Essential Mathematics for GCSE Higher

Michael White

Elmwood Press

In memory of Jackie Gilday,
Head of Mathematics and
Deputy Head of the Blue School, Wells

i

First published 2006 by
Elmwood Press
80 Attimore Road
Welwyn Garden City
Herts AL8 6LP
Tel. 01707 333232

Typeset and illustrated by Domex e-Data Pvt. Ltd.

Printed by Mateu Cromo

Preface

This book covers the material required for the GCSE Higher Tier (grades A* to D).

Nowadays there is a wealth of ICT and internet resources available to teachers. This book can be used alongside these to enable students to work at topics in a systematic way which helps to build up their confidence.

To help facilitate the range of abilities within a class, each section of work is identified as being 'M' or 'E', 'M' sections cover the main part of the syllabus (mainly grades B, C and D) accounting for 70% of the final examination questions. 'E' sections cover the extended part of the syllabus (mainly grades A* and A) accounting for 30% of the final examination questions.

Constant revisiting of topics is essential for exam success. Throughout this book, the author provides 'Can you still?' sections to encourage this continual reviewing process.

Questions are provided at the end of each unit for students to test themselves against each learning objective stated at the start of the unit. These are then backed up with a selection of GCSE examination questions.

The author is most concerned about students' awareness of money matters. Each unit contains a 'Watch your money!' section. The purpose of this is to encourage discussion and highlight each area. Questions are provided in each money section because it gives a focus. These questions do not require a high level of mathematical knowledge. The important issue is that students think about how these matters might affect them.

Thanks are due to AQA, CCEA, Edexcel, OCR and WJEC for kindly allowing the use of questions from their past examination papers. The answers are solely the work of the author and are not ratified by the examining groups.

The author is indebted to the contributions from Paul Williams, Hilary White and Peter Gibson.

Michael White

Contents

In the 'M' sections (mainly grades B, C, D) you will learn how to:
- deal with non calculator arithmetic, particularly + / - / × / ÷ decimals
- use fractions
- use a calculator
- convert fractions and decimals

In the 'E' sections (mainly grades A*, A) you will learn how to:
- convert recurring decimals into fractions
- simplify surds
- expand brackets containing surds and rationalise denominators

Also you will learn how to:
- ⟨WATCH YOUR MONEY!⟩ – mobile phones

M | Non calculator arithmetic

The questions in this section are to check that you have not gone 'rusty' with basic arithmetic, particularly problems involving decimals.

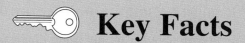

Key Facts

+/– decimals

line up the decimal points

× decimals

$0.\underline{4} \times 0.\underline{7} = 0.\underline{28}$

$0.\underline{8} \times 0.\underline{03} = 0.\underline{024}$

÷ decimals

multiply both numbers by 10, 100, 1000,... so that the decimal you are dividing by becomes a whole number.

$3.6 \div 0.04$

$= 360 \div 4$

$= 90$

Do not use a calculator

1 Work out

(a) $4 \times 7 + 3$ (b) $5 \times 12 + 1$ (c) $7 \times 11 + 4$

(d) $3 \times (2 + 9)$ (e) $4 \times (18 - 15)$ (f) $11 \times (13 - 2)$

(g) $(8 - 3) \times (9 - 2)$ (h) $(18 - 12) \times (17 - 11)$ (i) $(15 - 2)^2$

2 Find the value of each calculation below:

(a) $\dfrac{5 \times 7 + 1}{12}$ (b) $\dfrac{2 \times 3 + 5 \times 7}{45 - 2 \times 2}$ (c) $\dfrac{(13 + 2) \times (5 - 2)}{3^2}$

(d) $\dfrac{(13 + 5) \times (12 - 9)}{5 \times 4 - 7 \times 2}$ (e) $\dfrac{11^2 - 1}{3 \times 4 \times 5}$ (f) $\dfrac{12^2 - 9^2}{3^2}$

3 Work out

(a) 37×46 (b) 246×42 (c) 57×318

(d) $782 \div 17$ (e) $1764 \div 28$ (f) $1224 \div 34$

4 How many 27p stamps can I buy with a £20 note?

5 Tom has to put 1000 bottles into crates. One crate will take 24 bottles. How many crates will Tom need?

6 Find the value of $8 \times 8 \times 8 \times 8$.

7 Write down the answer to each of the following:

(a) $9 - 3.07$ (b) 0.03×0.5 (c) 0.9×0.003 (d) 0.1^2

(e) 0.04×30 (f) $16 - 0.713$ (g) 0.21×0.6 (h) 0.3×500

(i) $0.63 \div 0.7$ (j) $14.98 \div 0.7$ (k) $0.57 \div 0.6$ (l) $0.496 \div 0.08$

(m) 0.28^2 (n) 31.6×0.27 (o) $0.065 \div 0.002$ (p) 0.48×3.77

8 Tom, Sally and Cherie club together to buy some flowers for their dear old Gran. The flowers cost £37.35. How much does each person pay?

9 A box of sweets contains 2.4 kg. How many packets can be filled from this box if each packet holds 0.15 kg?

10 Work out

(a) $2\sqrt{25}$ (b) $\sqrt{36} + 3\sqrt{49}$ (c) $4\sqrt{121} - 5\sqrt{4}$

(d) $\left(2\sqrt{9} + 1\right)^2$ (e) $5\sqrt{4} + 3\sqrt{100}$ (f) $7\sqrt{9} - 2\sqrt{16}$

(g) $\dfrac{6\sqrt{4}}{\sqrt{9}}$ (h) $\dfrac{2\sqrt{9} + \sqrt{16}}{\sqrt{4} + \sqrt{9}}$ (i) $\dfrac{2\sqrt{100} + \sqrt{16}}{\sqrt{4} + 1}$

(j) $\left(\sqrt{225} - \sqrt{196}\right)^2$ (k) $\left(\sqrt{49} + \sqrt{16}\right)\left(\sqrt{49} - \sqrt{16}\right)$ (l) $\left(\sqrt{169} - \sqrt{64}\right)^2$

(a) $3\frac{1}{5} \times 1\frac{2}{3} = \frac{16}{\cancel{5}_1} \times \frac{\cancel{5}^1}{3}$

$\qquad = \frac{16}{3}$

$\qquad = 5\frac{1}{3}$

(b) $2\frac{3}{4} \div 7\frac{1}{3} = \frac{11}{4} \div \frac{22}{3}$

$\qquad = \frac{\cancel{11}^1}{4} \times \frac{3}{\cancel{22}_2}$

$\qquad = \frac{3}{8}$

(c) $2\frac{2}{3} - 1\frac{3}{4}$

$\qquad = \frac{8}{3} - \frac{7}{4}$

$\qquad = \frac{32}{12} - \frac{21}{12}$

$\qquad = \frac{11}{12}$

M1.2

1 Work out and give the answer in its simplest form:

(a) $\frac{5}{6}$ of 42

(b) $\frac{1}{3}$ of $\frac{1}{8}$

(c) $\frac{2}{7} \times \frac{3}{4}$

(d) $\frac{3}{8} \times \frac{4}{5}$

(e) $3\frac{2}{3} \times 1\frac{4}{5}$

(f) $3\frac{1}{4} \times 2\frac{1}{2}$

(g) $\frac{8}{9} \times 12$

(h) $\frac{4}{5} \times 20$

(i) $\frac{1}{9} \div \frac{1}{8}$

(j) $\frac{2}{7} \div \frac{5}{9}$

(k) $\frac{3}{8} \div 6$

(l) $5\frac{1}{2} \div 3$

(m) $\frac{1}{6} \div \frac{4}{9}$

(n) $\frac{2}{5} \div \frac{1}{2}$

(o) $8\frac{1}{2} \div 5\frac{1}{4}$

(p) $4\frac{5}{6} \div 4\frac{2}{3}$

2 A recipe for a cake uses $\frac{2}{3}$ lb of sugar. How many cakes can be made from 6lb of sugar?

3 How many whole rods of length $2\frac{1}{3}$ cm can be cut from a pole of length $19\frac{1}{4}$ cm?

4 Work out and give the answer in its simplest form:

(a) $\frac{3}{7} + \frac{2}{5}$

(b) $\frac{8}{9} - \frac{2}{3}$

(c) $\frac{4}{5} - \frac{3}{8}$

(d) $\frac{3}{20} + \frac{1}{3}$

(e) $\frac{1}{5} + \frac{4}{9}$

(f) $\frac{2}{3} + \frac{1}{4}$

(g) $\frac{5}{6} - \frac{1}{2}$

(h) $\frac{7}{8} - \frac{4}{7}$

5 Work out and give the answer in its simplest form:

(a) $3\frac{3}{4} + \frac{2}{3}$

(b) $1\frac{7}{8} - \frac{3}{4}$

(c) $3\frac{1}{2} - 2\frac{5}{8}$

(d) $3\frac{1}{6} + 1\frac{2}{5}$

6 Which room below has the larger area and by how much?

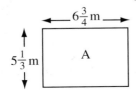

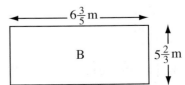

7 Match each question to the correct answer:

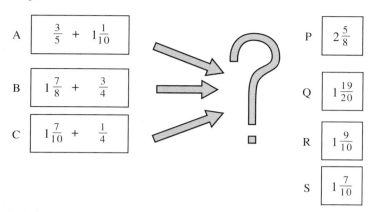

A $\quad \frac{3}{5} + 1\frac{1}{10}$

B $\quad 1\frac{7}{8} + \frac{3}{4}$

C $\quad 1\frac{7}{10} + \frac{1}{4}$

P $\quad 2\frac{5}{8}$

Q $\quad 1\frac{19}{20}$

R $\quad 1\frac{9}{10}$

S $\quad 1\frac{7}{10}$

8 A person gives one third of his earnings to his son and one quarter to his daughter. The person gives the rest to his partner. What fraction did his partner get?

9 One eighth of candidates pass an exam at the first attempt. Two-fifths pass on the second attempt. What fraction of candidates do *not* pass after two attempts?

10 A car is two-thirds of a mile ahead of a lorry on a long, straight motorway. A motorbike is half a mile behind the lorry. What is the distance between the motorbike and the car?

11 Carol has a lawn which measures $6\frac{1}{2}$ m by $7\frac{3}{4}$ m. She inserts a pond which measures $1\frac{1}{4}$ m by $1\frac{1}{2}$ m into the middle of the lawn. Find the new area of the lawn (as a fraction).

12 Copy each square and fill in the missing numbers or symbols (+, −, ×, ÷). The arrows act as equals signs.

(a)

	−	$\frac{1}{6}$	→	$\frac{1}{3}$
×		÷		
$\frac{1}{4}$	÷	$\frac{1}{5}$	→	
↓		↓		
	×		→	

(b)

	×	$\frac{1}{3}$	→	$\frac{2}{9}$
		÷		
$\frac{1}{2}$	+	$\frac{3}{8}$	→	
↓		↓		
$\frac{1}{6}$	+		→	

13 Work out and give the answer in its simplest form.

(a) $\dfrac{3}{5} \times \dfrac{2}{3} \times \dfrac{5}{6}$

(b) $\dfrac{3}{4} \times \dfrac{2}{5} \times \dfrac{15}{16}$

(c) $\left(\dfrac{3}{5} + \dfrac{2}{3}\right) \times \dfrac{5}{7}$

(d) $\left(\dfrac{2}{5} + \dfrac{1}{2}\right) \times \left(\dfrac{1}{3} + \dfrac{1}{4}\right)$

(e) $\left(1\dfrac{3}{5} + 2\dfrac{2}{7}\right) \div \dfrac{4}{7}$

(f) $\left(\dfrac{3}{7} + \dfrac{2}{5}\right) \times \left(\dfrac{3}{10} + \dfrac{4}{5}\right)$

14 How many whole rods of length $2\frac{1}{3}$ cm can be cut from a pole of length $19\frac{1}{4}$ cm?

15 The floor of a room measures $4\frac{2}{3}$ m by $3\frac{1}{2}$ m. A carpet measures $5\frac{1}{2}$ m by $3\frac{2}{3}$ m. What is the area of the carpet left over when the carpet is fitted?

16 Work out $\frac{1}{2} + \frac{1}{3} + \frac{1}{4} + \frac{1}{5} + \frac{1}{6} + \frac{1}{7}$.

17 Harry begins his journey with his petrol tank two-thirds full. When he stops for lunch, he notices that the amount of petrol in his tank is three-quarters of the *starting amount*. What fraction of the full tank is this?

18 The organizer of a cup final gives three eighths of the tickets to each of the clubs playing. These clubs then give two thirds of their allocation to season ticket holders. What fraction of the tickets at the cup final will be given to season ticket holders from the two clubs?

Can you still?

1A **Round off**

1. Round off the numbers below to the given number of decimal places (d.p.).

   (a) 0.218 (1 d.p.)   (b) 0.863 (1 d.p.)   (c) 2.639 (2 d.p.)

   (d) 0.053 (1d.p.)   (e) 36.718 (2 d.p.)   (f) 14.18276 (3 d.p.)

2. Copy the grid below.

   Use a calculator to fill in the grid using the clues (*ignore any decimal points*).
   You *must* round answers to the number of significant figures (s.f.) shown

Clues across	**Clues down**
1. 1.9×9.46 (4 s.f.)	**1.** $18 \div 9.1$ (3 s.f.)
3. $3 \div 0.27$ (2 s.f.)	**2.** 30.8^2 (1 s.f.)
6. 2754.4×0.3 (2 s.f.)	**4.** $1797.4853 \div 13$ (6 s.f.)
8. 3.81^2 (4 s.f.)	**5.** 0.24×0.17 (2 s.f.)
9. $\frac{38 + 69.4}{0.48}$ (3 s.f.)	**7.** $0.36^2 + 1.7^2$ (3 s.f.)
11. 2.3^3 (2 s.f.)	**9.** $29 \div 13$ (3 s.f.)
12. $(3.6 + 5.12) \times 1.01$ (2 s.f.)	
13. $5.6^2 + 0.417$ (3 s.f.)	**10.** $\frac{33}{0.12} + 142.9$ (3 s.f.)
14. $\frac{3.1}{(2.83 - 1.9)}$ (2 s.f.)	**12** $99 - 16.182$ (2 s.f.)

5

Powers

$2^4 = 2 \times 2 \times 2 \times 2 = 16$ We say '2 to the power 4' equals 16.

Calculator button $\boxed{y^x}$ or $\boxed{x^y}$

Find the button on your calculator.

Key in $\boxed{2}$ $\boxed{x^y}$ $\boxed{4}$ $\boxed{=}$ The answer should be 16.

Fractions

Key in $\boxed{3}$ $\boxed{a\frac{b}{c}}$ $\boxed{4}$ This is $\frac{3}{4}$

$$3 \lrcorner 4$$

Use the fraction button to work out $\frac{5}{6} - \frac{3}{4}$

The display should show $\boxed{1 \lrcorner 12}$ because the answer is $\frac{1}{12}$.

M1.3

1 Use a calculator to match each question below to the correct answer:

A	3^5	P	256
B	2^8	Q	4096
C	5^5	R	243
D	7^4	S	3125
E	4^6	T	7776
F	6^5	U	2401

2 A cab driver fills up his car with petrol costing 64.9p per litre. If he was charged £29.33 then how many litres did he get (give your answer to 1 decimal place)?

3 A minibus hire company charges £45 for the day plus 28p per kilometre travelled.

(a) How much would it cost to hire a minibus for a day-trip for a journey of 350 km?

(b) How many kilometres did a woman travel if she paid the company £96.80 for the day?

4 Use a calculator to work out

(a) $\dfrac{4}{9} - \dfrac{2}{11}$ (b) $3\dfrac{1}{5} \times 4\dfrac{1}{2}$ (c) $8\dfrac{1}{4} \div \dfrac{3}{5}$ (d) $\left(4\dfrac{1}{5}\right)^2$

5 Copy the grid below.

Use a calculator to fill in the grid using the clues (*ignore any decimal points*).

Clues across

1. $3.8 + 1.7 + 1.42$

3. $7 \times (3.6 - 1.9)$

5. $\dfrac{17.6}{0.4} - 3.88$

7. 4.9×150

9. $(0.62 + 0.08) \times 70$

10. $-24.1 - 2.3 + 61.2$

11. $-900 \times (-0.09)$

12. $4.9 \times \left(\dfrac{40}{0.8}\right)$

Clues down

1. $\dfrac{5.1 - 1.7}{0.5}$

2. $3.9 \times 4.8 \times 13.4$

3. $(3.1 + 1.8) \times (6.1 - 3.8)$

4. $121 - (31.2 - 4.85)$

6. $\dfrac{13.8 + 9.12}{0.25}$

8. $(15.1 - 7.6) \times 3.5 + 5.2$

10. $\dfrac{18.1 - 1.1}{0.38 + 0.12}$

6 Calculate the following, giving each answer to 2 decimal places.

(a) $3.1^3 \times (5.9 - 1.312)$

(b) $\dfrac{5.12}{(7.8 + 0.314)}$

(c) $\dfrac{17.2 + 11.25}{3.89 + 1.63}$

(d) $\dfrac{16.18 - 3.892}{12.62 + 19.31}$

(e) $\dfrac{5.1^2 + 6.34}{17.162 - 2.8^2}$

(f) $\dfrac{3.81^2 + 2.6^3}{1.41^2 - 1.317}$

7 Copy and use a calculator to complete the table opposite.

+	$\frac{3}{8}$		$2\frac{1}{2}$	$1\frac{2}{3}$
$\frac{1}{4}$				
$\frac{3}{5}$	$\frac{19}{20}$			
		$4\frac{5}{6}$		
	$2\frac{13}{20}$			

8 Calculate the following, giving each answer to 3 significant figures.

(a) $\left(\sqrt{5} + \sqrt{3}\right)^3$

(b) $\dfrac{\sqrt{5} + \sqrt{3}}{\sqrt{5} - \sqrt{3}}$

(c) $4.7 - (1.8^2 - 0.5^3)$

(d) $\dfrac{84 \times 9 + 37 \times 72}{3.2 + 18.2 \times 1.1}$

(e) $\dfrac{(-3)^2 - (2 - \sqrt{3})}{\sqrt{2} + 1}$

(f) $\dfrac{-3.19 + 2.1 \times 11.9}{(-9.8) \times (-3.5) + 4.7}$

1B   **Use negative numbers**

Do not use a calculator

1. Work out

   (a) $3 \times (-4)$

   (b) $(-7) \times 6$

   (c) $(-8) \times 2$

   (d) $9 \div (-3)$

   (e) $(-24) \div (-3)$

   (f) $(-15) \div 5$

   (g) $(-8) \times (-4)$

   (h) $(-16) \times (-5)$

   (i) $(-20) \div (-4)$

   (j) $\dfrac{-30}{-6}$

   (k) $\dfrac{-48}{-8}$

   (l) $\dfrac{-56}{7}$

2. Work out

   (a) $-5 + 2$

   (b) $-6 - 3$

   (c) $-10 + 6$

   (d) $-4 - (-2)$

   (e) $-9 - (-4)$

   (f) $6 + (-9)$

   (g) $-10 + 12$

   (h) $-3 - 2$

   (i) $-8 - (-7)$

3. Copy and fill in the empty boxes.

   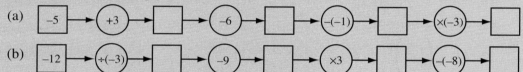

   (a) $\boxed{-5} \rightarrow \bigcirc{+3} \rightarrow \boxed{} \rightarrow \bigcirc{-6} \rightarrow \boxed{} \rightarrow \bigcirc{-(-1)} \rightarrow \boxed{} \rightarrow \bigcirc{\times(-3)} \rightarrow \boxed{}$

   (b) $\boxed{-12} \rightarrow \bigcirc{\div(-3)} \rightarrow \boxed{} \rightarrow \bigcirc{-9} \rightarrow \boxed{} \rightarrow \bigcirc{\times 3} \rightarrow \boxed{} \rightarrow \bigcirc{-(-8)} \rightarrow \boxed{}$

4. Work out

   (a) $2 \times (-3) \times (-5)$

   (b) $(-7) \times 6 \times (-2)$

   (c) $5 \times 4 \times (-2)$

   (d) $\dfrac{(-3) \times (-8)}{12}$

   (e) $\dfrac{(-4) \times 5}{2}$

   (f) $\dfrac{(-8) \times (-9)}{2 \times (-12)}$

   (g) $4.5 \times (-2)$

   (h) $5.5 \times (-4)$

   (i) $(-7.5) \times 6$

5. Write down the missing number for each question below:

   (a) $\boxed{} + (-3) = -2$

   (b) $\boxed{} - (-7) = -3$

   (c) $-3 \times \boxed{} = 36$

   (d) $\boxed{} \div (-4) = -5$

   (e) $-28 \div \boxed{} = 14$

   (f) $-8 - \boxed{} = -13$

6. Work out

   (a) $(-8)^2$

   (b) $0.04 \times (-0.08)$

   (c) $(-0.4) \times (-0.01)$

   (d) $(-0.7) \times 0.6$

   (e) $(-6)^2$

   (f) $(-3)^3$

   (g) $5 \times (-6) - 2 \times 4$

   (h) $-4 + (-5) \times 3$

   (i) $\dfrac{(-6) \times 5 + 2}{7}$

   (j) $\dfrac{(-3) \times (-10) + 4}{15 - (-2)}$

   (k) $\dfrac{(-5)^2 \times (-2)^2}{40 - (-10)}$

   (l) $\dfrac{(-9) \times (-8) - 12}{15 \times (-2)}$

$\dfrac{7}{20} = \dfrac{35}{100} = 0.35$ | change the denominator into a power of 10 if possible | $\dfrac{21}{200} = \dfrac{105}{1000} = 0.105$

$\dfrac{2}{9} \longrightarrow$ | cannot change the denominator easily into a power of 10 so divide to get a decimal answer | $\longrightarrow$

$$\begin{array}{r} 0.\ 2\ 2\ 2 \\ 9\overline{)2.\ ^20^20^20} \end{array}$$

so $\dfrac{2}{9} = 0.222... = 0.\dot{2}$

(0.2 recurring)

Remember $0.\dot{6}\dot{3}$ means 0.63 63 63 .... $0.1\dot{8}2\dot{7}$ means 0.1827 827.....

1 Convert the decimals below into fractions in their lowest form:
   (a) 0.6   (b) 0.08   (c) 0.75   (d) 0.215

   (e) 0.836   (f) 0.517   (g) 0.7275   (h) 0.0625

2 Pair off each fraction with an equivalent decimal:

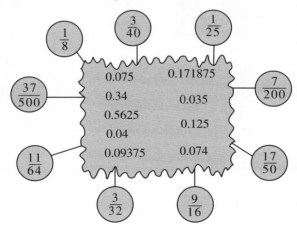

3 Use division to convert the fractions below into recurring decimals:

   (a) $\dfrac{2}{11}$ (b) $\dfrac{5}{9}$ (c) $\dfrac{2}{3}$ (d) $\dfrac{7}{11}$

   (e) $\dfrac{7}{15}$ (f) $\dfrac{4}{9}$ (g) $\dfrac{1}{6}$ (h) $\dfrac{7}{12}$

4 Use division to convert $\frac{4}{7}$ into a recurring decimal.

5 Convert $\frac{6}{7}$ and $\frac{11}{13}$ into recurring decimals. Which is the larger fraction?

 **Key Facts**

All recurring decimals can be written as exact fractions.

(a) Change $0.\dot{8}3\dot{7}$ to a fraction.

let f = 0.837837.....

number of repeating digits = **3**
multiply both sides of equation
by $10^3 = 1000$

1000f = 837.837.....

we have f =   0.837.....

note these 3 recurring
digits match up with the
3 digits above

subtract

999f = 837

$f = \dfrac{837}{999}$ this can be cancelled down

$0.\dot{8}3\dot{7} = \dfrac{31}{37}$

(b) Change $0.4\dot{2}\dot{6}$ to a fraction.

let f = 0.42626.....

2 repeating digits
multiply both sides of equation
by $10^2 = 100$

100f = 42.626.....

we have f =   0.426.....

note these 2 recurring
digits match up with the
2 digits above

subtract

99f = 42.2

$f = \dfrac{42.2}{99}$ $\dfrac{(\times 10)}{(\times 10)} = \dfrac{422}{990}$ cancel down

$0.4\dot{2}\dot{6} = \dfrac{211}{495}$

E1.1

1 (a) Copy and complete to change
0.$\dot{7}$ to a fraction.

let f = 0.7777...

10f = ☐ (multiply both sides by 10)

we have f = 0.7777...

subtract

9f = ☐

$f = \dfrac{☐}{☐}$

(b) Copy and complete to change
0.$\dot{3}\dot{1}$ to a fraction.

let f = 0.313131...

100f = ☐

we have f = 0.313131...

subtract

99f = ☐

$f = \dfrac{☐}{☐}$

2 Express the following recurring decimals as fractions in their lowest form:

(a) $0.\dot{8}$

(b) $0.898989\ldots$

(c) $0.\dot{1}\dot{7}$

(d) $0.7\dot{3}$

(e) $0.153153153\ldots$

(f) $0.2\dot{4}\dot{9}$

(g) $0.\dot{9}\dot{1}$

(h) $0.59\dot{4}$

(i) $0.16666\ldots$

(j) $0.4\dot{3}$

(k) $0.8\dot{1}\dot{3}$

(l) $4.3\dot{4}\dot{7}$

E | Surds 1

Simplifying surds

Use a calculator to work out $\sqrt{2}$.

$\sqrt{2} = 1.41421356\ldots$ is a non-terminating, non-recurring decimal. The decimal value would probably have to be rounded off when using it in calculations which could lead to errors. To avoid this we might leave $\sqrt{2}$ in the calculation to ensure we get 'exact' answers. $\sqrt{2}$ is known as a 'surd'.

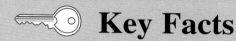

Key Facts

$\sqrt{a}$ is known as a surd.

Rules

$$\sqrt{a} \times \sqrt{b} = \sqrt{ab} \qquad \frac{\sqrt{a}}{\sqrt{b}} = \sqrt{\frac{a}{b}}$$

(you can verify these rules by trying out some numbers)

warning ($\neq$ means 'is *not equal to*')

$$\sqrt{a} + \sqrt{b} \neq \sqrt{a+b} \qquad \sqrt{a} - \sqrt{b} \neq \sqrt{a-b}$$

(use numbers to show these)

Simplifying a single surd

Simplify $\sqrt{27}$

if you can find a factor of 27 which is a square number, the surd can be simplified

$$\sqrt{27} = \sqrt{9 \times 3} = \sqrt{9} \times \sqrt{3} = 3\sqrt{3}$$

square number

Note. a surd $\sqrt{9}$ means 'the positive square root of 9' $\sqrt{9}$ means 3 *not* ± 3

11

(a) $\sqrt{7} \times \sqrt{3} = \sqrt{21}$

(b) $\sqrt{8} \times \sqrt{2} = \sqrt{16} = 4$

(c) $3\sqrt{5} \times 2\sqrt{2} = 3 \times 2 \times \sqrt{5 \times 2} = 6\sqrt{10}$

(d) $3\sqrt{2} + 5\sqrt{2} = 8\sqrt{2}$

(e) $\sqrt{18} \div \sqrt{3} = \sqrt{\dfrac{18}{3}} = \sqrt{6}$

(f) Simplify $\sqrt{32}$ $\Rightarrow$ $\sqrt{32} = \sqrt{16 \times 2} = \sqrt{16}\sqrt{2} = 4\sqrt{2}$

(g) Simplify $\sqrt{18} - \sqrt{8}$ $\Rightarrow$ $\sqrt{9 \times 2} - \sqrt{4 \times 2}$

simplify each surd separately first $= \sqrt{9}\sqrt{2} - \sqrt{4}\sqrt{2}$

$= 3\sqrt{2} - 2\sqrt{2}$

$= \sqrt{2}$

E1.2

1 Simplify

(a) $\sqrt{12}$ (b) $\sqrt{44}$ (c) $\sqrt{45}$ (d) $\sqrt{50}$

(e) $\sqrt{75}$ (f) $\sqrt{24}$ (g) $\sqrt{63}$ (h) $\sqrt{200}$

(i) $\sqrt{160}$ (j) $\sqrt{150}$ (k) $\sqrt{48}$ (l) $\sqrt{135}$

(m) $\sqrt{180}$ (n) $\sqrt{216}$ (o) $\sqrt{245}$ (p) $\sqrt{343}$

2 Simplify as far as possible

(a) $\sqrt{5} \times \sqrt{3}$ (b) $\sqrt{7} \times \sqrt{4}$ (c) $\sqrt{5} \times \sqrt{11}$

(d) $\left(\sqrt{3}\right)^2$ (e) $\left(\sqrt{6}\right)^2$ (f) $\sqrt{3} \times \sqrt{4} \times \sqrt{2}$

(g) $\sqrt{5} \times \sqrt{6} \times \sqrt{2}$ (h) $\sqrt{18} \times \sqrt{2}$ (i) $\sqrt{8} \times \sqrt{6}$

3 Simplify as far as possible

(a) $\sqrt{28} \div \sqrt{2}$ (b) $\dfrac{\sqrt{40}}{\sqrt{8}}$ (c) $\dfrac{\sqrt{6}}{\sqrt{2}}$

(d) $\dfrac{\sqrt{60}}{\sqrt{30}}$ (e) $\sqrt{80} \div \sqrt{10}$ (f) $\sqrt{12} \div \sqrt{6}$

4 Which of the statements below are true?

(a) $\sqrt{8} \times \sqrt{11} = \sqrt{88}$ (b) $\sqrt{4} + \sqrt{4} = \sqrt{8}$ (c) $\sqrt{18} \div \sqrt{2} = 3$

(d) $\sqrt{20} - \sqrt{15} = \sqrt{5}$ (e) $\sqrt{6} + \sqrt{9} = \sqrt{15}$ (f) $\sqrt{27} - \sqrt{12} = \sqrt{3}$

5 Simplify as far as possible

(a) $5\sqrt{2} \times 3\sqrt{5}$

(b) $2\sqrt{3} \times 3\sqrt{7}$

(c) $6\sqrt{3} \times \sqrt{3}$

(d) $7\sqrt{6} \times 3\sqrt{2}$

(e) $\left(5\sqrt{2}\right)^2$

(f) $\left(3\sqrt{5}\right)^2$

(g) $9\sqrt{5} \times 7\sqrt{3}$

(h) $8\sqrt{2} \times 3\sqrt{3}$

(i) $\left(\sqrt{2}\right)^3$

(j) $3\sqrt{7} \times 5\sqrt{3}$

(k) $3\sqrt{2} \times 3\sqrt{3} \times 2\sqrt{3}$

(l) $\left(3\sqrt{3}\right)^3$

6 Write down which of these expressions are equal to the number in the circle.

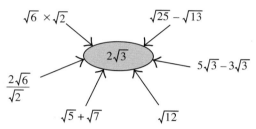

7 Simplify as far as possible

(a) $5\sqrt{2} - 3\sqrt{2}$

(b) $2\sqrt{3} + 5\sqrt{3}$

(c) $8\sqrt{5} - 5\sqrt{5}$

(d) $9\sqrt{3} - 5\sqrt{3} + \sqrt{3}$

(e) $\sqrt{3} + \sqrt{12}$

(f) $\sqrt{27} + 2\sqrt{3}$

(g) $5\sqrt{5} + \sqrt{45}$

(h) $7\sqrt{2} + \sqrt{50}$

(i) $\sqrt{18} + \sqrt{200}$

(j) $\sqrt{60} + \sqrt{135}$

(k) $\sqrt{180} - \sqrt{20}$

(l) $\sqrt{48} + \sqrt{20} - \sqrt{12}$

Can you still?

1C **Estimate**

Can you still?

1. There are 42 matches in a matchbox. *Estimate* how many matches there are in 89 matchboxes.

2. Josh burns off 590 kcals each time he visits the Gym. *Estimate* how many kcals he burns off during 21 trips to the Gym.

3. Estimate, correct to 1 significant figure:

(a) $41.56 \div 7.88$

(b) $\dfrac{5.13 \times 18.777}{0.952}$

(c) $\dfrac{1}{5}$ of £14892

(d) $\dfrac{0.0974 \times \sqrt{104}}{1.03}$

(e) 52% of 0.394 kg

(f) $\dfrac{6.84^2 + 0.983}{5.07^2}$

(g) $\dfrac{2848.7 + 1024.8}{51.2 - 9.98}$

(h) $\dfrac{2}{3}$ of £3124

(i) $18.13 \times (3.96^2 + 2.07^2)$

Expanding brackets containing surds

(see Unit 4 if 'expanding brackets' not yet covered. In particular $(a + b)^2 = (a + b)(a + b)$ *not $a^2 + b^2$*)

(a) $\left(\sqrt{5} + \sqrt{2}\right)\left(\sqrt{3} - \sqrt{2}\right)$

$= \sqrt{15} - \sqrt{10} + \sqrt{6} - 2$

cannot be simplified any further because no individual surds can be simplified

(b) $\left(\sqrt{6} - \sqrt{2}\right)\left(\sqrt{3} + 2\right)$

$= \sqrt{18} + 2\sqrt{6} - \sqrt{6} - 2\sqrt{2}$

↓ simplify

$= 3\sqrt{2} + 2\sqrt{6} - \sqrt{6} - 2\sqrt{2}$

$= \sqrt{2} + \sqrt{6}$

c) $\left(3 + \sqrt{5}\right)^2$

$= \left(3 + \sqrt{5}\right)\left(3 + \sqrt{5}\right)$

$= 9 + 3\sqrt{5} + 3\sqrt{5} + 5$

$= 14 + 6\sqrt{5}$

Rationalising the denominator

If we get an answer which is a fraction, we prefer not to have a surd in the denominator. We can deal with this issue by multiplying the numerator and denominator by the surd in question.

(a) $\dfrac{1}{\sqrt{2}} = \dfrac{1 \times \sqrt{2}}{\sqrt{2} \times \sqrt{2}} = \dfrac{\sqrt{2}}{2}$ $\qquad \left(\text{sometimes written as } \dfrac{1}{2}\sqrt{2}\right)$

(b) $\dfrac{3}{2\sqrt{3}} = \dfrac{3 \times \sqrt{3}}{2\sqrt{3} \times \sqrt{3}} = \dfrac{3\sqrt{3}}{2 \times 3} = \dfrac{3\sqrt{3}}{6} = \dfrac{\sqrt{3}}{2}$

Key Facts

$$\frac{a}{\sqrt{b}} \quad = \quad \frac{a}{\sqrt{b}} \times \frac{\sqrt{b}}{\sqrt{b}} \quad = \quad \frac{a\sqrt{b}}{b}$$

The surd in the denominator has been removed. We say the denominator has been *rationalised*.

1 Expand and simplify

(a) $\left(\sqrt{3}+2\right)\left(\sqrt{3}+3\right)$ (b) $\left(\sqrt{5}-1\right)\left(\sqrt{5}+2\right)$ (c) $\left(\sqrt{3}-4\right)\left(2+\sqrt{5}\right)$

(d) $\left(\sqrt{2}+\sqrt{3}\right)\left(\sqrt{3}+\sqrt{5}\right)$ (e) $\left(\sqrt{5}-\sqrt{2}\right)\left(\sqrt{3}+\sqrt{2}\right)$ (f) $\left(\sqrt{7}+\sqrt{3}\right)\left(\sqrt{5}+\sqrt{2}\right)$

2 Jan says that $\left(\sqrt{2}+\sqrt{3}\right)^2 = 5$.

Show whether she is correct or not.

3 Expand and simplify

(a) $\left(\sqrt{2}+1\right)^2$ (b) $\left(\sqrt{3}+\sqrt{5}\right)^2$ (c) $\left(\sqrt{5}-\sqrt{2}\right)^2$

(d) $\left(\sqrt{2}+1\right)\left(\sqrt{2}-1\right)$ (e) $\left(\sqrt{7}+\sqrt{3}\right)\left(\sqrt{7}-\sqrt{3}\right)$ (f) $\left(\sqrt{5}+2\right)\left(\sqrt{5}-2\right)$

(g) $\left(\sqrt{7}-\sqrt{3}\right)^2$ (h) $\left(\sqrt{11}+\sqrt{7}\right)\left(\sqrt{11}-\sqrt{7}\right)$ (i) $\left(\sqrt{5}+2\right)^2$

4 Rationalise the denominator in each of the following:

(a) $\dfrac{1}{\sqrt{5}}$ (b) $\dfrac{1}{\sqrt{3}}$ (c) $\dfrac{1}{\sqrt{7}}$ (d) $\dfrac{6}{\sqrt{2}}$

(e) $\dfrac{10}{\sqrt{5}}$ (f) $\dfrac{21}{\sqrt{7}}$ (g) $\dfrac{15}{2\sqrt{5}}$ (h) $\dfrac{33}{5\sqrt{11}}$

(i) $\dfrac{\sqrt{3}}{\sqrt{5}}$ (j) $\dfrac{\sqrt{2}}{\sqrt{7}}$ (k) $\dfrac{5\sqrt{3}}{\sqrt{7}}$ (l) $\dfrac{4\sqrt{2}}{\sqrt{8}}$

5 Expand and simplify

(a) $\sqrt{2}\left(1+\sqrt{3}\right)$ (b) $\sqrt{5}\left(2-\sqrt{5}\right)$ (c) $\sqrt{3}\left(\sqrt{2}+\sqrt{5}\right)$ (d) $2\sqrt{2}\left(3-\sqrt{3}\right)$

6 Rationalise the denominator in each of the following:

(a) $\dfrac{1+\sqrt{3}}{\sqrt{2}}$ (b) $\dfrac{5-\sqrt{2}}{\sqrt{5}}$ (c) $\dfrac{\sqrt{2}+\sqrt{5}}{\sqrt{3}}$ (d) $\dfrac{\sqrt{6}-1}{\sqrt{2}}$

7 (a) Given that $\left(\sqrt{5}-2\right)\left(\sqrt{5}+2\right) = 1$, can you find a way to rationalise the denominator of $\dfrac{3}{\sqrt{5}-2}$?

(b) Given that $\left(1+\sqrt{2}\right)\left(1-\sqrt{2}\right) = -1$, can you find a way to rationalise the denominator of $\dfrac{5}{1+\sqrt{2}}$?

(c) Describe how to rationalise the denominator of $\dfrac{c}{a+\sqrt{b}}$?

8 Simplify the following as far as possible:

(a) $5\sqrt{2}\times 2\sqrt{2}$

(b) $\sqrt{3}\times\sqrt{27}$

(c) $\sqrt{50}\times 2\sqrt{2}$

(d) $\dfrac{4\sqrt{2}}{\sqrt{8}}$

(e) $\dfrac{10\sqrt{6}}{\sqrt{150}}$

(f) $\dfrac{3\sqrt{28}}{\sqrt{7}}$

(g) $\left(\sqrt{5}+3\right)\left(\sqrt{2}-1\right)$

(h) $\left(\sqrt{7}-3\right)\left(\sqrt{7}+3\right)$

(i) $3\sqrt{5}\left(\sqrt{2}-\sqrt{3}\right)$

(j) $\dfrac{\sqrt{8}+\sqrt{12}}{\sqrt{2}+\sqrt{3}}$

(k) $\left(\sqrt{2}+\sqrt{3}\right)^{3}$

(l) $\left(\sqrt{5}+2\right)^{3}$

9 Find the 'exact' area of each shape. All units are in cm.

(a)

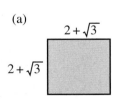

$2+\sqrt{3}$

$2+\sqrt{3}$

(b)

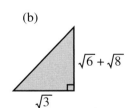

$\sqrt{6}+\sqrt{8}$

$\sqrt{3}$

(c)

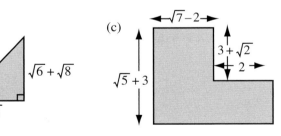

$\sqrt{7}-2$

$3+\sqrt{2}$

2

$\sqrt{5}+3$

10 Find the 'exact' volume of each prism. All units are in cm.

(a)

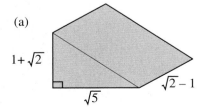

$1+\sqrt{2}$

$\sqrt{2}-1$

$\sqrt{5}$

(b)

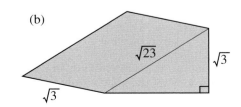

$\sqrt{23}$

$\sqrt{3}$

$\sqrt{3}$

1 Do you have a mobile phone?

2 If yes, which one?

3 Why did you choose this phone?

4 When do you usually use your phone the most?

| Monday to Friday (during the day) | or | Monday to Friday (during the evening) | or | at the weekend |

5 How many minutes do you spend on the phone per day?

| 0 | or | 1 – 5 | or | 6 – 15 | or | 16 – 30 | or | 31 – 60 | or | more than 60 |

6 How many texts do you send per day?

| 0 | or | 1 – 5 | or | 6 – 10 | or | 11 – 15 | or | more than 15 |

7 What are the advantages and disadvantages of having a mobile phone?

8 *Collect the above class data together with your teacher. Discuss the main findings.*

Mobile phone bills

Contract

You often pay a fixed monthly amount which allows you a certain number of minutes of phone calls and a certain number of text messages. You may have to pay extra if you exceed your limit.

Pay As You Go

You pay money in advance (sometimes by buying cards which allow you a certain amount of money on your phone). As soon as you have used up all your money, you have to buy more phone credit in advance.

Remember

Text messages are usually cheaper to send than making phone calls.

The best deal?

A tariff is a way of paying to use a mobile phone. The best tariff depends on how many minutes you use your phone for and what time of the day you use the phone.

Compare these two tariffs.

TARIFF P
4p per minute
anytime

TARIFF Q
£9 per month
plus 1p per minute

The best choice depends on how many minutes are used.

1 20 minutes on tariff P would cost 20 × 4p = 80p. Copy and complete this table for tariff P.

minutes	0	20	40	100	300	400
cost (£)	0	0.80	1.60			

2 20 minutes on tariff Q would cost £9 then add on (20 × 1p) which is £0.20. 20 minutes cost £9.20.

Copy and complete this table for tariff Q.

minutes	0	50	100	200	300	400
cost (£)	9					

3 (a) Copy the axes opposite onto squared paper.

(b) Plot points from the tariff P table and join them up to make a straight line.

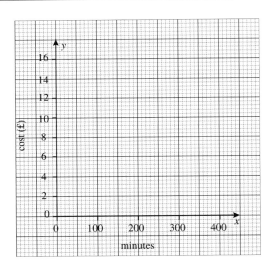

4 Plot points from the tariff Q table using the *same axes* as before. Join them up to make a straight line.

Your graph should look like this.

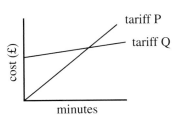

5 After how many minutes do the 2 lines cross?

6 What is the cost on both tariffs when the 2 lines cross?

7 If the number of minutes you use your mobile phone is less than your answer to Question **5**, which tariff is cheaper for you?

18

8 If the number of minutes you use your mobile phone is more than your answer to Question **5**, which tariff is cheaper for you?

9 Compare these two tariffs.

TARIFF Y
£5 per month
plus 2p per minute

TARIFF Z
4.5p per minute
anytime

(a) Repeat Questions **1** to **4** for these new tariffs.

(b) After how many minutes is the cost the same for both tariffs?

(c) Which tariff would you advise if you use your mobile phone for 150 minutes?

(d) Which tariff would you advise if you use your mobile phone for 320 minutes?

TEST YOURSELF ON UNIT 1

1. Dealing with non calculator arithmetic

Do not use a calculator

Work out

(a) $(17 - 3)^2$

(b) $\dfrac{9 + 2 \times 3}{5}$

(c) 73×216

(d) $962 \div 37$

(e) $4 \times 4 \times 4 \times 4$

(f) $\dfrac{8 + (4 \times 3)}{\sqrt{16}}$

(g) Find the missing values A, B, C and D below:

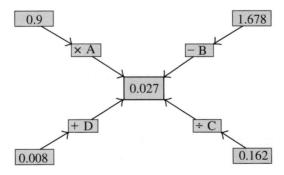

2. Using fractions

Work out

(a) $\dfrac{3}{10} + \dfrac{2}{3}$

(b) $\dfrac{7}{9}$ of 45

(c) $3\dfrac{2}{5} - 1\dfrac{5}{6}$

(d) $2\dfrac{3}{4} \div \dfrac{5}{12}$

(e) A film is $1\dfrac{3}{4}$ hours long. Sam watches $\dfrac{3}{8}$ of the film. What fraction of an hour does Sam watch the film for?

19

(f)

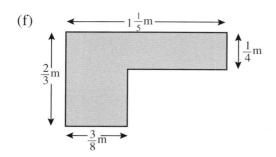

Find the area of this shape. Give the answer as a fraction in its simplest form.

---

3. Using a calculator

Calculate the following, giving each answer to 3 significant figures.

(a) $\dfrac{5.1 + 7.9}{3.68 - 1.5}$

(b) $\dfrac{2.16 + 3.8^2}{5.97^2}$

(c) $\dfrac{15.21 \div 0.083}{0.018^2}$

(d) $\dfrac{\left(\sqrt{8} + \sqrt{3}\right)^2}{\sqrt{15}}$

(e) $\dfrac{\dfrac{5}{9} - \dfrac{1}{8}}{\left(2\frac{1}{2}\right)^2}$

(f) $(3.7)^4 - (2.4)^3$

---

4. Converting fractions and decimals

(a) Each fraction has an equivalent decimal value. Write down each pair.

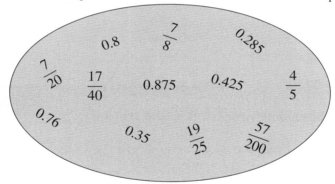

Convert the fractions below into recurring decimals:

(b) $\dfrac{7}{9}$

(c) $\dfrac{8}{15}$

---

5. Converting recurring decimals into fractions

Express the following recurring decimals as fractions in their lowest form:

(a) $0.\dot{2}\dot{3}$

(b) $0.4\dot{8}$

(c) $0.\dot{7}1\dot{9}$

---

6. Simplifying surds

(a) Which of the statements below are true?

(i) $\sqrt{10} - \sqrt{7} = \sqrt{3}$

(ii) $\sqrt{5} + \sqrt{11} = 4$

(iii) $\sqrt{3} \times \sqrt{7} = \sqrt{21}$

(iv) $2 \times \sqrt{5} = \sqrt{10}$

(v) $\sqrt{30} \div \sqrt{6} = \sqrt{5}$

(vi) $\left(\sqrt{3}\right)^2 = 3$

(b) Simplify as far as possible

(i) $\sqrt{27}$ (ii) $\sqrt{80}$ (iii) $4\sqrt{2} \times 3\sqrt{5}$

(iv) $\left(4\sqrt{3}\right)^2$ (v) $7\sqrt{2} - 3\sqrt{2}$ (vi) $\sqrt{32} - \sqrt{18}$

---

7. Expanding brackets containing surds and rationalising denominators

Expand and simplify

(a) $\left(\sqrt{2} + \sqrt{5}\right)\left(\sqrt{3} - \sqrt{2}\right)$ (b) $\left(1 + \sqrt{3}\right)\left(\sqrt{5} - 3\right)$ (c) $\left(2 + \sqrt{11}\right)\left(2 - \sqrt{11}\right)$

(d) $\sqrt{5}\left(2 - \sqrt{3}\right)$ (e) $\left(1 + \sqrt{3}\right)^2$ (f) $\left(\sqrt{5} - 7\right)^2$

Rationalise the denominator in each of the following:

(g) $\dfrac{1}{\sqrt{11}}$ (h) $\dfrac{3}{\sqrt{2}}$ (i) $\dfrac{\sqrt{5}}{\sqrt{7}}$ (j) $\dfrac{\sqrt{3} - 5}{\sqrt{2}}$

(k)

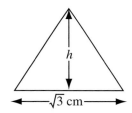

The area of this triangle is $\sqrt{48}$ cm².

Find the height h of the triangle.

Mixed examination questions

1   (a) Write these five fractions in order of size.
Start with the smallest fraction.

$$\frac{3}{4} \qquad \frac{1}{2} \qquad \frac{3}{8} \qquad \frac{2}{3} \qquad \frac{1}{6}$$

(b) Write these numbers in order of size.
Start with the smallest number.

$$65\% \qquad \frac{3}{4} \qquad 0.72 \qquad \frac{2}{3} \qquad \frac{3}{5}$$ (EDEXCEL)

2   Work out an estimate for $\dfrac{97.4 \times 4.18}{62.3 - 9.78}$ (CCEA)

3   Calculate

$$\frac{56.2}{7.1 \times 4.3}$$

Give your answer correct to 2 decimal places.   (OCR)

4

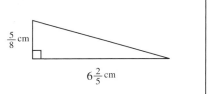 

$\frac{5}{8}$ cm

$6\frac{2}{5}$ cm

The area of the square is 18 times the area of the triangle.

Work out the **perimeter** of the square. (EDEXCEL)

5 (a) Write the following fractions in order of size with the smallest first. Show how you found your answer.

$$\frac{3}{5} \qquad \frac{1}{2} \qquad \frac{4}{7}$$

(b) Work out.

$$\frac{2}{3} \times \frac{3}{7}$$

Give your answer as a fraction in its lowest terms. (OCR)

6 $1.54 \times 450 = 693$

Use this result to write down the answer to

(i) 1.54×45

(ii) 1.54×4.5 \qquad (iii) 0.154×0.45 (EDEXCEL)

7 (a) Write $\sqrt{6} \times \sqrt{3}$ in the form $a\sqrt{b}$ where a and b are prime numbers.

(b) Simplify fully $5\sqrt{2} + \sqrt{8}$. (AQA)

8 (a) Find the value of $\sqrt{5} \times \sqrt{20}$.

$\sqrt{5} + \sqrt{20} = k\sqrt{5}$, where k is an integer.

(b) Find the value of k. \qquad (c) Find the value of $\dfrac{\sqrt{5} + \sqrt{45}}{\sqrt{20}}$

(EDEXCEL)

9 (a) You are given that $\sqrt{12} + \sqrt{27} = a\sqrt{3}$ where a is an integer.

Find the value of a.

(b) Find the value of $(m + p)^2$ when $m = \sqrt{2}$ and $p = \sqrt{8}$ (AQA)

10 Find the fractions equivalent to the following recurring decimals.

(a) $0.\dot{7}$ \qquad (b) $0.4\dot{7}$ (OCR)

11 (a) Expand and simplify $\left(7 + \sqrt{3}\right)\left(7 - \sqrt{3}\right)$

(b) Write $\dfrac{24}{\sqrt{6}}$ in the form $d\sqrt{e}$, where d and e are integers. (OCR)

In the 'M' sections (mainly grades B, C, D) you will learn how to:

– find percentage increases and decreases

– find a percentage change (including percentage profit/loss)

– solve compound interest–type problems

– work out reverse percentages

– use ratios

– multiply and divide using indices

In the 'E' sections (mainly grades A*, A) you will learn how to:

– use negative indices

– use fractional indices

– find indices from equations

Also you will learn how to:

– WATCH YOUR MONEY! – pricing your holiday

M **Percentage increase/decrease**

Zoe earns £500 each week.

She is given a 3% pay rise.

How much does she now earn each week?

$$3\% \text{ of } 500 = \overset{1\%}{(500 \div 100)} \times 3 = 15$$

Zoe now earns 500 + 15 = 515

↑

increase

Using percentage multipliers

In the example above, instead of finding 3% of £500 and adding it on, we could say:

Zoe now earns 100% of 500 + 3% of 500

$$= 103\% \text{ of } 500$$
$$= \frac{103}{100} \times 500$$
$$= 1.03 \times 500 = 515$$
⇧

1.03 is the '*percentage multiplier*'

so the quickest way to increase £7100 by 9% is

$$1.09 \times 7100 = £7739$$
⇧
$$100\% + 9\% = 109\% = 1.09$$

Decrease a price of £620 by 3%:

$$100\% - 3\% = 97\% = 0.97 \quad \text{This is the percentage multiplier.}$$

Answer: $0.97 \times 620 = £601.40$

M2.1

Use a calculator when needed.

1 Copy the 2 grids below:

60	38	3		63	90	38	11		66	15

40	12	63	50	9		9	50	90	9	50

There is a hidden message.

Answer the questions listed below then write the letter under the answer number in your grids.

Example. Letter B is 50% of 40   *Answer:* 20. Write the letter 'B' under all the 20's in the grid.

Letter A is 40% of 30	Letter O is 10% of 380
Letter E is 20% of 250	Letter S is $33\frac{1}{3}\%$ of 27
Letter I is 75% of 88	Letter T is 30% of 50
Letter K is 90% of 70	Letter U is 15% of 20
Letter M is 80% of 50	Letter W is 5% of 220
Letter N is 25% of 360	Letter Y is $66\frac{2}{3}\%$ of 90

2 Find the odd one out

(a) 3% of £68   (b) 8% of £32   (c) 12% of £17

3 9% of a cereal is sugar. How much sugar is there in a 750g box of cereal?

4 Which is larger:

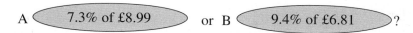

A 7.3% of £8.99 or B 9.4% of £6.81 ?

5 Rory earns £22000 each year. He gets a pay rise of 4%. How much does he now earn each year?

6 The price of a house was £160,000. During one year, the price increases by 3.5%. What is the new price of the house?

7 What is the sale price for each item below?

(a)

Digital radio £90
SALE
$33\frac{1}{3}$% off

(b)

Bed £450
SALE
35% off

8 A railcard gives a 20% discount. How much would a £9.65 train journey cost if the railcard was used?

9 Write down the percentage multiplier that would be used for the following (e.g. 'increase of 4%' means the percentage multiplier is 1.04)

(a) Increase of 25%   (b) Increase of 17.5%   (c) Decrease of 6%

(d) Reduction of 3.5%   (e) Decrease of 63%   (f) Increase of p%

10 (a) Decrease £320 by 8.5%   (b) Increase £48 by 26%

(c) Reduce £21 by 6.3%   (d) Decrease £9.85 by 3.2%

11 The population of Hatton is 11500. If the population decreases by 2%, what is the new population?

12 A car is worth £4650. After an accident its value falls by 38%. How much is it worth now?

13 A bike costs £412 + VAT. If VAT is 17.5%, work out how much the bike costs altogether.

14 A computer costs £1099. Tom gets a 14% discount. How much will Tom pay for the computer?

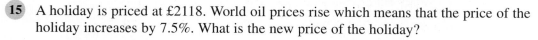

15 A holiday is priced at £2118. World oil prices rise which means that the price of the holiday increases by 7.5%. What is the new price of the holiday?

16 A new car costs £2320 + VAT (17.5%). Its value decreases by 27% after one year.

(a) What is the total price of the new car?

(b) How much does the car cost after 1 year?

17 A new watch costs £275 + VAT (17.5%). After a year-and-a-half the shop puts the watch in a sale when the price is reduced by 15%.

(a) What is the total price of the new watch?

(b) How much does the watch cost in the sale?

18 A new TV costs £550 + VAT (17.5%). In the New Year sales, the price of the TV is reduced by 18%.

(a) What is the total price of the new TV?

(b) How much does the TV cost in the New Year sales?

M Finding a percentage change

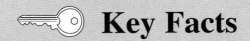

Key Facts

The price of a car increases from £9000 to £9090.

increase = £90

The price of a guitar increases from £300 to £390.

increase = £90

The *actual* increase of £90 is the same for both items but the increase is far more significant for the guitar.

A good way of comparing price changes (up or down) is to work out the *percentage* change.

For an increase,

$$\text{percentage increase} = \left(\frac{\text{actual increase}}{\text{original value}}\right) \times 100$$

For a decrease,

$$\text{percentage decrease} = \left(\frac{\text{actual decrease}}{\text{original value}}\right) \times 100$$

For the car above, % increase = $\left(\dfrac{90}{9000}\right) \times 100 = 1\%$

For the guitar, % increase = $\left(\dfrac{90}{300}\right) \times 100 = 30\%$

Note

Percentage *profit* or *loss* are calculated in the same way, changing the words 'increase' to 'profit' and 'decrease' to 'loss'.

(a) A holiday firm reduces its price of a holiday from £1740 to £1479.

Find the percentage decrease.

actual decrease $= 1740 - 1479$

$= 261$

Percentage decrease $= \left(\dfrac{261}{1740}\right) \times 100$

$= 15\%$

(b) Roger buys a box of shirts for £180 and sells them for £232.20.

Find the percentage profit.

actual profit $= 232.20 - 180$

$= 52.20$

Percentage profit $= \left(\dfrac{52.20}{180}\right) \times 100$

$= 29\%$

M2.2

Use a calculator when needed.
Give answers to one decimal place if necessary.

1. Eddie's wages were increased from £120 to £129.60 per week. What was the percentage increase?

2. A CD player is bought for £60 and sold for £69. What is the percentage profit?

3. The value of a bike drops from £240 to £160 in one year. What is the percentage decrease in that year?

4. The population of a country increases from 2,374,000 to 2,445,220. What is the percentage increase?

5. 'Dobbs Autos' has to reduce its workforce from 120 people to 93 people. What is the percentage decrease?

6. Kevin bought a car for £7350 and sold it quickly for £8100. Calculate the percentage profit.

7. The 'King's Arms' pub buys some of its items at the costs shown below and sells them at the prices shown below. Find the percentage profit on each item.

item	cost price	selling price
pint of lager	£1.20	£2.70
packet of crisps	25p	60p
pint of bitter	£1.15	£2.50
packet of nuts	27p	75p

8. Sinan buys 300 cans of drink at 30p for each can. The cans are sold at a school disco for 36p a can. What is the percentage profit if all the cans are sold?

9. The cost of a first-class stamp is increased from 28p to 29p. What is the percentage increase?

10 Arnie the grocer bought 100 cabbages at 30p each. He sold 80 of the cabbages at 65p each. The other 20 cabbages went 'rotten' and had to be thrown away. Find the percentage profit Arnie made on the 100 cabbages.

11

25 cm

15 cm

The base and height are both increased by 20%.

What is the percentage increase in the area of the triangle?

12 In 2004 a company makes a profit which is 25% higher than in 2003. In 2005 the profit drops back to the level of 2003. What was the percentage decrease from 2004 to 2005?

Can you still?

Can you still?

2A **Use decimals (see Unit 1)**

Do not use a calculator

Work out

1. 17 – 0.063   **2.** 42.6 – 3.712   **3.** 0.4 × 0.12

4. 2.6 × 1.8   **5.** 0.72 ÷ 0.8   **6.** 0.48 ÷ 0.15

7. Marcus has £50. He needs to buy 7 calculators each costing £5.39 and a book costing £12.25. Does he have enough money?

8. $0.6^2 - 0.179$ **9.** $\dfrac{0.12 - 0.0282}{0.34}$ **10.** $\dfrac{0.72 + 0.45}{0.72 + 0.18}$

M   Compound interest – type problems

£2000 is invested at 10% per annum (year) *compound* interest. How much money will there be after 2 years?

'Compound' interest here means that the interest must be worked out separately for each year.

After 1 year: total money = 2000 + 10% of 2000 = £2200

(or 1.1 × 2000 = £2200)

↑

'percentage multiplier' = 100% + 10% = 110% = 1.1

After 2 years: total money = 2200 + 10% of 2200 = £2420

money at start of 2nd year

(or (1.1 × 2000) × 1.1 = 1.1^2 × 2000 = £2420)

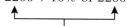

money after 1 year   'percentage multiplier' for the 2nd year

Method

Work out each year separately *or* using one calculation, total money after n years is £$(1.1^n \times 2000)$.

Simple interest

This means work out the interest for one year then multiply by the number of years.

£2000 is invested at 10% per annum (year) *simple* interest. How much money will there be after 2 years?

Interest = 10% of 2000   = 200

Total interest for 2 years   = $200 \times 2 = 400$

Total money after 2 years   = $2000 + 400 = £2400$

A car is bought for £12000. Each year, its value depreciates (goes down) by 5% of its value at the start of the year. How much is the car worth after 2 years?

Method 1	**Method 2**
After 1 year: loss = 5% of 12000	'percentage multiplier' = 100% − 5%
= 600	= 95%
value of car = 12000 − 600	= 0.95
= 11400	
After 2 years: loss = 5% of 11400	value of car after 2 years = $0.95^2 \times 12000$
= 570	= £10830
value of car = 11400 − 70	
= £10830	

M2.3

Use a calculator when needed.
Give answers to the nearest penny if necessary.

1   Ben invests £6000 in a bank at 5% per annum compound interest. How much money will he have in the bank after 2 years?

2   A bank pays 6% per annum compound interest. How much will the following people have in the bank after the number of years stated?

    (a) Kim: £9000 after 2 years.   (b) Freddie: £4000 after 3 years.

    (c) Les: £2500 after 2 years.   (d) Olive: £600 after 2 years.

3   A stereo loses 30% of its value every year.
    Tim bought it for £800. How much would it be worth after:

    (a) 2 years   (b) 3 years

4 The population of a country decreases by 4% every year. If the population is 8 million, what will it be after 3 years?

5 A bacteria culture starts with 4000 bacteria. Each hour the number of bacteria increases by 20%. How many bacteria will there be after 3 hours?

6 Inflation is how much more expensive things in the shop get each year. Inflation is about 3%.
If a pair of shoes costs £50, how much will the pair of shoes cost after:

(a) 2 years   (b) 3 years   (c) 15 years

7 Mohammed puts £200 in a bank at 6% p.a. (per annum) compound interest.
Geena puts £210 in a bank at 4% p.a. compound interest.

a) Who will have more money in the bank after 2 years?   b) By how much?

8 £3000 is invested at 6% per annum *simple* interest. How much money will there be after 10 years?

9 A bank pays 7% p.a. compound interest. If you put £1200 into the building society, how much would you have 5 years later?

10 (a) What is the percentage multiplier to find a 15% decrease?

(b) The value of a car depreciates by 15% of its value each year. Sally buys the new car for £16000.
How much will the car be worth after 7 years?

11 A bank account gives 5% compound interest each year. Jack put £600 into the bank. Copy and complete the table below:

after	money in bank
1 year	
3 years	
5 years	
10 years	

12 A population decreases by 11% each year. At the end of year 2000, the population was 3,000,000. Copy and complete the table below, giving your answers to the nearest whole number.

end of year	population
2001	
2002	
2003	
2004	

13 If a 15-year old person put £500 in a bank at 9% p.a. compound interest and left it in the bank for 50 years until retirement, how much money would be in the bank?

14 Imran invests some money in a bank at 8% p.a. compound interest. After how many years will his money have doubled?

15 The number of burglaries in a certain country rose by 8% for two years in a row from 2001 to 2003. If there were 20,000 burglaries in 2001 then:

(a) How many burglaries were there in 2002?

(b) How many burglaries were there in 2003?

(c) What was the overall percentage increase in burglaries over the two years? (note: the answer is *not* 16%).

M   Reverse percentages

A radio costs £100. Its price is increased by 10% so the radio now costs £110.

If you are told that a radio costs £110 after a 10% increase, you do *not* find the original price by finding 10% of £110 and subtracting because:

10% of 110 = 11 then 110 – 11 = £99   *This is not the original price of £100.*

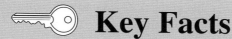

Key Facts

Any percentage increase or decrease refers to the *original* (old) amount *not* the new amount.

In the example above,

£110 is 110% of the original price (original 100% plus 10% extra)

{ Find 1% of original price }

$\dfrac{110}{110}$ is 1% of the original price

{ Find 100% of original price }

$\dfrac{110}{110} \times 100$ is 100% of the original price

so original price = £100

Rose reduces her hours at work a little and takes an 8% pay cut. She now earns £202.40 each week. What was her weekly pay before she reduced her hours?

8% decrease so £202.40 is 92% of original pay
$$(100\% - 8\%)$$

$$\dfrac{202.40}{92} \text{ is 1% of original pay}$$

$$\dfrac{202.40}{92} \times 100 \text{ is 100% of original pay}$$

original pay = £220

You may use a calculator when needed

1 Harry earns £27300 each year after a 5% pay rise. How much did he earn before the pay rise?

2 Martin's weight has increased by 8% over the last year. If he now weighs 73.44 kg, how much did he weigh one year ago?

3 Carla collects CDs. She now has 30% more CDs than 2 years ago. If she now has 91 CD's, how many did she have 2 years ago?

4 Jasmine earns £2852 each month after a 15% pay rise. How much did she earn each month before the rise?

5 A garden table is selling for £48 with a sign saying '*Reduction of 20%.*' What was the price before the sale?

6 In a sale all items are reduced by 15%. A carpet is selling for £15.30 per square metre. What was it before the sale?

7 A train ticket costs £38.76 after a 14% increase in prices. How much would the train ticket have cost before the price increase?

8 Copy and complete the table below:

	old price	% change	new price
(a)		7% increase	£28.89
(b)		20% increase	£58.20
(c)		30% decrease	£6.51
(d)		19% increase	£130.90

9 A drill costs £66.27 after VAT has been added at 17.5%. How much would the drill cost a builder who did *not* have to pay VAT?

10 A TV costs £733.20 including 17.5% VAT. How much did the TV cost before VAT was added?

11 A car repair bill is £131.60 including 17.5% VAT. How much was the repair bill before VAT was added?

12 Colin buys a car for £1500 and sells it a year later for a 22% loss. How much did Colin sell the car for?

13 Agnes sells a hockey stick for £21.60 which is a 20% loss. How much did Agnes pay for the hockey stick?

14 A school claims that the pupils' average mark in an exam has increased by 15% over 5 years. Two pupils are told that the average mark is now 85.1. George thinks that the average mark five years ago was 72.335 but Jane thinks it was 74. Who is right and how is the correct answer obtained?

15 4200 copies of a certain book were sold in March which was a decrease of 25% on the number sold in February. In April there was an increase of 40% on the number sold in March.

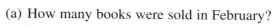

(a) How many books were sold in February?

(b) How many books were sold in April?

16 The price of a litre of petrol rose in line with inflation to 89.44p. If the annual rate of inflation was 4%, what was the price of a litre of petrol one year earlier?

17 Will pays £323.36 each month on rent. This is 43% of his monthly pay. How much is his monthly pay?

18 Jackie has £663 stolen from her whilst on holiday. This is 65% of her total holiday money. What was her total holiday money?

19 A picture is reduced by 15%. The dimensions of the reduced copy are 102 mm by 136 mm. What were the dimensions of the original picture?

 *Can you still?*

 *Can you still?*

(2B) **Use fractions (see Unit 1)**

Do not use a calculator

Work out

1. $\dfrac{3}{8} \times \dfrac{4}{5}$

2. $\dfrac{2}{3} \div \dfrac{7}{9}$

3. $1\dfrac{1}{4} \div 4\dfrac{1}{6}$

4. $2\dfrac{2}{3} \times \dfrac{9}{10}$

5. Copy and complete

+	$\dfrac{1}{10}$		$\dfrac{2}{9}$
	$\dfrac{1}{2}$		
$\dfrac{3}{8}$		$\dfrac{5}{8}$	
		$\dfrac{7}{12}$	

6. Cho has a piece of wood $2\dfrac{3}{5}$ m long. She cuts off a piece $1\dfrac{2}{3}$ m long. How long is the remaining piece of wood?

7. Charlie has 3 pieces of carpet. Their lengths are $4\dfrac{1}{6}$ m, $2\dfrac{2}{3}$ m and $1\dfrac{1}{2}$ m. What is the total length of carpet he has?

(a) $9:15 = \dfrac{9}{15} = \dfrac{3}{5} = 3:5$
simplest form

(b) 25cm:2m = 25cm:200cm
Get units the same

= 1:8
simplest form

(c) 5 doughnuts cost 80p

1 doughnut costs 16p

12 doughnuts cost $16 \times 12 = 192p = £1.92$

(d) Share £480 between Carol, Maggie and Peter in the ratio 5:3:4.

Carol : Maggie : Peter
= 5 : 3 : 4
Total of 12 shares

£480
so each share   = 480 ÷ 12
                = £40

Carol gets 5 shares
        = 5 × 40 = £200
Maggie gets 3 shares
        = 3 × 40 = £120
Peter gets 4 shares
        = 4 × 40 = £160

M2.5

1   In a hall there are 45 chairs and 9 tables. Find the ratio of chairs to tables in its *simplest form*.

2   In a class of 30 children, 18 are boys. Find the ratio of boys to girls in its *simplest form*.

3   Change the following ratios to their *simplest form*:

(a) 42:49   (b) 40:25   (c) 40:15:25   (d) 2m:20cm

(e) 5p:£2   (f) 30p:£9   (g) 75cm:3m:0.5m   (h) 0.6kg:20kg

4   5 pints of beer cost £13.30. Find the cost of 7 pints of beer.

5   17 adults can go to the cinema for £116.45. How much would 12 adults pay?

6   £320 is shared between Omar, Molly and Sachin in the ratio 3:1:4. How much will each person get?

7   A green paint is mixed from blue and yellow in the ratio 2:5. How much of each colour is needed to make 56 litres of paint?

8 The angles *p*, *q*, *r* and *s* in a quadrilateral are in the ratio 3:1:2:4.

Find the sizes of angles *p*, *q*, *r* and *s*.

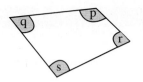

9 This recipe for pancakes serves 4 people.

> 120g plain flour
> 280 ml milk
> 2 eggs

How much of each ingredient is needed for 6 people?

10 This recipe for chocolate sponge serves 8 people.

> 220g butter
> 240g sugar
> 2 tablespoons of boiling water
> 4 eggs
> 200g self-raising flour
> 2 tablespoons of cocoa

How much of each ingredient is needed for 12 people?

11 Gravel and cement are mixed in the ratio 5:3 to make mortar.

(a) If 30 shovels of gravel are used, how many shovels of cement are needed?

(b) If 12 shovels of cement are used, how many shovels of gravel are needed?

12 A father's and son's ages are in the ratio 9:4. If the father is 45 years old, how old is the son?

13 In a factory the ratio of men to women is 5:2. If there are 235 men, how many women are there?

14 £8000 is shared between Carl and Anna in the ratio 11:5. Carl then divides his share between himself and his two brothers in the ratio 5:3:3 respectively. How much money does Carl keep?

15 Some sweets are shared between Jan and Dom in the ratio 6:5. If Jan gets *y* sweets, how many sweets does Dom get? (give the answer in terms of *y*)

16 The seven dwarves are given some money. It is shared between Dopey, Doc, Happy, Bashful, Grumpy, Sneezy and Sleepy in the ratio 8:9:4:3:10:7:12 respectively. If Grumpy gets £150, how much money do each of the seven dwarves get? What is the total amount of money?

Key Facts

3^4 ⇦ the 'power' 4 is also called the 'index' ('indices' for more than one index)

⇧

this number is called the 'base'

> To multiply numbers with indices, add the indices. The base numbers must be the same
> $a^m \times a^n = a^{m+n}$

> To divide numbers with indices, subtract the indices. The base numbers must be the same
> $a^m \div a^n = a^{m-n}$

$(5^3)^2$ $= 5^3 \times 5^3 = (5 \times 5 \times 5) \times (5 \times 5 \times 5)$

               $= 5 \times 5 \times 5 \times 5 \times 5 \times 5$

               $= 5^6$

               $(= 5^{3 \times 2})$

> To raise an index number to another power, multiply the indices.
> $(a^m)^n = a^{mn}$

$a^n \div a^n = a^{n-n} \quad = a^0$

$a^n \div a^n = \dfrac{\cancel{a^n}}{\cancel{a^n}}_1 \quad = 1$ ➜ $\boxed{a^0 = 1}$

> $a^0 = 1$
> for any number a
> (apart from $a = 0$)

(a) $(6^2)^3 \times 6^2 = 6^6 \times 6^2 = 6^8$

(b) $\dfrac{a^7}{a^3} = a^4$

(c) $\dfrac{b^8 \times (b^3)^2}{(b^2)^4} = \dfrac{b^8 \times b^6}{b^8} = \dfrac{b^{14}}{b^8} = b^6$

(d) $3a^2 \times 2a^3$

        $= (3 \times 2) \times (a^2 \times a^3)$

        $= 6a^5$

(e) $\dfrac{\overset{12}{\cancel{48}}a^7}{\underset{1}{\cancel{4}}a^4} = \dfrac{12a^7}{a^4} = 12a^3$

(f) $(6a^2)^3 = 6^3(a^2)^3 = 216a^6$

M2.6

1   Copy and complete the following:

(a) $2^4 = 2 \times 2 \times 2 \times 2 = \boxed{}$

(b) $3^5 = 3 \times 3 \times 3 \times 3 \times 3 = \boxed{}$

(c) $2^5 = \boxed{}$

(d) $5^3 = \boxed{}$

(e) $2^3 \times 3^2 = 2 \times 2 \times 2 \times 3 \times 3 = \boxed{}$

(f) $5^2 \times 2^2 = \boxed{}$

2 Copy and complete the following, giving each answer in index form.

(a) $3^4 \times 3^2 = 3^{\square}$ (b) $2^3 \times 2^5 = 2^{\square}$ (c) $8^7 \div 8^4 = 8^{\square}$

(d) $6^7 \div 6^5 = 6^{\square}$ (e) $(9^2)^3 = 9^{\square}$ (f) $(4^3)^4 = 4^{\square}$

3 Work out and write each answer as a number in index form.

(a) $5^2 \times 5^4$ (b) $7^2 \times 7^3$ (c) $6^5 \times 6^2$

(d) $9^8 \div 9^5$ (e) $5^5 \div 5^2$ (f) $4^6 \div 4^5$

(g) $(5^3)^2$ (h) $(7^4)^2$ (i) 8^0

(j) $(5^6)^3$ (k) 9^0 (l) $4^7 \times 4^3$

4 Copy and complete. Write the number in index form.

(a) $(3^4)^2 \times 3^3$ (b) $(2^3)^4 \times 2^6$ (c) $6^5 \times (6^2)^2$

(d) $\dfrac{7^3}{7^0}$ (e) $\dfrac{(5^2)^4}{(5^3)^2}$ (f) $\dfrac{9 \times (9^3)^3}{9^7}$

(g) $\dfrac{8^2 \times 8^6}{(8^2)^3}$ (h) $\dfrac{4^3 \times (4^5)^2}{4^7}$ (i) $\dfrac{(2^3)^2 \times (2^3)^2}{2^4 \times 2^3}$

5 Copy and complete

(a) $3^4 \times 3^2 = \boxed{}$ (b) $\boxed{} \times 6^4 = 6^6$ (c) $\boxed{} \times 9^4 = 9^7$

(d) $4^6 \times \boxed{} = 4^8$ (e) $9^3 \times \boxed{} = 9^4$ (f) $4^8 \div 4^2 = \boxed{}$

(g) $3^8 \div \boxed{} = 3^2$ (h) $8^{10} \div \boxed{} = 8^5$ (i) $\boxed{} \div 4^5 = 4^7$

6 Simplify the expressions below.

(a) $a^4 \times a^3$ (b) $x^7 \times x^4$ (c) $x^9 \div x^4$

(d) $(n^3)^2$ (e) $a^{10} \div a^6$ (f) $(x^3)^3$

(g) n^0 (h) $p^8 \times p$ (i) $m^{14} \div m^8$

(j) $(x^2)^0$ (k) $(a^2)^4 \times a^5$ (l) $x^p \div x^p$

7 Which is larger?

A $\dfrac{(3^3)^2 \times 3^2}{3^3 \times (3^2)^2}$ or   B $\dfrac{(3^2)^3 \times 3^3}{3^5 \times 3^2}$

8 Simplify the expressions below.

(a) $\dfrac{x^5 \times x^3}{x^6}$ (b) $\dfrac{a^2 \times a^6}{(a^2)^2}$ (c) $\dfrac{(m^3)^2 \times m^4}{(m^3)^3}$

(d) $\dfrac{a^8}{a^3 \times a}$ (e) $\dfrac{n^9 \times (n^2)^4}{(n^3)^5}$ (f) $\dfrac{(x^8) \times x^4}{(x^3)^2 \times x^2}$

9 Write down the area of this square in index form:

3^4 cm

10 Find a in each of the following:

    (a) $2^3 \times 2^a = 2^7$
        (b) $x^5 \times x^a = x^6$
        (c) $y^2 \times y^a = y^2$

    (d) $r^a \div r^{11} = r^9$
        (e) $5^a \div 5^9 = 5^7$
        (f) $2^9 \div 2^a = 2^2$

    (g) $(3^5)^a = 3^{20}$
        (h) $(y^a)^a = y^9$
        (i) $(x^a)^{a+1} = x^{42}$

11 Simplify the expressions below.

    (a) $5a^3 \times 2a^4$
        (b) $3a^2 \times 5a^6$
        (c) $5p^3 \times 2p^2$

    (d) $-8a^2 \times -3a^4$
        (e) $5a^3 \times a^6$
        (f) $-6b^4 \times 3b^3$

12 Simplify the expressions below

    (a) $12a^6 \div 4a^2$
        (b) $25a^7 \div 5a^5$
        (c) $\dfrac{32c^{10}}{8c^3}$

    (d) $\dfrac{40m^9}{10m^4}$
        (e) $56a^8 \div 7a^4$
        (f) $63m^{12} \div 9m^7$

13 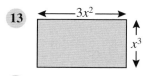 Write down the area of this rectangle in index form.

14 What is the value of $(4^0)^6$?

15 Simplify the following.

    (a) $(3a^2)^2$
        (b) $(2b^3)^3$
        (c) $(5p^4)^3$
        (d) $(7a^3)^2$

16 Multiply out the brackets below, leaving each answer in index form.

    (a) $x^3(x^3 + x^2)$
        (b) $n^4(n^5 - n)$
        (c) $x^7(x^2 + x^5)$

Can you still?

2C   **Simplify surds (see Unit 1)**

Can you still?

Simplify as far as possible:

1. $\sqrt{48}$
        2. $\sqrt{75}$
        3. $\sqrt{75} - \sqrt{48}$
        4. $(2\sqrt{5})^2$

5. $\dfrac{\sqrt{27} \times \sqrt{5}}{\sqrt{15}}$
        6. $(\sqrt{3} - 1)(\sqrt{3} + 1)$
        7. $(\sqrt{5} + 2)(\sqrt{3} - 1)$

8. Find the 'exact' area of this square.

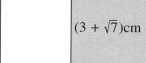 $(3 + \sqrt{7})$cm

9. Rationalise the denominator in each of the following:

    (a) $\dfrac{1}{\sqrt{5}}$
        (b) $\dfrac{6}{\sqrt{3}}$
        (c) $\dfrac{1 + \sqrt{2}}{\sqrt{2}}$

10. Show that $\dfrac{\sqrt{5}}{10} + \dfrac{2}{\sqrt{5}} = \dfrac{\sqrt{5}}{2}$ (can be written as $\frac{1}{2}\sqrt{5}$)

Key Facts

$$a^0 \div a^n = \frac{a^0}{a^n} = \frac{1}{a^n}$$

$$a^0 \div a^n = a^{0-n} = a^{-n}$$

$$a^{-n} = \frac{1}{a^n}$$

Note $\frac{1}{a}$ is known as the *reciprocal* of a

so a^{-n} is the *reciprocal* of a^n $\left(\frac{1}{a^n}\right)$

(a) $5^{-2} = \frac{1}{5^2} = \frac{1}{25}$

(b) $8^{-1} = \frac{1}{8^1} = \frac{1}{8}$

(c) $7^{-3} = \frac{1}{7^3} = \frac{1}{343}$

(d) $\left(\frac{1}{4}\right)^{-2} = \frac{1}{\left(\frac{1}{4}\right)^2} = \frac{1}{\frac{1}{16}} = 16$

E2.1

Do not use a calculator

1 Copy and complete the following:

(a) 6^{-2}

(b) 3^{-1}

(c) 6^{-3}

$= \dfrac{1}{6^{\square}}$

$= \dfrac{1}{3^{\square}}$

$= \dfrac{1}{6^{\square}}$

$= \dfrac{1}{\square}$

$= \dfrac{1}{\square}$

$= \dfrac{1}{\square}$

2 Write the following as ordinary numbers.

(a) 3^{-2} (b) 10^{-3} (c) 2^{-1} (d) 10^{-1}

(e) 8^{-2} (f) 2^{-2} (g) 3^{-3} (h) 2^{-4}

(i) 7^{-2} (j) 4^{-4} (k) 20^{-1} (l) 5^{-4}

3 Which of the statements below are true?

(a) $\dfrac{1}{4} = 4^{-1}$ (b) $\dfrac{3}{4} = 4^{-3}$ (c) $\dfrac{2}{5} = 5^{-2}$ (d) $\dfrac{1}{3^4} = 3^{-4}$

4 Write the following in negative index form.

(a) $\dfrac{1}{5^3}$ (b) $\dfrac{1}{6^4}$ (c) $\dfrac{1}{3^7}$ (d) $\dfrac{1}{9^5}$

5 Express the following in negative index form using the stated numbers.

(a) $\dfrac{1}{36}$ as a power of 6

(b) $\dfrac{1}{16}$ as a power of 2

(c) $\dfrac{1}{125}$ as a power of 5

(d) $\dfrac{1}{1024}$ as a power of 2

6 Write the following as ordinary numbers

(a) $\left(\dfrac{1}{3}\right)^{-1}$

(b) $\left(\dfrac{3}{5}\right)^{-2}$

(c) $\left(\dfrac{7}{3}\right)^{-2}$

7 Write the following as ordinary numbers.

(a) $\left(\dfrac{1}{2}\right)^{-1}$

(b) $\left(\dfrac{2}{7}\right)^{-1}$

(c) $\left(\dfrac{2}{3}\right)^{-2}$

(d) $\left(\dfrac{1}{4}\right)^{-3}$

(e) $\left(\dfrac{2}{9}\right)^{-2}$

(f) $\left(\dfrac{3}{10}\right)^{-1}$

(g) $\left(\dfrac{1}{4}\right)^{-4}$

(h) $\left(\dfrac{5}{9}\right)^{-2}$

8 Which of the statements below are true?

(a) $5^3 \times 5^{-1} = 5^2$

(b) $7^{-2} \times 7^{-2} = 7^4$

(c) $\left(\dfrac{1}{4}\right)^{-1} = -3$

(d) $6^2 \div 6^5 = 6^{-3}$

(e) $8^{-1} = -8$

(f) $3^{-1} > 4^{-1}$

(g) $\left(\dfrac{1}{2}\right)^0 = -1$

(h) $\left(\dfrac{2}{5}\right)^{-2} = \dfrac{25}{4}$

(i) $6^{-1} \times 6^{-1} = 6^{-2}$

9 Simplify the expression below.

(a) $(x^{-1})^{-2}$

(b) $\dfrac{a^2 \times a^{-5}}{a^3}$

(c) $\dfrac{(x^2)^{-3}}{x^3 \times x^{-1}}$

(d) $(3x^{-2})^2$

(e) $\dfrac{2b^{-3} \times 3b^{-2}}{12b^3}$

(f) $\dfrac{(4a^{-3})^3}{2a^4 \times 4a^2}$

10 Express the following in the form 8^n

(a) $\dfrac{1}{8}$

(b) 8

(c) 1

(d) 64

(e) $\dfrac{1}{64}$

(f) $\dfrac{1}{512}$

E   **Indices 3 – Fractional indices**

$3^{\frac{1}{2}} \times 3^{\frac{1}{2}} = 3^{\frac{1}{2}+\frac{1}{2}} = 3^1 = 3$

$3^{\frac{1}{2}} \times 3^{\frac{1}{2}} = (3^{\frac{1}{2}})^2$

$(3^{\frac{1}{2}})^2 = 3$
so $3^{\frac{1}{2}} = \sqrt{3}$

$5^{\frac{1}{3}} \times 5^{\frac{1}{3}} \times 5^{\frac{1}{3}} = 5^{\frac{1}{3}+\frac{1}{3}+\frac{1}{3}} = 5^1 = 5$

$5^{\frac{1}{3}} \times 5^{\frac{1}{3}} \times 5^{\frac{1}{3}} = (5^{\frac{1}{3}})^3$

$(5^{\frac{1}{3}})^3 = 5$
so $5^{\frac{1}{3}} = \sqrt[3]{5}$

 **Key Facts**

$$a^{\frac{1}{2}} = \sqrt{a} \qquad a^{\frac{1}{3}} = \sqrt[3]{a} \qquad a^{\frac{1}{4}} = \sqrt[4]{a}$$

$$a^{\frac{1}{n}} = \sqrt[n]{a}$$

A fractional index indicates '*rooting*'.

(a) $64^{\frac{1}{3}} = \sqrt[3]{64} = 4$

(b) $16^{\frac{-1}{4}} = \dfrac{1}{16^{\frac{1}{4}}} = \dfrac{1}{\sqrt[4]{16}} = \dfrac{1}{2}$

(c) $\left(\dfrac{81}{100}\right)^{\frac{-1}{2}} = \left(\dfrac{100}{81}\right)^{\frac{1}{2}} = \dfrac{\sqrt{100}}{\sqrt{81}} = \dfrac{10}{9}$

(d) $\sqrt[3]{8a^{12}} = (8a^{12})^{\frac{1}{3}} = 8^{\frac{1}{3}}(a^{12})^{\frac{1}{3}}$
$$= \sqrt[3]{8}\, a^{12 \times \frac{1}{3}} = 2a^4$$

E2.2

Do not use a calculator.

1 Copy and complete the following:

(a) $9^{\frac{1}{2}}$

$= \sqrt{\boxed{}}$

$= \boxed{}$

(b) $27^{\frac{1}{3}}$

$= \sqrt[3]{\boxed{}}$

$= \boxed{}$

(c) $36^{\frac{-1}{2}}$

$= \dfrac{1}{\boxed{}^{\frac{1}{2}}}$

$= \dfrac{1}{\sqrt{\boxed{}}}$

$= \dfrac{1}{\boxed{}}$

2 Evaluate the following:

(a) $4^{\frac{1}{2}}$ (b) $8^{\frac{1}{3}}$ (c) $125^{\frac{1}{3}}$ (d) $64^{\frac{1}{6}}$

(e) $81^{\frac{1}{4}}$ (f) $27^{\frac{-1}{3}}$ (g) $32^{\frac{-1}{5}}$ (h) $64^{\frac{-1}{2}}$

(i) $169^{\frac{-1}{2}}$ (j) $1000^{\frac{-1}{3}}$ (k) $9^{\frac{-1}{2}}$ (l) $1024^{\frac{-1}{10}}$

3 Find a in each of the following:

(a) $\sqrt{6} = 6^a$ (b) $\dfrac{1}{\sqrt[3]{23}} = 23^a$ (c) $\dfrac{1}{\sqrt{37}} = 37^a$ (d) $\sqrt[3]{5} = 5^a$

4 Express the following as powers of 64:

(a) 64   (b) 8   (c) 4

(d) 2   (e) 1   (f) $\dfrac{1}{64}$

(g) $\dfrac{1}{8}$ (h) $\dfrac{1}{2}$ (i) $\dfrac{1}{4}$

5 Evaluate the following:

(a) $9^{\frac{1}{2}}$ (b) $64^{\frac{1}{3}}$ (c) $81^{\frac{1}{2}}$ (d) $10000^{\frac{1}{4}}$

(e) $32^{\frac{1}{5}}$ (f) $121^{\frac{1}{2}}$ (g) $144^{-\frac{1}{2}}$ (h) $49^{-\frac{1}{2}}$

(i) $125^{-\frac{1}{3}}$ (j) $\left(\dfrac{4}{9}\right)^{\frac{1}{2}}$ (k) $\left(\dfrac{1}{27}\right)^{\frac{1}{3}}$ (l) $\left(\dfrac{27}{64}\right)^{\frac{1}{3}}$

(m) $\left(\dfrac{125}{64}\right)^{-\frac{1}{3}}$ (n) $\left(\dfrac{36}{49}\right)^{-\frac{1}{2}}$ (o) $\left(\dfrac{216}{125}\right)^{\frac{1}{3}}$ (p) $\left(\dfrac{16}{625}\right)^{\frac{1}{4}}$

6 Simplify the following:

(a) $(f^4 \times f^5)^{\frac{1}{3}}$ (b) $\sqrt[3]{r^6}$ (c) $\sqrt[5]{s^{15}}$

(d) $\dfrac{1}{\sqrt{q^3 \times q^7}}$ (e) $\dfrac{e^3}{\sqrt[3]{e^2 \times e^{13}}}$ (f) $\sqrt{(x^2)^3 \times (x^2)^2}$

(g) $\sqrt{4x^2}$ (h) $\sqrt[3]{27y^6}$ (i) $(64z^{12})^{\frac{1}{2}}$

(j) $(16w^{20})^{\frac{1}{4}}$ (k) $(32q^{10})^{\frac{1}{5}}$ (l) $(4k^8)^{-\frac{1}{2}}$

(m) $\sqrt{9a^4b^2}$ (n) $(16m^4n^2)^{\frac{1}{2}}$ (o) $\sqrt[3]{8h^3k^6}$

Can you still?

2D   **Convert recurring decimals into fractions (see Unit 1)**

Express the following recurring decimals as fractions in their lowest form:

1. $0.\dot{4}$ **2.** $0.\dot{3}\dot{9}$ **3.** $0.5\dot{2}\dot{8}$

4. $0.712712712......$ **5.** $0.0\dot{9}\dot{2}$

Can you still?

Key Facts

$a^{m/n}$ can be written as $a^{m \times \frac{1}{n}} = (a^m)^{\frac{1}{n}}$

so $a^{m/n} = \sqrt[n]{a^m}$

$a^{m/n}$ can also be written as $a^{\frac{1}{n} \times m} = \left(a^{\frac{1}{n}}\right)^m$

so $a^{m/n} = (\sqrt[n]{a})^m$

Use whichever form is most convenient.

(a) $36^{\frac{3}{2}} = (36^{\frac{1}{2}})^3 = (\sqrt{36})^3 = 6^3 = 216$

Note that this is easier to work out by finding the roots first.

(b) $\left(\dfrac{27}{8}\right)^{-\frac{2}{3}} = \left(\dfrac{8}{27}\right)^{\frac{2}{3}} = \left(\dfrac{8^{\frac{1}{3}}}{27^{\frac{1}{3}}}\right)^2 = \left(\dfrac{\sqrt[3]{8}}{\sqrt[3]{27}}\right)^2 = \left(\dfrac{2}{3}\right)^2 = \dfrac{4}{9}$

E2.3

Do not use a calculator.

1 Evaluate the following:

(a) $64^{\frac{2}{3}}$

(b) $4^{\frac{5}{2}}$

(c) $100^{-\frac{3}{2}}$

2 Evaluate the following:

(a) $25^{\frac{3}{2}}$ (b) $32^{\frac{2}{5}}$ (c) $9^{\frac{3}{2}}$ (d) $16^{\frac{3}{4}}$

(e) $1000^{\frac{4}{3}}$ (f) $4^{-\frac{5}{2}}$ (g) $32^{-\frac{4}{5}}$ (h) $125^{-\frac{2}{3}}$

(i) $81^{-\frac{3}{4}}$ (j) $64^{-\frac{2}{3}}$ (k) $49^{\frac{3}{2}}$ (l) $1024^{-\frac{3}{5}}$

3 (a) $\dfrac{4}{9}$ can be written in the form $\left(\dfrac{2}{3}\right)^a$. Find a.

(b) $\dfrac{4}{9}$ can be written in the form $\left(\dfrac{8}{27}\right)^b$. Find b.

(c) $\dfrac{4}{9}$ can be written in the form $\left(\dfrac{27}{8}\right)^c$. Find c.

4 Evaluate the following:

(a) $\left(\dfrac{64}{27}\right)^{\frac{2}{3}}$ (b) $\left(\dfrac{8}{125}\right)^{-\frac{4}{3}}$ (c) $\left(\dfrac{49}{81}\right)^{-\frac{3}{2}}$

5 Evaluate the following:

(a) $\left(\dfrac{100}{121}\right)^{\frac{3}{2}}$　　　(b) $\left(\dfrac{1}{32}\right)^{-\frac{3}{5}}$　　　(c) $\left(\dfrac{9}{16}\right)^{-\frac{3}{2}}$　　　(d) $\left(\dfrac{27}{1000}\right)^{-\frac{4}{3}}$

6 Which of the statements below are true?

(a) $27^{\frac{2}{3}} = 18$　　　(b) $16^{-\frac{1}{2}} = 8$　　　(c) $25^{-\frac{3}{2}} = \dfrac{1}{125}$

(d) $\left(\dfrac{216}{27}\right)^{-\frac{2}{3}} = \dfrac{1}{4}$　　　(e) $\left(\dfrac{1}{64}\right)^{-\frac{3}{2}} = 512$　　　(f) $\left(\dfrac{9}{25}\right)^{-\frac{1}{2}} = \dfrac{-3}{5}$

7 Simplify the following:

(a) $(8p^9)^{\frac{2}{3}}$　　　(b) $(8a^3b^6)^{\frac{2}{3}}$　　　(c) $(27j^{18})^{-\frac{2}{3}}$

(d) $\left(\dfrac{8}{f^9}\right)^{-\frac{4}{3}}$　　　(e) $\left(\dfrac{16a^4}{b^8}\right)^{\frac{3}{4}}$　　　(f) $\left(\dfrac{a^2}{25b^{10}}\right)^{-\frac{3}{2}}$

(g) $\dfrac{\sqrt{(4z)}}{z^3}$　　　(h) $\sqrt{r} \times \sqrt[3]{r}$　　　(i) $\dfrac{12x^3\sqrt{x}}{4x^2}$

E　Indices 5 – Finding indices from equations

Solve　　　$3^x = 81$　　　　　　　$4^{1-x} = 8$

get the base number
to be the same

get the base number
to be the same

$3^x = 3^4$　　　　　　　　　$(2^2)^{1-x} = 2^3$

so $x = 4$　　　　　　　　　$2^{2(1-x)} = 2^3$

so $2(1 - x) = 3$

$2 - 2x = 3$

$-1 = 2x$

$x = \dfrac{-1}{2}$

1 Solve the equations

(a) $5^x = \dfrac{1}{125}$

(b) $2^x = 1$

(c) $2^x = 64$

(d) $6^x = 216$

(e) $4^x = \dfrac{1}{16}$

(f) $10^x = 0.001$

(g) $2^x = \dfrac{1}{8}$

(h) $2^x = 0.25$

(i) $6^x = \dfrac{1}{36}$

2 Copy and complete

(a) $2^x = \dfrac{1}{32}$

$2^x = \dfrac{1}{2^\square}$

$2^x = 2^\square$

$x = \boxed{}$

(b) $\left(\dfrac{1}{5}\right)^{\frac{x}{2}} = 125$

$(5^\square)^{\frac{x}{2}} = 5^\square$

$\dfrac{-x}{2} = \boxed{}$

$x = \boxed{}$

3 Find x in the following:

(a) $32^x = 2$

(b) $81^x = 3$

(c) $125^x = 5$

(d) $49^x = 7$

(e) $121^x = 11$

(f) $27^x = 3$

(g) $243^x = 3$

(h) $256^x = 16$

(i) $3^x = \dfrac{1}{3}$

(j) $81^x = \dfrac{1}{3}$

(k) $125^x = \dfrac{1}{5}$

(l) $512^x = \dfrac{1}{2}$

4 Find x in the following:

(a) $m^3 \times \sqrt[3]{m} = m^x$

(b) $m^x \times \dfrac{1}{m^4} = \dfrac{1}{m^5}$

(c) $\dfrac{\sqrt{m}}{m^x} = m^2$

(d) $\sqrt[4]{a} \times (a^x)^2 = a^3$

(e) $\dfrac{n^3}{\sqrt{n^x}} = \dfrac{1}{n^2}$

(f) $\dfrac{m^{x-3}}{m^4} = \dfrac{1}{\sqrt{m}}$

5 Solve

(a) $4^{\frac{x}{2}} = \dfrac{1}{32}$

(b) $49^x = \dfrac{1}{343}$

(c) $1000^x = 0.01$

(d) $2^{x+3} = 4^{2x}$

(e) $4^x = (\sqrt{2})^6$

(f) $5^{\frac{4x}{3}} = 125^{\frac{2}{3}}$

6 Solve

(a) $\left(\dfrac{2}{3}\right)^x = \dfrac{9}{4}$

(b) $\left(\dfrac{3}{5}\right)^x = \dfrac{27}{125}$

(c) $\left(\dfrac{2}{5}\right)^x = \dfrac{125}{8}$

(d) $\left(\dfrac{10}{7}\right)^x = \dfrac{49}{100}$

(e) $\left(\dfrac{9}{4}\right)^x = \dfrac{32}{243}$

(f) $\left(\dfrac{1}{2}\right)^x = 1024$

(g) $\left(\dfrac{8}{27}\right)^x = \dfrac{81}{16}$

(h) $\left(\dfrac{3}{4}\right)^x = \dfrac{16}{9}$

(i) $\left(\dfrac{8}{125}\right)^x = \dfrac{25}{4}$

The 'power' button on a calculator is x^y or y^x or $\wedge$

| 4 | $y.x$ | 3 | = | | 64 (4^3) |

| 9 | $y.x$ | 0 | . | 5 | = | 3 | ($9^{0.5} = \sqrt{9}$) |

E2.5

Do the problems *without using a calculator*. Whenever appropriate, check answers by using a calculator.

1 Evaluate the following:

(a) 4^{-2}

(b) $49^{\frac{1}{2}}$

(c) 9^{-1}

(d) $25^{\frac{3}{2}}$

(e) $\left(\frac{1}{5}\right)^{-1}$

(f) $\left(\frac{1}{7}\right)^{0}$

(g) $\left(\frac{49}{81}\right)^{\frac{1}{2}}$

(h) $\left(\frac{125}{8}\right)^{-\frac{1}{3}}$

2 Write each expression below as a power of 2:

(a) $8^3 \times 16^2$

(b) $\dfrac{16 \times 32^2}{8^3}$

(c) $16\sqrt{2}$

3 Simplify

(a) $(2a^2)^3$

(b) $(5ab^2)^2$

(c) $\sqrt{(64a^4)}$

(d) $\sqrt{(25a^2b^6)}$

(e) $(2a^3)^5$

(f) $(3m^2n^4)^4$

4 There are estimated to be 10^{12} bacteria in a dish. After an antibiotic is added, the number of bacteria is reduced to one millionth of the original. How many bacteria are left?

5

The volume of this cuboid is 81 cm^3.

Find the value of h, giving your answer in index notation.

6 Simplify

(a) $\dfrac{12a^{14}b^8}{(3a^4b^3) \times (2a^2b^3)}$

(b) $\dfrac{(36m^6n^2) \times (3m^2n^4)}{(3m^2n)^2}$

(c) $\dfrac{(4a^2b^3)^2}{\sqrt{(64a^2)}}$

7 Find x in the following

(a) $4^x = 32$

(b) $25^x = 125$

(c) $64^x = \dfrac{1}{4}$

(d) $2^{4x+1} = 4^{x+1}$

(e) $9^{2x-1} = 27^{x+2}$

(f) $32^{3x-1} = 16^{4x-3}$

8 Sarwan has £(2^{16}) to share equally between 8 people. How much does each person get (leave your answer in index form)?

9 Which is true: $\boxed{3m^{-1} = \dfrac{3}{m}}$ or $\boxed{3m^{-1} = \dfrac{1}{3m}}$?

10 Given that $4y^{-2} = 4(y^{-2}) = 4\left(\dfrac{1}{y^2}\right) = \dfrac{4}{y^2}$, find the value of:

(a) $5m^{-2}$ when $m = 2$

(b) $8y^{-1}$ when $y = 4$

(c) $10n^{-3}$ when $n = 5$

(d) $6a^{-2}$ when $a = 4$

11 Evaluate the following:

(a) $\left(2\frac{1}{4}\right)^{-\frac{1}{2}}$

(b) $\left(2\frac{7}{9}\right)^{\frac{3}{2}}$

(c) $\left(\frac{3}{7}\right)^{-2}$

(d) $\left(2\frac{10}{27}\right)^{-\frac{2}{3}}$

12 (a) Find x if $\dfrac{8^x \times 64^3}{16^7} = 32$

(b) Find x if $\dfrac{81^x \times 9^2}{27^4} = 1$

WATCH YOUR MONEY! – Pricing your holiday

The table below shows the prices in £'s per person for two adults to share a twin/double room in different hotels in a European city. The price includes travelling by air from the UK and includes breakfast in the hotel.

Hotels	Hotel Rio		Tulip Hotel		Carling Hotel		Hotel Eden	
departure date	1 night	extra night	1 night	extra night	1 night	extra night	1 night	extra night
01 Apr – 27 Oct	174	77	185	84	210	99	216	105
28 Oct – 10 Nov	161	62	185	84	198	86	191	85
11 Nov – 5 Dec	161	62	171	73	210	99	190	84
6 Dec – 21 Dec	161	62	171	73	210	99	216	105
22 Dec – 5 Jan	174	77	187	88	219	103	216	105
6 Jan – 10 Jan	174	77	185	84	214	101	212	101
11 Jan – 20 Jan	159	60	171	73	187	81	186	75
21 Jan – 2 Mar	159	62	171	73	187	81	188	77
3 Mar – 10 Mar	161	63	175	74	192	83	218	107
11 Mar – 18 Mar	161	62	175	74	198	86	220	109
19 Mar – 31 Mar	179	81	191	86	215	103	228	117

Weekend supplement: £12 per person for Friday and Saturday departures.

Seasonal supplement of £12 per person applies for departures between: 28 Apr – 3 May, 28 – 31 May, 26 – 30 Aug, 24 – 27 Dec, 30 Dec – 2 Jan.

'Weekend supplement' means each person pays £12 extra if they depart on a Friday or Saturday.

'Seasonal supplement' means each person pays £12 extra if they depart on the dates shown.

£

£

£

£

£

47

(a) 2 people want to spend 4 nights at the Carling Hotel, leaving on 15th November. How much will this cost?

Look along the '11 Nov – 5 Dec' row and stop at the Carling Hotel column. The cost per person is £210 plus £99 for each extra night.

Total cost per person for 4 nights = 210 + 99 × 3 = £507

Total cost for 2 people = 507 × 2 = £1014

(b) 4 people want to spend 3 nights at the Tulip Hotel. They want to depart for their holiday on 7th August which is a Saturday. How much will the holiday cost for these 4 people?

Look along the '01 Apr – 27 Oct' row and stop at the Tulip Hotel column. The cost per person is £185 plus £84 for each extra night.

Total cost per person for 3 nights = 185 + 84 × 2 = £353

Depart on Saturday so weekend supplement = £12

Total cost per person = £365

Total cost for 4 people = 365 × 4 = £1460

Remember

There is also the cost of getting to the airport, spending money, money for main meals, travel insurance and other items.

WYM2

1. 2 people want to spend 3 nights at the Hotel Eden leaving on 23rd January. How much will this cost?

2. Mr. and Mrs. Rowan want to spend 2 nights at the Carling Hotel, leaving on 10th May which is a Friday. How much will the holiday cost?

3. 4 people want to spend 5 nights at the Hotel Rio leaving on the 3rd March. What is the total cost of this holiday?

4. 2 people want to spend 4 nights at the Hotel Rio leaving on 20th September which is a Saturday. How much will the holiday cost for these 2 people?

5. A party of 10 people want to spend 2 nights at the Tulip Hotel leaving on the 27th August (a seasonal supplement will be payable). What is the total cost of the holiday?

6 Jack and Susan are celebrating their Silver Wedding anniversary by spending 3 nights at the Carling Hotel. They plan to depart on 9th December which is a Friday. How much will this holiday cost?

7 6 people want to spend 7 nights at the Hotel Eden, departing on the 20th March. What is the total cost of this holiday?

8 4 people want to spend 6 nights at the Hotel Rio leaving on 28th May (a seasonal supplement will be payable). How much will this holiday cost?

9 Mr. and Mrs. Harris want to spend 14 nights at the Tulip Hotel departing on the 2nd June which is a Friday. How much will this holiday cost?

10 20 people want to stay at the Carling Hotel for two nights for a wedding, departing on the 25th March. What is the total cost of this stay?

TEST YOURSELF ON UNIT 2

1. Finding percentage increases and decreases

(a) Callum bought a car for £800 and sold it a year later for a loss of 25%. How much did he sell the car for?

(b) Bethan's annual salary of £18200 is increased by 7%. What is her new annual salary?

(c) The profits of a company in 2004 were £7,000,000. In 2005 the profits rose by 15%. What were the profits in 2005?

(d) An internet company claims to offer holidays at prices which are 18% cheaper than in the high street.
How much would it charge for a holiday which cost £450 in the high street?

(e) A computer costs £1250 + VAT.
If VAT is 17.5%, work out how much the computer costs altogether.

2. Finding a percentage change (including percentage profit/loss)

(a) A bike is selling for £180. The shop then reduces the price by £21.60. What percentage does this reduction represent?

(b) The fees for a nursery were £450 in April and £517.50 in May. What is the percentage increase?

(c) Luke was paid £20,000 one year. The next year he was paid £23,000. What was his percentage increase?

(d) The population of Ireland in 1901 was 3,221,823. In 1936 it was 2,968,420. By what percentage did the population of Ireland decrease from 1901 to 1936? (give the answer to 3 significant figures)

3. Solving compound interest-type problems

(a) Megan invests £4000 in a bank at 6% per annum compound interest. How much money will she have in the bank after 2 years?

(b) In a certain area, the population of rabbits is 1600. Each year the rabbit population is decreasing by 6% of its number at the start of the year. What will the rabbit population be in three years time? (give the answer to the nearest whole number)

(c) The shares of a certain company fell by 10% per month for three consecutive months. If they were 780p before the fall then what were they after the fall?

4. Working out reverse percentages

(a) Jenny sold a vase for £250. This was a profit of 25%. How much did she buy the vase for?

(b) Daniel's salary is increased by 5%. He now earns £27,090. What did he earn before the pay rise?

(c) A garage sold a car at a loss of 4%. If it sold the car for £11,100, what did the garage pay for the car?

(d) A washing machine costs £615.70 including 17.5% VAT. How much was the washing machine before VAT was added?

5. Using ratios

(a) 45 sweets were shared between Chloe and Lewis in the ratio 7:2. How many sweets did each person get?

(b) The angles x, y and z in a triangle are in the ratio 9:7:4.

Find the sizes of angles x, y and z.

(c) 8 bottles of wine cost £51.12. Find the cost of 5 bottles of wine.

(d) Write the ratio 30 cm: 2 m in its simplest form.

(e) A photo is enlarged in the ratio 2:5. If the original measures 8 cm by 12 cm, what will the area of the enlarged photo be?

6. Multiplying and dividing using indices

Work out and write each answer as a number in index form.

(a) $7^8 \div 7^3$

(b) $(6^3)^2$

(c) $5^9 \times 5^3 \times 5^4$

(d) $\dfrac{3^4 \times (3^2)^3}{3^7}$

(e) $\dfrac{8^3 \times 8^4}{(8^0)^3}$

(f) $\dfrac{6^2 \times (6^3)^3}{(6^2)^2 \times 6^5}$

Simplify the following:

(g) $\dfrac{a^8}{a^5}$

(h) $\dfrac{n^4 \times n}{n^3}$

(i) $\dfrac{x^3 \times x^7}{(x^2)^4}$

(j) $3n^4 \times 2n^2$

(k) $\dfrac{12a^6}{4a^4}$

(l) $(4a^2)^3$

Write the following as ordinary numbers.

(a) 6^{-2} (b) 5^{-1} (c) 2^{-3} (d) $\left(\dfrac{2}{5}\right)^{-2}$

(e) $\left(\dfrac{7}{3}\right)^{-1}$ (f) $\left(\dfrac{1}{2}\right)^{-4}$ (g) $\left(\dfrac{10}{3}\right)^{-2}$ (h) $\left(\dfrac{4}{3}\right)^{-3}$

Simplify

(i) $\dfrac{a^{-6} \times a^2}{a}$ (j) $(4a^2)^{-1}$ (k) $\dfrac{(m^3)^{-1}}{m^{-2} \times m^4}$

8. Using fractional indices

Evaluate the following:

(a) $64^{\frac{1}{2}}$ (b) $125^{\frac{1}{3}}$ (c) $125^{\frac{2}{3}}$

(d) $\left(\dfrac{1}{64}\right)^{-\frac{1}{3}}$ (e) $\left(\dfrac{9}{100}\right)^{-\frac{1}{2}}$ (f) $\left(\dfrac{125}{216}\right)^{-\frac{2}{3}}$

Simplify the following:

(g) $\sqrt[6]{a^{18}}$ (h) $\sqrt{(25m^4)}$ (i) $(27a^9b^3)^{\frac{2}{3}}$

9. Finding indices from equations

Solve

(a) $3^x = 81$ (b) $2^x = \dfrac{1}{32}$ (c) $10^x = 0.01$

(d) $64^x = 4$ (e) $16^x = \dfrac{1}{2}$ (f) $3^{2x+1} = 27^x$

(g)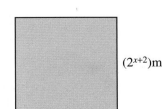
125^{2n} 25^{n-1}

The area of this rectangle is 625 cm².

Find the value of n.

(all units are in cm)

(h) The area of this square is $\dfrac{1}{8}$ m².

Find the value of x.

(2^{x+2})m

51

1 Gail and Marion shared £86 808 in the ratio 5:1.
How much did each receive? (OCR)

2 Tatyana invested £5000 at 4.5% simple interest per annum.
Oleg invested £5000 at 4.2% compound interest per annum.
Whose investment was worth more after 5 years and by how much?
You must show how you decided. (OCR)

3 In a sale all the prices are reduced by 30%.
The sale price of a jacket is £28.

Work out the price of jacket before the sale. (EDEXCEL)

4 Sachin paid £250 for 36 sweatshirts.
He sold them all at £11.99 each.
Calculate his percentage profit. (OCR)

5 A recipe for a fruit crumble includes these ingredients.

200 g	flour
125 g	margarine
100 g	sugar
20 g	ginger
750 g	rhubarb

(a) Paul has 300 g of flour.
He uses it all to make a larger fruit crumble with the recipe.
What weight of sugar should he use?

(b) Sally has 600 g of rhubarb.
She uses it to make a smaller crumble with the recipe.
What weight of margarine should she use? (OCR)

6 (a) Simplify (b) Simplify (c) Simplify

$$x^3 \times x^5 \qquad y^6 \div y^2 \qquad \frac{8w^7}{2w^2 \times w^3} \qquad \text{(EDEXCEL)}$$

7 (*a*) Simplify

(i) $\dfrac{a^5}{a^2}$ (ii) $p^3 \times p$ (iii) $(3n^3)^2$

(b) Simplify

(i) $3a^2 \times 2a^3b^2$ (ii) $(3a^2)^{-1}$ (AQA)

8 (a) Simplify $27^{\frac{2}{3}} \times 7^{-2}$ leaving your answer in fractional form.

(b) Simplify $(5ab^4)^3$. (WJEC)

52

9 Simplify

(i) $f^3 \times f^2$ 　　　　　(ii) $\dfrac{k^8}{k^2}$ 　　　　　　　　　　　　(OCR)

10 Simplify

(a) $3a^2b \times 4a^3b^2$ 　　(b) $\left(\dfrac{5p^3}{q}\right)^3$ 　　　　(c) $\dfrac{12t^5}{u^4} \times \dfrac{u^3}{3t^2}$ 　　(EDEXCEL)

11 Find the exact value of $64^{\frac{1}{3}} \times 196^{-\frac{1}{2}}$.

Give your answer as a fraction in its simplest form. 　　　　　　(AQA)

12 In 2003 the State Pension was increased by 2% to £78.03
What was the State Pension before this increase? 　　　　　　　(AQA)

13 In a sale, normal prices are reduced by 20%.

Andrew bought a saddle for his horse in the sale.
The sale price of the saddle was £220.

SALE
20% OFF

Calculate the normal price of the saddle. 　　　　　　　　　(EDEXCEL)

14 (a) Evaluate

(i) $225^{\frac{1}{2}}$

(ii) $36^{-0.5} \times 36^{\frac{1}{2}}$

(b) Given that $8^{\frac{2}{3}} \times 4^{-\frac{5}{2}} = 2^p$, find the value of p. 　　　(OCR)

15 Find the values of n, p and q for which

(a) $2^n = 128$ 　　　　(b) $2^p = 1$ 　　　　(c) $2^q = (\sqrt{2})^5$ 　　(CCEA)

16 A company bought a van that had a value of £12 000.
Each year the value of the van depreciates by 25%.

(a) Work out the value of the van at the end of three years.

The company bought a new truck.
Each year the value of the truck depreciates by 20%.
The value of the new truck can be multiplied by a single number to find its value at
the end of four years.

(b) Find this single number as a decimal. 　　　　　　　　(EDEXCEL)

In the 'M' sections (mainly grades B, C, D) you will learn how to:

– deal with basic angle problems, including the isosceles triangle

– find angles with parallel lines

– find angles in polygons

In the 'E' sections (mainly grades A*, A) you will learn how to:

– use circle properties, including cyclic quadrilaterals and tangents

– prove circle properties

Also you will learn how to:

– WATCH YOUR MONEY! – money for your holiday

M   Finding angles

🔑 Key Facts

Reminder

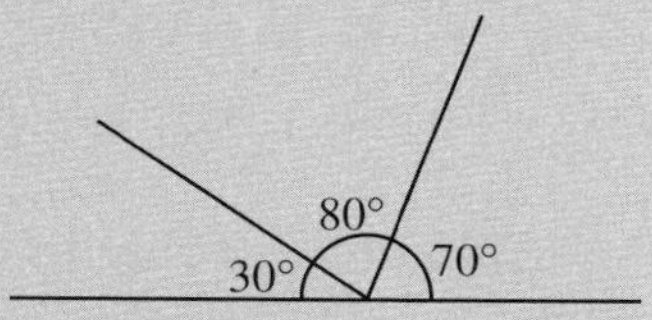

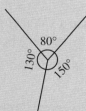

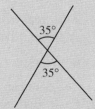

The angles on a straight line add up to 180°

The angles at a point add up to 360°

Vertically opposite angles are equal

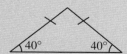

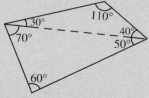

An isosceles triangle has two equal sides and two equal angles. (The sides marked with a dash are equal)

The angles in a quadrilateral add up to 360° (made from two triangles)

Find the angles marked with letters.

1

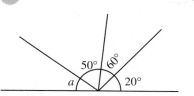

2

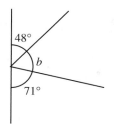

3

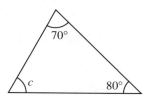

4

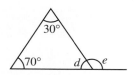

5

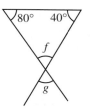

6

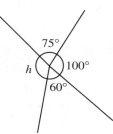

7

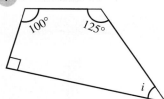

8

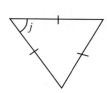

9

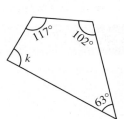

10

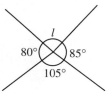

11

12

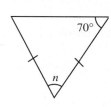

13

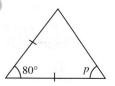

14

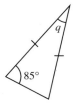

15

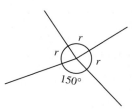

16

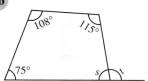

17

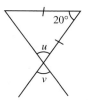

18

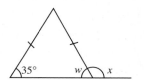

19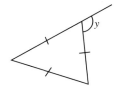

20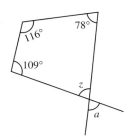

21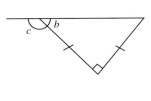

22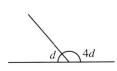

23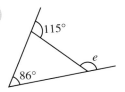

24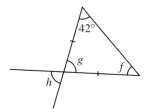

M	Finding angles with parallel lines

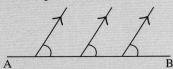

🔑 Key Facts

Reminder

In this diagram all the arrow lines are parallel.

The arrows all make the same angle with the line AB. These angles are called *corresponding* angles.

angle a = angle b
These are called *alternate* angles.

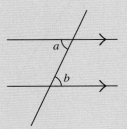

(a)

$a = 70°$ (corresponding angles)
$b = 110°$ (a and b are angles
　　　　 on a straight line
　　　　 which add up to $180°$)

(b)

$a = 72°$ (corresponding)
$b = 108°$ (angles on a straight line add up to $180°$)
$c = 101°$ (alternate)
$d = 79°$ (angles on a straight line add up to $180°$)

56

Find the angles marked with letters.

1

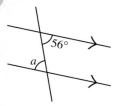

2

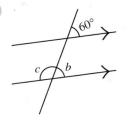

3

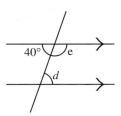

4

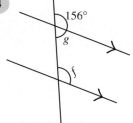

5

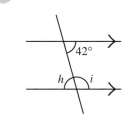

6

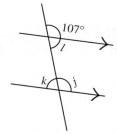

7

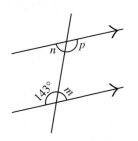

8

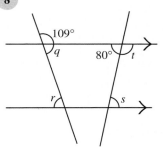

9

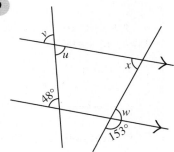

10

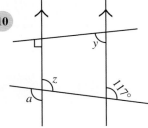

11

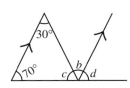

12

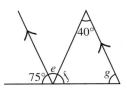

13

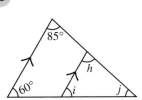

14

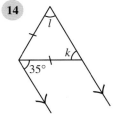

15

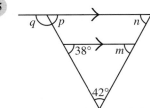

57

3A **Mixed percentages (see Unit 2)**

1. A petrol station increased all its prices by 3% from October to November.

   (a) In October a litre of unleaded petrol cost 80p.

      What did it cost in November?

   (b) In November a litre of diesel cost 80.34p.

      What did it cost in October?

2. An electrical shop offers a 35% reduction off all its products. What is the reduced price for a CD player costing £150?

3. A dishwasher costs £320 + VAT. What is the total cost of the dishwasher if VAT is 17.5%?

4. In 2004 a school had 1200 pupils. The following year it had 1260 pupils. By what percentage did the school increase over the year?

5. A vintage car increases in value over ten years from £25,000 to £31,250. What percentage is this increase?

6. The price of a new car fell by 5% of its value at the start of each month for the first three months of the year 2006. The car cost £16,800 at the start of the year. What did the car cost after three months?

7. Hamish invests £1200 in a building society offering 6% interest per year compound interest. How much will Hamish have in his account after

   (a) 2 years?   (b) 10 years?

8. The price of a camera fell from £150 to £112.50. Find the percentage decrease.

9. Find the original price of a motorbike which was sold at £2720 at a loss of 15%.

10. Lucy buys a computer for £1492.25 including VAT (17.5%). What was the cost of the computer before the VAT was added?

M | Angles in polygons

A polygon is a shape with straight sides. Each angle *inside* a polygon is called an *interior* angle.

We can find the sum of the interior angles of any polygon by splitting the polygon into triangles (the triangles must not overlap).

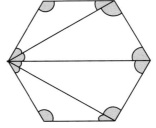

A hexagon can be split into 4 triangles.
The angles in each triangle add up to 180°.
The *sum* of the *interior angles* of a hexagon is
4 × 180° = 720°.

polygon with 4 sides can be split into 2 triangles so interior angles add up to 2 × 180° = 360°
polygon with 5 sides can be split into 3 triangles so interior angles add up to 3 × 180° = 540°
polygon with 6 sides can be split into 4 triangles so interior angles add up to 4 × 180° = 720°
polygon with *n* sides can be split into (*n*–2) triangles so interior angles add up to (*n*–2) × 180°

> The sum of interior angles of a polygon with n sides is 180 (n–2)°

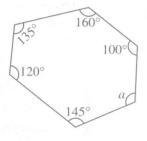

Find the value of angle *a*.

The polygon has 6 sides

so sum of interior angles = $\underbrace{180 \times (6 - 2)}_{180\,(n-2)}$ = 180 × 4 = 720°

angle *a* = 720° − (145° + 120° + 135° + 160° + 100°)

   = 720° − 660°

   = 60°

M3.3

1

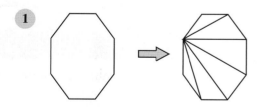

Copy and complete below:

An octagon can be split into ---- triangles.

Sum of interior angles = ----- × 180°

   = -----°

2 Find the sum of the interior angles of:

(a) a nonagon (polygon with 9 sides).

(b) a heptagon (polygon with 7 sides).

(c) a decagon (polygon with 10 sides).

(d) a dodecagon (polygon with 12 sides).

3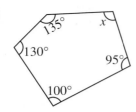

Copy and complete below:

This polygon can be split into ---- triangles.

Sum of interior angles = ----- × 180°

            = -----°

Add up all the given angles:

95° + 100° + 130° + 135° = -----°

angle x = -----°

In the questions below, find the angles marked with letters.

4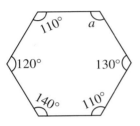

5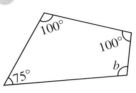

6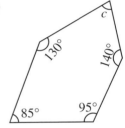

7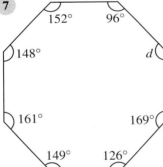

8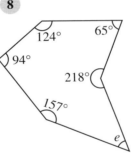

9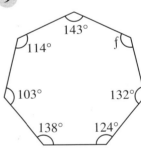

10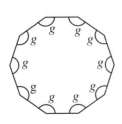

11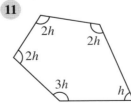

12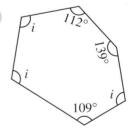

13 Find the sum of the interior angles in a polygon with 23 sides.

14 A polygon has 30 sides. If each interior angle is equal, what is the size of each interior angle?

60

🔑 Key Facts

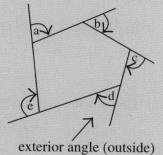

Exterior angles of a polygon add up to 360°

In a *regular* polygon, all *exterior angles* are *equal*.

If the regular polygon has *n* sides, each exterior angle $= \dfrac{360°}{n}$

exterior angle (outside)

All the exterior angles add up to 360°.

There are 8 sides so 8 equal exterior angles.

One exterior angle = 360 ÷ 8 = 45°

interior angle + 45° = 180°

interior angle *x* = 135°

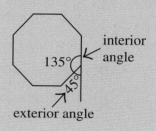

interior angle

exterior angle

M3.4

1 Each shape below is a *regular* polygon. Using any method, find the angles marked with letters.

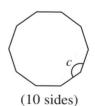

(10 sides)

2 Find the angles marked with letters.

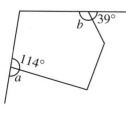

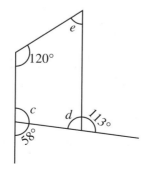

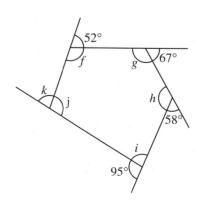

61

3 A dodecagon has 12 sides.

(a) Find the size of each exterior angle of a *regular* dodecagon.

(b) Write down the size of the interior angle for the same shape.

4 (a) Find the size of each exterior angle of a *regular* nonagon (9 sides).

(b) Write down the size of the interior angle for the same shape.

5 Find the exterior angles of *regular* polygons with

(a) 15 sides   (b) 20 sides   (c) 60 sides   (d) 90 sides

6 Find the interior angle of each polygon in Question **5** .

7 Each exterior angle of a *regular* polygon is 8°. How many sides has the polygon?

8 Each exterior angle of a *regular* polygon is 20°. How many sides has the polygon?

9 This diagram shows the interior and exterior angles of a regular polygon.

How many sides has the polygon?

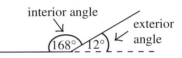

10 Find the size of the *interior* angle of a *regular* polygon with 45 sides.

11 The diagram shows part of a *regular* polygon where O is the centre of the polygon.

How many sides has the polygon?

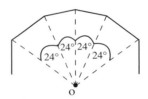

12 A nonagon (9 sides) has 8 equal angles *x* and one angle 4*x*. Find the value of *x*.

13 Find each angle marked with a letter in this 20-sided *regular* polygon. O is the centre of the polygon.

14 In a *regular* polygon each interior angle is 160° greater than each exterior angle. How many sides has the polygon?

15 The diagram shown is formed by joining regular pentagons. Find the angles *x* and *y*.

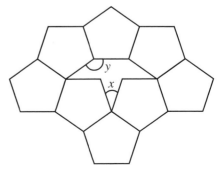

62

3B   **Quadrilaterals**

1. Use a ruler to sketch the 6 quadrilaterals below:

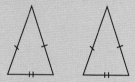

2. Which quadrilaterals above have 4 lines of symmetry?

3. Which quadrilaterals above have 2 diagonals of equal length?

4. Which quadrilaterals above have 2 diagonals which are perpendicular to each other?

5. 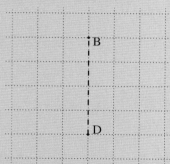   If you put the equal sides together from these two triangles, how many different quadrilaterals can you make? Name each quadrilateral.

6. 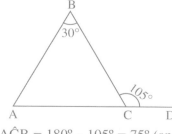   Line BD is one *diagonal* of a rhombus ABCD. Copy BD and draw *two* possible rhombuses ABCD.

7. If you cut along the diagonal of a rectangle to make two triangles, what shapes can you make by joining the diagonals together in a different way?

M   **Mixed angle problems including proof**

Prove that triangle ABC is isosceles.

Give all your reasons clearly.

$A\hat{C}B = 180° − 105° = 75°$ (angles on a straight line)

$B\hat{A}C = 180° − 30° − 75° = 75°$ (angles in a triangle add up to 180°)

$A\hat{C}B = B\hat{A}C$ so triangle ABC is isosceles.

63

1

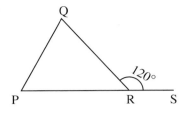

QR = PR.

Prove that triangle PQR is equilateral.

Give all your reasons clearly.

2

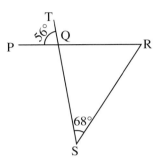

Prove that triangle QRS is isosceles.

Give all your reasons clearly.

3

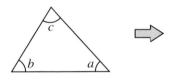 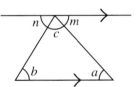

(a) Which angle is equal to angle m?

(b) Which angle is equal to angle n?

(c) Prove that the sum of the angles in a triangle is 180°.

4

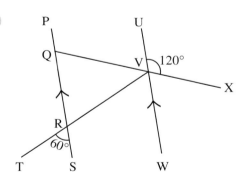

Prove that triangle QRV is equilateral.

Give all your reasons clearly.

5

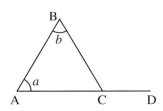

Prove that $B\hat{C}D = a + b$ (ie. 'an exterior angle of a triangle is equal to the sum of the two opposite interior angles')

In Questions **6** to **14**, find the angle marked with letters.

6
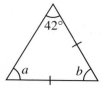
42°

a   b

7
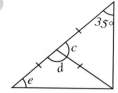
35°
c
d
e

8
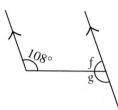
108°
f
g

9
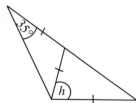
35°
h

10
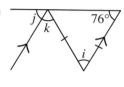
j
k
76°
i

11

l

12
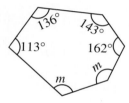
136°   143°
113°   162°
m
m

13
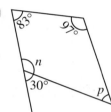
83°   97°
n
30°
p

14
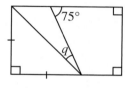
75°
q

15 Prove that opposite angles in a parallelogram are equal (hint: alternate and corresponding angles)

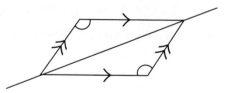

16 D

C 2x

x A

B

Prove that triangle ABC is isosceles.

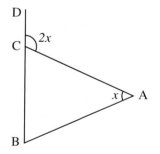

17

A
x

x
B   C   D

AĈD is double the size of AĈB.

Prove that triangle ABC is equilateral.

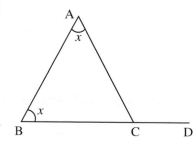

65

In the circle work that follows, O is always the centre of the circle.

Key Facts

1. **The angle in a semi-circle is 90°**

2. **The angle at the centre of a circle is twice the angle at the circumference, if the angles stand on the same arc.**

3. **Angles at the circumference are equal, if the angles stand on the same arc.**

Note

A 'chord' is a straight line joining any two points on the circumference of a circle.

If a triangle is formed using two radii and a chord, the triangle is isosceles.

We will prove these rules formally later in this unit.

Find the angles marked with letters.

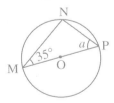

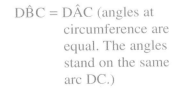

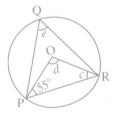

MN̂P = 90° (angle in a semi-circle)

$a = 55°$ (sum of angles in a triangle = 180°)

DB̂C = DÂC (angles at circumference are equal. The angles stand on the same arc DC.)

$b = 47°$

$c = 55°$ (isosceles triangle OPR)

$d = 70°$ (sum of angles in a triangle = 180°)

$e = 35°$ (angle at the centre d is twice the angle at the circumference)

Find the angles marked with letters.

1
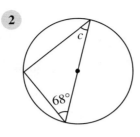

2
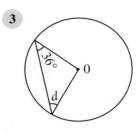

3
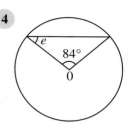

4

5
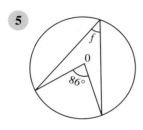

6
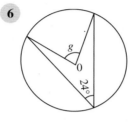

7
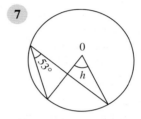

8
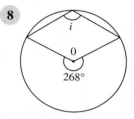

9
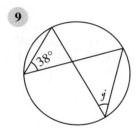

10
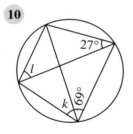

11
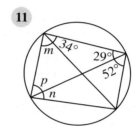

12
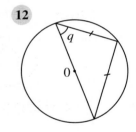

13
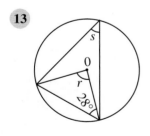

14
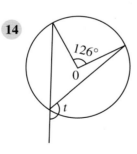

15
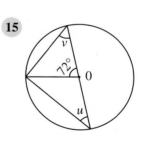

16
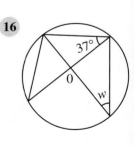

17
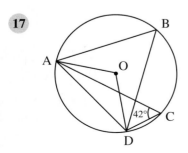

In this question, write down *all the reasons* for your answers.

Find

(a) AB̂D

(b) AÔD

(c) AD̂O

18 Find UV̂T. Write down *the reasons* for your answer.

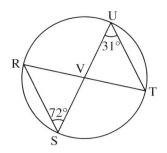

19

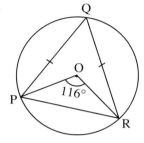

In this question, write down *all the reasons* for your answers.

Find

(a) OP̂R

(b) PQ̂R

(c) RP̂Q

(d) OP̂Q

20 In this question, write down *all the reasons* for your answers.

Find

(a) BĈD

(b) AB̂C

(c) OD̂C

(d) CD̂E

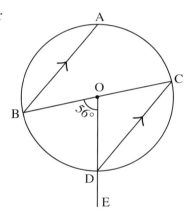

In Questions **21** to **26**, find the value of each letter.

21

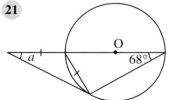

22

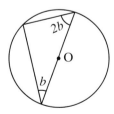

23

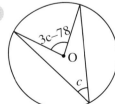

24

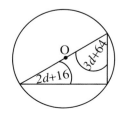

25

26

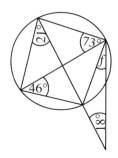

Key Facts

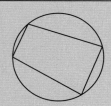

A *cyclic quadrilateral* is a quadrilateral whose four vertices lie on the circumference of a circle.

4. The opposite angles of a cyclic quadrilateral add up to 180°.

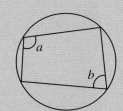

$a + b = 180°$

5. The exterior angle of a cyclic quadrilatral equals the opposite interior angle.

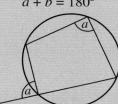

Again, we will prove these rules formally later in this unit.

Find the angles marked with letters.

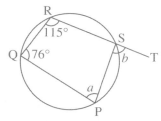

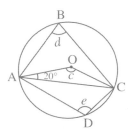

$a = 65°$ (opposite angles in a cyclic quadrilateral add up to 180°)

$T\hat{S}P = P\hat{Q}R$ (exterior angle of a cyclic quadrilateral equals the opposite interior angle)

$b = 76°$

$A\hat{C}O = 20°$ (isosceles triangle ACO)

$c = 140°$ (sum of angles in a triangle = 180°)

$A\hat{B}C = \frac{1}{2} A\hat{O}C$ (angle at centre is twice the angle at the circumference)

$d = 70°$

$A\hat{D}C + A\hat{B}C = 180°$ (opposite angles in a cyclic quadrilateral add up to 180°)

$e = 110°$

Find the angles marked with letters.

1

2

3

4
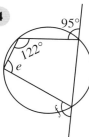

5
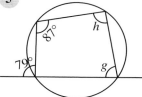

6
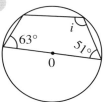

7
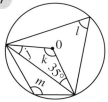

8
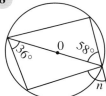

9
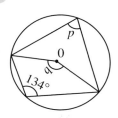

10
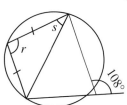

11
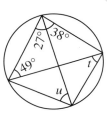

12
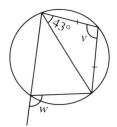

13 In this question, write down *all the reasons* for your answers.

Find

(a) AB̂O

(b) AD̂O

(c) AÔD

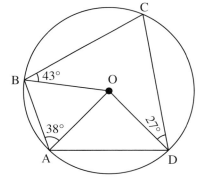

14 In this question, write down *all the reasons* for your answers.

Find

(a) AB̂C

(b) CÔA

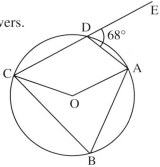

In Questions **15** to **20** , find the value of each letter.

15

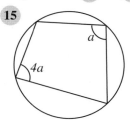

16

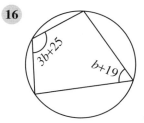

17

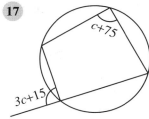

18

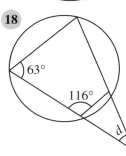

19

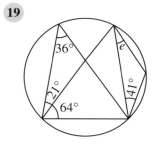

20

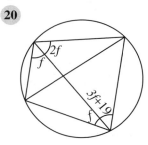

Key Facts

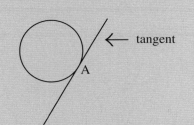 ← tangent

A *tangent* is a line which touches a circle at one point only (i.e. at point A).

6. The angle between a tangent and a radius is 90°.

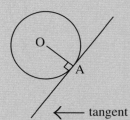

← tangent

7. Tangents from a point to a circle are equal in length.

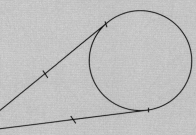

We will prove these rules later in this unit.

71

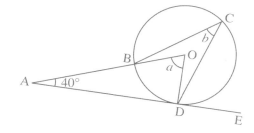

ADE is a tangent to the circle.

AD̂O = 90° (angle between tangent and radius is 90°)

a = 50° (sum of angles in a triangle = 180°)

BĈD = ½ × BÔD (angle at centre is twice the angle at the circumference)

b = 25°

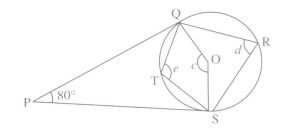

PQ and PS are tangents to the circle.

PQ̂O = PŜO = 90° (angle between tangent and radius is 90°)

QÔS = 360° − (90° + 90° + 80°) (sum of angles in a quadrilateral = 360°)

c = 100°

QR̂S = ½ × QÔS (angle at centre is twice the angle at the circumference)

d = 50°

QT̂S + QR̂S = 180° (opposite angles in a cyclic quadrilateral add up to 180°)

e = 130°

E3.3

Find the angles marked with letters.

1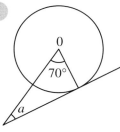

70°, a

2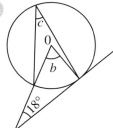

c, b, 18°

3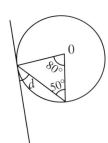

80°, 50°, d

4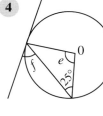

f, e, 25°

5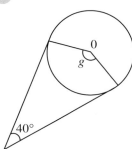

g, 40°

6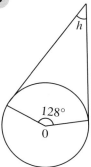

128°

7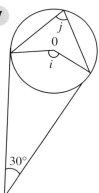

j, i, 30°

8

l, k, 63°

72

9 In this question, write down *all the reasons* for your answers.

Find

(a) OQ̂S

(b) OŜQ

(c) QÔS

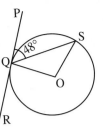

10 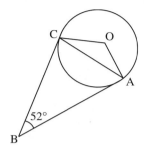 Find BÂC and CÂO. Write down *the reasons* for your answers.

11 In this question, write down *all the reasons* for your answers.

Find

(a) PÔR

(b) PQ̂R

(c) PŜR

(d) PR̂S

(e) PR̂T

(f) SR̂T

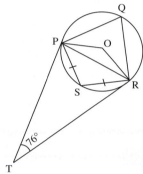

In Questions **12** to **15** , you will have to use Pythagoras or trigonometry (this work is reviewed/tackled in Unit 10). Give your answers to one decimal place.

12 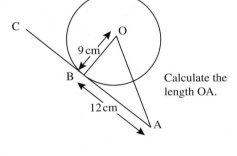 Calculate the length OA.

13 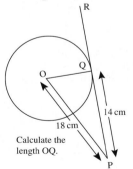 Calculate the length OQ.

14 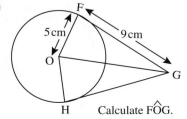 Calculate FÔG.

15 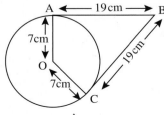 Calculate AB̂C.

73

In Questions **16** to **19** , find the value of each letter.

16

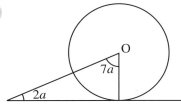

17

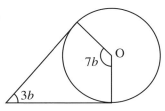

18

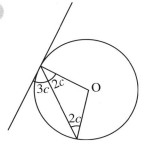

19

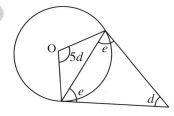

Can you still?

Can you still?

3C   **Indices (see Unit 2)**

1. Which of the statements below are true?

   (a) $7^2 \times 7^3 = 7^6$ (b) $(5^2)^3 = 5^6$ (c) $3^0 = 0$

   (d) $\dfrac{3^8}{3^4} = 3^2$ (e) $4^{-1} = -4$ (f) $3^{-2} = \dfrac{1}{9}$

2. Which of the expressions below simplify to 5^4?

   (a) $5^6 \div 5^2$ (b) $(5^2)^2$ (c) $\left(\dfrac{1}{5^{-4}}\right)^{-1}$ (d) $5^8 - 5^4$ (e) $\sqrt{(5^8)}$

3. Evaluate the following:

   (a) 2^{-4} (b) $\left(\dfrac{9}{4}\right)^{\frac{1}{2}}$ (c) $\left(\dfrac{64}{27}\right)^{-\frac{2}{3}}$ (d) $\left(\dfrac{5}{2}\right)^{-3}$

4. Solve

   (a) $2^{3x} = 128$ (b) $3^x = \dfrac{1}{27}$ (c) $8^{x+1} = 16^{2x}$

5. Simplify the following:

   (a) $(4m^3)^3$ (b) $\dfrac{a^2 \times a^{-6}}{(a^3)^2}$ (c) $(8m^6n^9)^{\frac{1}{3}}$

Key Facts

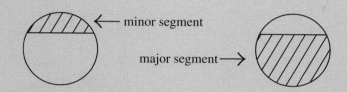

minor segment ←

major segment →

8. The angle between a tangent and a chord
    is equal to the angle at the circumference
    in the alternate segment (known as the
    alternate segment theorem).

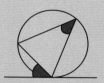

9. The perpendicular bisector of a chord
    passes through the centre of the circle.

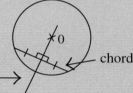

perpendicular
bisector →

chord

We will prove these rules later in this unit.

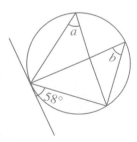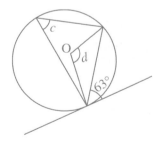

$a = 58°$ (alternate segment theorem)

$b = 58°$ (alternate segment theorem)

$c = 63°$ (alternate segment theorem)

$d = 2c$ (angle at centre is twice the angle at the
circumference)

$d = 126°$

Find the angles marked with letters.

1

2

3

4

5
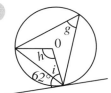

6

7
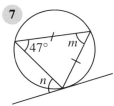

8

9
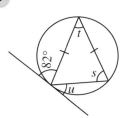

10
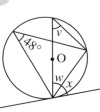

11
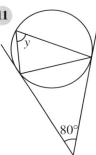

12
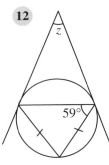

13
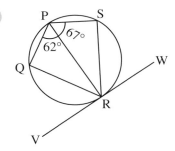

In this question, write down *all the reasons* for your answers.

Find

(a) SR̂W

(b) QR̂V

(c) QR̂S

14 In this question, write down *all the reasons* for your answers.

Find

(a) BÂC

(b) CÔD

(c) BÂD

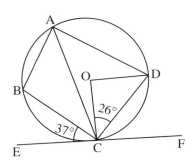

76

15

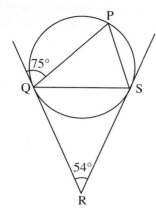

In this question, write down *all the reasons* for your answers.

Find

(a) QŜR

(b) QP̂S

(c) PŜQ

(d) PQ̂S

16 In this question, write down *all the reasons* for your answers.

Find

(a) ED̂A

(b) AD̂C

(c) AĈB

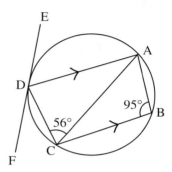

In Questions **17** to **21**, find the angles marked with letters.

17

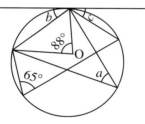

18

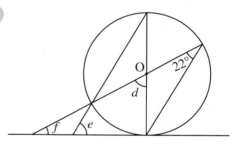

19

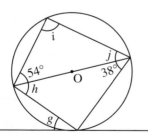

20

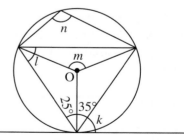

21

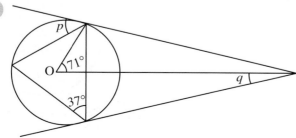

Prove that 'the angle at the centre is twice the angle at the circumference in any circle'.

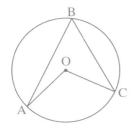

Use algebra

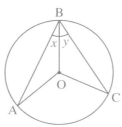

$O\hat{A}B = x$ (triangle OAB is isosceles)

$A\hat{O}B = 180 - 2x$ (sum of angles in a triangle = 180°)

$O\hat{C}B = y$ (triangle OCB is isosceles)

$B\hat{O}C = 180 - 2x$ (sum of angles in a triangle = 180°)

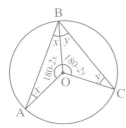

$A\hat{O}C = 360 - (180 - 2x) - (180 - 2y)$

                  (sum of angles at a point add up to 360°)

$A\hat{O}C = 360 - 180 + 2x - 180 + 2y$

$A\hat{O}C = 2x + 2y = 2(x + y)$

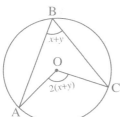

This proves that $A\hat{O}C = 2 \times A\hat{B}C$

ie. the angle at the centre is twice the angle at the circumference.

The questions in the Exercise below will guide you through the proofs of many of the circle properties used in this unit. You should become familiar with these proofs for your GCSE exams.

E3.5

1. Copy and complete the following proof that 'opposite angles in a cyclic quadrilateral add up to 180°.'

    $x = \boxed{}$ (angle at centre is twice angle at circumference)

    $y = 2q$ $\left(\boxed{}\right)$

    $x + y = \boxed{}$ $\left(\text{sum of angles at a point} = \boxed{}\right)$

    $\boxed{} + 2q = \boxed{}$

    $p + q = \boxed{}$ so opposite angles in a cyclic quadrilateral add up to 180°.

2 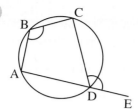 Prove that $A\hat{B}C = C\hat{D}E$ (ie. the exterior angle of a cyclic quadrilateral equals the opposite interior angle).

3 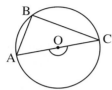 Copy and complete the following proof that 'the angle in a semi-circle is 90°.'

$A\hat{O}C = 2 \times \boxed{}$ (angle at centre is $\boxed{}$ angle at circumference)

$A\hat{O}C = \boxed{}$ (a straight line)

$A\hat{B}C = \frac{1}{2}$ of $\boxed{}$

$A\hat{B}C = \boxed{}$ so the angle in a semi-circle is 90°.

4 Copy and complete:

$P\hat{Q}S = \boxed{}$ (angle at centre is twice angle at circumference)

$P\hat{R}S = \boxed{}$ (angle at centre is $\boxed{}$ angle at circumference)

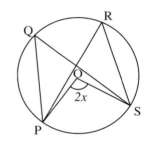

so $P\hat{Q}S = P\hat{R}S$ so angles at the circumference are $\boxed{}$
      if the angles stand on the same arc.

5 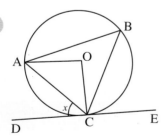 Copy and complete the following proof for the alternate segment theorem.

$A\hat{C}O = \boxed{}$ (angle between tangent and radius is 90°)

$C\hat{A}O = \boxed{}$ (triangle CAO is isosceles)

$A\hat{O}C = 180° - C\hat{A}O - A\hat{C}O$ (sum of angles in a triangle is 180°)

$A\hat{O}C = 180° - \left(\boxed{}\right) - \left(\boxed{}\right)$

$A\hat{O}C = 180° - \boxed{} + \boxed{} - \boxed{} + \boxed{}$

$A\hat{O}C = \boxed{}$

$A\hat{B}C = \frac{1}{2} \times \boxed{}$ (angle at centre is twice angle at circumference)

$A\hat{B}C = \boxed{} = A\hat{C}D$ This proves the alternate segment theorem.

79

6

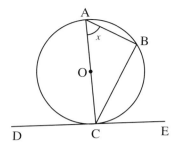

Copy and complete:

B$\hat{C}$E = ☐ (alternate segment theorem)

A$\hat{B}$C = ☐ (angle in a semi-circle is ☐)

A$\hat{C}$B = ☐ (sum of angles in a triangle is 180°)

A$\hat{C}$E = A$\hat{C}$B + B$\hat{C}$E

A$\hat{C}$E = ☐ + ☐

A$\hat{C}$E = ☐ This proves that 'the angle between a tangent and a radius is 90°.'

7 Use this diagram to prove that 'the angle at the centre is twice the angle at the circumference'. (Look at the earlier example if you need to but try to avoid it if possible. You need to learn this proof).

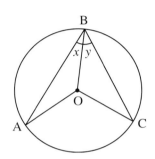

8

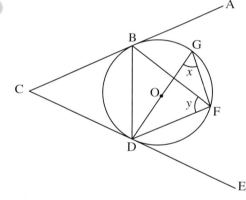

Find the following angles in terms of x and y.

(a) G$\hat{D}$F

(b) D$\hat{B}$F

(c) C$\hat{B}$D

(d) B$\hat{G}$F

WATCH YOUR MONEY! – Money for your holiday

Exchange rate

This is the amount of foreign money you will get in exchange for £1.

At the time of writing:

£1 = 1.45 euros (Europe)	£1 = 51.18 rubles (Russia)
£1 = 1.82 dollars (USA)	£1 = 19.84 pesos (Mexico)
£1 = 196 yen (Japan)	£1 = 6.84 riyals (Saudi Arabia)
£1 = 11.98 rand (South Africa)	£1 = 2.39 dollars (Australia)

Converting pounds into foreign money

> Multiply the number of pounds by the chosen exchange rate

Examples

£1 = 1.82 dollars (USA)

so £10 = 10 × 1.82 = 18.2 dollars.

£1 = 51.18 rubles (Russia)

so £300 = 300 × 51.18 = 15354 rubles.

Converting foreign money into pounds

> Divide the foreign money by the chosen exchange rate

Examples

£1 = 196 yen (Japan)

4508 yen = 4508 ÷ 196 = £23

£1 = 1.45 euros

150 euros = 150 ÷ 1.45 = £103.448276

= £103.45 (to the nearest penny)

> Beware!

When converting your money, the bank (or whatever organisation you use) will charge you a fee. This is called the *'commission'*.

Different organisations charge different amounts of commission. Always look around for the best deal.

WYM3

Using the exchange rate at the start of this section, convert the following amounts of money.

1 £200 into euros.

2 £350 into pesos.

3 £150 into australian dollars.

4 £900 into rand.

5 300.3 american dollars into pounds.

6 11904 pesos into pounds.

7 13328 yen into pounds.

8 £454 into riyals.

9 1015 euros into pounds.

10 17970 rand into pounds.

11 A digital radio costs £164 in the UK. Sarah sees a similar digital radio for 31360 yen in Japan. In which country is the digital radio cheaper?

81

12 Jonathan was lucky enough to have two holidays last year, one in France and one in Austria. A can of cola was 1.16 euros in France and 1.68 dollars in Australia. In which country was the can of cola cheaper?

13 Candice comes back from holiday in Mexico with 992 pesos. Shalina returns from holiday in the USA with 98.28 dollars. Who has more money left?

14 Stephen takes 547.2 riyals to a Bureau de Change to convert them into pounds. The Bureau de Change charges 4% commission. How much money does Stephen get back?

15 Maggie takes 2047.2 rubles to a bank to change them into pounds. The bank charges 3% commission. How much money does Maggie get back?

TEST YOURSELF ON UNIT 3

> **1.** Dealing with basic angle problems, including the isosceles triangle

Find the angles marked with letters.

(a)

131°   43°

b a

142°

(b)

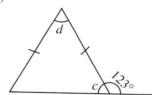

d

c 123°

(c)

e

$3e$

$4e$

e

(d)

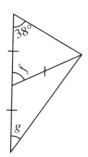

38°

f

g

(e)

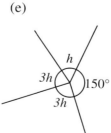

h

$3h$ 150°

$3h$

(f)

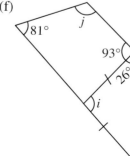

81° j

93°

26°

i

82

2. Finding angles with parallel lines

Find the angles marked with letters.

(a)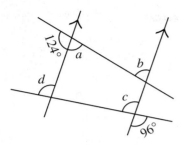

(b)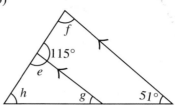

(c)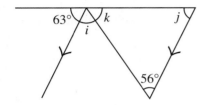

3. Finding angles in polygons

(a) Find the sum of the interior angles of a
   regular octagon.

(b) What is the size of one interior angle in a *regular* octagon?

(c) Write down the size of each exterior angle of a *regular* pentagon.

(d) Each interior angle of a *regular* polygon is 165°. How many sides has the
   polygon?

(e) 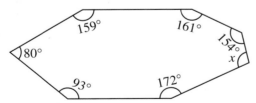   Find the value of angle *x*.

4. Using circle properties, including cyclic quadrilaterals and tangents

Find the angles marked with letters. O is always the centre of the circle.

(a)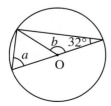

(b)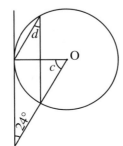

(c)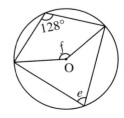

83

(d)

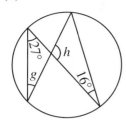

(e)

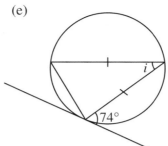

(f)

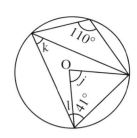

(g)

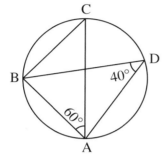

Explain why AC *cannot* be the diameter of this circle.

(a)

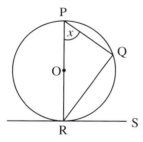

Prove that PR̂S = 90° (the angle between the tangent and the radius = 90°).

(b) *Prove* that the opposite angles in a cyclic quadrilateral add up to 180°.

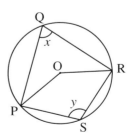

(c) *Prove* that the angles at the circumference are equal if the angles stand on the same arc.

Mixed examination questions

1 In the diagram the lines AB and CD are parallel.

They are crossed by two straight lines.

Find the angles x and y, giving reasons for your answer.

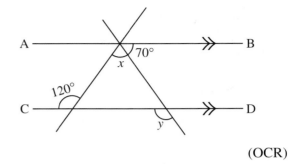

(OCR)

2 The diagram shows a pentagon.

$AB = AE$

$BC = CD = DE$

Find the size of the angle marked $x°$.

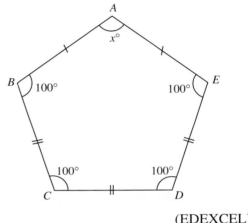

(EDEXCEL)

3 The diagram shows a quadrilateral $ABCD$ and a straight line CE.

AB is parallel to CE.

(a) Work out the size of the angle marked $x°$.

(b) (i) Write down the size of the angle marked $y°$.

(ii) Give a reason for your answer.

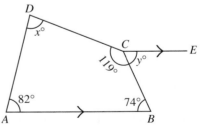

(EDEXCEL)

4 The diagram shows part of a regular polygon.

How many sides does the polygon have?

(OCR)

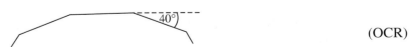

5 A, B, C, and D are points on the circumference of a circle.

BD is a diameter of the circle and PA is a tangent to the circle at A.

Angle ADB = 25° and angle CDB = 18°.

(a) Write down the value of angle.

(i) BCD.

(ii) PAB.

(b) Calculate angle ABC.

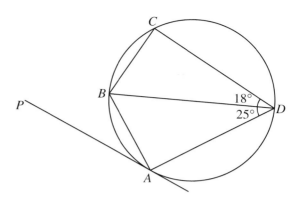

(AQA)

6 O is the centre of the circle.

P, Q, R and S are points on the circumference of the circle.

Angle PQR = 51°.

(a) Work out angle PSR, giving a reason for your answer.

TS is a tangent on the circle at S.

Angle PST = 32°.

(b) Find angle PRS, giving a reason for your answer.

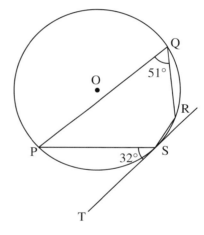

(OCR)

7 (a) O is the centre of the circle, AB is a diameter and BX is a tangent. The lines OC and DB are parallel. (This diagram is not drawn to scale.)

Angle ABD = 50°

Find the sizes of:

(i) angle COB,

(ii) angle OBC,

(iii) angle CBX,

(iv) angle BXC,

(v) angle CAB.

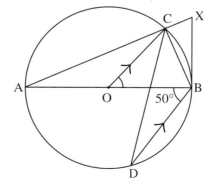

(b) Prove that OC bisects angle ACD. State your answers clearly.

(CCEA)

86

8 W, X, Y and Z are points on the circumference of the circle. The line WY passes through O, the centre of the circle. Angle YWX = 49°.

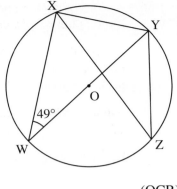

Find the following angles, giving a reason for each answer.

(a) Angle WXY

(b) Angle YZX

(c) Angle YOX

(OCR)

9 P, Q, R, and S are four points on the circumference of the circle centre O. TSV is a tangent which touches the circle at S. $R\hat{P}S = 54°$ and $P\hat{S}R = 68°$.

(a) Find the values of

   (i) $P\hat{Q}R$.

   (ii) $P\hat{O}R$ (obtuse).

(b) Explain clearly why $T\hat{S}P = 58°$.

(c) Find the value of $O\hat{R}S$.

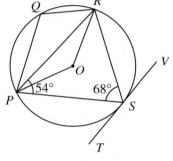

(WJEC)

87

In the 'M' sections (mainly grades B, C, D) you will learn how to:

- substitute into expressions and formulas
- multiply out single brackets
- multiply out two brackets
- factorise by taking out common factors
- factorise quadratics with coefficient of $x^2 = 1$

In the 'E' sections (mainly grades A*, A) you will learn how to:

- use the difference of 2 squares
- factorise by grouping
- factorise quadratics with coefficient of $x^2 > 1$
- solve quadratic equations by factorising
- deal with problems leading to quadratic equations

Also you will learn how to:

- WATCH YOUR MONEY! – VAT

M **Substitution**

$a = 2,\ b = -3,\ c = -4$

(a) $a(b - c)$

$= 2(-3 - -4)$

$= 2(-3 + 4)$

$= 2 \times 1$

$= 2$

(b) $5b^2 = 5 \times b^2$

$= 5 \times (-3)^2$

$= 5 \times 9$

$= 45$

(c) $\dfrac{8b + 3c}{2a}$

$= \dfrac{8(-3) + 3(-4)}{2(2)}$

$= \dfrac{-24 + -12}{4}$

$= \dfrac{-24 - 12}{4}$

$= -9$

In this Exercise find the value of each expression.

In questions **1** to **15** $x = 3$, $y = 0$, $z = 8$

1 $6x$

2 $4z + x$

3 $3z + 7$

4 $3x - 2y$

5 $y^2 + x^2$

6 xy

7 xyz

8 $x^2 + y^2 + z^2$

9 $3(2x + z)$

10 $x(z - y)$

11 $4x^2$

12 $\dfrac{5z}{x + 2}$

13 $\dfrac{z - 2x}{3x - 7}$

14 $4(x^2 + z^2)$

15 $(2x)^2$

In questions **16** to **30** $a = 4$, $b = -2$, $c = -6$

16 bc

17 $3b$

18 c^2

19 $2c^2$

20 $5a^2$

21 $(4b)^2$

22 $9b^2$

23 $a^2 + c^2$

24 $ab + c$

25 $bc - a$

26 abc

27 $\dfrac{3a}{2b}$

28 $\dfrac{c}{b} + \dfrac{5a}{2b}$

29 $(2a)^2 - 2a^2$

30 $b^2(2a - c)$

In questions **31** to **45** $x = -3$, $y = 5$, $z = -1$

31 $z(2x + y)$

32 $x^2 - z$

33 $x^2 + 2x$

34 $5y^2 - 2x^2$

35 z^3

36 $x^2 (2y + 3z)$

37 $\dfrac{4y + 2x^2}{z^2}$

38 $x^2 (y^2 - z^2)$

39 $z^2 - 3z + 2$

40 $x^3 + z^3$

41 $\dfrac{2y - 5z}{5x}$

42 $\dfrac{x(x^2 - z)}{3y}$

43 $\dfrac{(2x)^2 + z}{y}$

44 $(2x + 4z)(3y + z)$

45 $x^3 z^3 (x^2 - z)$

M   Formulas

The acceleration a of a car is found from the formula

$$a = \frac{v - u}{t}$$

where v is the final speed

      u is the speed at the start

      t is the time taken

Find a when $v = 38$, $u = 13$ and $t = 5$.

$$a = \frac{v - u}{t} = \frac{38 - 13}{5} = \frac{25}{5} = 5$$

1  The surface area A of a cone is roughly given by the formula

$$A = 3rl$$

Find the value of A when

(a) $r = 2, l = 10$ (b) $r = 5, l = 3$ (c) $r = 8, l = 5$

2 The position P of the middle value of some numbers is found from the formula

$$P = \frac{1}{2}(n + 1)$$

where n is how many numbers there are.

Find P when   (a) $n = 7$ (b) $n = 99$

3 The interest I made by some money P is given by the formula

$$I = \frac{PTR}{100}$$

where T is the time and R is the rate of interest. Find the value of I when

(a) P = 800, T = 2, R = 5   (b) P = 40, T = 5, R = 8

4 A ball is dropped. The distance s it travels is given by the formula

$$s = 4.9\,t^2$$

where t is the time taken.

Find the value of s when   (a) $t = 10$ (b) $t = 2$

5 The temperature in degrees Fahrenheit F can be changed into degrees Centigrade C by using the formula

$$C = \frac{5}{9}(F - 32)$$

Find the value of C when   (a) F = 50   (b) F = 68

6 Using the formula $h = \sqrt{(a^2 - b^2)}$, find the value of h when

(a) $a = 13, b = 12$ (b) $a = 25, b = 24$

7 The volume V of a ball is roughly given by the formula

$$V = 4r^3$$

where r is the radius of the ball.

Find the value of V when   (a) $r = 5$ (b) $r = 10$

8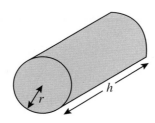

The surface area A of a cylinder is roughly given by the formula

$$A = 6rh + 3r^2$$

Find the value of A when

(a) $r = 2$, $h = 5$ (b) $r = 4$, $h = 20$

In Questions **9** to **12** you may *use a calculator* if you wish.

9 The formula $v = \sqrt{u^2 + 2as}$ gives the final speed v of a particle whose initial speed is u, acceleration is a and displacement is s. Find the value of v (to 3 significant figures if necessary) when

(a) $u = 10$, $a = 3$, $s = 7$ (b) $u = -3.6$, $a = 9.8$, $s = 15.3$

10 The formula $s = vt - \frac{1}{2}at^2$ gives the displacement s of a particle after time t. The final speed is v and acceleration is a. Find s (to 3 significant figures if necessary) when

(a) $v = 5$, $a = 3$, $t = 2$ (b) $v = 0$, $a = 9.81$, $t = 1.03$

11 The formula $A = \sqrt{s(s-a)(s-b)(s-c)}$ gives the area A of a triangle with sides a, b and c where s is half the perimeter. Find the area A (to 2 significant figures if necessary) of the following triangles (by first finding and stating the value of s).

(a) $a = 3$, $b = 4$, $c = 5$ (b) $a = 7.8$, $b = 18.72$, $c = 20.28$

12 The total resistance R in a circuit with resistors R_1 and R_2 in parallel is given by the formula

$$\frac{1}{R} = \frac{1}{R_1} + \frac{1}{R_2}$$

Find R in the following cases (to 3 significant figures if necessary).

(a) $R_1 = 2$ ohms and $R_2 = 2$ ohms

(b) $R_1 = 3$ ohms and $R_2 = 4$ ohms

M   Multiplying out brackets

Multiply out $2(a + b)$ means $2 \times a$ add $2 \times b = 2a + 2b$

Expand $3(5a - 4)$ means $3 \times 5a$ subtract $12 = 15a - 12$

Expand $a(b + c)$ means $a \times b$ add $a \times c = ab + ac$

Multiply out $p(2q - 3)$ means $p \times 2q$ subtract $p \times 3 = 2pq - 3p$

Expand $n(n + 2)$ means $n \times n$ add $n \times 2 = n^2 + 2n$

Expand $5n(2n + 3)$ means $5n \times 2n$ add $5n \times 3 = 10n^2 + 15n$

Note that 'expand' means 'multiply out'.

1 Simplify

(a) $4y \times 2$ (b) $6 \times 8x$ (c) $2a \times 4b$ (d) $c \times 5c$

(e) $7a \times 2a$ (f) $24x \div 4$ (g) $42n \div 6$ (h) $64p \div 8$

(i) $6c \times 9c$ (j) $3a \times 2b \times 2c$ (k) $-9y \times 4$ (l) $-4c \times 5d$

(m) $-6c \times -3d$ (n) $-9y \div 3$ (o) $28q \div -4$ (p) $-7p \times -5p$

In Questions **2** to **10** answer 'true or false'.

2 $3 \times a = a \times 3$ **3** $3a - a = 3$ **4** $8n \times 4n = 32n^2$

5 $4n + 4n = 8n^2$ **6** $2 \times 3n = 5n^2$ **7** $10a \div 2 = 5a$

8 $a \times 3a = 3a^2$ **9** $a + a^2 = a^3$ **10** $12p \div 3 = 9p$

Multiply out

11 $2(a + 3)$ **12** $6(4x - 2)$ **13** $7(3x - 5)$ **14** $5(a - b)$

15 $7(3x + y)$ **16** $6(3x + 2)$ **17** $4(p + 2q)$ **18** $9(4c + 8d)$

19 $x(2x + y)$ **20** $a(b + a)$ **21** $c(2c + d)$ **22** $a(a - 7)$

23 $a(3a - 4)$ **24** $5x(y + 2)$ **25** $4a(a + 2b)$ **26** $6a(4b - 8c)$

Expand

27 $-2(x + 6)$ **28** $-3(a - 2)$ **29** $-5(c + 10)$ **30** $-4(3p - 5)$

31 $-3(2c + 4)$ **32** $-a(b + c)$ **33** $-p(2p + q)$ **34** $-a(a + b)$

35 $-x(2x - y)$ **36** $-m(m - n)$ **37** $-(2p + 5q)$ **38** $-6a(4 - 2b)$

Expand

39 $a(a^2 - 2b)$ **40** $x^2(4x + y)$ **41** $5b^2(2b + 3)$ **42** $3p(pq + 2p^2)$

M | **Expanding and simplifying brackets**

(a) Simplify $2(3n + 1) + 3n$

$\boxed{\text{multiply out brackets first}}$

$= 6n + 2 + 3n$

$\boxed{\text{now collect like terms}}$

$= 9n + 2$

(b) Simplify $3(2a + 2) + 4(a + 1)$

$= 6a + 6 + 4a + 4$

$= 10a + 10$

(c) Simplify $5(2a + 1) - 3(a - 2)$

$= 10a + 5 - 3a + 6$

⇧
Note

$= 7a + 11$

(d) Simplify $8(x + 3) - 2(2x + 4)$

$= 8x + 24 - 4x - 8$

⇧
Note

$= 4x + 16$

Expand and simplify

1 $2(x + 3) + 5$ **2** $5(2x + 1) + 3$ **3** $4(3x + 2) + 2x$

4 $9(2x + 3) - 14$ **5** $3(2a + 4) - 2a$ **6** $9(3y + 2) - 6$

Expand and simplify

7 $5(a + 2) + 2(2a + 1)$ **8** $3(x + 4) + 6(x + 2)$ **9** $6(x + 1) + 3(2x + 4)$

10 $3(4a + 8) + 2(a - 3)$ **11** $7(2x + 3) + 4(3x + 1)$ **12** $4(2d + 2) + 6(3d + 4)$

Simplify

13 $3(4a + 2) - 2(a - 2)$ **14** $5(3x + 1) - 3(3x + 2)$ **15** $6(2x + 3) - 4(2x + 2)$

16 $5(3a + 2) - 3(2a + 1)$ **17** $3(4d + 1) - 2(6d - 5)$ **18** $7(2c + 6) - 4(c + 5)$

Expand and simplify

19 $9y - 5(y + 2) - 3$ **20** $11x + 2 - 3(2x - 5)$ **21** $6a + 2(3a + 1) - 7 + 2a$

22 $15(n + m) - 6(2n - m)$ **23** $8(2a + b) - 3(3a + 2b)$ **24** $8x + 6(2 - x) + 2(3x + 5)$

Simplify

25 $a(3a + 2) + 5a(2a + 1)$ **26** $4x(3x + 2) - 3x(x - 3)$

27 $2y(4y + 5) - 5y(y + 2)$ **28** $3a(a + 2b) + 2b(5a + 2b)$

29 $4m(3m + 2p) - 3m(p - 2m)$ **30** $6x(2x + 3y) - 3x(x - 4y)$

31 $5a(a + 2b) + 4b(3a - c)$ **32** $7x(2x + 3y + z) - 3y(3x - 2z)$

Can you still?  Can you still?

4A Use ratios (see Unit 2)

1. The ratio of butter to flour in a certain recipe is 2:3. If 150g of butter was used then how much flour was used?

2. The angles a, b and c on a straight line are in the ratio 5:6:1 respectively.

   Find the sizes of angles a, b and c.

   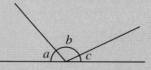

3. Write the ratio 20 g:0.16 kg:0.1 kg in its simplest form.

4. £1105 was shared out between Yasmin, Janet and Wayne in the ratio 4:7:6 respectively. How much does each person get?

5. A photocopier is set to reduce in the ratio 7:3.

   (a) A picture of length 14 cm is photocopied. How long will it be in the photocopy?

   (b) On the photocopy the letter A has height 18 mm. How high will the letter A be on the original?

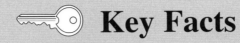 **Key Facts**

Each term in one bracket must be multiplied by each term in the other bracket.

Consider $(a + b)(c + d)$

F $(a + b)(c + d)$ multiply the <u>F</u>irst terms in each bracket $\Rightarrow$ ac

O $(a + b)(c + d)$ multiply the <u>O</u>uter terms in each bracket $\Rightarrow$ $+ ad$

I $(a + b)(c + d)$ multiply the <u>I</u>nner terms in each bracket $\Rightarrow$ $+ bc$

L $(a + b)(c + d)$ multiply the <u>L</u>ast terms in each bracket $\Rightarrow$ $+ bd$

First

Outer   Follow this order each
         time to make sure you $\Rightarrow$ $(a + b)(c + d) = ac + ad + bc + bd$

Inner   do not miss any terms

Last

(a) Expand $(x + 5)(x - 2)$

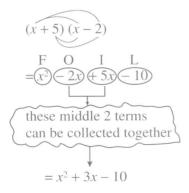

$(x + 5)(x - 2)$

     F   O   I   L
$= x^2 - 2x + 5x - 10$

these middle 2 terms
can be collected together

$= x^2 + 3x - 10$

(b) Expand $(2x + 3)(5x - 1)$

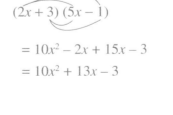

$(2x + 3)(5x - 1)$

$= 10x^2 - 2x + 15x - 3$

$= 10x^2 + 13x - 3$

(c) Expand $(x - 5)^2$

$(x - 5)(x - 5)$

$= x^2 - 5x - 5x + 25$

$= x^2 - 10x + 25$

WARNING!

$(x - 5)^2$ is **not**
$x^2 - 25$ or $x^2 + 25$
Similarly
$(x + 4)^2$ is **not** $x^2 + 16$

1 Copy and complete the following.

(a)

$(x + 3)\ (x + 4)$

$= x^2 + 4x\ +\Box + 12$

$= x^2 +\Box + 12$

(b)

$(a - 5)\ (a + 3)$

$=\Box + 3a - 5a -\Box$

$=\Box - 2a -\Box$

(c) $(m - 7)^2$

$(m - 7)\ (m - 7)$

$= m^2 -\Box -\Box +\Box$

$= m^2 -\Box +\Box$

Expand the following:

2 $(x + 2)(x + 6)$

3 $(p + 1)(p + 5)$

4 $(a + 3)(a + 7)$

5 $(m + 3)(m - 1)$

6 $(y + 2)(y - 6)$

7 $(n - 5)(n + 2)$

8 $(b - 8)(b + 3)$

9 $(x - 6)(x + 8)$

10 $(c - 8)(c - 3)$

11 $(q - 2)(q - 7)$

12 $(f - 2)(f - 10)$

13 $(a + 9)(a - 4)$

Multiply out the following:

14 $(2x + 1)(3x + 4)$

15 $(5y + 2)(y + 3)$

16 $(4p + 2)(2p + 7)$

17 $(3a - 4)(5a + 2)$

18 $(6f - 1)(2f + 3)$

19 $(9y - 4)(4y - 2)$

20 $(3x - 4)(7x + 2)$

21 $(3q - 4)(7q - 1)$

22 $(4b - 3)(5b - 3)$

23 $(4z - 6)(2z - 3)$

24 $(x + 7)(4x - 9)$

25 $(6a - 5)(5a + 4)$

Expand the following:

26 $(x + 6)(x + 6)$

27 $(x + 5)^2$

28 $(a + 10)^2$

29 $(y - 1)^2$

30 $(p - 3)^2$

31 $(b - 9)^2$

32 $(2a - 1)^2$

33 $(5x + 4)^2$

34 $(3y - 5)^2$

Multiply out the following:

35 $(3 + 2a)(4 + a)$

36 $(2 + 5y)(3 - 2y)$

37 $(4 + 3x)(x - 2)$

38 $(7 - 3p)(4 - 2p)$

39 $(x + 3y)(2x - 4y)$

40 $(3a - 5b)(2a - 3b)$

Expand and simplify the following:

41 $(x + 1)^2 + (x + 3)^2$

42 $(a - 4)^2 - (a + 2)^2$

43 $(y - 3)^2 - (y - 1)^2$

44 $(p + 5)^2 + (p + 4)^2 + (p + 2)^2$

Find the area of each rectangle below:

45

46

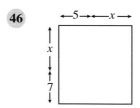

47 Expand $(x + 2)(x + 3)(x + 4)$

48 Expand $(x + 5)(x + 2)(x + 1)$

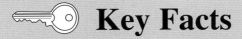

Key Facts

We know that $3(a + b)$ is the same as $3a + 3b$ so $3a + 3b = 3(a + b)$

Consider $(3a)$ + $(3b)$

           $3 \times a$ $3 \times b$ 3 is a *factor* of both $3a$ and $3b$

                            so 3 is the *common factor* of $3a$ and $3b$

Common factors can be extracted from algebraic expressions.

> $3a + 3b$ $\Rightarrow$ Take out common factor 3. $\Rightarrow$ $3(a + b)$
>   Write remaining terms
>   in a bracket.
> This is called '*factorising*' $3a + 3b$ by *taking out a common factor.*

Always multiply out the bracket at the end to check you have the same expression you started with.

'*Factorising*' an expression means writing it as a *product of its factors*.

Factorise each expression below:

(a) $8p - 24$ (b) $xy + xz$ (c) $5ac + 15bc$ (d) $4x^2 - 6x$

   $= 8(p - 3)$ $= x(y + z)$ $= 5c(a + 3b)$ $= 2x(2x - 3)$

| Common factor | Common factor | Common factor | Common factor |

Note

     In example (c) above, $5ac + 15bc = 5(ac + 3bc)$
                   and $5ac + 15bc = c(5a + 15b)$

     Both answers are a correct use of algebra but have not been factorised completely.

     '*Factorise completely*' means '*take out the largest common factor possible*'.

Copy and complete

1 $6a + 15 = 3\left(2a + \boxed{}\right)$

2 $7n - 35 = 7\left(\boxed{} - \boxed{}\right)$

3 $48b - 40 = 8\left(\boxed{} - \boxed{}\right)$

4 $ab - ac = a\left(\boxed{} - \boxed{}\right)$

5 $x^2 + 6x = x\left(x + \boxed{}\right)$

6 $3b^2 - 12b = 3b\left(\boxed{} - \boxed{}\right)$

7 $3xy + 15xz = 3x\left(y + \boxed{}\right)$

8 $12x^2 - 8x = \boxed{}\left(3x - \boxed{}\right)$

9 $6m^2 - m = \boxed{}\left(6m - \boxed{}\right)$

10 $a^3 + 5a^2b = a^2\left(\boxed{} + \boxed{}\right)$

Factorise these expressions completely:

11 $6m + 42$

12 $25a - 35$

13 $24m - 20n$

14 $16x - 4$

15 $56a + 32b$

16 $27p + 18$

17 $10a + 15b + 25c$

18 $28x - 36y + 16$

19 $ef + fg$

20 $x^2 - 8x$

21 $a^2 + 5a$

22 $2pq + 4pr$

23 $8ab - 12bc$

24 $6xy - 9yz$

25 $5x^2 - 15x$

26 $5st + 35s$

27 $8pr - 40pq$

28 $6ab + 4b$

29 $3a^2 + 8a$

30 $12x - 16x^2$

31 $3x^2 + 21xy$

32 $a^2b - a^2c$

33 $a^2 + abc$

34 $5x^2 - 6xy$

35 $20p^2 - 30pq$

36 $36abc - 16b^2$

37 $49x^2 + 42xy$

38 $63a^2 - 35ab$

39 $9x^2y + 6xy^2$

40 $10pqr + 15pq^2$

41 $16ab^2 + 8abc$

42 $25fgh - 20efg$

43 $8ab^2 - 6ab$

44 $12x^3 + 8x^2$

45 $6p^2q + 15p^3$

46 $18a^2b^2 - 12abc$

Factorise completely:

47 $9abc + 15a^2b - 6ab^2$

48 $12x^2y^2 - 9xy^2z - 18x^2yz$

49 $42p^3q^2r^2 + 28pq^3r^2 - 49p^2q^2r$

50 $32a^2b^3c^3 - 24a^3b^2c^3 + 40a^2bc^2$

M Factorising – quadratics

We have seen that $(x + 2)(x + 5) = x^2 + 5x + 2x + 10 = x^2 + 7x + 10$

$x^2 + 7x + 10$ is a *quadratic* expression (x^2 is the highest power).

Since $(x + 2)(x + 5) = x^2 + 7x + 10$, we can reverse the process to show that $x^2 + 7x + 10 = (x + 2)(x + 5)$.

$(x + 2)$ multiplied by $(x + 5)$ gives $x^2 + 7x + 10$ so $(x + 2)$ and $(x + 5)$ are both *factors* of $x^2 + 7x + 10$.

Expressing $x^2 + 7x + 10$ as $(x + 2)(x + 5)$ is known as *factorising the quadratic* $x^2 + 7x + 10$. The process is vital to solving many mathematical equations and for making algebraic expressions simpler.

(a) Factorise $x^2 - 2x - 8$

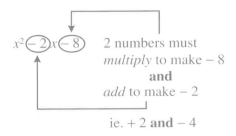

$x^2 \boxed{-2}x \boxed{-8}$ 2 numbers must
multiply to make -8
and
add to make -2

ie. $+2$ **and** -4

$x^2 - 2x - 8 = (x + 2)(x - 4)$

(b) Factorise $x^2 - 8x + 12$

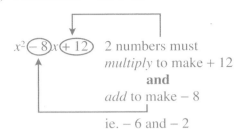

$x^2 \boxed{-8}x \boxed{+12}$ 2 numbers must
multiply to make $+12$
and
add to make -8

ie. -6 **and** -2

$x^2 - 8x + 12 = (x - 6)(x - 2)$

Check each answer by multiplying back out

M4.7

Copy and complete

1 $x^2 + 10x + 21$

$= (x + 3)(x + \boxed{})$

2 $x^2 - 7x + 12$

$= (x - \boxed{})(x - \boxed{})$

3 $x^2 + 3x - 10$

$= (x + \boxed{})(x - 2)$

Factorise the following quadratics:

4 $a^2 + 11a + 30$

5 $y^2 + 8y + 15$

6 $b^2 + 12b + 20$

7 $p^2 + 5p + 6$

8 $x^2 + 4x + 4$

9 $f^2 + 10f + 25$

10 $c^2 + 5c + 4$

11 $y^2 + 3y + 2$

12 $x^2 + 12x + 35$

Factorise the following:

13 $m^2 - 6m + 5$

14 $x^2 - 17x + 30$

15 $n^2 - 9n + 8$

16 $a^2 - 8a + 16$

17 $q^2 - 14q + 13$

18 $w^2 + 5w - 24$

19 $x^2 - 3x - 28$

20 $m^2 - 2m - 35$

21 $y^2 - 4y - 12$

22 $n^2 + 5n - 14$

23 $p^2 + p - 6$

24 $x^2 - x - 20$

25 $y^2 - 7y + 10$

26 $a^2 + 3a - 40$

27 $q^2 - q - 42$

28 $x^2 + 2x - 24$

29 $n^2 - 5n + 6$

30 $y^2 - 4y - 60$

31   Find the length of PQ in terms of x.

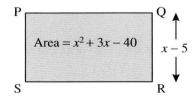

Area $= x^2 + 3x - 40$
$x - 5$

32   Find the length of FG in terms of a.

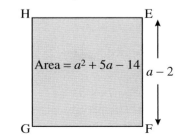

Area $= a^2 + 5a - 14$
$a - 2$

98

Factorise the following quadratics:

33 $x^2 - 20x + 99$ **34** $y^2 - 10y + 25$ **35** $m^2 + 13m + 42$

36 $p^2 - 14p + 24$ **37** $n^2 - 17n + 70$ **38** $z^2 - 18z - 40$

39 $h^2 + 15h + 26$ **40** $m^2 - 3m - 130$ **41** $q^2 + 7q - 60$

Can you still?

4B   **Simplify surds (see Unit 1)**

Can you still?

Simplify

1. $\sqrt{80}$ **2.** $\sqrt{125}$ **3.** $\sqrt{125} - \sqrt{80}$ **4.** $\sqrt{2} \times \sqrt{8}$

5. $\left(\sqrt{7}\right)^2$ **6.** $\dfrac{\sqrt{30}}{\sqrt{2}}$ **7.** $\sqrt{54} \div \sqrt{6}$ **8.** $3\sqrt{3} \times 2\sqrt{5}$

9. $6\sqrt{3} - 4\sqrt{3}$ **10.** $\left(1 + \sqrt{3}\right)\left(2 - \sqrt{3}\right)$ **11.** $\left(\sqrt{7} - \sqrt{2}\right)\left(\sqrt{7} + \sqrt{2}\right)$

12. $\left(5 + \sqrt{2}\right)\left(3 + \sqrt{3}\right)$ **13.** $\sqrt{7}\left(\sqrt{3} - \sqrt{2}\right)$ **14.** $\left(3 - \sqrt{5}\right)^2$

15. Find the area of this triangle
(the units are in cm).

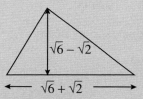

$\sqrt{6} - \sqrt{2}$

$\sqrt{6} + \sqrt{2}$

Rationalise the denominator in each of the following:

16. $\dfrac{1}{\sqrt{2}}$ **17.** $\dfrac{3}{\sqrt{5}}$ **18.** $\dfrac{4}{3\sqrt{3}}$ **19.** $\dfrac{1 - \sqrt{5}}{\sqrt{2}}$

E | Factorising – the difference of 2 squares

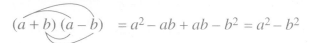

$(a + b)(a - b) = a^2 - ab + ab - b^2 = a^2 - b^2$

so $a^2 - b^2$ can quickly be factorised into $(a + b)(a - b)$

Factorise the expressions below:

(a) $x^2 - y^2$

$= (x + y)(x - y)$

(b) $x^2 - 9y^2$

$= x^2 - (3y)^2$

$= (x + 3y)(x - 3y)$

(c) $m^2 - 25$

$= m^2 - 5^2$

$= (m + 5)(m - 5)$

Always check answers at the end by multiplying back out.

Copy and complete

1 $a^2 - 4$

$= a^2 - \boxed{}\,^2$

$= (a + \boxed{})(a - \boxed{})$

2 $4x^2 - y^2$

$= \boxed{}\,^2 - y^2$

$= (\boxed{} + y)(\boxed{} - y)$

3 $9p^2 - 4q^2$

$= \boxed{}\,^2 - \boxed{}\,^2$

$= (\boxed{} + \boxed{})(\boxed{} - \boxed{})$

Factorise the following expressions:

4 $m^2 - n^2$

5 $p^2 - q^2$

6 $a^2 - 4^2$

7 $n^2 - 7^2$

8 $n^2 - 49$

9 $x^2 - 4$

10 $y^2 - 81$

11 $m^2 - 1$

12 $64 - a^2$

13 $100 - y^2$

14 $x^2 - \dfrac{1}{16}$

15 $4b^2 - c^2$

16 $p^2 - 16q^2$

17 $25m^2 - 4$

18 $9x^2 - 1$

19 $36y^2 - 25$

20 $81b^2 - 4c^2$

21 $49a^2 - 16b^2$

22 $100x^2 - 49y^2$

23 $25m^2 - \dfrac{n^2}{4}$

24 Use the difference of 2 squares to evaluate $1003^2 - 997^2$ without using a calculator.

25 Find the value of $200002^2 - 199998^2$.

26 Use the difference of 2 squares to evaluate $19.5^2 - 0.5^2$ without using a calculator.

 # Key Facts

Factorising completely.

Always take out common factors first then try to factorise what remains in the bracket.

Examples.

Factorise *completely* the expressions below:

(a) $4y^2 - 16$

$= 4(y^2 - 4)$

$= 4(y + 2)(y - 2)$

(b) $x^3 - 9x$

$= x(x^2 - 9)$

$= x(x + 3)(x - 3)$

(c) $4x^2 - 8x - 32$

$= 4(x^2 - 2x - 8)$

$= 4(x - 4)(x + 2)$

Copy and complete questions **27** to **29** :

27 $16a - a^3$

$= \boxed{}(16 - a^2)$

$= \boxed{}(4 + \boxed{})(4 - \boxed{})$

28 $3n^2 + 9n - 30$

$= 3(n^2 + \boxed{} - \boxed{})$

$= 3(n + \boxed{})(n - \boxed{})$

29 $4p^2 - 4$

$= 4(\boxed{} - \boxed{})$

$= 4(\boxed{} + \boxed{})(\boxed{} - \boxed{})$

Factorise completely the expressions below:

30 $m^3 - 25m$

31 $6p^2 - 24$

32 $n^3 - n$

33 $5s^2 + 10s + 5$

34 $3t^2 + 9t + 6$

35 $27 - 12x^2$

36 $10y^2 - 20y - 80$

37 $2x^2 + 6x - 56$

38 $7a^2 - 49a + 42$

E   Factorising by grouping

🔑 Key Facts

If an expression has 4 terms, it may be possible to pair off the terms and to factorise as follows:

Consider $ac + bd + ad + bc$

find pairs of terms with a common factor

common factor c

$ac + bd + ad + bc$

common factor d

$= \underbrace{ac + bc} + \underbrace{bd + ad}$ (group 'pairs' together)

$= c(a + b) + d(b + a)$ (take out common factors)

(a+b) is now a common factor. Take this out.

$= (a + b)\ (c + d)$ (the expression is 'factorised')

E4.2

Copy and complete

1 $ab + bc - ad - cd$

$= b\left(\boxed{} + \boxed{}\right) - d\left(a + \boxed{}\right)$

$= \left(\boxed{} + \boxed{}\right)(b - d)$

2 $xz + yz - xy - y^2$

$= z\left(\boxed{} + \boxed{}\right) - y\left(\boxed{} + \boxed{}\right)$

$= \left(\boxed{} + \boxed{}\right)(z - y)$

Factorise the expressions below:

3 $ef + fh + eg + gh$

4 $mq - mp + nq - np$

5 $ab - cd - bd + ac$

6 $mn + xy + ny + mx$

7 $ad - ac - bd + bc$

8 $qr + ps - rs - pq$

9 $eh + ef - fg - gh$

10 $ac - 3a + 2c - 6$

11 $3 - d - 3e + de$

12 $6ac + 2bd + 4ad + 3bc$

13 $12yz - 6wx + 8xy - 9wz$

14 $8mp - 12mq - 10np + 15nq$

Factorise $6x^2 + 11x - 10$

Part 1

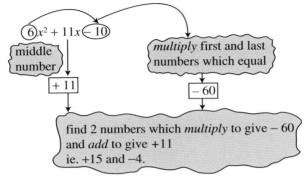

Part 2 Rewrite the middle term using the 2 numbers +15 and –4

$$6x^2 + 11x - 10 = 6x^2 + 15x - 4x - 10$$

Part 3 Factorise by grouping

$$6x^2 + 15x - 4x - 10 = 3x(2x + 5) - 2(2x + 5)$$
$$= (2x + 5)(3x - 2)$$

Factorise the expressions below:

(a) $2x^2 + 5x - 12$

Find 2 numbers which multiply

to make –24 and add to make +5

ie. +8 and –3.

$2x^2 + 5x - 12$

$= 2x^2 + 8x - 3x - 12$

$= 2x(x + 4) - 3(x + 4)$

$= (2x - 3)(x + 4)$

(b) $5x^2 + 13x + 8$

Find 2 numbers which multiply

to make +40 and add to make +13

ie. +8 and +5.

$5x^2 + 13x + 8$

$= 5x^2 + 8x + 5x + 8$

$= x(5x + 8) + (5x + 8)$

$= (5x + 8)(x + 1)$

E4.3

Copy and complete

1 $3x^2 + 11x + 6$

$= 3x^2 + 9x + \boxed{} + 6$

$= 3x\left(\boxed{} + \boxed{}\right) + 2\left(\boxed{} + \boxed{}\right)$

$= \left(\boxed{} + \boxed{}\right)\left(3x + 2\right)$

2 $5q^2 - 8q - 4$

$= 5q^2 - 10q + \boxed{} - 4$

$= 5q\left(\boxed{} - \boxed{}\right) + \boxed{}\left(\boxed{} - \boxed{}\right)$

$= \left(\boxed{} - \boxed{}\right)\left(5q + \boxed{}\right)$

Factorise the following quadratics:

3 $2x^2 + 7x + 6$ **4** $3x^2 + 14x + 8$ **5** $6a^2 + 11a + 4$

6 $4y^2 + 20y + 9$ **7** $4z^2 + 13z + 3$ **8** $6q^2 - 11q + 4$

9 $4p^2 - 13p + 9$ **10** $8h^2 + 5h - 3$ **11** $10t^2 + 13t - 3$

12 $12r^2 - 13r - 4$ **13** $25e^2 - 49$ **14** $16s^2 - 25$

15 $3x^2 - 14x + 8$ **16** $2a^2 + a - 21$ **17** $4p^2 - 15p - 4$

18 $15u^2 - 17u - 4$ **19** $6x^2 + 19x + 10$ **20** $4b^2 + 12b + 5$

21 $4p^2 + 20p + 9$ **22** $8w^2 - 19w - 15$ **23** $42x^2 - 5x - 3$

Can you still?   **(4C) Find angles (see Unit 3)**   *Can you still?*

Find the angles marked with letters.

1.

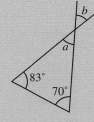

2.

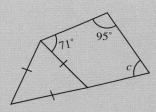

3.

4.

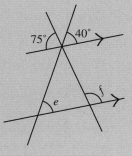

5.

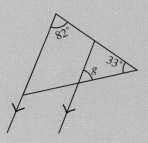

6.

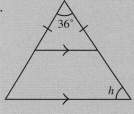

7.

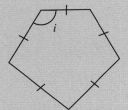

8.

9.

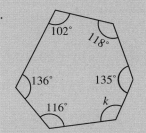

103

Key Facts

Part 1 Solve $x^2 - 3x = 18$

> Always rearrange to make one side of the equation = 0

$x^2 - 3x - 18 = 0$

Part 2

> Factorise by taking out a common factor, using the difference of 2 squares or factorising into 2 brackets

$(x - 6)(x + 3) = 0$

Part 3

> Consider the equation A × B = 0.
> The only way A × B can equal 0 is if A = 0 or B = 0 or both A and B = 0

Consider $(x - 6) \times (x + 3) = 0$

$x - 6 = 0$ or $x + 3 = 0$

$x = 6$ or $x = -3$

> There are usually 2 solutions (answers) but sometimes there is only 1 solution or no solutions.

Solve the following equations.

(a) $x^2 - 7x + 12 = 0$

$(x - 3)(x - 4) = 0$

$x - 3 = 0$ or $x - 4 = 0$

$x = 3$ or $x = 4$

(b) $2y^2 = 4y$

$2y^2 - 4y = 0$

$2y(y - 2) = 0$

$2y = 0$ or $y - 2 = 0$

$y = 0$ or $y = 2$

(c) $n^2 - 10n + 25 = 0$

$(n - 5)(n - 5) = 0$

$n - 5 = 0$ or $n - 5 = 0$

$n = 5$ or $n = 5$

so $n = 5$ only

E4.4

Copy and complete

1 $x^2 + 9x + 20 = 0$

$(x + 5)\left(x + \boxed{}\right) = 0$

$x + 5 = 0$ or $x + \boxed{} = 0$

$x = \boxed{}$ or $x = \boxed{}.$

2 $m^2 - 6 = 5m$

$m^2 - \boxed{} - 6 = 0$

$\left(m - \boxed{}\right)(m + 1) = 0$

$m - \boxed{} = 0$ or $m + \boxed{} = 0$

$m = \boxed{}$ or $m = \boxed{}$

3 $r^2 - 6r = 0$

$r\left(\boxed{} - \boxed{}\right) = 0$

$r = 0$ or $\boxed{} - \boxed{} = 0$

$r = 0$ or $r = \boxed{}$

Solve the following equations

4 $x^2 + 7x + 12 = 0$ **5** $x^2 + 5x + 6 = 0$ **6** $n^2 + 8n + 16 = 0$

7 $y^2 + 9y + 18 = 0$ **8** $p^2 - 6p + 8 = 0$ **9** $a^2 - 10a + 21 = 0$

10 $m^2 - 10m + 24 = 0$ **11** $b^2 - 7b + 10 = 0$ **12** $n^2 - n - 6 = 0$

13 $q^2 - 8q - 20 = 0$ **14** $x^2 - 2x - 15 = 0$ **15** $m^2 + 7m - 30 = 0$

Solve these equations

16 $x^2 - x - 20 = 0$ **17** $(n + 9)(n - 1) = 0$ **18** $(p - 3)(p - 8) = 0$

19 $(a - 8)(a + 7) = 0$ **20** $y^2 + 2y = 0$ **21** $w^2 - 3w = 0$

22 $(b - 2)(b + 10) = 0$ **23** $z^2 + 2z + 1 = 0$ **24** $k^2 + k = 0$

Rearrange then solve these equations

25 $x^2 - 3x = -2$ **26** $a^2 + 30 = 11a$ **27** $n^2 + 6n = 7$

28 $2u^2 = u + 10$ **29** $r^2 = 2r$ **30** $c^2 + 15c = -36$

31 $z^2 - 12 = 4z$ **32** $h(h - 4) + 1 = 6$ **33** $t(t - 4) - 14 = t$

The remaining questions involve coefficients of the squared term >1. Make sure you have tackled Exercise E4.3 before attempting these questions.

Copy and complete

34 $(7t - 1)(4t + 3) = 0$

$7t - 1 = 0$ or $\boxed{} + \boxed{} = 0$

$7t = \boxed{}$ or $\boxed{} = \boxed{}$

$t = \dfrac{\boxed{}}{\boxed{}}$ or $t = \dfrac{\boxed{}}{\boxed{}}$

35 $6x^2 - 5x - 4 = 0$

$6x^2 - 8x + \boxed{} - 4 = 0$

$2x\left(\boxed{} - \boxed{}\right) + \left(\boxed{} - 4\right) = 0$

$\left(\boxed{} - \boxed{}\right)(2x + 1) = 0$

$\boxed{} - \boxed{} = 0$ or $2x + 1 = 0$

$\boxed{} = \boxed{}$ or $2x = \boxed{}$

$x = \dfrac{\boxed{}}{\boxed{}}$ or $x = \dfrac{\boxed{}}{\boxed{}}$

Solve the following equations

36 $3a^2 + 13a + 4 = 0$ **37** $6g^2 - 13g + 5 = 0$ **38** $2x^2 - 5x - 3 = 0$

39 $6y^2 + 11y - 10 = 0$ **40** $20x^2 + 21x + 4 = 0$ **41** $4x^2 - 8x - 21 = 0$

42 $9n^2 + 7n - 2 = 0$ **43** $y^2 - 36 = 0$ **44** $9p^2 - 1 = 0$

45 $25a^2 - 16 = 0$ **46** $9n^2 - 27n + 20 = 0$ **47** $49y^2 - 4 = 0$

Solve these equations

48 $4h^2 - 8h = 5$

49 $4q^2 = 20q - 9$

50 $4z(z - 1) = 3$

51 $5u^2 = 4u$

52 $9u^2 = 4$

53 $8x^2 = -19x - 6$

54 $\frac{1}{2}y^2 - y = 0$

55 $(3x + 2)(2x + 1) = 1$

56 $(2t + 3)(t + 2) = 3$

Can you still?

Can you still?

4D **Use circle properties (see Unit 3)**

In these questions O is the centre of the circle.

1.

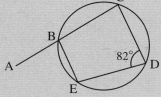

Find AB̂E.

2.

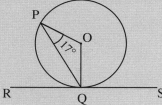

Find PQ̂R.

3.

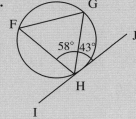

Find FĜH.

4.

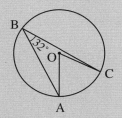

Find AÔC.

5.

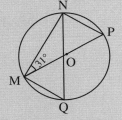

Find MQ̂N.

6.

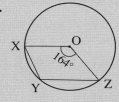

Find XŶZ.

7.

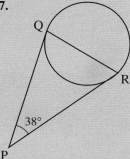

Find PQ̂R.

8.

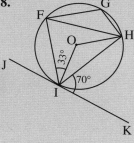

Find IF̂H *and* FĜH.

9.

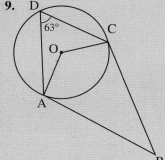

Find AÔC *and* AB̂C.

A right–angled triangle has a width of x. Its height is 2 cm more than its width. The hypotenuse is 4 cm more than its width.

(i) Write down expressions for the height and the hypotenuse of the triangle.

(ii) Use Pythagoras' theorem to write down a quadratic equation involving x (see Unit 10 if Pythagoras' theorem not yet covered).

(iii) Solve this equation to find x and state the length of each side of the triangle.

(i) height $= x + 2$

hypotenuse $= x + 4$

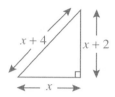

(ii) $x^2 + (x + 2)^2 = (x + 4)^2$ using Pythagoras.

$x^2 + x^2 + 2x + 2x + 4 = x^2 + 4x + 4x + 16$

$2x^2 + 4x + 4 = x^2 + 8x + 16$

$x^2 - 4x - 12 = 0$

(iii) $(x - 6)(x + 2) = 0$

$x - 6 = 0$ or $x + 2 = 0$

$x = 6$ or -2 x is a length so cannot be negative therefore $x = 6$.

Hence the sides of the triangle are 6 cm, 8 cm and 10 cm.

E4.5

1 A triangle of area 30 cm² is such that its height is 4 cm greater than its base. If its base is x cm then:

(a) Write down an expression for the height in terms of x.

(b) Use the area of the triangle to write down an equation which x satisfies and hence show that $x^2 + 4x - 60 = 0$.

(c) Solve this equation to find the base of the triangle.

2  The width of a rectangle is x cm. The length of the rectangle is 5 cm more than its width.

(a) Write down an expression for the length of the rectangle in terms of x.

(b) Write down an expression for the area of the rectangle in terms of x.

(c) If the area of the rectangle is 36 cm², write down a quadratic equation involving x.

(d) Solve this equation to find x.

3

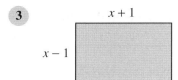

These 2 rectangles have the same area.

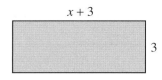

(a) Use the fact that they have the same area to write down an equation involving x.

(b) Show that this equation can be written in the form $x^2 - 3x - 10 = 0$.

(c) Hence find x.

4 A triangle has an area of 52 cm^2 and its height is 5 cm greater than its base. If its base is x cm then:

(a) Write down an expression for the height in terms of x.

(b) Hence write down an expression for the area of the triangle in terms of x.

(c) Write an equation and solve this to find x.

5 A right-angled triangle has a width of x cm. Its height is 7 cm more than its width. The hypotenuse is 13 cm.

(a) Write down an expression for the height of the triangle in terms of x.

(b) Use Pythagoras' theorem to write down a quadratic equation involving x (see Unit 10 if Pythagoras' theorem not yet covered).

(c) Solve this equation to find x.

6

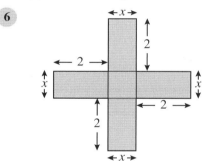

(a) All units are in cm. If the total area of this shape is 33 cm^2, write down a quadratic equation involving x.

(b) Solve this equation to find x.

7 (a) Write down the dimensions, in terms of x, of the larger rectangle.

(b) Find the area, in terms of x, of the shaded area.

(c) If the shaded area is 64 cm^2, find x.

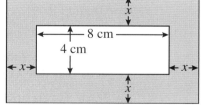

8 The length of the base of a rectangular box is 3 cm longer than twice its width. The area of the base is 44 cm^2.

(a) Let the width of the box = x. Write down a quadratic equation involving x.

(b) Find the width of the box.

9 A rectangle that measures x by $x - 1$ has the same area as a rectangle that measures $x - 3$ by 10.

(a) Write down a quadratic equation involving x.

(b) Solve this to find two possible values of x.

10

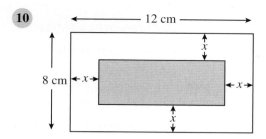

A piece of paper measures 12 cm by 8 cm. A strip of width x cm is cut off from each side. The area (shaded) is now 32 cm².

(a) Find the dimensions of the new piece of paper in terms of x.

(b) Find the area (shaded) of the new piece of paper, in terms of x.

(c) Write down a quadratic equation involving x.

(d) Show that this equation simplifies to $x^2 - 10x + 16 = 0$.

(e) Solve this to find the value of x.

11 28 m of fencing is arranged so that it encloses a rectangular area of 40 m². If w is the width of the rectangle then:

(a) Find the length of the rectangle in terms of w.

(b) Write down a quadratic equation involving w.

(c) Solve this equation to find w.

12 Two positive numbers differ by 2. The sum of their squares is 244.

(a) If n is the smaller of the two numbers then write down the larger number in terms of n.

(b) Hence write down an equation.

(c) Show that this can be re-written as $n^2 + 2n - 120 = 0$.

(d) Solve this to find n.

13 Find two consecutive integers so that the sum of their squares is 61.

14 The sum of the first n positive whole numbers is $\dfrac{n(n+1)}{2}$.

(a) Find the sum of the first 20 positive whole numbers.

(b) If the sum of the first n numbers is 55 then write down a quadratic equation involving n.

(c) Solve this to find n.

15

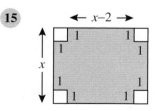

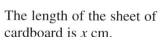

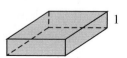

An open box is made by cutting 1 cm squares from the corners of a square sheet of cardboard and then folding.

The length of the sheet of cardboard is x cm.

If the volume of the box is 81 cm³, find the value of x.

WATCH YOUR MONEY! – VAT – Value Added Tax

This is money added to the prices of goods and services. This money is collected by the government.

The usual rate of VAT is 17.5%. Fuel for homes is charged at a lower rate of 5%. Some things like books are zero-rated. This means there is no VAT on books.

A TV costs £500 + VAT at 17.5%. How much does the TV cost?

VAT *without* a calculator.

10% of 500 = $\frac{1}{10}$ of 500 = 50

5% of 500 = 25

2.5% of 500 = 12.50

Total: 17.5% of 500 = 87.50

VAT *with* a calculator.

17.5% means $\frac{17.5}{100}$

so 17.5% of 500 = $\frac{17.5}{100} \times 500$

$(17.5 \div 100 \times 500)$

so 17.5% of 500 = 87.50

TV costs £500 + £87.50 = £587.50

$\underbrace{}_{VAT}$

WYM4

VAT is 17.5% in this exercise.

1   How much will each of the following cost?

(a) a computer costing £820 + VAT.

(b) a washing machine costing £450 + VAT.

(c) a cooker costing £630 + VAT.

2

'ELECTRICS'
Digital radio

£160
including VAT

Which digital radio is cheaper?

'SPARKS'
Digital radio

£140
plus VAT

3   Lionel has a checkup and a filling at the dentist. He is charged £182 + VAT. How much does Lionel have to pay?

4   Raneer has some new windows fitted. The windows cost £2750 + VAT. How much does Raneer pay?

110

5 Copy and complete the garage bill below.

brake pads	£ 43
brake fluid	£ 4
labour	£ 45
total	
VAT	
total bill	

6 Callie has a £400 limit. Can she afford to buy a dishwasher which costs £360 + VAT?

7 Mary's grandparents offer her £300 towards a new music system. Mary has saved £200. She wants a music system which costs £420 + VAT. Has she enough money to buy this?

8 Copy and complete the bill below for certain bathroom items.

bath	£ 199.50
sink	£ 89.70
toilet	£ 112
mirror	£ 26.80
total	
VAT	
total bill	

9 An electrical shop sells a washing machine for £434.75 including VAT. How much did the washing machine cost before VAT was added?

10 A local garage sells a car for £13395 including VAT. How much did the car cost before VAT was added?

TEST YOURSELF ON UNIT 4

1. Substituting into expressions and formulas

If $x = 6$, $y = -2$ and $z = -3$, find the value of

(a) $3x + 2y$ (b) $y^2 + z^2$ (c) $3y^2$ (d) $\dfrac{(4y)^2}{z^2 + x + 1}$ (e) $y^2(2x - z)$

(f) The area A of a triangle with base b and height h is given by the formula $A = \frac{1}{2}bh$. Find the value of A when $b = 18$ and $h = 7$.

(g) Using the formula $v = u + at$, find the value of v when $u = 37$, $a = 5$ and $t = 6$.

(h) Given that $s = \dfrac{v^2 - u^2}{2a}$ find s when $u = 60$, $v = 80$ and $a = 400$.

(i) If $x = \sqrt{\dfrac{py + q}{r}}$ find x when $p = 25$, $y = 10$, $q = -8$ and $r = 2$.

2. Multiplying out single brackets

Multiply out

(a) $5(x + 3)$ (b) $3(2a - 4)$ (c) $y(y - 5)$ (d) $4b(2b + 1)$

Expand and simplify

(e) $3(a + 2) + 5(a + 3)$ (f) $4(2x + 3) - 3(x - 5)$

(g) $14y + 5 - 6(2y + 3)$ (h) $3p(2p + 4) - 2p(2p - 1)$

3. Multiplying out two brackets

Expand the following:

(a) $(x + 3)(x + 7)$ (b) $(y + 2)(y - 6)$ (c) $(a - 3)(a - 5)$

(d) $(p - 2)^2$ (e) $(3b - 2)(5b + 3)$ (f) $(3x + 2)^2$

4. Factorising by taking out common factors

Factorise these expressions *completely*:

(a) $5x + 15$ (b) $cd - ce$ (c) $35p - 21$ (d) $x^2 - 4xy$

(e) $6pq - 10qr$ (f) $5a^2 + 30ab$ (g) $8y^2z + 20yz$ (h) $18ab^2 - 12a^2b$

5. Factorising quadratics with coefficient of $x^2 = 1$

Factorise the following quadratics:

(a) $x^2 + 3x + 2$ (b) $m^2 - 7m + 6$ (c) $b^2 + b - 6$

(d) $u^2 + 2u - 8$ (e) $h^2 + 15h + 26$ (f) $y^2 - 13y - 48$

6. Using the difference of 2 squares

Factorise *completely* the expressions below:

(a) $y^2 - z^2$ (b) $m^2 - 16$ (c) $9x^2 - 25$

(d) $36n^2 - 49p^2$ (e) $100 - 81a^2$ (f) $x^3 - 36x$

7. Factorising by grouping

Factorise the expressions below:

(a) $km + kn + lm + ln$ (b) $qx + py - xy - pq$ (c) $8a - 3b + 6ab - 4$

8. Factorising quadratics with coefficient of $x^2 > 1$

Factorise the following quadratics:

(a) $3x^2 - 8x + 4$ (b) $4y^2 - 8y - 5$ (c) $4n^2 - 11n + 6$ (d) $6p^2 - 13p - 5$

9. Solving quadratic equations by factorising

Solve the following equations:

(a) $x^2 + 9x + 14 = 0$ (b) $n^2 - 5n + 6 = 0$ (c) $y^2 - 10y - 24 = 0$

(d) $m^2 - 8m = 0$ (e) $4a^2 + 4a - 3 = 0$ (f) $15p^2 = p + 6$

10. Dealing with problems leading to quadratic equations

(a) A photograph of area 40 cm^2 is 3 cm longer than it is wide.

If its width is x cm then:

(i) Write down an expression for the length in terms of x.

(ii) Write down an equation which x satisfies and hence show that $x^2 + 3x - 40 = 0$.

(iii) Find the two solutions to this equation.

(iv) Hence write down the width of the photograph.

(b)

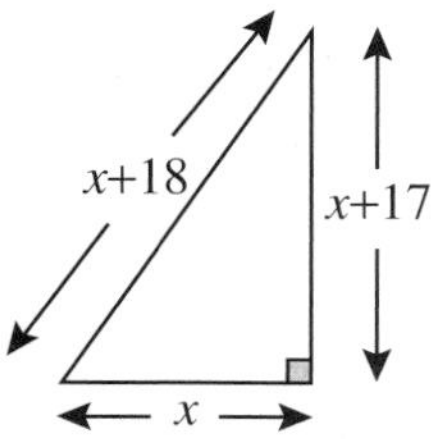

All units are in cm.

Use Pythagoras' theorem to write down a quadratic equation involving x.

Solve this equation to find x and state the length of each side of the triangle.

(c)

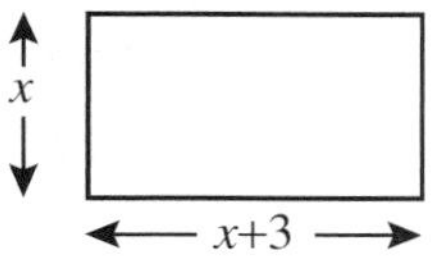

The rectangle and triangle have the same area.

All units are in cm.

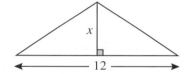

(i) Write down a quadratic equation involving x.

(ii) Find the 2 solutions to this equation.

(iii) Hence write down the one possible value of x in the above diagrams.

Mixed examination questions

1 (a) Expand $4a(2a + 3)$

(b) Expand and simplify $(2x + 1)(3x - 2)$

(c) Expand and simplify $(3x + 2y)(2x - y)$ (EDEXCEL)

2 (a) Expand the brackets $x(y^2 - x)$

(b) Expand and simplify $4(3n + 2) - 3(2n - 1)$

3 Expand and simplify $2x(x + 5y) - y(2x + 5y)$

4 Factorise (i) $10x + 5$ (ii) $x^2 + 7x$ (OCR)

5 Factorise completely $6a^2 + 10ab$

6 (a) Simplify $(3x + y)(x - y) + 2y(x + y)$

(b) Factorise $a^2 - b^2$ (CCEA)

7 (i) Factorise $x^2 - 6x + 8$

   (ii) Solve the equation $x^2 - 6x + 8 = 0$ (EDEXCEL)

8 A rectangle has length $(x + 5)$ cm and width $(x - 1)$ cm.
   A corner is removed from the rectangle as shown.

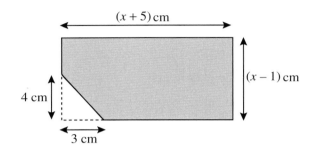

   Show that the shaded area is given by $x^2 + 4x - 11$.   (OCR)

9 Solve $x^2 + 8x + 12 = 0$.

10 Factorise

   (a) $3d + 6e$ (b) $4x^2 + 8xy$ (c) $x^2 - 11x + 30$ (d) $25x^2 - 1$

                                                                                           (CCEA)

11 (a) Expand and simplify $4(x + 3) + 3(2x - 3)$

   (b) Expand and simplify $(2x - y)(3x + 4y)$ (EDEXCEL)

12 (a) Expand and simplify $(2x - 7)(x + 3)$.

   (b) (i) Factorise $x^2 + 4x - 5$

       (ii) Solve the equation $x^2 + 4x - 5 = 0$.   (EDEXCEL)

13 Factorise completely $6a^2 - 7ab + 2b^2$ (EDEXCEL)

14 The diagram below shows a 6-sided shape.
   All the corners are right angles.
   All measurements are given in centimetres.

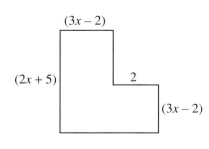

   The area of the shape is 25 cm².

   (a) Show that $6x^2 + 17x - 39 = 0$

   (b) (i) Solve the equation

           $6x^2 + 17x - 39 = 0$

       (ii) Hence work out the length of the
            longest side of the shape.

                                                                                           (EDEXCEL)

15 Solve by factorizing $2x^2 + 5x + 2 = 0$ (OCR)

16 Expand and simplify (i) $(3x - 1)(x + 5)$

(ii) $(x^2 + y)^2$

(iii) $(x + y)^2 - (x - y)^2$ (EDEXCEL)

17 Factorise completely (i) $p^3r^4 + p^5r^3$

(ii) $25p^2 - 4q^2$ (OCR)

In the 'M' sections (mainly grades B, C, D) you will learn how to:

– find factors, multiples, products of prime factors, HCF's and LCM's

– write numbers in standard form

– use standard form numbers without a calculator

– use standard form numbers with a calculator

– find upper/lower bounds

In the 'E' sections (mainly grades A*, A) you will learn how to:

– calculate with upper/lower bounds

– use direct proportion

– use inverse proportion

Also you will learn how to:

– 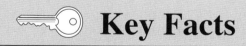 – bank accounts 1

M   **Factors, multiples and prime numbers**

🔑 Key Facts

A *factor* is a number which divides exactly into another number (there will be no remainder).

Multiples are the numbers in a multiplication table. 6, 12, 18, 24, 30, ... are multiples of 6.

A *prime number* can only be divided by two different numbers (these are the numbers 1 and itself). The first four prime numbers are 2, 3, 5, 7, ...

Highest Common Factor (HCF) – the highest number which divides exactly into 2 or more given numbers.

Lowest Common Multiple (LCM) – the smallest number which each of two or more given numbers will divide into.

1 Write down *all* the factors of (a) 28 (b) 50 (c) 48

2 Harry picks his National Lottery numbers by choosing the first six prime numbers. The winning numbers are drawn as below:

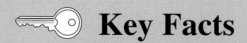

Does Harry win a small prize for picking 3 correct numbers?

3 Which numbers between 20 and 30 have 7 as a factor?

4 Add together all the prime numbers less than 20.

5 (a) Write down the first 5 multiples of 12.

(b) Write down the first 5 multiples of 15.

(c) Write down the LCM (Lowest Common Multiple) of 12 and 15.

6 Find the LCM of:

(a) 12 and 20   (b) 10 and 7   (c) 4, 5 and 6

7 (a) List all the factors of 32.

(b) List all the factors of 40.

(c) Write down the HCF (Highest Common Factor) of 32 and 40.

8 Find the HCF of:

(a) 16 and 48   (b) 36 and 60   (c) 10, 20 and 45

9 Is 93 a prime number?

10 In the game of 'Fizzbuzz', people take it in turns to count up one number at a time. When a multiple of 3 is reached, the person must say 'Fizz'. When a multiple of 5 is reached the person must say 'Buzz'. If a multiple of both 3 and 5 is reached, the person says 'Fizzbuzz.'

Write down the first 2 numbers when the person would have to say 'Fizzbuzz'.

M   Prime factors

🔑 Key Facts

Factors of a number which are also prime numbers are called prime factors.

For example, $42 = 2 \times 3 \times 7$

We can find these prime factors by using a 'factor tree' or by dividing by prime numbers again and again.

Find the prime factors of 36.

Factor tree

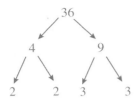

split into 4 and 9
because $4 \times 9 = 36$

split 4 into 2×2
split 9 into 3×3

stop splitting when all numbers are prime
numbers.

We can say $36 = \underbrace{2 \times 2 \times 3 \times 3}_{\text{prime factors}}$

Dividing by prime numbers

Divide by any prime number

$\downarrow$

$2\overline{)36}$
$2\overline{)18}$ ← $36 \div 2 = 18$
$3\overline{)\ 9}$ ← $18 \div 2 = 9$
$3\overline{)\ 3}$ ← $9 \div 3 = 3$
$\quad\ 1$ ← $3 \div 3 = 1$

stop when you get to 1

These are the prime factors.

We can say $36 = 2 \times 2 \times 3 \times 3$

The product of prime factors

When we write $36 = 2 \times 2 \times 3 \times 3$, the prime factors 2, 2, 3 and 3 are multiplied together. This is called a product.

$2 \times 2 \times 3 \times 3$ is the *product of its prime factors*.

Index form

$2 \times 2 = 2^2$ $\qquad$ $3 \times 3 = 3^2$

so $36 = 2 \times 2 \times 3 \times 3$ can be written as $2^2 \times 3^2$

The answer written like this using powers is said to be in *index* form.

M5.2

1 Work out

(a) $2 \times 2 \times 5$ $\qquad$ (b) $2 \times 3 \times 5$ $\qquad$ (c) $3 \times 3 \times 5$

(d) $2 \times 3 \times 7$ $\qquad$ (e) $3 \times 5 \times 11$ $\qquad$ (f) $2 \times 2 \times 5 \times 5$

2 Copy and complete the boxes below:

(a)

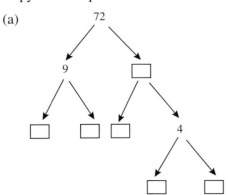

$72 = \square \times \square \times \square \times \square \times \square$

(b)

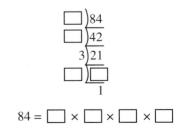

$84 = \square \times \square \times \square \times \square$

118

3 Using any method, write the following numbers as *products of prime factors*:

   (a) 18   (b) 28   (c) 22   (d) 32   (e) 81   (f) 96

   (g) 200   (h) 120   (i) 196   (j) 385   (k) 420   (l) 392

4 Write all your answers to Question **3** in *index form* if you have not already done so.

Finding HCFs

Find the HCF of 64 and 672.

Write the numbers as products of prime factors.

$64 = \boxed{2} \times \boxed{2} \times \boxed{2} \times \boxed{2} \times \boxed{2} \times 2$

$672 = \boxed{2} \times \boxed{2} \times \boxed{2} \times \boxed{2} \times \boxed{2} \times 3 \times 7$

Pick out all the common factors.

Both numbers have the common factors
$2 \times 2 \times 2 \times 2 \times 2$

so HCF of 64 and 672

$= 2 \times 2 \times 2 \times 2 \times 2 = 32$

Finding LCMs

Find the LCM of 28 and 44.

Write the numbers as products of prime factors.

$28 = 2 \times 2 \times 7$

$44 = 2 \times 2 \times 11$

Identify the common factors then cross them out in the second number as shown below.

$28 = \boxed{2} \times \boxed{2} \times 7$

$44 = \cancel{2} \times \cancel{2} \times 11$

The LCM is the product of all the remaining factors.

$LCM = 2 \times 2 \times 7 \times 11 = 308$

---

5 $\boxed{154 = 2 \times 7 \times 11}$ and $\boxed{1365 = 3 \times 5 \times 7 \times 13}$

Find the HCF of 154 and 1365.

6 $\boxed{975 = 3 \times 5 \times 5 \times 13}$ and $\boxed{550 = 2 \times 5 \times 5 \times 11}$

   (a) Find the HCF of 975 and 550.

   (b) Find the LCM of 975 and 550.

7 Use Question **3** to find the HCF of the following pairs of numbers.

   (a) 28 and 120   (b) 200 and 420   (c) 196 and 420

8 Use Question **3** to find the LCM of the following pairs of numbers.

   (a) 28 and 32   (b) 96 and 120   (c) 200 and 420

9 Find   (a) the HCF and   (b) the LCM of 675 and 375

10 Find   (a) the HCF and   (b) the LCM of 336 and 308

11 Two cars complete laps of a circuit. One takes 315 seconds per lap, the other takes 525 seconds per lap. They start their circuits of the laps at the same time.

(a) Express 315 and 525 as the product of their primes.

(b) Find the lowest common multiple of 315 and 525.

(c) Use this to find how many laps the faster car will do before the cars first get to the starting point at the same time.

12 (a) Find the highest common factor and lowest common multiple of 210 and 550.

(b) Multiply the two numbers that you found in part (a) together.

(c) Multiply 210 and 550 together.

(d) What do you notice about the answers to parts (b) and (c)?

(5A)   **Use fractions (see Unit 1)**

Do not use a calculator

1. A flower measuring 20 cm increases in length by four-fifths. What is its new length?

2. A rectangular mat has dimensions $\frac{4}{5}$ m and $\frac{17}{20}$ m. What is the area of the mat?

3. Work out $\left(\frac{3}{4} - \frac{2}{3}\right) \div \frac{1}{2}$

4. Callum is $1\frac{7}{8}$ m tall. Mariah measures $1\frac{5}{12}$ m. How much taller is Callum than Mariah?

5. A large box weighs $47\frac{1}{2}$ kg. The box is full of packets each weighing $\frac{5}{8}$ kg. How many packets are inside the box?

6. Find A, B, C and D to make this diagram correct.

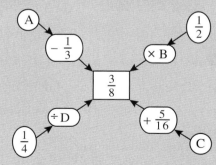

7. A snooker club charges £4.50 per hour to play on a snooker table. If Kye and Frances play for $1\frac{3}{5}$ hours, how much will it cost them?

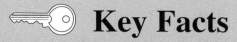

Key Facts

A number written in standard form will have the form

$$A \times 10^n$$

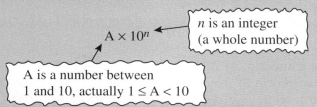

n is an integer (a whole number)

A is a number between 1 and 10, actually $1 \le A < 10$

Very large numbers and very small numbers are usually written in standard form.

Changing ordinary numbers into standard form

$$6000 = 6 \times 1000 \qquad = 6 \times 10^3$$

$$1980 = 1.98 \times 1000 \quad = 1.98 \times 10^3$$

$$5300000 = 5.3 \times 1000000 = 5.3 \times 10^6$$

Numbers between 0 and 1

Quick method

$$0.0082 = 8.2 \times 10^{-3} \leftarrow \text{the decimal point moves to the right 3 places from A to B.}$$
$$\uparrow \quad \uparrow$$
$$\text{A} \quad \text{B}$$

M5.3

1 Copy each statement below and fill in the empty boxes.

(a) $400000 = 4 \times 10^{\square}$ (b) $82000 = \square \times 10^{\square}$ (c) $6400 = \square \times 10^3$

(d) $0.08 = 8 \times 10^{\square}$ (e) $0.000067 = 6.7 \times 10^{\square}$ (f) $0.052 = 5.2 \times 10^{\square}$

(g) $0.4 = \square \times 10^{-1}$ (h) $42000 = 4.2 \times 10^{\square}$ (i) $0.00082 = \square \times 10^{-4}$

2 Write the numbers below in standard form.

(a) 60000   (b) 900   (c) 5800   (d) 690000

(e) 850   (f) 74000000   (g) 47000   (h) 4 million

(i) 0.0008   (j) 0.003   (k) 0.00000007   (l) 0.95

(m) 0.2   (n) 0.0061   (o) 0.000062   (p) 72 million

(q) 42 thousand   (r) 0.0625   (s) 0.812   (t) 213 million

3 150000 tonnes of tea are consumed by people in the UK each year. Write this number in standard form.

4 500 million litres of rain can fall from a single thunderstorm. Write this in standard form.

5 The annual budget for the Holland High School is £4126000. Write this in standard form.

6 The hairs on the knee of the common flea are of length 0.000007 m. Write this in standard form.

7 In 1902, the cost of a pint of beer was 0.8 pence! Write this in standard form.

8 A hydrogen atom has a mass of 0.000 000 000 000 000 000 000 0017 grams. Write this in standard form.

9 Angling in the most popular participant sport in Britain. There are 3500000 anglers in Britain. Write this number in standard form.

10 Write each number below as an *ordinary number*.

(a) 5×10^2 (b) 6.8×10^3 (c) 8.1×10^5 (d) 7×10^{-2}

(e) 9.8×10^{-4} (f) 6.12×10^4 (g) 3.7×10^{-3} (h) 8.41×10^{-2}

(i) 2.5×10^6 (j) 4.6×10^{-1} (k) 1.72×10^{-4} (l) 5.36×10^5

11 Write down which numbers below are *not* written in standard form.

(a) 7.1×10^{-2} (b) 0.32×10^8 (c) 48×10^3

(d) 59×10^{-3} (e) 5.6×10^{-3} (f) 0.02×10^7

12 Write the numbers below in standard form.

(a) 0.02 (b) 0.0006 (c) 209 (d) 31600

(e) 5800000 (f) 316.8 (g) 32.71 (h) 0.0065

(i) three thousand million (j) 0.073 (k) five thousandths (l) 590000

M | **Using standard form numbers without a calculator**

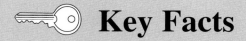 # Key Facts

To multiply standard form numbers: multiply the numbers, add the powers.

To divide standard form numbers: divide the numbers, subtract the powers.

To add or subtract: make sure the powers of 10 are the same before adding or subtracting.

(a) $\dfrac{9 \times 10^{14}}{2 \times 10^3} = 4.5 \times 10^{11}$

(b) $(7 \times 10^4) \times (3 \times 10^3) = 21 \times 10^7$

$\qquad\qquad\qquad\qquad\quad = (2.1 \times 10^1) \times 10^7$

$\qquad\qquad\qquad\qquad\quad = 2.1 \times 10^8$

(c) $(3.6 \times 10^8) - (7.1 \times 10^7)$

Convert 7.1×10^7 into 0.71×10^8

so $(3.6 \times 10^8) - (7.1 \times 10^7) = (3.6 \times 10^8) - (0.71 \times 10^8)$

$\qquad\qquad\qquad\qquad\qquad\qquad\quad = 2.89 \times 10^8$

M5.4

Do not use a calculator

1 Write each number below in *standard form*.

(a) 36×10^5 (b) 21×10^9 (c) 47×10^{-4} (d) 0.38×10^7

(e) 0.8×10^{12} (f) 0.71×10^{-6} (g) 586×10^{10} (h) 413×10^{-9}

2 Work out the following, leaving each answer in *standard form*.

(a) $(4 \times 10^3) \times (2 \times 10^5)$ (b) $(3 \times 10^8) \times (3 \times 10^4)$ (c) $(2 \times 10^7) \times (3 \times 10^5)$

(d) $(5 \times 10^9) \times (1.5 \times 10^6)$ (e) $(2 \times 10^6) \times (8 \times 10^2)$ (f) $(4 \times 10^7) \times (3 \times 10^6)$

(g) $(2.5 \times 10^{-4}) \times (3 \times 10^9)$ (h) $(9 \times 10^{16}) \times (4 \times 10^{-8})$ (i) $(3 \times 10^{-4}) \times (5 \times 10^{14})$

3 Evaluate the following, leaving your answers in *standard form*.

(a) $(8 \times 10^{14}) \div (2 \times 10^6)$ (b) $(9 \times 10^{17}) \div (3 \times 10^4)$ (c) $\dfrac{6 \times 10^{21}}{2 \times 10^8}$

(d) $(3 \times 10^{26}) \div (2 \times 10^{13})$ (e) $\dfrac{8.1 \times 10^{42}}{3 \times 10^{17}}$ (f) $(8 \times 10^7) \div (4 \times 10^{17})$

(g) $(4.5 \times 10^{12}) \div (3 \times 10^{-6})$ (h) $\dfrac{2 \times 10^{27}}{4 \times 10^9}$ (i) $(6.6 \times 10^{-8}) \div (2.2 \times 10^{-19})$

4 UK households produce 29 million tonnes of general waste per year – half of which could be recycled. How many tonnes could be recycled? Give your answer in standard form.

5 $3.6 \times 10^{-9}\text{m}$

$3 \times 10^{-8}\text{m}$

Work out the area of this rectangle. Give the answer in standard form.

6 The average speed of a plane is 2.3×10^7 metres per hour. How long will it take to travel a distance of 4.6×10^8 metres? (time = distance ÷ speed)

7 The area of a country is given as 9.2×10^4 km². Express this in m² in standard form (1 km² $= 10^6$ m²).

8 Use Einstein's formula $E = mc^2$ to work out E when $m = 2 \times 10^6$ and $c = 3 \times 10^8$. Give the answer in standard form.

9 Every day, 2×10^7 text messages are sent in the UK. How many text messages are sent in the UK in one year? (Assume 1 year = 365 days).

10 Copy and complete:

(a) $(4 \times 10^7) + (3 \times 10^6)$

$= (4 \times 10^7) + (3 \times 10^7 \times 10^{\square})$

$= (4 \times 10^7) + \left(\boxed{} \times 10^7\right)$

$= \boxed{} \times 10^7$

(b) $(8.6 \times 10^{-8}) - (3 \times 10^{-9})$

$= (8.6 \times 10^{-8}) - (3 \times 10^{-8} \times 10^{-1})$

$= (8.6 \times 10^{-8}) - \left(\boxed{} \times 10^{-8}\right)$

$= \boxed{} \times 10^{-8}$

11 Work out the following, leaving each answer in *standard form*.

(a) $(6 \times 10^3) + (3 \times 10^4)$

(b) $(8 \times 10^9) + (5 \times 10^8)$

(c) $(3.1 \times 10^{11}) + (5.6 \times 10^{12})$

(d) $(5 \times 10^3) - (4 \times 10^2)$

(e) $(2 \times 10^5) - (6 \times 10^4)$

(f) $(3.5 \times 10^3) - (2.1 \times 10^2)$

(g) $(4 \times 10^{-7}) - (8 \times 10^{-8})$

(h) $(6.1 \times 10^{-12}) - (2 \times 10^{-13})$

(i) $(9.3 \times 10^{-6}) + (4.9 \times 10^{-5})$

12 $m = 5.6 \times 10^8$ and $n = 3.7 \times 10^9$

Find the values of:

(a) $m + n$ (b) $n - m$ (c) $2m + 3n$

Leave each answer in standard form.

13 Two electronic components have widths of (8×10^{-7}) m and (3.4×10^{-6}) m respectively. What is their combined width if they are placed side by side? Give the answer in standard form.

14 Square 2.1×10^{-7}.

15 At a time when Jupiter, Pluto and the Sun are in a line, the distances of Jupiter and Pluto from the Sun are respectively 7.9×10^8 km and 6×10^9 km.

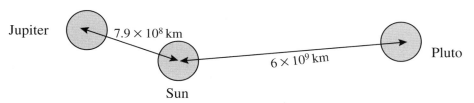

What is the distance (in standard form) between Pluto and Jupiter when the two planets and the Sun are in line with:

(a) the planets on opposite sides of the Sun?

(b) the planets on the same side of the Sun?

A number like 720000000000000 is too large to type into a calculator. Write it in standard form as 7.2×10^{14}.

 Key Facts

Use the EXP button to enter numbers in standard form.

7.2×10^{14} is typed in as 7 · 2 EXP 1 4

Note. You do *not* press the × button before or after pressing the EXP button!

The calculator display may be 7.2¹⁴ or 7.2 14 but more and more calculators now show 7.2 × 10¹⁴

'On paper' the standard form number must be written properly as 7.2×10^{14}

Example

Work out $(5.1 \times 10^{12}) \times (2.8 \times 10^{-38})$ leaving your answer in standard form.

5 · 1 EXP 1 2 × 2 · 8 EXP 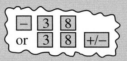 =

The answer is 1.428×10^{-25}

M5.5

1 Use a calculator to work out the following and write each answer in standard form.

(a) $(3 \times 10^{16}) \times (5 \times 10^{-9})$

(b) $(1.8 \times 10^6) \times (2.3 \times 10^{14})$

(c) $(7.2 \times 10^{-6}) \times (4 \times 10^{-12})$

(d) $(8 \times 10^{-14}) \times (3.6 \times 10^{-17})$

(e) $(7.2 \times 10^{34}) \div (3 \times 10^{-16})$

(f) $(4.8 \times 10^{16}) \div (4 \times 10^{-6})$

(g) $(5.1 \times 10^{-8}) \div (1.7 \times 10^{-19})$

(h) $(4.9 \times 10^{-11}) + (2.6 \times 10^{-10})$

(i) $(5.1 \times 10^{19}) - (2.8 \times 10^{18})$

2 The distance of the Earth from the Sun is about 1.496×10^{11} m. The distance of Pluto from the Sun is about 5.91×10^{12} m. How many times further from the Sun is Pluto compared to the Earth (Give your answer to the nearest whole number)?

3 The radius of this circle is 4.7×10^{-8} m. Calculate the area of the circle (Give your answer to 3 significant figures).

4 $m = 7.1 \times 10^{19}$ and $n = 3.6 \times 10^{33}$. Work out the following, leaving each answer in standard form correct to 3 significant figures.

(a) $m \times n$ (b) $m \div n$ (c) m^2 (d) $m^2 \div n^2$

5 The mass of an electron is 9.1×10^{-28} grams. What is the total mass of 5×10^{12} electrons?

6 A book says that the Earth is known to be 149,600,000 km from the Sun. It then says that the Earth is 1.58×10^{-5} light years from the Sun. Use these two pieces of information to find what distance (in km to 2 significant figures) a light year represents. Leave your answer in standard form.

7 Work out the following, leaving each answer in standard form correct to 3 significant figures.

(a) $\dfrac{(2.1 \times 10^{9}) \times (4.6 \times 10^{16})}{4 \times 10^{7}}$

(b) $\dfrac{(3.8 \times 10^{21}) \times (6.1 \times 10^{32})}{4.6 \times 10^{19}}$

(c) $\dfrac{(2.7 \times 10^{31}) \times (8.6 \times 10^{-14})}{5.6 \times 10^{-12}}$

(d) $\dfrac{(5.6 \times 10^{37}) \times (3.1 \times 10^{8})}{6.2 \times 10^{-12}}$

(e) $\dfrac{(4.3 \times 10^{9}) \times (2.6 \times 10^{24})}{(6.6 \times 10^{5})^2}$

(f) $\dfrac{(3.7 \times 10^{-9}) \times (2.6 \times 10^{-18})}{(5.3 \times 10^{17}) \times (1.8 \times 10^{-4})}$

8 A thunderstorm is taking place 6 km away. Light travels 3×10^{5} km in one second. Sound travels 1.226×10^{3} km in one hour.

(a) How long does it take for the light from the lightning to travel 6 km? (Give your answer in standard form).

(b) Show that sound travels approximately 340 m in one second.

(c) How long (to the nearest second) does it take for the sound of the thunder to travel 6 km?

9 The centre of the Milky Way is 2.6×10^{4} light years from earth, and the nearest galaxy is 1.6×10^{5} light years from the Earth.

(a) (i) Which of these distances is greater?

(ii) By how many light years?

(b) If one light year is 9.46×10^{12} km then find the distance of the nearest galaxy from the Earth in km. Leave your answer in standard form correct to 3 significant figures.

When you measure something, the measurement is never exact. If you measure the diameter of a 5 pence coin with a ruler, you might read 1.7 cm. If you use a more accurate device for measuring you might read the diameter as 1.71 cm. An even more accurate device might give the diameter as 1.712 cm. None of these figures is precise.

They are all approximations to the actual diameter. This means that there is always an error in making any kind of measurement such as length, weight, time, temperature and so on. This kind of error cannot be avoided.

Suppose the width of a book is measured at 16 cm to the nearest cm.

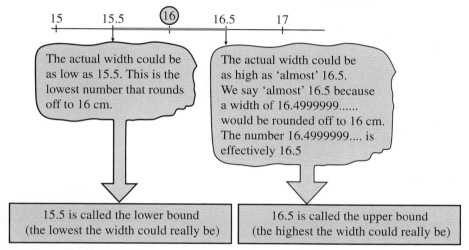

The actual width could be as low as 15.5. This is the lowest number that rounds off to 16 cm.

The actual width could be as high as 'almost' 16.5. We say 'almost' 16.5 because a width of 16.4999999...... would be rounded off to 16 cm. The number 16.4999999.... is effectively 16.5

15.5 is called the lower bound (the lowest the width could really be)

16.5 is called the upper bound (the highest the width could really be)

We can say $15.5 \leqslant \text{width} < 16.5$

If a measurement of 16 cm is taken to the nearest cm, it could be in error by as much as 0.5 cm in either direction.

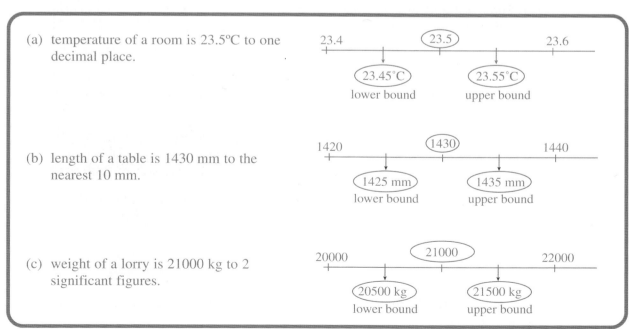

(a) temperature of a room is 23.5°C to one decimal place.

(b) length of a table is 1430 mm to the nearest 10 mm.

(c) weight of a lorry is 21000 kg to 2 significant figures.

1 The length of a pen is measured at 14 cm to the nearest cm.

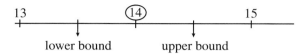

Write down (a) the lower bound (b) the upper bound

2 The height of a church tower is 42 m, measured to the nearest metre.
Write down (a) the lower bound (b) the upper bound.

3 The diameter of a one pound coin is 21.5 mm, measured to the nearest 0.1 mm.
Write down (a) the lower bound (b) the upper bound

4 A baby weighs 3.6 kg, measured to the nearest 0.1kg.
Write down (a) the lower bound (b) the upper bound.

5 Copy and complete the table.

		lower bound	upper bound
(a)	length = 79 cm, to nearest cm		
(b)	mass = 32.3 kg, to nearest 0.1 kg		
(c)	length = 9.1 cm, to nearest 0.1 cm		
(d)	volume = 15.7 m³, to nearest 0.1 m³		
(e)	width = 6.32 cm, to nearest 0.01 cm		
(f)	mass = 8.17 g, to nearest 0.01 g		

6 A coin weighs 10.3 g, correct to one decimal place. What is the least possible weight of the coin?

7 A famous rock singer has a fortune of £24,712,000, correct to the nearest £1000. What is the least amount of money the rock singer might have?

8 The width of a field is 530 m, correct to the nearest 10 m. What is the least possible width of the field?

9 In a 100 m race a sprinter is timed at 10.12 seconds to the nearest 0.01 second. Write down the least possible time.

10 Copy and complete each statement. Part (a) is done as an example.

   (a) A mass m is 48 g, to the nearest g, so $47.5 \leqslant m < 48.5$.

   (b) A length l is 92.6 mm, to the nearest 0.1 mm, so $92.55 \leqslant l < \boxed{}$.

   (c) A diameter d is 16.2 cm, to the nearest 0.1 cm, so $\boxed{} \leqslant d < \boxed{}$.

   (d) A capacity c is 1200 l, to the nearest 100 l, so $\boxed{} \leqslant c < 1250$.

   (e) A height h is 3.86 m, to the nearest 0.01 m, so $\boxed{} \leqslant h < \boxed{}$.

11 The volume of a liquid is measured at 1.4 litres, correct to the nearest 0.2 litres. Write down the upper and lower bounds.

12 The length of a park is measured at 2.2 km, correct to the nearest 50 m. Write down the upper and lower bounds.

Can you still?

5B **More percentages (see Unit 2)**

Can you still?

1. The attendance at a rugby match was 45,000 in 2005 and 54,000 in 2006. What was the percentage increase in attendance?

2. A bus company reduces its prices by 4%. What is the new price of a ticket which originally costs £3.50.

3. A builder charges £5900 + VAT to do a garage conversion. If VAT is 17.5%, how much does the garage conversion cost in total?

4. A shop is selling a jacket for £120. In a sale it sells for £90. What percentage was taken off in the sale?

5. A girl sees a bike for sale with the notice 'price £105.75 (incl. VAT 17.5%)'. What was the price before VAT?

6. Vinny is paid £20,000 one year. The next year he was paid £23,000. What was his percentage increase?

7. The value of a company rose by 60% to £32 million from 2005 to 2006. What was the value in 2005?

8. The population of a small island decreases each year by 10% of its value at the start of the year. At the start of 2004, the population is 200. How many people are there at the start of 2006?

9. A company employs 1300 people. One day 156 are absent through illness. What percentage of the workers were absent that day?

10. Ed invests £800 in a bank offering 4.5% interest per year compound interest. How much will Ed have in his account after 3 years?

When measurements are used in calculations, any initial errors can become larger.

The base of this triangle is 10 cm to the nearest cm.
The height of this triangle is 7 cm to the nearest cm.

Find the upper and lower bounds for the area.

$$9.5 \leqslant \text{base} < 10.5 \text{ and } 6.5 \leqslant \text{height} < 7.5$$

$$\text{Area} = \frac{1}{2} \times \text{base} \times \text{height}$$

to find lower bound for area, use both lower bounds for base and height

$$\text{area} = \frac{1}{2} \times 9.5 \times 6.5 = 30.875 \text{ cm}^2$$

to find upper bound for area, use both upper bounds for base and height

$$\text{area} = \frac{1}{2} \times 10.5 \times 7.5 = 39.375 \text{ cm}^2$$

so $30.875 \leqslant \text{area} < 39.375$

E5.1

1 The length and width of a field are measured to the nearest 0.1m.

71.8 m
156.3 m

(a) Write down the lower and upper bounds for the length of the field.

(b) Write down the lower and upper bounds for the width of the field.

(c) Calculate the lower and upper bounds for the area of the field, giving your answers to 2 decimal places.

2 Find the lower bound for the perimeter of this shape. Each length has been measured to the nearest 0.1 cm.

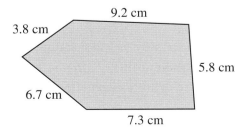

9.2 cm
3.8 cm
5.8 cm
6.7 cm
7.3 cm

3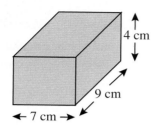

The length, width and height of the cuboid are measured to the nearest cm.

Volume = length × width × height

What is the *greatest* possible value of the volume of the cuboid?

4 If $a = 3.1$, $b = 8.6$ and $c = 7.9$, all measured to one decimal place, calculate:

(a) the greatest value of $a + b$

(b) the smallest value of ab

(c) the largest value (to 3 sig. figs) of $\frac{a}{c}$

(d) the smallest value (to 3 sig. figs) of $\frac{bc}{a}$

(e) the largest value of $c - a$

5 The area of a rugby field is given as 6950 m², correct to 3 sig. figs. The length of the field is given as 95 m, correct to 2 sig. figs.

(a) Find the upper and lower bounds for the area of the field.

(b) Find the upper and lower bounds for the length of the field.

(c) Use these to calculate the upper and lower bounds for the width of the field (to 2 dec. places).

6 The formula for the distance, s, travelled by a body with initial speed u, constant acceleration a after a time t is given by

$$s = ut + \frac{1}{2}at^2$$

Find the greatest and least possible values (to 3 sig. figs) of s when $u = 6.1$, $a = 4.5$ and $t = 13.6$, all measured correct to 1 decimal place.

7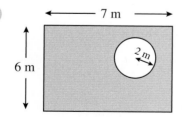

A rectangular piece of metal measures 7 m by 6 m (to the nearest metre). A circle of radius 2 m (to the nearest metre) is cut out from the sheet.

(a) Calculate the upper and lower bounds for the area of the rectangle.

(b) Calculate the upper and lower bounds for the area of the circle (to 3 sig. figs).

(c) Use your answers to (a) and (b) to find the upper and lower bounds for the shaded area (to 3 sig. figs).

8 Consider the formula $V = \dfrac{3P}{Q} - R$.

If $P = 7.1$, $Q = 4.6$ and $R = 0.6$, measured correct to 1 decimal place, calculate:

(a) the maximum possible value for V (to 3 sig. figs).

(b) the minimum possible value for V (to 3 sig. figs).

9 A person runs a 100 m race in a measured time of 10.3 s. If the track length is accurate to the nearest metre and the time is accurate to the nearest 0.1 s, find the upper and lower bounds (to 1 decimal place) for the person's average speed (average speed = distance ÷ time).

10 The total resistance R in an electrical circuit in which there are two resistors in parallel (of resistance R_1 and R_2 respectively) is given by the formula

$$R = \dfrac{1}{\dfrac{1}{R_1} + \dfrac{1}{R_2}}$$

R_1 is measured as 7.16 ± 0.005 ohms (this means $7.155 \le R_1 < 7.165$)

R_2 is measured as 4.8 ± 0.05 ohms.

(a) What is the least possible value for R (to 3 sig. figs)?

(b) What is the greatest possible value for R (to 3 sig. figs)?

Can you still?

Can you still?

5C **More indices (see Unit 2)**

1. Simplify

(a) $\dfrac{5^7}{5^3}$ (b) $(3^2)^4$ (c) $\dfrac{5^2 \times 5^9}{5^4}$ (d) 8^0

2. Evaluate

(a) 2^{-1} (b) 3^{-3} (c) $25^{\frac{1}{2}}$ (d) $81^{-\frac{1}{2}}$

3. Simplify

(a) $3xy \times 4y$ (b) $\dfrac{9m^2n}{6mn^2}$ (c) $(3a^2)^3$ (d) $\sqrt{(36n^4)}$

4. Evaluate

(a) $\left(\dfrac{1}{4}\right)^{-1}$ (b) $\left(\dfrac{1}{3}\right)^{-2}$ (c) $\left(\dfrac{9}{25}\right)^{-\frac{1}{2}}$ (d) $\left(\dfrac{8}{27}\right)^{\frac{2}{3}}$

5. Solve

(a) $5^x = \dfrac{1}{125}$ (b) $49^{2x} = \dfrac{1}{7}$ (c) $8^{\frac{x}{2}} = 32$ (d) $9^{2x} = 27^{x+1}$

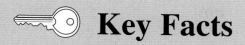 **Key Facts**

The 'proportional' symbol is '∝'.

If y is 'directly proportional' to x we write '$y \propto x$'.

Two quantities are 'directly proportional' if one quantity is a multiple of the other. This multiple is usually indicated by the letter k.

> If $y \propto x$ we say that $y = kx$

where k is known as the *'constant of proportionality'* or the *'constant of variation'*.

If we know a pair of values for x and y, we can substitute them into $y = kx$ to find the value of k. The formula can then be used to find other values for y and x.

Note

'y varies as x' means the same as 'y is directly proportional to x'.

A force F on an object is directly proportional to its acceleration a. When F = 9, a = 2. Find

(i) the relationship between F and a.

(ii) the force when $a = 12$.

(iii) the acceleration when F = 72.

(i) F $\propto a$ so F = ka [write a formula involving k first]

   F = 9, a = 2   so 9 = 2k [substitute the F and a values in the formula]

$$k = \frac{9}{2} = 4.5 \text{ [leave } k \text{ as a fraction unless it is a simple decimal]}$$

$$F = 4.5a \text{ [this is the relationship between F and } a]$$

(ii) $a = 12$ so F = 4.5 × 12 = 54

(iii) F = 72   so 72 = 4.5a

$$a = \frac{72}{4.5} = 16$$

133

1 In the following tables, y is directly proportional to x, that is $y = kx$ for some constant k. In each case find the value of k then copy and complete the tables.

(a)

x	5	13		23
y	10		30	

(b)

x	8	14		20
y	12		27	

(c)

x		10	24	38
y	20		60	

2 The number of arrests, A, in a town is directly proportional to the number of policemen, P, on patrol. It is recorded that when there were 16 policemen on patrol the number of arrests was 48.

(a) Write down an equation giving A in terms of P, having calculated the constant of proportionality.

(b) How many arrests will be made when there are 24 policemen on patrol?

(c) How many policemen are there on patrol if 72 arrests are made?

3 When a car is accelerating from rest at a constant rate its speed, v, is directly proportional to time, t.

(a) Write down this statement using the symbol $\propto$.

(b) Rewrite this statement using the symbol $=$.

(c) After 5 seconds the car is travelling at 15 m/s. How fast will the car be travelling after 7 seconds?

(d) After how long will the car be travelling at 42 m/s?

4 The cost, C, of a rug is directly proportional to its thickness, T.

(a) Write down a relationship between C and T and a constant k.

(b) A rug which is 4 cm thick costs £75. How much does it cost to buy a rug which is 3 cm thick?

(c) How thick is the rug which costs £15?

5 It is known that s varies as t (ie. that s is directly proportional to t). It is also known that $s = 21$ when $t = 6$.

(a) Find a formula for s in terms of t, having calculated the constant of proportionality.

(b) Find s when $t = 16$.

(c) Find t when $s = 28$.

6 h is directly proportional to T and $h = 63$ when $T = 15$.

(a) Find a formula for h in terms of T, having calculated the constant of proportionality.

(b) Find h when $T = 35$.

(c) Find T when $h = 210$.

7 u is directly proportional to t and it is known that $u = 18$ when $t = 9$.

(a) Find a formula for u in terms of t.

(b) Find the increase in u when t increases from 10 to 17.

(c) By how much has t decreased when u falls from 20 to 15?

The mass, m, of an object is directly proportional to the cube of its side length, l. The mass of a cube with side length 3 cm is found to be 216 g.

(a) Write down an equation for m in terms of l, having calculated the constant of proportionality.

(b) Find the mass of the object with side length 7 cm.

(c) Find the side length of the object which has mass 9261 g.

note

(a) $m \propto l^3$ so $m = kl^3$

    $m = 216, l = 3$ so $216 = k \times 3^3 \Rightarrow 216 = 27k$

$$k = \frac{216}{27} = 8$$

$$m = 8l^3$$

(b) $l = 7$ so $m = 8 \times 7^3 = 8 \times 343 = 2744$ g

(c) $m = 9261$ so $9261 = 8l^3$

$$l = \sqrt[3]{\frac{9261}{8}} = 10.5 \text{ cm}$$

E5.3

1 An object accelerates from rest at a constant rate. Its distance (s) is directly proportional to the square of its velocity (v).

When it has travelled 45 m it has a velocity of 15 m/s.

(a) Copy and complete:

$s \propto v^{\square}$ so $s = \boxed{} v^{\square}$

$s = 45, v = 15$ so $45 = \boxed{} \times 15^{\square}$

$$45 = 225 \boxed{}$$

$$\boxed{} = \frac{45}{225} = \frac{1}{5}$$

so $s = \frac{1}{5} v^{\square}$

(b) How far will it have gone when its velocity is 45 m/s?

2 y is directly proportional to the square of x so $y = kx^2$ for some constant k. Find the value of k then copy and complete the table.

x	2	4		8
y	8		50	

3 y is directly proportional to the cube of x. Write down a formula relating x and y. Copy and complete the table.

x	2	3		8
y	40		1080	

4 The mass m of a block is directly proportional to the cube of the side length l.

(a) Write down an equation involving m, l and a constant k.

It is given that a block of side length 3 cm has mass 54 kg.

(b) Calculate k.

(c) What is the mass of a block of side length 8 cm?

(d) What is the side length of the block which has mass 250 kg?

5 The energy, E, stored in a spring is directly proportional to the square of the extension, e.

(a) Write down the relationship between E, e and a constant k.

(b) When the extension is 5 cm, the energy stored is 150 joules. Find k.

(c) How much energy is stored when the extension is 3 cm?

(d) What is the extension in the spring when the energy stored in 384 joules?

6 It is known that the time, T, taken for a pendulum to swing back and forth once is proportional to the square root of its length, l.

(a) If the time taken for a pendulum of length 9 cm to swing back and forth once is 2.4 seconds then write down an equation involving T and l.

(b) Find the time for a pendulum to swing back and forth once if the pendulum has length 16 cm.

(c) Find the length of the pendulum which takes 5.6 seconds to swing back and forth once.

7 y is directly proportional to the cube root of x.

(a) Write down a formula relating x and y.

(b) Copy and complete the table.

x	8		216	
y	12	24		60

8 The current I in an electrical circuit varies as the square root of the power P. If the current is 18 amps when the power is 25 watts, find the current when the power is 144 watts.

9 H is directly proportional to the cube root of r. When $r = 27$ it is known that H = 15.

(a) Write down an equation for H in terms of r, having calculated the constant of proportionality.

(b) Find H when r = 1000.

(c) Find r when H = 20.

10 The table shows some values of x and y.

(a) Write down a relationship between x and y using the symbol $\propto$.

x	2	3	4	5
y	24	81	192	375

(b) Write down an equation involving x and y.

(c) What will x be when $y = 3993$?

 *Can you still?*

 *Can you still?*

5D **Factorise (see Unit 4)**

Copy and complete

1. $2x^2 + 4x$

$= 2x\left(\boxed{} + \boxed{}\right)$

2. $x^2 - 4x - 21$

$= (x + \boxed{})(x - \boxed{})$

3. $x^2 - 25$

$= (x + \boxed{})(x - \boxed{})$

Factorise *completely* the expressions below:

4. $x^2 + 5x + 6$

5. $x^2 - 7x - 18$

6. $x^2 - 6x$

7. $x^2 + 3x - 18$

8. $x^2 - 81$

9. $x^2 - 7x + 10$

10. $8x^2 + 6x$

11. $x^2 - x - 12$

12. $x^2 - 1$

Copy and complete

13. $mp - np + mq - nq$

$= p\left(m - \boxed{}\right) + q\left(m - \boxed{}\right)$

$= \left(m - \boxed{}\right)\left(\boxed{} + \boxed{}\right)$

14. $10x^2 - x - 2$

$= 10x^2 - 5x + \boxed{} - 2$

$= 5x\left(\boxed{} - 1\right) + \boxed{}\left(\boxed{} - 1\right)$

$= \left(\boxed{} - 1\right)\left(5x + \boxed{}\right)$

15. $x^3 - 4x$

$= x\left(\boxed{} - 4\right)$

$= x\left(x + \boxed{}\right)\left(\boxed{} - 2\right)$

Factorise completely the expressions below:

16. $ac - bc - ad + bd$

17. $xy - y^2 + xz - yz$

18. $3x^2 + 14x + 15$

19. $12x^2 - x - 6$

20. $x^3 - 36x$

21. $4x^2 - 49$

22. $x^3 + 2x^2 + x$

23. $32x^2 - 2$

24. $45x^2 - 30x + 5$

Two quantities are 'inversely proportional' if one quantity is directly proportional to the reciprocal of the other ('reciprocal' of $x = \frac{1}{x}$).

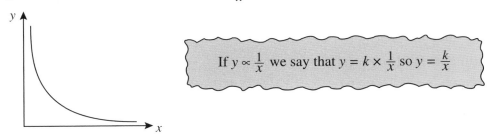

If $y \propto \frac{1}{x}$ we say that $y = k \times \frac{1}{x}$ so $y = \frac{k}{x}$

M is inversely proportional to the square root of N. When M = 2, N = 25.

(a) Write down an equation for M in terms of N.

(b) Find M when N = 81.

(c) Find N when M = 15.

(a) $M \propto \dfrac{1}{\sqrt{N}}$ so $M = \dfrac{k}{\sqrt{N}}$ *note*

M = 2, N = 25   so $2 = \dfrac{k}{\sqrt{25}}$

$2 = \dfrac{k}{5}$

$k = 10$, so $M = \dfrac{10}{\sqrt{N}}$

(b) N = 81

so $M = \dfrac{10}{\sqrt{81}} = \dfrac{10}{9} = 1\dfrac{1}{9}$

(c) M = 15

so $15 = \dfrac{10}{\sqrt{N}}$

$15\sqrt{N} = 10$

$\sqrt{N} = \dfrac{10}{15} = \dfrac{2}{3}$

$N = \left(\dfrac{2}{3}\right)^2 = \dfrac{4}{9}$

E5.4

1   F is inversely proportional to r. When F = 8000, r = 15.

(a) Write down an equation for F in terms of r.

(b) Find F when r = 24.

(c) Find r when F = 1000.

2 y is inversely proportional to the square of x. When y = 3, x = 4.

(a) Write down an equation for y in terms of x.

(b) Find y when x = 2.

(c) Find x when y = 192.

3 The volume V of a given mass of gas varies inversely as the pressure P. When V = 2 m³, P = 400 N/m².

(a) Write down an equation for V in terms of P.

(b) Find the volume when the pressure is 200 N/m².

(c) Find the pressure when the volume is 16 m³.

4 The force of attraction F between 2 magnets is inversely proportional to the square of the distance d between them. When the magnets are 3 cm apart the force of attraction is 12 N.

(a) Write down an equation for F in terms of d.

(b) What is the attractive force when they are 1 cm apart?

(c) How far apart are they if the attractive force is 27 N?

5 It is known that the quantity Q is inversely proportional to the square root of t. It is also found that Q = 12 when $t = 9$.

(a) Find an equation to express Q in terms of t having first found the constant of proportionality.

(b) Use this to find Q when $t = 16$.

(c) Find also the value of t when Q = 18.

6 It is known that the quantity P is inversely proportional to r^3. It is also found that P = 8 when $r = 5$.

(a) Find an equation to express P in terms of r.

(b) Use this to find P when $r = 10$.

(c) Find also the value of r when P = 125.

7 (a) If y is inversely proportional to x then by what factor does y increase/decrease when x doubles?

(b) If y is inversely proportional to x^2 then by what factor does y increase/decrease when x doubles?

8 In a set of similar shapes the length l is inversely proportional to the cube root of the volume V. When the length is 10 cm, the volume is 27000 cm³.

(a) Find an equation for l in terms of V.

(b) Find the length of the shape which has a volume of 1000 cm³.

(c) Find the volume of a shape which has a length of 12 cm.

9 Given that y is inversely proportional to the square of x, copy and complete the table below:

x	2	3		10
y		100	25	

10 It is known that H is inversely proportional to the cube root of u. It is also known that H = 12 when $u = 27$. Find u when H = 18.

11 It is found that, when $x = 5$, y is 8 and that when $x = 10$, $y = 2$. Given that y is inversely proportional to one of the following; x, x^2, x^3, $\sqrt{x}$ or $\sqrt[3]{x}$, write down an equation for y in terms of x.

Most people have an account with a bank or a building society. Money is kept safely in the bank. Bills can be paid directly from the bank or with a debit card. Cash can be withdrawn or cheques can be used.

Writing a cheque

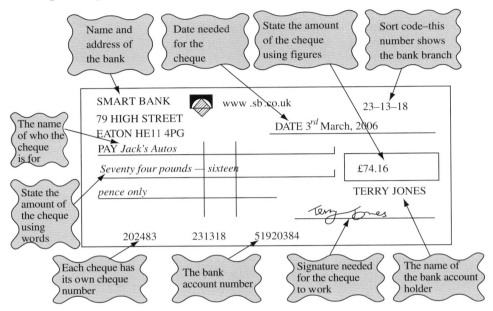

Note

- The amount in words must match the amount in figures.
- The cheque must be used within six months of the date.
- If you make a mistake when filling out a cheque, you may correct it so long as you write your signature by the mistake.
- The bank will not pay the money for your cheque if you do not have enough money in your bank account.

Cheque guarantee card

Once you are over 18, your bank may allow you a cheque guarantee card. If the cheque guarantee card number is written on the back of the cheque, the bank will definitely pay the money (the maximum amount is usually £100).

Being overdrawn

If you spend more money than is in your bank account without arranging with the bank beforehand, you will go overdrawn. The bank will charge you extra money and you will *owe* them *even more money*. You will then have to sort it out quickly or could run into even greater difficulties.

Opening a bank account

You can open a bank account now if you have not already done so. Visit any bank and they will help you to open an account but *shop around*. Some banks will *pay you extra money* if you have some money in your bank account. This is called *'interest on your bank account'*. Also find out how *'kind'* the bank is if you go *'slightly'* overdrawn. Will the bank charge you lots of money?

WYM5

1 Pat has £56 in her account. Her bank will charge her £30 if she goes overdrawn. She pays out two cheques, one of £39.19 and another of £27. How much will she now owe the bank?

2 Zak's bank has agreed that he may go up to £50 overdrawn without paying a penalty. If he breaks the agreement, he will have to pay a £35 charge.
Zak has £32 in his account. He makes 3 payments of £28, £16.29 and £34.96. How much will Zak now owe the bank?

3 Chloe has the same agreement with her bank as Zak in Question **2** . Chloe has £93 in her account. She makes 3 payments of £61.14, £73.06 and £25.32. How much will Chloe now owe the bank?

4 Colin sends the following cheque to his phone company.

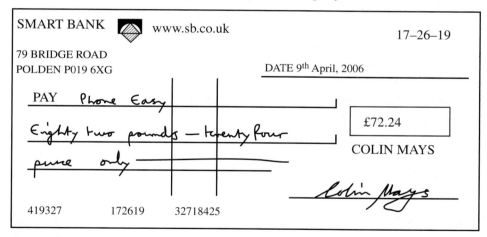

By looking at the cheque earlier in this section, write down:

(a) the sort code

(b) the bank account number

(c) the website address for the bank

(d) the cheque number

(e) The bank will *not* cash this cheque. Explain why.

5 Lara has £128.16 in her bank account. She makes payments of £17.11, £32.68 and £41.23. What is the biggest cheque she could now pay out *without* going overdrawn?

6 Investigate different banks. Find out if they pay interest on bank accounts. How much can you go overdrawn before you are charged? How much would the bank charge you if you went too much overdrawn? Discuss as a class.

1. Finding factors, multiples, products of prime factors, HCFs and LCMs

(a) Write down three multiples of 17 between 50 and 100.

(b) Write down *all* the factors of 45.

(c) Express 150 as the product of its prime factors.

(d) $936 = 2^x \times 3^y \times z$. Find the values of x, y and z.

(e) Write 105 and 330 as products of their prime factors. Use these to find the HCF and LCM of 105 and 330.

2. Writing numbers in standard form

Write the numbers below in standard form.

(a) 273000   (b) 380   (c) 52 thousand   (d) 0.8

(e) 0.0018   (f) 9 million   (g) 712.6   (h) 0.0000087

Write each number below as an ordinary number.

(i) 7.2×10^2 (j) 5.21×10^{-2} (k) 5.9×10^{-4} (l) 6.14×10^6

3. Using standard form numbers *without* a calculator

Evaluate the following, leaving your answers in standard form.

(a) $(2 \times 10^9) \times (1.5 \times 10^3)$ (b) $(3 \times 10^7) \times (5 \times 10^6)$

(c) $(6.9 \times 10^{16}) \div (2.3 \times 10^5)$ (d) $(6.6 \times 10^4) \div (1.1 \times 10^{-7})$

(e) $(5 \times 10^7) + (3 \times 10^6)$ (f) $(7.2 \times 10^{-6}) - (9 \times 10^{-7})$

4. Using standard form numbers *with* a calculator

Work out the following, leaving your answers in standard form (to 3 significant figures if necessary).

(a) $(5.7 \times 10^{-7}) \div (1.9 \times 10^{-18})$ (b) $(7.8 \times 10^{12})^2$

(c) $\dfrac{(4.2 \times 10^8) \times (3.6 \times 10^{11})}{(2.7 \times 10^5)^2}$ (d) $\dfrac{(5.1 \times 10^9) + (6.3 \times 10^8)}{(3.8 \times 10^{-7}) - (5.8 \times 10^{-8})}$

(e) The speed of light is approximately 300000 km/s. Calculate how far in km (standard form to 2 significant figures) light travels in one year (365 days).

5. Finding upper/lower bounds

Copy and complete the table.

	lower bound	upper bound
(a) mass = 58 kg, to nearest kg		
(b) width = 3.7 m, to nearest 0.1 m		
(c) height = 72.6 cm, to nearest 0.1 cm		
(d) capacity = 8.12 l, to nearest 0.01 l		

6. Calculating with upper/lower bounds

If $x = 5$, $y = 7$ and $z = 2$, all measured to the nearest whole number, calculate:

(a) the smallest value of $\frac{x}{z}$

(b) the smallest value of $x + y - z$

(c) the largest value of $y(x - z)$

(d) Carl measures a piece of wood as 2.31m (to the nearest cm). He cuts off a piece and measures it as 0.83 m (to the nearest cm).

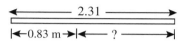

What is the largest possible length of wood Carl has left?

7. Using direct proportion

(a) In the table below, y is directly proportional to x. Copy and complete the table.

x	5	8		13
y		40	55	

(b) The distance s travelled by an object is directly proportional to the square of the time t for which it has been travelling:

$s = 75$ when $t = 5$.

(i) Write down an equation for s in terms of t.

(ii) Find s when $t = 7$.

(iii) Find t when $s = 363$.

(c) The speed of a particle v is directly proportional to the square root of its potential energy P. The potential energy of a particle travelling at 10 m/s is found to be 400 joules. Find the potential energy of the particle with speed 18 m/s.

8. Using inverse proportion

(a) M is inversely proportional to N. When M = 6, N = 40.

(i) Write down an equation for M in terms of N.

(ii) Find M when N = 15.

(iii) Find N when M = 24.

(b) The resistance R in a wire of fixed length is inversely proportional to the square of the diameter d. The resistance is 0.09 ohms when the diameter is 15 mm.

(i) Write down an equation for R in terms of d.

(ii) Find the resistance when the diameter is 9 mm.

(iii) Find the diameter when the resistance is 0.81 ohms.

143

1 (a) Write 24 as a product of prime factors.

(b) Find the lowest common multiple (LCM) of 24 and 60. (OCR)

2 (a) (i) Write the number 5.01×10^4 as an ordinary number.

(ii) Write the number 0.0009 in standard form.

(b) Multiply 4×10^3 by 6×10^5.

Give your answer in standard form. (EDEXCEL)

3 Work out

$(6.9 \times 10^{12}) \div (3 \times 10^5)$ (OCR)

4 Evaluate $(3 \times 10^{-2}) \times (8 \times 10^6)$ giving your answer in standard form. (OCR)

5 The number 1104 can be written as $3 \times 2^c \times d$, where c is a whole number and d is a prime number.

Work out the value of c and the value of d. (EDEXCEL)

6 The shutter speed, S, of a camera varies inversely as the square of the aperture setting, f. When $f = 8$, $S = 125$

(a) Find a formula for S in terms of f.

(b) Hence, or otherwise, calculate the value of S when $f = 4$ (EDEXCEL)

7 A notice board is a rectangle with a length of 80 cm and a width of 40 cm. Both measurements are correct to the nearest centimetre.

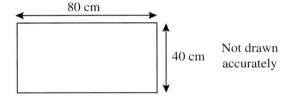

(a) What is the least possible length of the notice board?

(b) What is the greatest possible width of the notice board?

(c) What is the greatest possible area of the notice board? (AQA)

8 A company sells circular badges of different sizes.

The price, P pence, of a badge is proportional to the square of its radius, r cm.

The price of a badge of radius 3 cm is 180 pence.

(a) Find an equation expressing P in terms of r.

(b) Calculate the price of a badge of radius 4 cm. (AQA)

9 (a) (i) Write 30 000 000 in standard form.

(ii) Write 2×10^{-5} as an ordinary number.

(b) Work out the value of

$$2 \times 10^{-5} \times 30\,000\,000.$$

Give your answer in standard form.

10 A television soap has 280 episodes in one year.
During the year 1.95×10^5 words are spoken.
On average how many words are spoken in each episode? (OCR)

11 A coffee machine dispenses 130 millilitres of black
coffee into cups with a capacity of 172 millilitres.
These values are accurate to 3 significant figures.

Milk is supplied in small cartons which contain 21
millilitres, accurate to the
nearest millilitre.

Beryl likes milky coffee and always puts
2 cartons of milk in her coffee.

Will Beryl's cup ever overflow?

You **must** show all your working. (AQA)

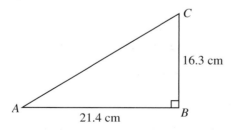

12 (a) Express 108 as the product of powers of its prime factors.

(b) Find the Highest Common Factor (HCF) of 108 and 24. (EDEXCEL)

13 W and P are both positive quantities.

W is directly proportional to the square root of P. When $W = 12$, $P = 16$.

(a) Express W in terms of P.

(b) What is the value of W when $P = 25$?

(c) What is the value of P when $W = 21$? (AQA)

14 Triangle ABC is right angled at B. The lengths of AB and BC are 21.4cm and 16.3cm
respectively correct to the nearest mm.

(a) Calculate the largest possible value of the area of triangle ABC, correct to the
nearest tenth of a cm^2.

(b) Use Pythagoras' Theroem to calculate the range of possible values of the length
of AC, correct to the nearest mm.

(c) Calculate the largest possible value of angle A. (WJEC)

15 The intensity of light L, measured in lumens, varies inversely as the square of the distance d m from the light.

When the distance is 2 m the light intensity is 250 lumens.

(a) Calculate the value of L when d is 2.5m.

(b) Calculate the value of d when L is 90 lumens.   (EDEXCEL)

16 A lorry is 3.8 m high to the nearest 0.1 m.
It is driven under a bridge 4.28 m high to the nearest cm.

(a) What is the least possible clearance of the lorry as it travels under the bridge?

The lorry tail lift can carry a safe working load of 1200 kg, to the nearest 50 kg.

It is used to load boxes that weigh 36 kg, to the nearest kg.

(b) What is the maximum number of boxes it can be sure to lift safely?   (OCR)

17 Two variables, x and y, vary in such a way that y is inversely proportional to the square of x.

(a) When $x = 4$, $y = 5$.
Find the formula giving y in terms of x.

(b) Find the value of y when $x = 5$.   (WJEC)

In the 'M' sections (mainly grades B, C, D) you will learn how to:

– solve linear equations

– set up linear equations

– solve problems using trial and improvement

– change the subject of a formula

– draw graphs of straight lines and quadratic curves

– find gradients of straight lines

– use the equation of a straight line $y = mx + c$

In the 'E' sections (mainly grades A*, A) you will learn how to:

– change the subject of a formula when the required subject appears more than once

– use function notation

– draw graphs of cubics and reciprocals, including real-life graphs

– find gradients of perpendicular lines

Also you will learn how to :

– 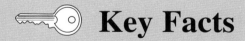 WATCH YOUR MONEY! – bank accounts 2

M | Linear equations

🔑 Key Facts

Remember:

(a) an equation contains an '=' sign

(b) 'solve' means 'find the value of the unknown quantity', often denoted by x

(c) you may 'add' the same quantity to *both sides* of an equation

  'subtract' the same quantity from *both sides* of an equation

  'multiply' *both sides* of an equation by the same quantity

  'divide' *both sides* of an equation by the same quantity

(d) collect all x terms on one side of the equation

Solve the following equations:

(a) $7x = 3$

$$\frac{7x}{7} = \frac{3}{7} \qquad \text{[divide both sides by 7]}$$

$$x = \frac{3}{7}$$

(b) $\dfrac{x}{9} = -4$

$$\frac{x}{9} \times 9 = -4 \times 9 \qquad \text{[multiply both sides by 9]}$$

$$x = -36$$

(c) $3x + 10 = 21 - 5x$

$$3x + 5x = 21 - 10 \qquad \text{[add } 5x \text{ onto both sides and subtract 10 from both sides]}$$

$$8x = 11$$

$$x = \frac{11}{8} \qquad \text{[divide both sides by 8]}$$

$$x = 1\frac{3}{8}$$

(d) $\dfrac{x}{5} - 7 = 2$

$$\frac{x}{5} = 2 + 7 \qquad \text{[add 7 onto both sides]}$$

$$\frac{x}{5} = 9$$

$$x = 9 \times 5 \qquad \text{[multiply both sides by 5]}$$

$$x = 45$$

M6.1

Solve the following equations:

1 $5x = 4$

2 $\dfrac{x}{8} = 7$

3 $x - 4 = -8$

4 $x - 12 = -2$

5 $4x = -20$

6 $-5n = 30$

7 $a + 7 = 0$

8 $\dfrac{m}{-2} = -2$

9 $2b = -9$

10 $4n = 3$

11 $\dfrac{c}{5} = -3$

12 $y + 9 = 4$

13 $\dfrac{n}{-5} = 4$

14 $p - 7 = -3$

15 $-9x = 27$

16 $2f = -1$

Copy and complete:

17 $4n + 11 = 8$

$$4n = 8 - \square$$

$$4n = \square$$

$$n = \frac{\square}{\square}$$

18 $8x - 4 = 6x + 14$

$$8x - \square = 14 + \square$$

$$\square = \square$$

$$x = \square$$

19 $\dfrac{a}{3} + 6 = 4$

$$\frac{a}{3} = 4 - \square$$

$$\frac{a}{3} = \square$$

$$a = \square \times 3$$

$$a = \square$$

148

Solve the following equations:

20 $7n + 6 = 34$

21 $3x - 8 = 22$

22 $8p - 4 = 84$

23 $4b + 9 = 5$

24 $6w + 10 = 5$

25 $9a + 4 = -32$

26 $8 = 33 + 5x$

27 $-6 = 9 + 3c$

28 $20 = 48 - 7x$

29 $10n + 2 = 7n + 14$

30 $7b - 3 = 4b + 12$

31 $8x - 22 = 2x + 8$

32 $5a + 2 = 3 - 2a$

33 $2p - 8 = 12 - 3p$

34 $9m + 4 = 3m - 1$

35 $11 - 5y = 26 - 2y$

36 $23 - 7x = 35 - 13x$

37 $\dfrac{b}{2} + 9 = 19$

38 $\dfrac{w}{3} + 12 = 19$

39 $\dfrac{a}{5} - 2 = 3$

40 $\dfrac{n}{6} + 3 = -2$

41 $\dfrac{3x}{4} = 6$

42 $\dfrac{3c}{5} - 4 = 2$

43 $9 = 3 - \dfrac{m}{2}$

44 $7 = 4 + \dfrac{a}{5}$

45 $\dfrac{x}{4} = \dfrac{2}{3}$

46 $\dfrac{3}{5} = \dfrac{n}{7}$

47 $\dfrac{21}{x} = -3$

M   Equations with brackets

Solve the following equations:

(a) $5(2x - 1) = 45$

    $10x - 5 = 45$ [multiply out brackets first]

    $10x = 45 + 5$ [add 5 onto both sides]

    $10x = 50$ [divide both sides by 10]

    $x = 5$

(b) $4(x - 2) = 3(x + 3) - 4$

    $4x - 8 = 3x + 9 - 4$ [multiply out brackets first]

    $4x - 3x = 9 - 4 + 8$ [subtract 3x from both sides and add 8 onto both sides]

    $x = 13$

M6.2

Solve these equations:

1 $4(x + 2) = 20$

2 $9(2n + 1) = 27$

3 $3(3n - 4) = 33$

4 $3(3b - 7) = 24$

5 $5(a + 3) = 10$

6 $2(2p + 3) = 5$

7 $5(2w + 4) = 0$

8 $33 = 3(2 - 3x)$

9 $5(2m + 1) = 2$

10 $5(4y + 3) = 8$

11 $7 = 2(6 - 3n)$

12 $25 = 8(4 + 5a)$

13 $3(3x + 4) = 4(2x - 2)$

$9x + 12 = \boxed{} - 8$

$9x - \boxed{} = -8 - 12$

$x = \boxed{}$

14 $5(2n - 1) - 6(n + 1) = 1$

$10n - \boxed{} - 6n - \boxed{} = 1$

$10n - 6n = 1 + \boxed{} + \boxed{}$

$\boxed{} = \boxed{}$

$n = \boxed{}$

Solve the following equations:

15 $7(x - 1) = 2(2x + 4)$

16 $8(w - 3) = 4(3 - w)$

17 $3(a + 2) = 4(1 - a)$

18 $3(2n + 1) = 4(7 - n)$

19 $5(2 - p) = 2(4 + 2p)$

20 $2(3 - 2m) = 5(2 - m)$

21 $4(a - 2) = 3(a + 3) - 4$

22 $3(2q + 3) + 4(q - 2) = 8$

23 $6(2x + 5) + 3(2 - 3x) = x$

24 $5(c - 2) + 1 = 3(c - 1)$

25 $7(2h + 1) - 1 = 5(3h + 2)$

26 $2(4w - 3) - 7(2w - 7) = 1$

27 $4(2y + 1) - 9(y - 1) = 3$

28 $3(x + 1) + 1 = 2(2x + 1) - 3$

29 $2(b + 1) + 1 = 3(3b - 5) - 10$

Mixed linear equations

Solve the following equations:

(a) $\dfrac{2x - 1}{3} = 5$

(b) $\dfrac{5}{x} = -2$

(c) $\dfrac{x - 3}{x + 2} = 7$ [multiply both sides by $(x + 2)$]

$2x - 1 = 5 \times 3$ [multiply both sides by 3]

$5 = -2x$ [multiply both sides by x]

$x - 3 = 7(x + 2)$ [multiply out brackets]

$2x - 1 = 15$

$x = \dfrac{5}{-2}$ [divide both sides by -2]

$x - 3 = 7x + 14$

$2x = 16$

$x = -2.5$

$-3 - 14 = 7x - x$

$x = 8$

$-17 = 6x$

$x = -2\tfrac{5}{6}$

Solve the following equations:

1 $\dfrac{x + 5}{4} = 5$

2 $\dfrac{n + 9}{3} = 7$

3 $\dfrac{a}{3} + 2 = 7$

4 $\dfrac{x - 8}{2} = 5$

5 $\dfrac{w}{6} - 8 = 1$

6 $2 = \dfrac{m - 10}{3}$

7 $5 - \dfrac{z}{4} = 2$

8 $\dfrac{3m - 1}{5} = 4$

9 $8 = \dfrac{6b + 2}{7}$

Copy and complete:

10 $\dfrac{16}{x} = 3$

$16 = \boxed{}$

$x = \dfrac{\boxed{}}{\boxed{}}$

$x = \boxed{} \dfrac{\boxed{}}{\boxed{}}$

11 $\dfrac{12}{x - 2} = 4$

$12 = \boxed{}(x - 2)$

$12 = \boxed{} - \boxed{}$

$12 + \boxed{} = \boxed{}$

$\boxed{} = \boxed{}$

$x = \boxed{}$

12 $\dfrac{3x + 2}{x + 4} = 5$

$3x + 2 = \boxed{}(x + 4)$

$3x + 2 = \boxed{} + \boxed{}$

$2 - \boxed{} = \boxed{} - 3x$

$-\boxed{} = \boxed{}$

$x = \boxed{}$

Solve the following equations:

13 $\dfrac{15}{a} = 3$

14 $\dfrac{24}{x + 1} = 6$

15 $\dfrac{36}{x - 2} = 4$

16 $\dfrac{18}{m - 8} = 3$

17 $4 = \dfrac{5}{a}$

18 $\dfrac{13}{m} = 6$

19 $-5 = \dfrac{9}{n}$

20 $\dfrac{3c + 1}{5} = 2$

21 $\dfrac{4x - 3}{3} = 7$

22 $\dfrac{x + 1}{x - 3} = 3$

23 $\dfrac{2a + 1}{a - 4} = 5$

24 $\dfrac{3m - 2}{m - 6} = 7$

25 $\dfrac{5w - 3}{w - 2} = 6$

26 $\dfrac{4b + 1}{b + 3} = 3$

27 $\dfrac{5}{n} - 4 = 4$

28 $\dfrac{3}{f} + 7 = 9$

29 $6(a - 2) = 4(2a + 1)$

30 $\dfrac{x}{9} + 7 = 10$

31 $5(2p + 3) + 2(3p + 5) = 33$

32 $\dfrac{7}{3m} = 1$

33 $8(a - 2) = 5(2a + 3) + 3(a - 4)$

Many problems can be solved by writing them as linear equations first. The unknown quantity is often chosen to be x.

The sum of four consecutive numbers is 42. Let the first number be x and write down the other three numbers in terms of x. Find the four numbers.

Other three numbers are $(x + 1)$, $(x + 2)$ and $(x + 3)$.

Sum is 42   so $x + (x + 1) + (x + 2) + (x + 3) = 42$

$$4x + 6 = 42$$
$$4x = 36$$
$$x = 9$$

The four numbers are 9, 10, 11 and 12.

M6.4

1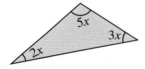

(a) Write down an equation using the angles.

(b) Find x.

(c) Write down the actual value of each angle in this triangle.

2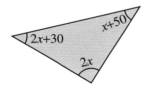

(a) Write down an equation using the angles.

(b) Find x.

(c) Write down the actual value of each angle in this triangle.

3 The sum of four consecutive numbers is 78. Let the first number be x. Set up an equation to find x then find the four numbers.

4 The perimeter of this rectangle is 58 cm.

(a) Write down an equation using the perimeter.

(b) Find x.

(c) Write down the actual length and width of the rectangle.

$3x + 2$

$x + 3$ $x + 3$

$3x + 2$

5 A rectangle has its length twice its width. If its perimeter is 42 cm, find the width of the rectangle.

6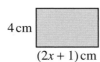

4 cm

$(2x + 1)$ cm

The area of this rectangle is 20 cm². Set up an equation to find x then write down the actual width of the rectangle.

7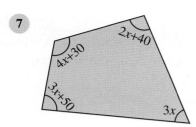

(a) Write down an equation using the angles.

(b) Find x.

(c) Write down the actual value of each angle in this triangle.

8 The length of a rectangle is 3 times its width. If the perimeter of the rectangle is 32 cm, find its length and width.

9 There are 3 children in a family. Each is 3 years older than the next and the sum of their ages is 21. How old is each child? (hint: let x = age of the youngest child)

10 A triangle has 2 angles which are each 4 times the size of the third angle. Find the size of each angle (hint: let x = the third angle).

11 The sum of four consecutive odd number is 216.

(a) If x is the smallest number, write down the other numbers in terms of x.

(b) Find the actual numbers.

12 The area of this rectangle is 46 cm². Find the perimeter of the rectangle.

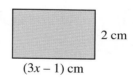

13 £190 is divided between Jack and Halle so that Jack receives £72 more than Halle. How much does each person get? (hint: let x = Halle's money)

14 You have three consecutive *even* numbers so that the sum of twice the smallest number plus three times the middle number is four times the largest number. Find the three numbers.

15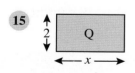

The area of rectangle P is five times the area of rectangle Q. Find x.

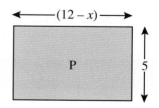

16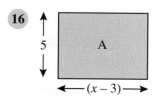

The area of rectangle A is equal to the area of rectangle B. Find the perimeter of rectangle B.

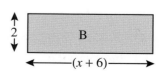

6A   **Expand brackets (see Unit 4)**

Multiply out:

1. $4(3a - 2)$ **2.** $x(5x + 3)$ **3.** $2p(p - 3q)$

Expand and simplify:

4. $5(b + 3) + 4(2 + 3b)$ **5.** $6(3y + 2) - 5(2y + 1)$

6. $a(b + 3) + b(a - 2)$ **7.** $m(2m + 1) - 3m(5m - 2)$

Expand the following:

8. $(x + 4)(x + 3)$ **9.** $(n - 4)(n + 1)$

10. $(w - 5)(w - 2)$ **11.** $(z + 4)(z - 6)$

12. $(2a + 5)(3a + 4)$ **13.** $(5m - 1)(3m + 5)$

14. Show that $(a + b)^2$ is *not* equal to $a^2 + b^2$.

Find the area of each square below in terms of x:

15.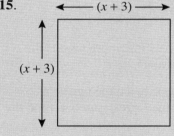

16.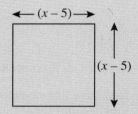

M   **Trial and improvement**

Sometimes it is not easy (or possible) to find the answer to a problem. We can try out different numbers with a calculator until we get closer and closer to the answer.

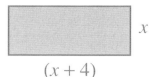

The area of this rectangle is 325 cm^2. Use trial and improvement to find x to 2 *decimal places*.

area $= x(x + 4) = 325$

Trial	calculation	too large or too small?
$x = 10$	$10 \times 14 = 140$	too small
$x = 20$	$20 \times 24 = 480$	too large
$x = 15$	$15 \times 19 = 285$	too small
$x = 17$	$17 \times 21 = 357$	too large
$x = 16$	$16 \times 20 = 320$	too small
so x is between 16 and 17		
$x = 16.2$	$16.2 \times 20.2 = 327.24$	too large
$x = 16.1$	$16.1 \times 20.1 = 323.61$	too small
so x is between 16.1 and 16.2		
$x = 16.15$	$16.15 \times 20.15 = 325.4225$	too large
$x = 16.14$	$16.14 \times 20.14 = 325.0596$	too large
$x = 16.13$	$16.13 \times 20.13 = 324.4969$	too small
so x is between 16.13 and 16.14		
Test the 'halfway' value to choose the correct answer.		
$x = 16.135$	$16.135 \times 20.135 = 324.878225$	too small

so x is between 16.135 and 16.14

so x is closer to 16.14

Answer: $x = 16.14$ to 2 decimal places.

M6.5

1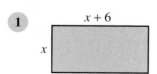

$x + 6$

x

The area of this rectangle is 270 cm². Use trial and improvement to find x to 1 decimal place. Show all your working out.

2 The volume of this cube is 226 cm³. Use trial and improvement to find x to 1 decimal place. Show all your working out.

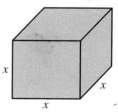

3 The area of a rectangle is 500 cm². Its length is 9 cm longer than its width. Use trial and improvement to find the length and width to 1 decimal place.

4 Solve these equations by trial and improvement. Give each answer to 1 decimal place.

(a) $x^2 + x = 24$ (b) $x^3 - x = 85$ (c) $x^3 + 2x = 170$

5 A cube has a volume of 650 cm³. Use trial and improvement to find the length of a side to *2 decimal places*.

6 A triangle has an area of 50 cm³. Its height is 3 cm more than its base. Use trial and improvement to find the height of the triangle to 2 decimal places.

7 Solve these equations by trial and improvement. Give each answer to 2 decimal places.

(a) $x^3 + x = 90$ (b) $x^3 - 2x = 120$ (c) $x(x^2 + 3) = 374$

8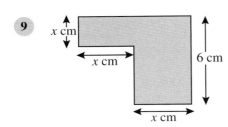

The volume of this cuboid is 300 cm³.

(a) Write down an equation in terms of x for the volume of the cuboid.

(b) Use trial and improvement to find x to 2 decimal places.

9

The total area of this shape is 74 cm².

Use trial and improvement to find x. Give your answer to 2 decimal places.

10 Solve the equations below by trial and improvement giving your answer to *1 decimal place*:

(a) $5^x = 62$ (b) $8^x = 200$

11 The length of a cuboid is 5 cm more than both its height *and* width. Use trial and improvement to find the dimensions of the cuboid if the volume is 90 cm³. Give your answers to 1 decimal place.

12 The shaded area opposite is 100 cm².

(a) Write down an equation in terms of x for the shaded area.

(b) Use trial and improvement to find x to 1 decimal place.

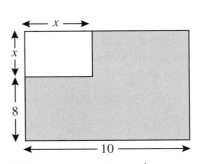

All measurements are in cm.

(a) Make q the subject of the formula $p = 5q + 8$

$$\boxed{p} = \boxed{5q} \boxed{+8}$$ [subtract 8 from both sides of the equation]

$p - 8 = 5q$ [divide both sides of the equation by 5]

$$\dfrac{p - 8}{5} = \dfrac{\cancel{5}q}{\cancel{5}}$$

$$q = \dfrac{p - 8}{5}$$

(b) Make y the subject of the formula

$$x = \dfrac{y}{w}$$

$$x = \dfrac{y}{w}$$ [multiply both sides of the equation by w]

$$w \times x = \cancel{w} \times \dfrac{y}{\cancel{w}}$$

$$y = wx$$

(c) Make x the subject of the formula $a(x - d) = y$

$\overparen{a(x - d)} = y$ [multiply out the brackets first]

$$\boxed{ax} \boxed{-ad} = \boxed{y}$$ [add ad onto both sides of the equation]

$ax = y + ad$ [divide both sides of the equation by a]

$$\dfrac{ax}{a} = \dfrac{y + ad}{a}$$

$$x = \dfrac{y + ad}{a}$$

(d) Make x the subject of the formula $y = \dfrac{ax + b}{c}$ [multiply both sides of the equation by c]

$$c \times y = \dfrac{ax + b}{\cancel{c}} \times \cancel{c}$$ [the c cancels down]

$$\boxed{cy} = \boxed{ax} \boxed{+b}$$ [subtract b from both sides of the equation]

$cy - b = ax$ [divide both sides of the equation by a]

$$\dfrac{cy - b}{a} = \dfrac{\cancel{a}x}{\cancel{a}}$$

$$x = \dfrac{cy - b}{a}$$

M6.6

Copy and complete each statement below:

1   If $a = 6b$ then $\dfrac{a}{\boxed{}} = b$

2   If $a = \dfrac{b}{8}$ then $\boxed{}\, a = b$

3   If $m = \dfrac{n}{p}$ then $n = \boxed{}\, p$

4   Make x the subject of each formula given below:

    (a) $y = x - 9$ (b) $y = \dfrac{x}{12}$ (c) $y = x + 20$ (d) $y = 8x$

    (e) $y = \dfrac{x}{3}$ (f) $y = x + b$ (g) $y = mx$ (h) $y = x - w$

5 Copy and fill each box below:

(a) $x = 3y + 2$

$x - \boxed{} = 3y$

$\dfrac{x - \boxed{}}{\boxed{}} = y$

(b) $x = 4y - 9$

$x + \boxed{} = 4y$

$\dfrac{x + \boxed{}}{\boxed{}} = y$

6 Make x the subject of each formula given below:

(a) $y = 2x + 8$

(b) $y = 6x - 5$

(c) $y = 8x - 10$

(d) $y = \dfrac{x}{3} + 2$

(e) $y = \dfrac{x}{5} - 6$

(f) $y = \dfrac{x}{2} - 4$

7 Make x the subject of each formula given below:

(a) $y = px + q$

(b) $y = cx - h$

(c) $y = rx - 2p$

(d) $q = cx + 3s$

(e) $bx + 5c = 2f$

(f) $y = ax + b - c$

8 Make x the subject of each formula given below:

(a) $c(x + d) = y$

(b) $m(x - n) = q$

(c) $r(x + 5) = y$

(d) $a(x + 7) = 3b$

(e) $y = f(x - g)$

(f) $4b = s(x - t)$

9 Copy and fill each box below:

(a) $y = \dfrac{fx - g}{h}$

$\boxed{} = fx - g$

$\boxed{} + g = fx$

$\dfrac{\boxed{} + g}{\boxed{}} = x$

(b) $\dfrac{px + 2h}{c} = y$

$px + 2h = \boxed{}$

$px = \boxed{} - \boxed{}$

$x = \dfrac{\boxed{} - \boxed{}}{\boxed{}}$

10 Make x the subject of each formula given below:

(a) $\dfrac{ax + d}{4} = e$

(b) $\dfrac{bx + 3c}{y} = p$

(c) $\dfrac{ax - r}{5} = q$

(d) $y = \dfrac{cx - 2d}{7}$

(e) $y = \dfrac{ax - 3c}{b}$

(f) $\dfrac{px + qr}{8} = y$

11 $h = 3g + m$ Make g the subject of the formula.

12 $x = u + fy$ Make y the subject of the formula.

13 Make x the subject of the formula $y = \dfrac{cx - 3}{a}$

14 Make b the subject of the formula $y = \dfrac{3(b + c)}{m}$

Powers and more fractions

(a) Make w the subject of the formula $w^2 = a + 6$

$w^2 = a + 6$ [square root both sides of the equation]

$w = \sqrt{(a + 6)}$

(b) Make x the subject of the formula $\sqrt[3]{(x - b)} = c$

$\sqrt[3]{(x - b)} = c$ [cube both sides of the equation to remove the cube root]

$x - b = c^3$ [add b onto both sides of the equation]

$x = c^3 + b$

(c) Make b the subject of the formula $\dfrac{a}{b} - 3m = 2n$

$\dfrac{a}{b} - 3m = 2n$ [add $3m$ onto both sides of the equation]

$\dfrac{a}{b} = 2n + 3m$ [multiply both sides of the equation by b]

$a = (2n + 3m)b$ [divide both sides of the equation by $(2n + 3m)$]

$\dfrac{a}{2n + 3m} = b$

(d) Make n the subject of the formula $\dfrac{4n^3}{p} + q = rx$

$\dfrac{4n^3}{p} + q = rx$ [subtract q from both sides of the equation]

$\dfrac{4n^3}{p} = rx - q$ [multiply both sides of the equation by p]

$4n^3 = p(rx - q)$ [divide both sides of the equation by 4]

$n^3 = \dfrac{p(rx - q)}{4}$ [cube root both sides of the equation to remove the cube]

$n = \sqrt[3]{\dfrac{p(rx - q)}{4}}$

1 Copy and complete:

(a) $x^2 - w = z$

$$x^2 = z + \boxed{}$$

$$x = \sqrt{\left(z + \boxed{}\right)}$$

(b) $3c = p - m^3$

$$\boxed{} + m^3 = p$$

$$m^3 = p - \boxed{}$$

$$m = \sqrt[3]{\left(p - \boxed{}\right)}$$

(c) $m\sqrt{y} = 4n$

$$\sqrt{y} = \frac{4n}{\boxed{}}$$

$$y = \left(\frac{4n}{\boxed{}}\right)^2$$

2 Make x the subject of each formula given below:

(a) $x^2 + 7 = b$

(b) $z = x^2 - t$

(c) $q + x^2 = 4p$

(d) $x^3 - a = c$

(e) $r = qx^3$

(f) $bx^2 = n$

(g) $\dfrac{x^2}{b} = c$

(h) $\sqrt{x} = m - n$

(i) $p + 2q = \sqrt[3]{x}$

(j) $\dfrac{\sqrt[3]{x}}{w} = y$

(k) $a = b\sqrt{x}$

(l) $2m = n - \sqrt{x}$

3 Copy and complete:

(a) $p = \sqrt{(x + q)} - r$

$$p + \boxed{} = \sqrt{(x + q)}$$

$$\left(p + \boxed{}\right)^2 = x + q$$

$$\left(p + \boxed{}\right)^2 - \boxed{} = x$$

(b) $\dfrac{\sqrt{A}}{3B} - M = N$

$$\frac{\sqrt{A}}{3B} = N + \boxed{}$$

$$\sqrt{A} = \boxed{}\left(N + \boxed{}\right)$$

$$A = \left(\boxed{}\left(N + \boxed{}\right)\right)^2$$

4 Make n the subject of each formula given below:

(a) $\sqrt{(n - r)} = p$

(b) $\sqrt{(n + 2r)} = 3q$

(c) $b = \sqrt[3]{(n + 5c)}$

(d) $(n + t)^2 = w$

(e) $(n - q)^2 + y = 2p$

(f) $8h = \sqrt{(n - g)} + m$

(g) $w = \sqrt{(y - n)}$

(h) $\sqrt{(n - h)} - 4k = 3m$

(i) $\dfrac{\sqrt{n}}{5} + c = d$

(j) $y = \dfrac{\sqrt{n}}{z} - 2w$

(k) $b = \dfrac{n^2}{e} + 3c$

(l) $\dfrac{(n - w)^3}{xz} = y$

5 Copy and complete:

(a) $\dfrac{M}{N} + Q = 3R$

$\dfrac{M}{N} = 3R - \boxed{}$

$M = \left(3R - \boxed{}\right)\boxed{}$

$\dfrac{M}{3R - \boxed{}} = \boxed{}$

(b) $\dfrac{v}{x - w} = y$

$v = y\left(x - \boxed{}\right)$

$v = xy - \boxed{}$

$v + \boxed{} = xy$

$\dfrac{v + \boxed{}}{y} = x$

6 Make w the subject of each formula given below:

(a) $\dfrac{m}{w} = q$

(b) $c = \dfrac{n}{w}$

(c) $3a = \dfrac{2m}{w}$

(d) $\dfrac{x}{w} - z = m$

(e) $\dfrac{2a}{w} + 3c = b^2$

(f) $q = \dfrac{r}{w} + 5n$

(g) $\dfrac{3d}{w} + 4c = 5a^2$

(h) $3r = q - \dfrac{t}{w}$

(i) $\dfrac{a}{w + c} = b^3$

(j) $\dfrac{c^2}{3a + w} = f$

(k) $5m = \dfrac{k}{w - 4n}$

(l) $\dfrac{m}{n + w} = 6p^2$

7 $\dfrac{f(e - h)}{m} = y$ Make e the subject of the formula.

8 $\sqrt[3]{\left(\dfrac{x}{y}\right)} = w$ Make y the subject of the formula.

9 Make v the subject of the formula $\sqrt{(v^2 + n)} = m$

10 Make x the subject of the formula $\sqrt[3]{(w^2 - x^2)} = n$

Can you still?

(**6B**)   **Convert recurring decimals into fractions (see Unit 1)**

Can you still?

Express the following recurring decimals as fractions in their lowest form:

1. $0.7\dot{8}$

2. $0.0\dot{4}$

3. $0.86868686\ldots$

4. $0.364364364\ldots$

5 $0.2\dot{6}\dot{3}$

161

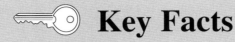

Key Facts

Collect all the terms containing the required subject on the same side of the equation and all the other terms on the other side of the equation.

The required subject usually has to be extracted as a *common factor* before it is finally isolated.

(a) Make m the subject of the formula $km + n = p - qm$

$km + n = p - qm$ [add qm onto both sides of the equation and subtract n from both sides of the equation]

$km + qm = p - n$ [take out m as a common factor]

$m(k + q) = p - n$ [divide both sides of the equation by $(k + q)$]

$m = \dfrac{p - n}{k + q}$

(b) Make x the subject of the formula $\dfrac{mx - ny}{fx} = k$

$\dfrac{mx - ny}{fx} = k$ [multiply both sides of the equation by fx]

$mx - ny = kfx$ [subtract kfx from both sides of the equation and add ny onto both sides of the equation]

$mx - kfx = ny$ [take out x as a common factor]

$x(m - kf) = ny$ [divide both sides of the equation by $(m - kf)$]

$x = \dfrac{ny}{m - kf}$

E6.1

1 (a) Continue the working to make b the subject of the formula $a^2b - c = fb + h^2$.

$a^2b - fb = h^2 + c$

$b(a^2 - f) = h^2 + c$

$b = ...$

(b) Make x the subject of the formula $\dfrac{mx - k}{p - qx} = r$

[Begin by multiplying both sides by $(p - qx)$]

2 Make m the subject of the formula $P = \dfrac{mn}{m + n}$

3 Make a the subject of the formula $Y = \dfrac{3ab}{b - a}$

4 Make x the subject of each formula given below:

(a) $fx + g = dx + e$ (b) $xy - wx = wz + y$ (c) $ax - b = 3c - bx$

(d) $m(x - y) = n(x + z)$ (e) $c(d - x) = b + fx$ (f) $y^2x = 3z - wx$

(g) $t + sx = p(x - r)$ (h) $\dfrac{a + bx}{dx - a} = c$ (i) $\dfrac{f - x}{g + kx} = m$

(j) $z = \dfrac{yx - 4}{x}$ (k) $\dfrac{mx + c}{kx + d} = n$ (l) $f = \dfrac{s - rx}{5x + d}$

5 Make x the subject of the formula $px - q + qx = r(q - x)$

6 (a) Make n the subject of the formula

$$\sqrt{\frac{m + n}{2m - n}} = p$$

[start by squaring both sides]

(b) Make f the subject of the formula $\dfrac{k}{3} = \dfrac{f + 2g}{g - f}$

7 Make w the subject of each formula given below:

(a) $\sqrt[3]{\dfrac{w + y}{w + 2y}} = z$ (b) $q = \sqrt{\dfrac{ax - w}{bw + c}}$ (c) $3y = \sqrt{\dfrac{w}{w - z}}$

(d) $\left(\dfrac{a - w}{w + c}\right)^2 = b$ (e) $z = \left(\dfrac{b + cw}{b - w}\right)^2$ (f) $\dfrac{mw}{n - pw} = \dfrac{2}{5}$

(g) $\dfrac{a}{b} = \dfrac{dw + m}{w - n}$ (h) $\dfrac{2p}{q} = \sqrt{\dfrac{aw}{w - b}}$ (i) $\sqrt[3]{\dfrac{mw + 1}{pw - 1}} = 2n$

8 Make m the subject of the formula $\dfrac{c - tm}{3p} = zm + 4$

9 Make x the subject of the formula $p - qx = \dfrac{nx + r^2 - wx}{m}$

E   Function notation

Key Facts

Consider $y = 3x - 1$ { put in x-value } → $\times 3$ → -1 → { gives a y-value }

This y-value is known as the 'function of x'

Another way of writing $y = 3x - 1$ is $f(x) = 3x - 1$

(a) If $f(x) = x^2 - 3x$

    (i) $f(3) = 3^2 - 3 \times 3 = 9 - 9 = 0$

    (ii) $f(-2) = (-2)^2 - 3 \times -2 = 4 + 6 = 10$

    (iii) $f(4z) = (4z)^2 - 3 \times 4z = 16z^2 - 12z$

(b) If $g(x) = 5x - 2$, find

    x if $g(x) = 18$

    $g(x) = 18$ so $5x - 2 = 18$

              $5x = 20$

                $x = 4$

E6.2

1 If $f(x) = 4x - 1$, find the value of:

    (a) $f(3)$ (b) $f(10)$ (c) $f(-2)$ (d) $f(0)$

2 If $g(x) = 7x + 5$, find the value of:

    (a) $g(4)$ (b) $g(-2)$ (c) $g(-5)$ (d) $g(\frac{1}{2})$

3 If $h(x) = x^2$, find the value of:

    (a) $h(7)$ (b) $h(0)$ (c) $h(\frac{1}{4})$ (d) $h(-4)$

4 If $f(x) = x^2 - 4x + 3$, find the value of:

    (a) $f(3)$ (b) $f(0)$ (c) $f(-1)$ (d) $f(-4)$

5 If $s(x) = (x - 4)^2$, find the value of:

    (a) $s(4)$ (b) $s(1)$ (c) $s(-3)$ (d) $s(w)$

6 If $h(x) = x^3 + x$, find the value of:

    (a) $h(2)$ (b) $h(-1)$ (c) $h(5)$ (d) $h(y)$

7 If $g(x) = \dfrac{3}{x} + 2$, find the value of:

    (a) $g(3)$ (b) $g(-1)$ (c) $g(z)$ (d) $g(0)$ Discuss this answer with your teacher

8 If $h(x) = \dfrac{x^2 - 7}{3x + 1}$, find the value of:

    (a) $h(1)$ (b) $h(0)$ (c) $h(p)$

9 If $f(x) = 6x + 3$, find the value of x when $f(x) = 45$.

10 If $h(x) = 1 - 9x$, find the value of x when $h(x) = 19$.

11 If $h(x) = x^2$, find the values of x when $h(x) = 25$.

12 $f(x) = x^2 - 2x$.

Copy and complete the following to find the values of q when $f(q) = q$.

$f(q) = q$ so $\underbrace{q^2 - 2q}_{f(q)} = q$

$q^2 - \boxed{} = 0$

$q\left(q - \boxed{}\right) = 0$

$q = 0$ or $q - \boxed{} = 0$

$q = 0$ or $q = \boxed{}$

13 $g(x) = x^2 + 6x - 18$

Copy and complete the following to find the values of a when $g(a) = 3a$

$g(a) = 3a$ so $\underbrace{a^2 + 6a - 18}_{g(a)} = 3a$

$a^2 + \boxed{} - 18 = 0$

$\left(a + \boxed{}\right)\left(a - \boxed{}\right) = 0$

$a + \boxed{} = 0$ or $a - \boxed{} = 0$

$a = -\boxed{}$ or $a = \boxed{}$

14 If $f(x) = x^2 + 4x - 8$, find the values of p when $f(p) = 2p$.

15 If $h(x) = x^2 + 3x - 12$, find the values of z when $h(z) = 4z$.

16 If $f(x) = x^2 + 8x + 9$, find the values of x when $f(x) = 9$.

17 If $g(x) = \dfrac{3x + 1}{x - 2}$, find the value of x when $g(x) = 2$.

18 If $f(x) = \dfrac{5x + 7}{x - 3}$, find the value of x when $f(x) = 3$.

19 If $f(x) = 5x + 2$, write down the function $4f(x) + 3$ by copying and completing below:

$4f(x) + 3 = 4(5x + 2) + 3$

$= \boxed{} + \boxed{} + 3$

$= \boxed{} + 11$

20 If $g(x) = 2x - 1$, write down each function below:

(a) $g(x) + 7$ (b) $3g(x)$ (c) $5g(x) - 3$ (d) $-g(x)$

21 If $h(x) = 9x + 4$, write down each function below:

(a) $2h(x)$ (b) $2h(x) - 7$ (c) $-h(x)$ (d) $-4h(x)$

22 If $h(x) = x^2 - 2x + 1$, write down each function below:

(a) $4h(x) + 1$ (b) $3h(x) - 6$ (c) $-2h(x)$ (d) $4 - h(x)$

23 If $g(x) = x^3 - x$, write down each function below:

(a) $-2g(x)$ (b) $g(x) - 9$ (c) $4 - 3g(x)$ (d) $-5g(x) - 3$

24 Find the function f so that $f(0) = 3$, $f(1) = 8$ and $f(2) = 13$.

Can you still?

Can you still?

6C   **Use circle properties (see Unit 3)**

In these questions O is the centre of the circle.

1.

Find $P\hat{R}Q$.

2.

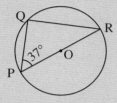

Find $C\hat{D}E$.

3.

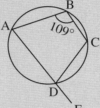

Find $F\hat{G}H$.

4.

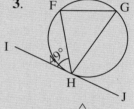

Find $O\hat{G}F$.

5.

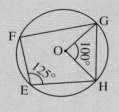

Find $B\hat{O}C$ if AB and AC are tangents to the circle.

6.

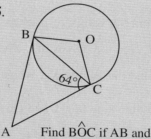

Find $P\hat{S}R$.

7.

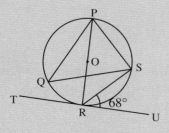

Find $P\hat{Q}S$.

8.

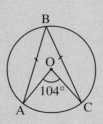

Find $O\hat{A}B$.

9.

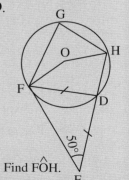

Find $F\hat{O}H$.

166

M6.8

Check all your graphs with a computer or graphical calculator if your teacher wants you to.

For Questions **1** to **3** , draw axes like those shown below:

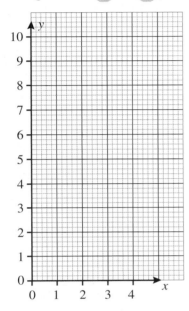

1 Copy and complete the table below then draw $y = 2x + 2$.

x	0	1	2	3
y				

2 Copy and complete the table below then draw $y = 3x + 1$.

x	0	1	2	3
y				

3 Copy and complete the table below then draw $y = 2x + 3$.

x	0	1	2	3
y				

4 Using x-values from 0 to 5, complete a table then draw the straight line $y = 6 - x$.

5 Copy and complete the table below then draw the straight line $y = 2x + 4$.

x	−2	−1	0	1	2
y		2			

6 Using x-values from − 3 to 3, complete a table then draw the straight line $y = 4x - 3$.

7 Draw $y = 3 - 2x$ using x-values from − 3 to 3.

8 Draw $y = \frac{1}{2}x$ using x-values from − 4 to 4.

9 Draw an x-axis from − 3 to 3 and a y-axis from − 12 to 12. Using the same set of axes,

draw $y = 4x$ $y = 2x - 3$

$y = 1 - 2x$ $y = 3x - 4$

Label each line clearly.

Draw $y = x^2 + 3$, using x-values from -3 to 3.

x	−3	−2	−1	0	1	2	3
y							

Draw a table

Use $y = x^2 + 3$ to find the y-values.

When $x = -3$, $y = (-3)^2 + 3 = 9 + 3 = 12$.

When $x = -2$, $y = (-2)^2 + 3 = 4 + 3 = 7$

and so on.

x	−3	−2	−1	0	1	2	3
y	12	7	4	3	4	7	12

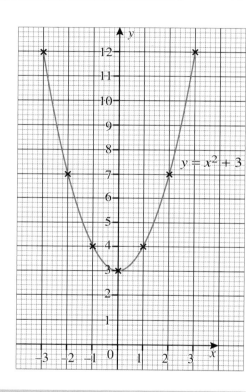

Draw axes so that all the points can be plotted.

Plot each point.

Join up all the points with a smooth curve.

Note

A curve should always be smooth.

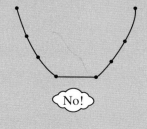

This indicates that an incorrect point has been calculated.

Label the curve with its equation.

Note

The top and bottom of curved graphs should *not* normally be straight lines.

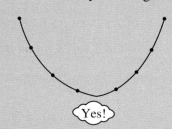

Check all your graphs with a computer or graphical calculator if your teacher wants you to.

1 Find the value of these expressions when $x = -4$:

(a) x^2 (b) $3x$ (c) $x^2 + 2$ (d) $x^2 - 6$ (e) $x^2 + x$

2 Find the value of these expressions when $x = -1$:

(a) $2x$ (b) x^2 (c) $x^2 + 3$ (d) $x^2 - x$ (e) $x^2 + 2x$

3 Complete the table below then draw the curve $y = x^2$ using axes like these shown opposite.

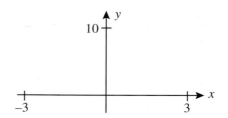

x	−3	−2	−1	0	1	2	3
y							

4 Using x-values from -3 to 3, complete tables of values then draw graphs for each of the following:

(a) $y = x^2 + 1$ (b) $y = x^2 - 2$ (c) $y = 2x^2$

[note: $2x^2$ means x^2 then 'multiply by 2']

(d) $y = 3x^2$ (e) $y = 2x^2 + 1$ (f) $y = 3x^2 - 7$

5 (a) Complete the table below for $y = x^2 + x + 2$.

add to get y
x	−4	−3	−2	−1	0	1	2
x^2		9					
$+x$		−3					
$+2$	2	2	2	2	2	2	2
y		8					

(b) Draw an x-axis from -4 to 2 and a y-axis from 0 to 14. Draw the curve $y = x^2 + x + 2$.

6 Complete the table below then draw the curve $y = x^2 + x$.

add to get y
x	−3	−2	−1	0	1	2	3
x^2			1				9
$+x$			−1				3
y			0				12

7 (a) Complete the table below then draw the curve $y = x^2 - x + 2$.

x	-3	-2	-1	0	1	2	3
x^2	9						
$-x$	3						
$+2$	2						
y	14						

(b) Read off the value of y from your curve when $x = 0.5$.

8 (a) Using x-values from -4 to 2, complete a table then draw $y = x^2 + 3x - 2$.

(b) Read off the value of y from your curve when $x = -1.5$.

9 Draw the graph of each function below using the given x-values.

(a) $y = x^2 + 4x - 3$ for x-values from -5 to 2.

(b) $y = x^2 - 3x + 3$ for x-values from -1 to 5.

(c) $y = 2x^2 + x - 6$ for x-values from -3 to 3.

(d) $y = 4 - 3x - x^2$ for x-values from -5 to 3.

(e) $y = 3x^2 - 5x + 6$ for x-values from -2 to 3.

(f) $y = x(3 - x)$ for x-values from -5 to 2.

(g) For each graph in parts (a) to (f), write down the co-ordinates of the vertex (the 'vertex' is the maximum point or the minimum point).

10 Every curve you have drawn in this Exercise has a similar shape. *Describe* this shape. All quadratic curves (x^2 term is the highest power) have this shape.

E | **Graphs of cubics and reciprocals**

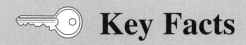 **Key Facts**

A *cubic* equation has an x^3 term as the highest power of x,
for example: $y = x^3 + 5x^2 + 3x + 2$ $\qquad$ $y = x^3 + x$

A *reciprocal* equation has the x term in the denominator of a fraction,

for example: $y = \dfrac{7}{x}$ $\qquad$ $y = \dfrac{3}{x - 2}$

Note
$\dfrac{4}{0} = 4 \div 0$ gives *no value*. You *cannot* divide by 0. If you use '0' in the denominator, the graph will have a 'break' in it (see example on next page)

Draw the graph of $y = \frac{4}{x}$ for x-values from –5 to 5.

Complete a table. Some y-values will have to be rounded off.

x	– 5	– 4	– 3	– 2	– 1	0	1	2	3	4	5
y	– 0.8	– 1	– 1.3	– 2	– 4	no value	4	2	1.3	1	0.8

What happens between $x = -1$ and $x = 1$?

Work out more y-values.

x	– 0.8	– 0.6	– 0.4	0.4	0.6	0.8
y	– 5	– 6.7	–10	10	6.7	5

There is no value for y when $x = 0$. As x gets nearer to 0, the curve approaches the y-axis but never touches it.

As x gets very large or very small, the curve approaches the x-axis but never touches it.

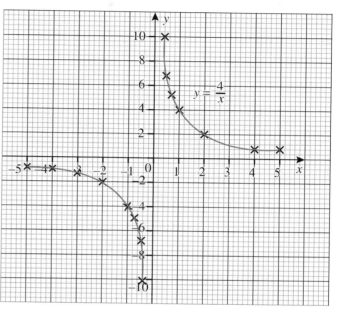

E6.3

Check all your graphs with a computer or graphical calculator if your teacher wants you to.

1 Complete the table below then draw $y = x^3$.

x	– 3	– 2	– 1	0	1	2	3
y	–27						

Remember to draw a smooth curve

2 (a) Complete the table below then draw $y = x^3 + x + 1$.

x	– 3	– 2	– 1	0	1	2	3
x^3		– 8					
$+x$		– 2					
$+1$		1					
y		– 9					

(b) Read off the value of y from your curve when $x = 1.5$

3 (a) Complete a table then draw $y = x^3 - x - 2$ using x-values from -3 to 3.

(b) Find the value of y when $x = -0.5$.

4 (a) Complete the table below then draw $y = x^3 - 5x + 3$.

x	-4	-3	-2	-1	0	1	2	3	4
x^3			-8						
$-5x$			$+10$						
$+3$			$+3$						
y			5						

To ensure a smooth curve you may wish to work out more y-values using extra x-values around where the curve is at a turning point.

(b) Read off the y-value when $x = -2.5$

5 Using x-values from -3 to 3 draw:

(a) $y = x^3 + 1$ (b) $y = x^3 + x$

(c) $y = x^3 + 3x - 4$ (d) $y = x^3 + x^2 + 1$

6 Using x-values from -2 to 4, draw $y = x^3 - 3x^2 + 2$.

7 Using x-values from -4 to 2, draw $y = x^3 + 2x^2 - 3x - 1$.

8 *Describe* the general shape of all the curves you have drawn in Questions

1 to **7** . All cubic curves (x^3 term is the highest power) have this shape.

9 (a) Complete the table below then draw $y = \dfrac{1}{x}$

x	-5	-4	-3	-2	-1	0	1	2	3	4	5
y						no value					

(b) Read off the y-value when $x = 2.5$

10 (a) Using x-values from -10 to 10, complete a table then draw $y = \dfrac{8}{x}$

(b) Read off the x-value when $y = 6.4$

11 Draw the graph of:

(a) $y = \dfrac{4}{x - 2}$ using x-values from -3 to 7 (b) $y = \dfrac{10}{x + 5}$ using x-values from -10 to 0

(c) $y = \dfrac{5}{x} + 2$ using x-values from -10 to 10 (d) $y = \dfrac{10}{x^2}$ using x-values from -5 to 5

(e) $y = \dfrac{5}{(x + 2)^2}$ using x-values from -7 to 3

12 Based on your earlier graphs, *sketch* the graph of any equation of the

form $y = \dfrac{a}{x}$ where a is a positive constant (fixed number).

13 For each curve below, write down if it is linear, quadratic, cubic or reciprocal.

(a)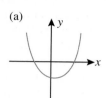

(b)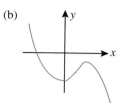

(c)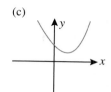

(d)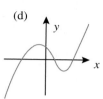

(e)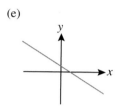

(f)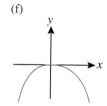

(g)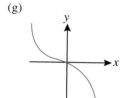

(h)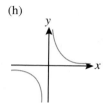

(i)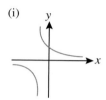

(j)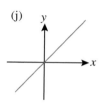

(k)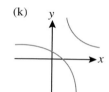

(l)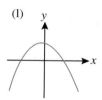

14 Match each equation to its graph below. One of the equations does not have a graph below.

(a) $y = x^2 - 4$

(b) $y = \dfrac{1}{x^2}$

(c) $y = x^3 - 2x^2 - 3x + 2$

(d) $y = \dfrac{3}{x}$

(e) $y = 6 - 2x$

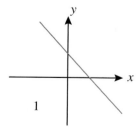

1

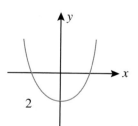

2

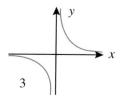

3

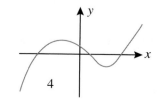

4

173 mHz

E6.4

1   Which of the graphs below shows:

(a) steady speed   (b) car that speeds up   (c) car that slows down

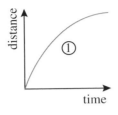  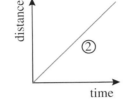

2   The cost, C, in £, of hiring a tile cutter is given by the formula $C = 15d + 28$ where d is the number of days the tile cutter is hired for.

(a) Draw a graph of C against d for values of d from 0 to 6.

(b) What is the fixed charge before the number of days hire is considered?

3   Which of the graphs below best fits each of the following statements:

(a) After a poor start, car sales have increased massively this year.

(b) The price of milk has remained the same over the past year.

(c) The world's population continues to rise rapidly.

(d) The price of computers has fallen steadily over the last year.

(e) The number of visitors to a seaside resort rose in the summer then dropped off towards winter.

(f) The number of people going to the cinema in the UK has increased steadily this year.

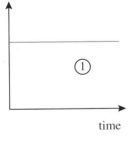 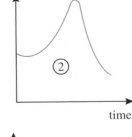 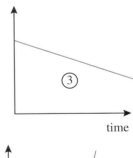

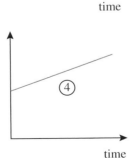 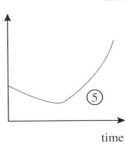 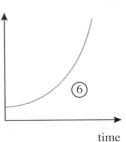

4 Water is poured at a constant rate into each of the containers A, B, and C. Which of the graphs below fits each container?

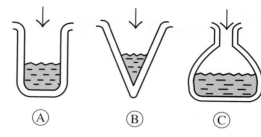

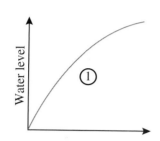

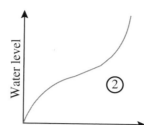

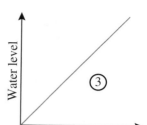

5 A ball is dropped from rest. The distance, s, it has travelled is given by the formula $s = 4.9t^2$ where t is measured in seconds and s in metres.

(a) Draw a graph of s against t for values of t from 0 to 10.

(b) Use the graph to find out how long it takes the ball to travel 70 m.

(c) Use the graph to find out how far the ball has travelled after 5.5 seconds.

6 In an electrical circuit, the resistance R is given by the formula $R = \dfrac{20}{I}$ where I is the current measured in amps and R is measured in ohms.

(a) Draw a graph of R against I for values of I from 1 to 10.

(b) Use the graph to find the value of R when I = 2.5.

(c) Use the graph to find the value of I when R = 7.5.

7

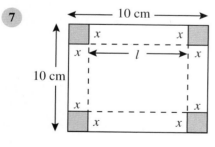

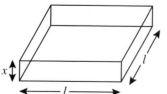

A square piece of cardboard is to be made into a box by cutting out squares from each corner as shown then folding.

(a) Express l in terms of x.

(b) Prove that the volume, V, of the box is given by $V = x(10 - 2x)^2$

(c) Draw a graph of V against x for values of x from 0 to 5.

(d) Use your graph to find the maximum possible volume.

(e) For what value of x does the maximum volume occur?

8 The total surface area of this cuboid is 40 cm^2.

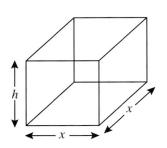

(a) Prove that $h = \dfrac{20 - x^2}{2x}$

(b) Volume $= x^2h = x^2\left(\dfrac{20 - x^2}{2x}\right)$

so V $= \dfrac{x}{2}(20 - x^2)$

Draw a graph of V against x for values of x from 0 to 4.

(c) Use your graph to find the value of x which gives the maximum volume.

(d) What is the maximum possible volume?

M | Gradient of a straight line

🔑 Key Facts

Gradient is a measure of 'steepness'.

Gradient $= \dfrac{\text{vertical distance}}{\text{horizontal distance}}$

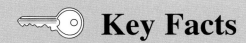

On a graph, the 'vertical distance' = difference between y coordinates

and the 'horizontal distance' = difference between x coordinates

so ⎰ gradient $= \dfrac{\text{difference between } y \text{ coordinates}}{\text{difference between } x \text{ coordinates}}$

Negative gradient

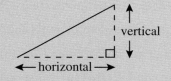

Sloping downwards to the right ⇨

If a line slopes downwards to the right, it has a *negative gradient*.

(a) Find the gradient of this line.

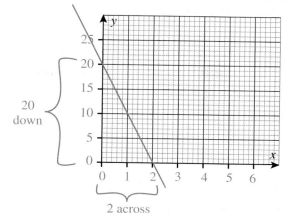

$$\text{Gradient} = \frac{20 \text{ down}}{2 \text{ across}}$$

$$= \frac{-20}{2}$$

$$= -10$$

(b) Find the gradient of the line which passes through $(-2, 3)$ and $(2, 15)$.

$$\text{Gradient} = \frac{\text{difference between } y \text{ co-ordinates}}{\text{difference between } x \text{ co-ordinates}}$$

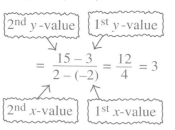

$$= \frac{15 - 3}{2 - (-2)} = \frac{12}{4} = 3$$

2nd y-value · 1st y-value
2nd x-value · 1st x-value

M6.10

1 Find the gradient of each line below:

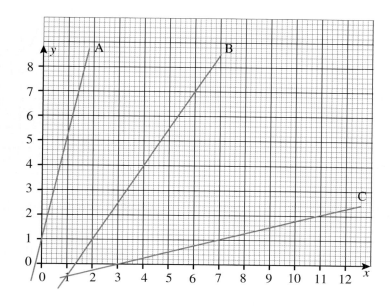

2 Find the gradient of each line below:

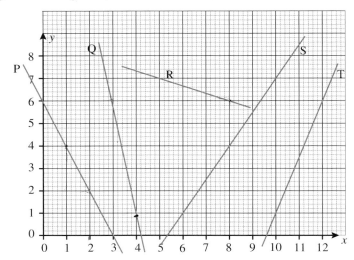

3 Find the gradient of the line joining each pair of points below:

(a) (1, 1) and (3, 5) (b) (2, 4) and (3, 7) (c) (3, 6) and (5, 2)

(d) (3, 1) and (5, 4) (e) (1, 4) and (3, 2) (f) (0, 5) and (2, 4)

(g) (5, 2) and (7, 3) (h) (− 1, 2) and (2, 7) (i) (5, − 2) and (9, − 2)

(j) (− 2, − 3) and (1, − 5) (k) (− 4, 6) and (2, 5) (l) (1, 2) and (1, − 5)

4 Find the gradient of the line joining:

(a) B and C

(b) C and D

(c) A and E

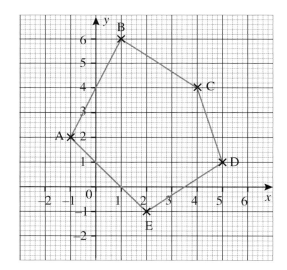

5 A line has a gradient of 6. One point on the line is (− 2, 5). A point P on the line has an *x*-value of 1. What is the *y*-value at P?

6 A line has a gradient of − 4. One point on the line is (3, 7). A point Q on the line has a *y*-value of − 5. What is the *x*-value at Q?

M6.11

Use a graphical calculator or computer if possible.

1   (a) Complete the table below then draw the straight line $y = 2x + 3$.

x	1	2	3
y			

   (b) Use another table to draw $y = 2x$ on the same grid.

   (c) Draw $y = 2x + 1$ on the same grid.

   (d) Draw $y = 2x - 1$ on the same grid.

   (e) Find the gradient of each line.

   (f) What do you notice about the gradient of each line and its equation?

   (g) Look at where each line cuts the y-axis. For each line what do you notice about this value and its equation?

2   Draw the following lines using the same set of axes and repeat parts (e), (f) and

   (g) from Question **1** :

$y = -3x + 1$ $y = -3x + 4$ $y = -3x$

$y = -3x - 2$ $y = -3x - 5$

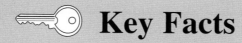 **Key Facts**

The equation of a straight line may be written in the form

$$y = mx + c$$

m is the gradient of the line

c is the y-value at the point where the line cuts the y-axis – this is known as the '*y-intercept*'

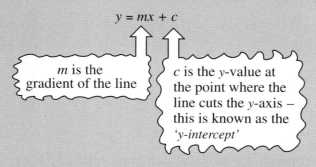

$y = mx + c$ is sometimes known as the 'gradient–intercept' form of the straight line.

(a) Write down the gradient and y-intercept of $y = \frac{1}{2}x - 3$

Gradient $= \frac{1}{2}$ y-intercept $= -3$

(b) Write down the gradient of $2x + 3y = 1$ and write down the co-ordinates of the point where the line cuts the y-axis

$$\boxed{\text{rearrange into form } y = mx + c} \qquad 2x + 3y = 1$$

$$3y = -2x + 1$$

$$\uparrow$$

$$\boxed{\text{write the } x\text{'s first}}$$

$$y = \frac{-2x}{3} + \frac{1}{3}$$

Gradient $= \dfrac{-2}{3}$ and line cuts y-axis at $\left(0, \dfrac{1}{3}\right)$

(c) Find the equation of the line which passes through $(3, 1)$ and $(6, 13)$.

$$\boxed{\text{find gradient } m \text{ first}} \qquad m = \frac{13 - 1}{6 - 3} = \frac{12}{3} = 4$$

we know $y = mx + c$ so $y = 4x + c$

$\boxed{\text{to find } c, \text{ substitute one pair of } x \text{ and } y \text{ values into the equation of the line}}$

$x = 3$ when $y = 1$

so $1 = 4 \times 3 + c$

$1 = 12 + c$

$c = -11$

equation of line is $y = 4x - 11$

M6.12

Write down the gradient and y-intercept of each of the following lines:

1 $y = 3x + 4$ **2** $y = 2x - 5$ **3** $y = 8x - 1$ **4** $y = x + 6$

5 $y = -4x - 2$ **6** $y = -4x + 3$ **7** $y = -x - 2$ **8** $y = -5x + 2$

9 $y = 3 - x$ **10** $y = 4 - 2x$ **11** $y = \frac{1}{3}x - 7$ **12** $y - 5x = 1$

13 $y + 4x = 5$ **14** $6x - y = 3$ **15** $2x + 5y = 3$ **16** $3x - 4y = 6$

17 $5x - 3y = 3$ **18** $4y - 2 = 5x$ **19** $4x + y - 6 = 0$ **20** $5x - 7y - 2 = 0$

Use your knowledge of $y = mx + c$ to *sketch* each of the following lines:

21 $y = 2x + 2$ **22** $y = 5 - x$ **23** $y - 3x = 1$ **24** $2x + 4y = 3$

180

25 Write down the equation of each of the 3 lines below:

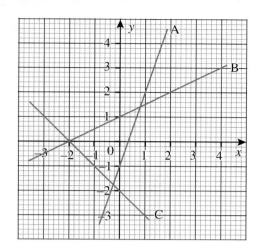

26 Which of the following lines are parallel?

(a) $y = 4x + 1$ (b) $y = 2 - 4x$ (c) $y = 2x + 4$

(d) $y - 4x = 2$ (e) $4x - y = 2$ (f) $y = 4 - 3x$

Find the equation of each line in questions **27** to **36**

27 The line passes through (0, 4) with gradient = 5.

28 The line passes through (0, 2) with gradient = -4.

29 The line passes through (3, 5) with gradient = 3.

30 The line passes through (5, -1) with gradient = 1.

31 The line passes through (3, 2) and (5, 8).

32 The line passes through (6, 1) and (8, 9).

33 The line passes through (-3, 4) and (-1, 10).

34 The line passes through (5, -3) and (8, -9).

35

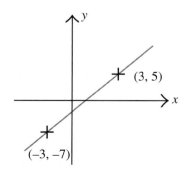

36

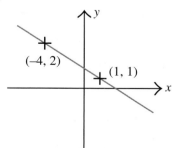

1

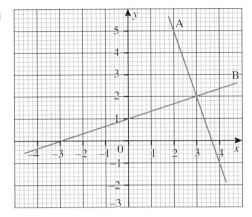

Line A and line B are perpendicular (at right angles).

(a) Find the gradient of line A.

(b) Find the gradient of line B.

(c) *Multiply* together the gradient of line A and the gradient of line B.

2 Line P and line Q are perpendicular (at right angles).

(a) Find the gradient of line P.

(b) Find the gradient of line Q.

(c) Find the *product* of the gradient of line P and the gradient of line Q.

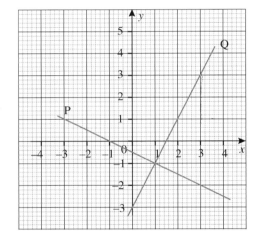

3 What do you notice about your answers to part (c) in both questions **1** and **2** ?

4 If a line has a gradient of 4, what is the gradient of a line perpendicular to this one?

5

Line R has a gradient of 4. Line S is perpendicular to line R.

Find the gradient of line S to check if your answer to Question **4** was correct.

Key Facts

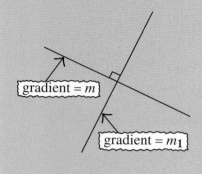

gradient = m

gradient = m_1

The product of the gradients of two perpendicular lines is -1

$m\, m_1 = -1$ so $m = \dfrac{-1}{m_1}$

Given a line with gradient $= m_1$, to find the gradient of a perpendicular line, find the reciprocal of m_1 $\left(\text{ie. } \dfrac{1}{m_1}\right)$ then change its sign $\left(\text{ie. } \dfrac{-1}{m_1}\right)$

Write down the gradient of a line which is perpendicular to a line of gradient (a) -5 (b) $\dfrac{2}{3}$

(a) $\dfrac{-1}{m_1} = \dfrac{-1}{-5} = \dfrac{1}{5}$

(b) $\dfrac{-1}{m_1} = \dfrac{-1}{2/3} \dfrac{(\times 3)}{(\times 3)} = \dfrac{-3}{2}$ [the simplest way is to turn the fraction upside down and change the sign]

(c) Find the equation of the line which passes through $(1, 3)$ and is perpendicular to the line $x + 2y = 3$.

Given line $x + 2y = 3$

$2y = -x + 3$

$y = \dfrac{-1x}{2} + \dfrac{3}{2}$ Gradient $= \dfrac{-1}{2}$

so gradient of perpendicular line is 2

equation of perpendicular line is $y = mx + c$

so $y = 2x + c$

passes through $(1, 3)$, ie. $x = 1$, $y = 3$

so $3 = 2 \times 1 + c$

$c = 1$

required equation is $y = 2x + 1$

1 Find the gradient of the line which is perpendicular to a line with each gradient given below:

(a) 7   (b) 1   (c) −4   (d) −8   (e) $\dfrac{1}{3}$ (f) $\dfrac{2}{5}$

(g) $\dfrac{-1}{6}$ (h) $\dfrac{-3}{4}$ (i) $\dfrac{-9}{2}$ (j) −0.5   (k) 0.2   (l) 0

2 Write down the gradient of any line which is perpendicular to:

(a) $y = 3x - 2$ (b) $y = -\dfrac{2}{3}x + 7$ (c) $5x + 8y = 3$

3 Find the equation of the line which passes through the given point and is perpendicular to the given line.

(a) $(0, 3)$ $y = \dfrac{1}{3}x + 6$ (b) $(0, -2)$ $y = -\dfrac{1}{5}x + 4$

(c) $(1, 1)$ $y = 8 - \dfrac{1}{4}x$ (d) $(2, 5)$ $y = 2x - 1$

(e) $(1, 4)$ $2y - x = 3$ (f) $(-6, 2)$ $3y + x = 5$

(g) $(-3, -3)$ $3x + y = 7$ (h) $(4, -1)$ $4x - 2y = 9$

(i) $(-1, 6)$ $x + y - 6 = 0$ (j) $(-4, -3)$ $6x + 3y - 5 = 0$

4 A line passes through $(3, 0)$ and is *parallel* to the line $y = 5x - 3$. Find the equation of the line.

5 A line passes through $(2, 5)$ and is *parallel* to the line $x + 2y = 1$. Find the equation of the line.

6 Without drawing any of these lines, put them into pairs of lines which are perpendicular to one another:

(a) $\boxed{3y - 2x = 7}$ (b) $\boxed{y = -\dfrac{1}{3}x + 5}$

(c) $\boxed{2y + x = 9}$ (d) $\boxed{5y + x = 9}$

(e) $\boxed{3x + 2y = 11}$ (f) $\boxed{y = 2x + 1}$

(g) $\boxed{y = x + 3}$ (h) $\boxed{y - 3x = 10}$

(i) $\boxed{y = 5x - 1}$ (j) $\boxed{y = -x + 5}$

To keep track of your money, the bank or building society will send you a regular **'statement'**.

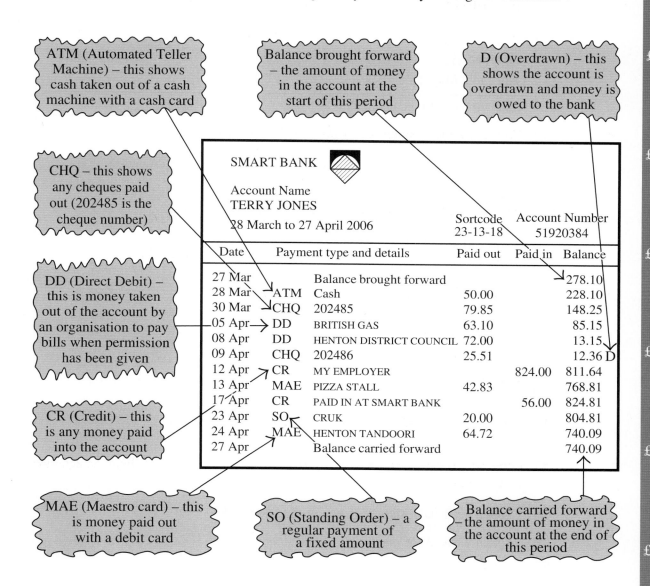

ATM (Automated Teller Machine) – this shows cash taken out of a cash machine with a cash card

Balance brought forward – the amount of money in the account at the start of this period

D (Overdrawn) – this shows the account is overdrawn and money is owed to the bank

CHQ – this shows any cheques paid out (202485 is the cheque number)

DD (Direct Debit) – this is money taken out of the account by an organisation to pay bills when permission has been given

CR (Credit) – this is any money paid into the account

MAE (Maestro card) – this is money paid out with a debit card

SO (Standing Order) – a regular payment of a fixed amount

Balance carried forward – the amount of money in the account at the end of this period

SMART BANK

Account Name
TERRY JONES

28 March to 27 April 2006

Sortcode
23-13-18

Account Number
51920384

Date	Payment type and details		Paid out	Paid in	Balance
27 Mar		Balance brought forward			278.10
28 Mar	ATM	Cash	50.00		228.10
30 Mar	CHQ	202485	79.85		148.25
05 Apr	DD	BRITISH GAS	63.10		85.15
08 Apr	DD	HENTON DISTRICT COUNCIL	72.00		13.15
09 Apr	CHQ	202486	25.51		12.36 D
12 Apr	CR	MY EMPLOYER		824.00	811.64
13 Apr	MAE	PIZZA STALL	42.83		768.81
17 Apr	CR	PAID IN AT SMART BANK		56.00	824.81
23 Apr	SO	CRUK	20.00		804.81
24 Apr	MAE	HENTON TANDOORI	64.72		740.09
27 Apr		Balance carried forward			740.09

SMART BANK

Account Name

| COLIN MAYS | Sort code | Account Number |
| 3 April to 2 May 2006 | 172619 | 32718425 |

Date	Payment type and details	Paid out	Paid in	Balance
2 Apr	Balance brought forward			416.25
3 Apr	CHQ 419330	63.10		①
5 Apr	DD POLDEN WATER	58.17		294.98
9 Apr	CR MY EMPLOYER		750.00	②
14 Apr	MAE PETROLGO	28.64		③
16 Apr	DD MID ELECTRICITY	67.00		949.34
18 Apr	CHQ 419331	④		823.74
19 Apr	SO MR. S. JONES	38.45		⑤
22 Apr	CR PAID IN AT SMART BANK		⑥	850.29
23 Apr	MAE HORTON STORE	43.26		⑦
28 Apr	MAE AQUAPLAY	21.95		⑧
2 May	Balance carried forward			⑨

For Questions **1** to **9**, write down the correct amount of money for each box above.

10 Explain what 'DD' shows on a bank statement.

11 Explain what 'ATM' shows on a bank statement.

12 Explain what 'D' shows on a bank statement.

TEST YOURSELF ON UNIT 6

1. Solving linear equations

Solve the following equations:

(a) $3x - 7 = 17$

(b) $9x + 6 = 36 - x$

(c) $\dfrac{3w}{8} = 2$

(d) $30 = 6(2n - 1)$

(e) $3(4y + 3) = 2(3y + 5)$

(f) $2m - 12 = 4(2 + 3m)$

(g) $\dfrac{2a + 5}{3} = 1$

(h) $9 = \dfrac{n}{4} - 2$

(i) $\dfrac{10}{x} = 4$

(a) A triangle has one angle 40° bigger than the smallest angle and the other angle 50° bigger than the smallest angle. Find the size of each angle (hint: let $x =$ smallest angle).

(b)

$3x - 1$

$x + 2$

The perimeter of this rectangle is 42 cm. Write down an equation involving x then work out the actual area of this rectangle.

(c) Three consecutive *odd* numbers add up to 105. Find the three numbers.

(a) Solve $x^3 + 5x = 300$ by trial and improvement, giving the answer to 1 decimal place.

(b) The length of a rectangle is 4 cm more than its width. The area of the rectangle is 80 cm². Use trial and improvement to find the dimensions of the rectangle, correct to 2 decimal places.

Make x the subject of each formula given below:

(a) $y = mx + c$ (b) $c(x - p) = q$ (c) $\frac{x}{a} + k = m$ (d) $\frac{wx + z}{y} = n$

(e) $\frac{a}{x} = m + p$ (f) $\frac{c}{x} - 4y = 3z$ (g) $x^3 = w - z$ (h) $3b = \sqrt{(x + n)}$

(a) Using x-values from -3 to 3, complete a table then draw the straight line $y = 2x - 5$.

(b) On the same axes as part (a), draw the straight line $x = -2$.

(c) Complete the table below then draw the curve $y = x^2 + 4$.

x	-3	-2	-1	0	1	2	3
y							

(d) Using x-values from -4 to 3, complete a table then draw $y = x^2 + 4x - 3$.

187

6. Finding gradients of straight lines

Find the gradient of each line below:

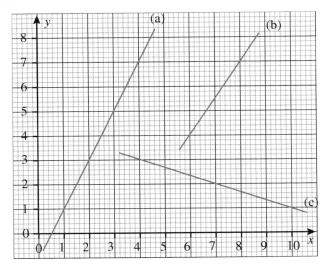

(d) A triangle has vertices (corners) A (1, 7), B(2, 11) and C(5, − 1). Calculate the gradients of the three lines which form this triangle.

7. Using the equation of a straight line $y = mx + c$

Write down the gradient and y-intercept of each of the following lines:

(a) $y = 2x - 6$ (b) $y = -x - 8$ (c) $3x + 5y = 8$

(d)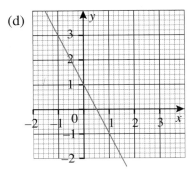

Write down the equation of this straight line.

(e) Find the equation of the straight line which passes through (2, 4) and (5, 19).

8. Changing the subject of a formula when the required subject appears more than once

Make n the subject of each formula given below:

(a) $m - nx = p + n$ (b) $a = \dfrac{cn - d}{b + n}$

(c) $k = \sqrt{\dfrac{fn - d}{n}}$ (d) $\sqrt[3]{a + kn - mn} = c$

188

9. Using function notation

(a) Find the value of $f(4)$ if $f(x) = 3 - 7x$.

(b) Find the value of $h(-3)$ if $h(x) = x^2 - x$.

(c) Find the value of $g(\frac{1}{2})$ if $g(x) = \dfrac{4}{x}$.

(d) If $g(x) = 4x + 5$, find the value of x when $g(x) = 29$.

(e) If $f(x) = x^2 - 5x + 3$, find the value of n when $f(n) = 3 + 2n$.

10. Drawing graphs of cubics and reciprocals, including real-life graphs

(a) Complete a table then draw $y = x^3 - 5x + 4$ using x-values from -3 to 3.

(b) Complete the table below then draw $y = \dfrac{40}{x}$.

x	-5	-4	-3	-2	-1	0	1	2	3	4	5
y						no value					

(c)

wall

Two sides of a rectangular yard are made by a wall. 20 m of fencing is used for the other two sides. The length of the rectangle is x.

(i)   Show that the width of the rectangle is $(20 - x)$.

(ii) Show that the area $A = 20x - x^2$.

(iii) Draw a graph of A against x for values of x from 0 to 20.

(iv) Find the length and width when $A = 70$ m^2.

(v)   Find the maximum possible area of the yard.

(vi) Write down the length and width of the yard with the maximum possible area.

11. Finding gradients of perpendicular lines

(a) Find the gradient of a line which is perpendicular to a line with a gradient of $\dfrac{-1}{4}$.

(b) Find the gradient of a line which is perpendicular to the line $5x + y = 3$.

(c) Which two lines below are perpendicular to each other?

$\boxed{x + 4y = 1}$ $\boxed{y = 4 - x}$ $\boxed{y = 4x - 3}$ $\boxed{-4x - y = 4}$

(d) Find the equation of the straight line which passes through $(12, -2)$ and is perpendicular to the line $3x - y = 2$.

1. Solve the equations   (a) $3p + 7 = 34$

    (b) $3(2q - 5) = 36$

    (c) $5r + 6 = 2r - 15$ (EDEXCEL)

2. A solution of the equation

$$x^3 + 3x^2 = 175$$

lies between $x = 4$ and $x = 5$.

Use the method of trial and improvement to find this solution.

Give your answer correct to one decimal place.

You **must** show all your trials.   (AQA)

3. The equation $x^3 + 3x = 47$

has a solution between 3 and 4.

Use a trial and improvement method to find this solution.

Give your answer correct to one decimal place.

You must show **ALL** your working.   (EDEXCEL)

4. Solve the following equation:

$$\frac{5x}{2} + \frac{3x + 1}{6} = \frac{5}{3}$$ (WJEC)

5. (a) Complete the table of values for $y = 2x + 3$

x	-2	-1	0	1	2	3
y		1	3			

   (b) Draw the graph of $y = 2x + 3$.

   (c) Use your graph to find

      (i) the value of y when $x = -1.3$

      (ii) the value of x when $y = 5.4$ (EDEXCEL)

6. (a) Complete the table of values for $y = x^2 - 2x - 2$.

x	-2	-1	0	1	2	3	4
y	6		-2			1	

   (b) Draw the graph of $y = x^2 - 2x - 2$ for values of x from -2 to 4.

   (c) Use your graph to solve the equation $x^2 - 2x - 2 = 0$.   (OCR)

7 Make q the subject of the formula

$$t = \frac{8(p + q)}{pq}$$

(EDEXCEL)

8 Make x the subject of the formula

$$y = \frac{x^2 + 4}{5}$$

(EDEXCEL)

9 The line l on the graph passes through the points A (0, 3) and B (–4, 11).

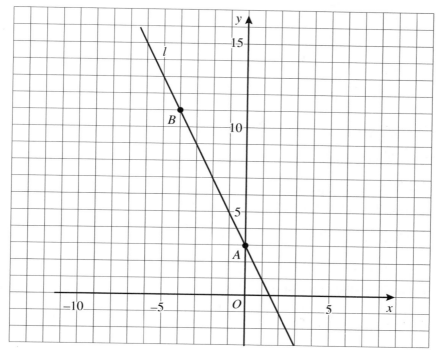

(a) Calculate the gradient of the line l.

(b) Write down the equation of the line l.

(c) Write down the equation of the line which also passes through the point (0, 3) but is perpendicular to line l.

(AQA)

10

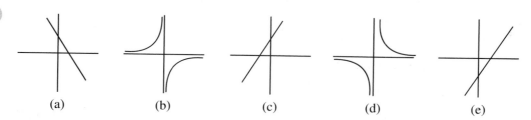

(a)　　　　(b)　　　　(c)　　　　(d)　　　　(e)

Which of the above graphs could represent the function

(i) $y = 2x + 3$　　　(ii) $y = \frac{6}{x}$

(CCEA)

11 (a) Find the equation of the straight line that passes through the points (2, –1) and (5, 8).

(b) State the gradient of a line perpendicular to the line in part (a).

(OCR)

12 (a) Complete the table of values for $y = 2x^2 - x - 3$.

x	-1.5	-1	-0.5	0	0.5	1	1.5	2
y	3		-2		-3		0	

(b) Draw the graph of $y = 2x^2 - x - 3$ for values of x from -1.5 to 2.

(c) Use your graph to solve the equation $2x^2 = x + 5$.   (AQA)

13 Rearrange this formula to make r the subject.

$$p = \frac{3(r^2 - 4)}{2}$$

(OCR)

14 You are given the formula $t = \sqrt{\dfrac{r}{s}}$.

Rearrange the formula to give r in terms of s and t.   (AQA)

15 The line L, shown is parallel to $y + 2x = 3$ and passes through the point $(0, 4)$.

(a) Write down the equation of L in the form $y = mx + c$.

(b) The line M is perpendicular to $y + 2x = 3$. Write down the gradient of the line M.

(OCR)

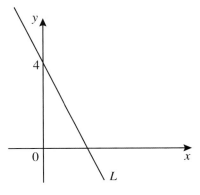

DATA 1

8

In the 'M' sections (mainly grades B, C, D) you will learn how to:

– find relative frequencies
– find probabilities
– work out 'expectation'
– list possible outcomes
– deal with mutually exclusive events including the 'OR' rule
– deal with independent events – the 'AND' rule
– use probability trees

In the 'E' sections (mainly grades A*, A) you will learn how to:

– deal with conditional probability

Also you will learn how to:

– WATCH YOUR MONEY! – electricity, gas and water

M Relative frequency

Sometimes it is useful to *estimate* the probability of something happening.

We collect data (maybe by doing an experiment). Each time the experiment is done is called a trial (eg. throwing a dice).

We use these results to estimate the chance of something happening. This estimate is called the *relative frequency*.

$$\text{Relative frequency of 'X' happening} = \frac{\text{number of times 'X' happens}}{\text{total number of trials}}$$

Maggie thinks her dice is biased (not fair). She throws the dice 600 times. The table below shows how many 3's she has in total after every 50 throws.

Number of throws	50	100	150	200	250	300	350	400	450	500	550	600
Number of 3's	22	35	45	62	75	96	105	124	144	155	165	186

$$\text{Relative frequency of throwing a '3'} = \frac{\text{number of times a '3' is thrown}}{\text{total number of throws}}$$

so after 50 throws, relative frequency of throwing a '3' = $\frac{22}{50}$ = 0.44

after 100 throws, relative frequency = $\frac{35}{100}$ = 0.35

after 150 throws, relative frequency = $\frac{45}{150}$ = 0.3

and so on.

Plot the relative frequency against the number of throws.

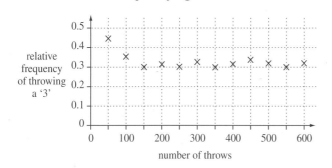

After many throws the relative frequency should settle down to a fairly constant number (around 0.31 in this example).

If the dice is fair, Maggie would expect a '3' 100 times for 600 throws ($\frac{1}{6}$ of the time).
The relative frequency of 0.31 from 186 3's strongly suggests that Maggie's dice is biased.

M8.1

1   Will thinks his dice is biased (not fair). He throws the dice 300 times. The table below shows his results.

score	1	2	3	4	5	6
frequency	51	46	47	54	53	49

(a) How many times should each number come up if the dice is fair?

(b) From Will's results, use a calculator to estimate the probability of getting a '4'.

(c) Do you think the dice is fair? Give reasons for your answer.

2   Lola keeps throwing a shoe in the air to see if it will land the 'right way up' (ie. 'laces up'). The table below shows the total number of times the shoe has landed 'laces up' after every 25 throws.

number of throws	25	50	75	100	125	150	175	200	225	250	275	300	325	350
number of 'laces up'	6	19	34	44	56	63	72	86	92	105	121	129	143	150

(a) Work out the relative frequency of the shoe landing 'laces up' after every 25 throws (round off to 2 decimal places if necessary).

(b) Plot a graph of the relative frequency of 'laces up' against the total number of throws (refer to the example before this exercise if necessary).

(c) Write down the number around which the relative frequency of 'laces up' is settling.

202

3 Four friends are using a spinner for a game and they wonder if it is perfectly fair. They each spin the spinner several times and record the results.

Name	Number of spins	Results			
		0	1	2	3
Hal	40	11	12	6	11
Rena	130	31	49	20	30
Maria	400	99	133	68	100
Ken	200	47	73	32	48

(a) Whose results are most likely to give the best estimate of the probability of getting each number?

(b) Collect together all the results into one single table. Use the table to decide whether you think the spinner is biased or unbiased.

(c) Use the results to work out the probability of getting a '3' with the spinner.

4 Do an experiment to investigate the relative frequency of an event happening. You might throw a shoe, use your own spinner (maybe biased), use a drawing pin, a biased dice or do anything that you and your teacher agree on.

(a) Do the experiment many times, working out a relative frequency after every 10, 20, 25,… trials (agree with your teacher).

(b) Plot a graph to show the relative frequency.

(c) Do the results settle down to a particular value?

Can you still?

8A **Using fractions and decimals (see Unit 1)**

Can you still?

Work out the following, leaving answers in their simplest form:

1. $\dfrac{7}{9} \times \dfrac{15}{28}$

2. $\dfrac{8}{17} \times \dfrac{13}{24} \times \dfrac{51}{39}$

3. $2\dfrac{1}{2} \times \dfrac{3}{10}$

4. $\dfrac{7}{10} + \dfrac{1}{9}$

5. $\dfrac{4}{25} + \dfrac{11}{30}$

6. $\dfrac{2}{3} - \dfrac{3}{8}$

7. 0.8×0.6

8. 0.03×0.7

9. $0.7 + 0.12$

10. Copy this square and fill in the missing numbers or symbols (+, −, ×, ÷). The arrows act as equal signs.

11. Work out $\left(\dfrac{3}{4} + \dfrac{1}{5}\right) \times \dfrac{10}{11}$

12. Work out $\left(2\dfrac{3}{4} \times 3\dfrac{1}{2}\right) - \left(1\dfrac{1}{2} \times 1\dfrac{1}{4}\right)$

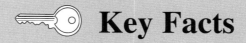

Key Facts

Probability of an event = $\dfrac{\text{the number of ways the event can happen}}{\text{the total number of possible outcomes}}$

Note

Use p (event) to mean 'probability of an event'.

Example

A bag contains 10 beads. 7 beads are green and the rest are white. If I take out one bead at random, what is the probability of taking out:

(a) a white bead

(b) a red bead

There are 3 white beads so $p(\text{white}) = \dfrac{3}{10}$

There are no red beads so $p(\text{red}) = \dfrac{0}{10} = 0$

M8.2

1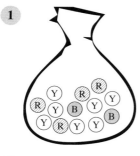

A bag contains 7 yellow discs, 4 red discs and 2 blue discs. One disc is taken out at random. What is the probability that it is:

(a) red

(b) yellow

(c) black

(d) blue

2 Billy has 9 cards as shown below:

Billy picks a card at random.

What is the probability that he picks the letter:

(a) C   (b) F   (c) a vowel

3 Rowan has a box of chocolates. There are 5 truffles, 4 toffees and 2 nuts.

Rowan picks a chocolate.

Find the probability that he chooses a:

(a) toffee   (b) truffle   (c) toffee or nut

4 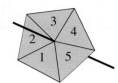 Thelma spins this spinner.

Find the probability that she gets a:

(a) 5   (b) even number   (c) odd number

5 Ten discs numbered 1, 2, 2, 2, 3, 6, 8, 9, 9, 9 are placed in a bag. One disc is selected at random. Find the probability that it is:

(a) an even number   (b) 2   (c) less than 6

6 Phil has 15 pencils in his pencil case. 7 pencils are red, 5 are blue and the rest are green. Phil takes out a pencil at random. What is the probability that he takes out:

(a) blue   (b) green   (c) red or green   (d) yellow

7 Sarah is taking part in a TV Quiz show. She must choose one box from a choice of 10 to win a prize. 4 boxes are empty, 5 boxes contain prizes for the home and 1 box has the 'star' prize.

What is the probability that Sarah will win:

(a) the 'star' prize

(b) nothing

(c) a prize for the home

8 One card is picked at random from a pack of 52.
Find the probability that it is:

(a) the Queen of clubs   (b) a red card

(c) a spade   (d) a picture card (ie. a King, Queen or Jack)

9  A bag contains 12 balls. There are 5 red, 4 white and 3 yellow.

(a) Find the probability of selecting a red ball.

(b) The 4 white balls are replaced by 4 yellow balls. Find the probability of selecting a yellow ball.

10 All the kings are removed from a pack of cards. If one card is now removed at random from the remaining cards, what is the probability of getting a:

(a) Queen   (b) black card   (c) an odd number?

11 I throw a dice once. What is the probability of getting:

(a) an odd number   (b) a multiple of 3   (c) a prime number?

12 Bag A contains 7 red discs and 4 blue discs. Bag B contains 5 blue discs and 2 red discs. Tony takes out one disc from Bag A.

(a) What is the probability that Tony takes out a blue disc?

(b) Tony removes a blue disc from Bag A and puts it in Bag B. Charlene now removes one disc from bag B. What is the probability that it is a red disc?

13 A bag contains 13 beads. x beads are yellow.

(a) How many beads are not yellow.

(b) If one bead is removed, what is the probability that it is yellow?

(c) If one bead is removed, what is the probability that it is not yellow?

14 One ball is selected from a bag containing m white balls and n green balls. What is the probability of selecting a white ball?

15 A bag contains 10 discs. x discs are red and the remaining discs are blue. y white discs are added to the bag.

(a) How many discs are there in total?

(b) How many discs are blue?

(c) If one disc is removed, what is the probability that it is blue?

M | Expectation

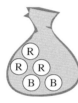

There are 3 red beads and 2 black beads in a bag. A bead is picked from this bag 75 times and replaced each time.

How many red beads would you expect to get?

probability of picking 'red' $= \dfrac{3}{5}$

expect to get $\dfrac{3}{5}$ of 75 = $(75 \div 5) \times 3 = 45$ reds

---

M8.3

1 A bag contains one white bead and 3 yellow beads. A bead is picked from the bag 80 times and replaced each time.

How many yellow beads would you expect to get?

2 A dice is thrown 180 times.

How many times would you expect to get a:

(a) 4   (b) 3   (c) even number   (d) 2 or 3

3 In a game this spinner is spun 60 times. How many wins would you expect?

4 The chance of Jim playing football in a Games lesson is $\frac{1}{4}$. There are 16 lessons in a term.

How many times will Jim expect to play football?

5 A bag contains 7 red discs, 8 black discs and 5 white discs. Sandra pulls out one at random and then puts it back. If she does this 80 times, how many times would she pick:

(a) a red disc   (b) a white disc   (c) a black disc

6 The probability that a train will arrive *on time* the next day at Swindon is 0.8. If 60 trains arrive at Swindon the next day, how many will be *on time*?

7 The probability of getting a grade C or better in an English GCSE is 0.6. If 300 young people take their English GCSE, how many would you expect to get a grade C or better?

8 Ann keeps trying her luck in the National Lottery. The probability that the first ball chosen will be hers is $\frac{6}{49}$. During one year, she plays 98 times. How many times would she expect the first ball chosen to be hers?

9 The probability of rain in November in Aberdeen is $\frac{5}{6}$. How many days would you expect it to rain in November?

10 3 in 10 cars are red.

(a) What is the probability that the next car you see on the road will be red?

(b) Of the next 5000 cars to join the M25 motorway, how many would you expect to be red?

M Listing possible outcomes

When more than one event occurs, it is usually helpful to make a list of all the possible outcomes. Use a system when making the list.

If you throw 2 coins, they could land as:

1st coin	2nd coin
head	head
head	tail
tail	head
tail	tail

There are 4 possible outcomes.

A list of all the possible outcomes is known as a **sample space**. A **sample space diagram** is a diagram or table which shows all the possible outcomes.

1 For breakfast, Ellie eats cereal or toast. She drinks juice or tea. Make a table to show *all* the different breakfasts she might have.

2 Four people, Tom, Sasha, Becky and Ronnie, work at a garage. Two people work at any one time. List *all* the possible pairs of people that could be working together at any one time.

3 Ivy throws a coin and a dice. She could get a 'head' and a '5' (H5). She could get a 'tail' and a '5'. List the 12 possible outcomes.

4 Three coins are thrown together.

(a) List *all* the possible outcomes for the three coins.

(b) What is the probability of getting 3 tails?

5 Jack has 2 spinners. He spins both spinners and adds up the numbers to get a total. For example a '4' and a '3' give a total of 7.

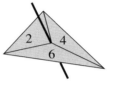 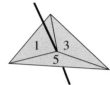

(a) Copy and complete this grid to show *all* the possible outcomes and totals.

(b) Find the probability of getting a total of 7.

+	1	3	5
2	3		
4		7	
6			

6 (a) List *all* the different ways of having had 4 children in terms of boys and girls (for example, B B G B).

(b) If it is assumed that the probability of having a boy or a girl is the same, what is the probability of having just 4 boys?

7   Here are 2 spinners. If I spin both spinners, I could get a 3 and a 9 (3, 9). List *all* the possible outcomes.

How many possible outcomes are there?

8 2 dice are thrown. The numbers are then added together to get a total.

(a) Copy and complete this grid to show all the possible outcomes and totals.

Find the probability of getting a total which is:

(b) 6

(c) an even number

(d) more than 9

(e) a square number

(f) 5 or 6

+	1	2	3	4	5	6
1						
2						
3		5				
4						
5		7				
6						

9 Four coins are thrown together.

(a) List all the possible outcomes for the four coins.

(b) What is the probability of getting:

   (i) 4 tails   (ii) 2 heads and 2 tails

  (iii) 1 head and 3 tails   (iv) *at least* 1 head

10 Calli and Pete play a game in which 2 coins and 1 dice are thrown.

Calli wins if both coins land the same and the dice gives a multiple of 3.

Pete wins if the coins land on one head and one tail as well as the dice giving a square number.

Any other outcome is a draw.

Is this game fair to both players? Give reasons for your answer.

 *Can you still?*

 *Can you still?*

8B   **Use standard form (see Unit 5)**

Write the numbers below in standard form:

1. 5140   **2.** 0.08   **3.** 0.72   **4.** 830000

5. Pair off each ordinary number and standard form number below (beware: one number has no pair):

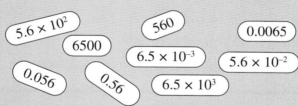

Evaluate the following, leaving your answer in standard form (*do not use a calculator*):

6. $(5 \times 10^8) \times (1.5 \times 10^4)$ **7.** $(3 \times 10^{11}) \times (6 \times 10^5)$

8. $(8 \times 10^{-14}) \div (2 \times 10^{-9})$ **9.** $(7.2 \times 10^{12}) \div (1.8 \times 10^{-6})$

10. $(5 \times 10^3) - (2 \times 10^2)$ **11.** $(8 \times 10^{19}) + (7 \times 10^{18})$

Use a calculator to evaluate the following, leaving your answer in standard form (to 3 significant figures if necessary):

12. $\dfrac{(5.2 \times 10^{26}) + (3.7 \times 10^{25})}{2.4 \times 10^{17}}$ **13.** $\dfrac{(4.3 \times 10^{-12})^2}{(5.8 \times 10^{11}) - (3.2 \times 10^{10})}$

14. Use the formula $v = at^2$ to work out v when $a = 3.1 \times 10^{-6}$ and $t = 5.5 \times 10^{-4}$. Give the answer in standard form.

15. The weekly turnover of a particular oil company is £16,780,000. What is the annual turnover (assume 1 year = 52 weeks). Give your answer in standard form.

Events are mutually exclusive if they cannot occur at the same time.

For example:

- selecting a queen }
  selecting a '3' } from the same pack of cards

- tossing a 'head'
  tossing a 'tail'

If there are no other possibilities, the sum of the probabilities of mutually exclusive events is 1

Adding probabilities ('OR' rule)

If events A and B are mutually exclusive,
$p(A \text{ } or \text{ } B) = p(A) + p(B)$

A bag contains balls which are either red, blue or yellow.

The probability of selecting a red is 0.3.

The probability of selecting a blue is 0.4.

What is the probability of selecting a yellow?

p(red or blue) = p(red) + p(blue) = 0.3 + 0.4 = 0.7

Sum of probabilities = 1

so p(yellow) = 1 – p(red or blue) = 1 – 0.7 = 0.3

M8.5

1 Which of the following pairs of events are mutually exclusive:

(a) choose a club or an ace from a pack of cards.

(b) win or lose a football match.

(c) the sun shines or it rains.

(d) wear a blue tie or brown shoes.

(e) get a '3' or a '4' on a dice.

2 Kerry has a drawer full of blue, black or red socks.
The probability of choosing blue socks is 0.5.
The probability of choosing black socks is 0.3.

(a) What is the probability of selecting blue or black socks?

(b) What is the probability of selecting red socks?

3 In a Games lesson, students play football, basketball or hockey.
The probability of playing football is 0.4.
The probability of playing basketball is 0.5.

(a) What is the probability of playing football or basketball?

(b) What is the probability of playing hockey?

4 In a football match the probability of Everton winning is 0.5. The probability of losing is 0.3. What is the probability of Everton drawing?

5 Emma has one drink for her breakfast. The table shows the probability of her choosing each drink.

tea	coffee	orange juice	grapefruit juice
0.4	x	0.3	0.1

(a) What is the probability of Emma choosing orange juice or grapefruit juice?

(b) What is the probability of Emma choosing coffee?

(c) During the month of April, how many days would you expect Emma to choose tea?

6 Terry has a selection of shirts. The table shows the probability of Terry choosing a particular shirt colour.

blue	white	yellow	red	green
0.3	0.3	0.15	x	0.05

(a) What is the probability of Terry choosing a yellow or green shirt?

(b) What is the probability of Terry choosing a red shirt?

(c) For every 50 times that Terry chooses a shirt, how many times would you expect him to choose a white shirt?

7 The probability of pulling out a Queen from a pack of cards is $\frac{1}{13}$. What is the probability of *not* pulling out a Queen?

8 4 people play a game of poker. The probability of each person winning the game is shown below in the table.

Darryl	Simon	Dan	Mark
0.35	0.25	0.25	x

(a) What is the probability of Darryl or Simon winning?

(b) What is the probability of Mark winning?

(c) If they play 60 times, how many times would you expect Dan to win?

9   Each time Cassie visits her grandfather he gives her some money. The table shows
    the probability of her getting a particular amount of money.

£2	£5	£10	£20
x	$\frac{1}{4}$	$\frac{1}{8}$	$\frac{1}{16}$

(a) Find the probability of getting £5 or £10.

(b) Find the probability of not getting £20.

(c) Find the probability of getting £2.

(d) For every 16 visits to her grandfather, how many times would Cassie expect to
    get £10?

10 It is found that in a car park the probability of a blue car is 0.2 and the probability of
    a car only having 2 doors is 0.15. If a car is chosen at random, which of the
    statements below are true?

(a) p (not 2 doors) = 0.85

(b) p (blue car or 2 doors) = 0.35

(c) p (not blue) = 0.8

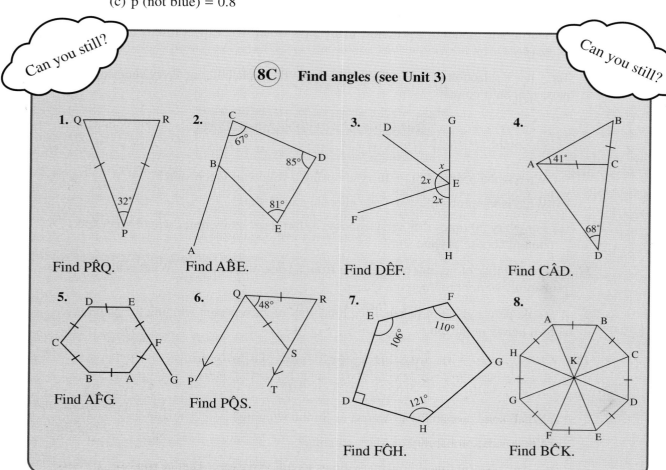

Can you still?

(8C) **Find angles (see Unit 3)**

Can you still?

1. Find PR̂Q.

2. Find AB̂E.

3. Find DÊF.

4. Find CÂD.

5. Find AF̂G.

6. Find PQ̂S.

7. Find FĜH.

8. Find BĈK.

212

Multiplying probabilities ('AND' rule)

> If events A and B are independent,
> $p(A \text{ and } B) = p(A) \times p(B)$

The probability that Jack walks to work is $\frac{1}{4}$.

The probability that Jack catches the bus to go home is $\frac{3}{5}$.

What is the probability that one day Jack does *not* walk to work and returns home by bus.

p(not walk and bus home to work) = p(not walk to work) × p(bus home)

$$= \frac{3}{4} \times \frac{3}{5}$$

$$= \frac{9}{20}$$

M8.6

1 A coin and a dice are thrown. Find the probability of getting 'tails' on the coin and a '4' on the dice.

2 A coin and a dice are thrown. Find the probability of getting tails on the coin and an even number on the dice.

3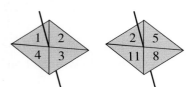
These two spinners are spun. What is the probability of getting:

(a) a '1' and an '8'?

(b) two odd numbers?

4 A card is taken from a pack of playing cards and a coin is thrown. What is the probability of obtaining:

(a) the King of Hearts and a 'head' on the coin?

(b) a picture card (J, Q or K) and 'tails' on the coin?

5 A bag contains 3 red beads and 5 green beads. If I remove one bead at random, replace it then take another bead, what is the probability that:

(a) both beads are red?

(b) both beads are green?

6 If a dice is thrown three times, what is the probability of obtaining three sixes?

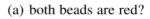

7 A card is taken from a pack of cards, replaced then another card is taken. What is the probability that:

(a) both cards are Kings?

(b) both cards are red?

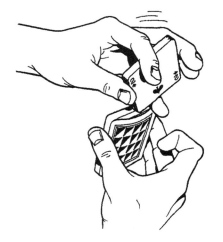

8

Each letter above is written on a card. The cards are shuffled and a card is chosen randomly. The card is replaced then another card is taken. What is the probability that:

(a) both cards are the letter 'C'?

(b) both cards are the letter 'I'?

(c) both cards are vowels?

9 The probability that Sam has toast for breakfast is 0.3. The probability that he has a cup of tea with his breakfast is 0.8.

On Tuesday morning what is the probability that Sam has:

(a) toast and tea?

(b) toast and no tea?

(c) no toast and no tea?

10 If a coin is thrown six times, what is the probability that the coin will land on tails each time?

11

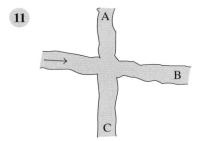

Every day Megan takes her dog for a walk. She always reaches a crossroads and has three choices of route. The probability of taking route A, B or C is equal.

On Monday to Friday, what is the probability that she takes route C everyday?

12 A bag contains 7 white beads and 4 green beads. If I remove one bead at random, replace it then take another bead, what is the probability that:

(a) both beads are green?

(b) one bead is white and one bead is green (*in any order*)?

A bag contains 4 yellow balls and 3 blue balls. One ball is removed at random then replaced. Another ball is then removed.

When a ball is removed, there are two possible outcomes, yellow or blue. These are represented by two branches.

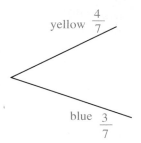

The probability of each event happening is written on the branch.

After the ball is replaced, another ball is removed still with two possible outcomes. Two more branches are needed following each set of previous branches.

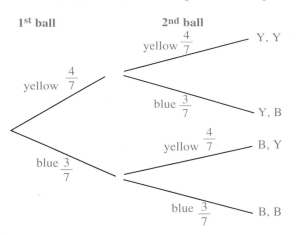

This tree diagram shows all the possible outcomes. If we want the probability of getting one ball of each colour, we can see that there are two ways this can happen, Y, B or B, Y.

The probability of an outcome is found by multiplying together the possibilities on the branches leading to that outcome.

$$p(Y, B) = \frac{4}{7} \times \frac{3}{7} = \frac{12}{49}$$

$$p(B, Y) = \frac{3}{7} \times \frac{4}{7} = \frac{12}{49}$$

The probability of getting one ball of each colour is P(Y, B or B, Y). 'Y, B' and 'B, Y' are mutually exclusive so add the probabilities.

$$p(Y, B \text{ or } B, Y) = p(Y, B) + p(B, Y)$$

$$= \frac{12}{49} + \frac{12}{49}$$

$$p(\text{one of each colour}) = \frac{24}{49}$$

1 A bag contains 8 green beads and 3 blue beads. One bead is removed at random then replaced. Another bead is then removed.
(a) Copy and complete the tree diagram to show all the outcomes.

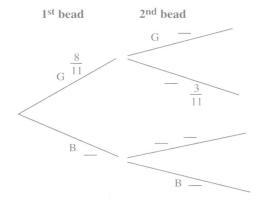

1st bead   2nd bead

Find the probability that:

(b) both beads are green.

(c) the first bead is blue and the second bead is green.

2 A bag contains 7 red discs and 5 green discs. One disc is removed at random then replaced. Another disc is then removed.

(a) Copy and complete the tree diagram to show all the outcomes.

Find the probability that:

(b) both discs are red.

(c) both discs are green.

(d) one disc is red and one disc is green (*in any order*).

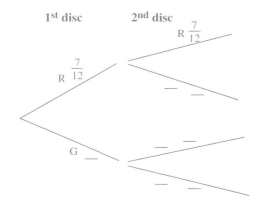

1st disc   2nd disc

3 A bag contains 15 balls, 7 of which are blue. The remaining balls are white. One ball is removed at random then replaced. Another ball is then removed.
(a) Draw a tree diagram to show all the outcomes.

Find the probability that:

(b) both balls are blue.

(c) there is one ball of each colour.

4 The probability of Roger eating 'Vital' flakes for breakfast is 0.6 or else he has a 'fry-up'.

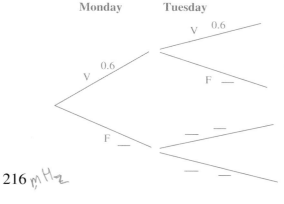

Monday   Tuesday

(a) Copy and complete the tree diagram showing what he eats for breakfast on Monday and Tuesday mornings (Use 'V' for 'Vital' flakes and 'F' for 'fry-up').

Find the probability that:

(b) Roger has a 'fry-up' on both mornings.

(c) He has 'Vital' flakes one morning and a fry-up on the other morning.

5 3 out of 10 children in a primary school are blonde haired. The tree diagram below shows the hair colour of the first child to get onto the playground on a Wednesday morning and a Thursday morning.

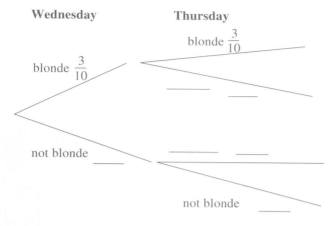

Wednesday   Thursday

blonde $\frac{3}{10}$

blonde $\frac{3}{10}$

not blonde

blonde $\frac{3}{10}$

not blonde

(a) Copy and complete the tree diagram.

Find the probability that:

(b) on both mornings the first child out has blonde hair.

(c) the first child out has blonde hair one morning and not blonde hair on the other morning.

6 A card is taken at random from a pack of cards then replaced. Another card is then taken. Draw a tree diagram to help you find the probability that:

(a) both cards are Queens.

(b) one card is a Queen and the other is not.

A card is taken at random from a pack of cards then replaced. This is done 3 times in total. What is the probability of getting

(a) no clubs

(b) *at least* one club

(a) p(no clubs) = p(not club) × p(not club) × p(not club)

$$= \frac{3}{4} \times \frac{3}{4} \times \frac{3}{4} = \frac{27}{64}$$

(b) p(*at least* one club) = 1 − p(no clubs) = $1 - \frac{27}{64}$

$$= \frac{64}{64} - \frac{27}{64} = \frac{37}{64}$$

---

7 A coin is thrown three times.

(a) Draw a tree diagram to show all outcomes.

Find the probability that the coin lands showing:

(b) 3 'heads'.

(c) *at least* one 'tail'.

(d) exactly 2 'heads' and one 'tail'.

8 A bag contains 3 red beads and 5 yellow beads. One bead is removed at random then replaced.

This is done three times in total.

(a) Draw a tree diagram to show all the outcomes.

Find the probability that:

(b) each bead is red.

(c) exactly two beads are red and one bead is yellow.

(d) *at least* one bead is red.

9 The probability of a successful heart operation is 0.7. On a particular day, 3 patients have the heart operation.

(a) Draw a tree diagram to show all outcomes.

Find the probability that:

(b) all three operations are successful.

(c) *at least* one operation is successful.

(d) exactly two operations are successful.

10 Chloe and Ellie play each other at tennis, badminton and squash. The probability of Chloe winning at tennis is 30%, at badminton is 50% and at squash is 60%.

Draw a tree diagram to help you find the probability that:

(a) Chloe wins all 3 games.

(b) Chloe wins exactly one game.

(c) Chloe wins *at least* one game.

11 The probability of Dave passing his driving test is $\frac{2}{3}$.

(a) Copy and complete this tree diagram.

Find the probability that:

(b) Dave passes at the second attempt.

(c) Dave passes at the third attempt.

(d) Dave passes within three tests.

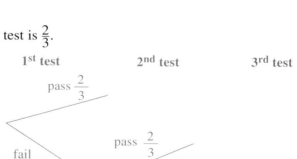

12 A dice is thrown three times. Find the probability that the dice lands on:

(a) *at least* one 5.

(b) exactly two 5's.

'Conditional probability' is when the probability of an event happening is *dependent* on the outcome of another event.

For example, if a ball is removed from a bag and not replaced then the probability for the next ball being removed will be affected.

Note

For all the questions that follow, using a tree diagram is often sensible but not always essential.

Two cards are taken at random from a pack of cards. Find the probability that:

(a) both cards are Kings

(b) at least one card is a King

(c) exactly one card is a King

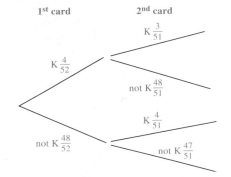

1st card   **2nd card**

K $\frac{4}{52}$ K $\frac{3}{51}$

not K $\frac{48}{51}$

not K $\frac{48}{52}$ K $\frac{4}{51}$

not K $\frac{47}{51}$

Note

Only 51 cards left in the pack when the 2nd card is removed.

The first branch that has been followed determines how many cards of each type are left in the pack before the 2nd card is removed.

(a) p (K, K) = p (K) × p (K) = $\dfrac{\overset{1}{\cancel{4}}}{\underset{13}{\cancel{52}}} \times \dfrac{\overset{1}{\cancel{3}}}{\underset{17}{\cancel{51}}} = \dfrac{1}{221}$

(b) p (no Kings) = $\dfrac{\overset{\overset{4}{\cancel{12}}}{\cancel{48}}}{\underset{13}{\cancel{52}}} \times \dfrac{47}{\underset{17}{\cancel{51}}} = \dfrac{188}{221}$

p (at least one K) = 1 − p (no K) = $1 - \dfrac{188}{221} = \dfrac{33}{221}$

(c) p (exactly one K) = p (K, not K) or p (not K, K)

$$= \left(\frac{4}{52} \times \frac{48}{51} \right) + \left(\frac{48}{52} \times \frac{4}{51} \right)$$

$$= \frac{16}{221} + \frac{16}{221} = \frac{32}{221}$$

1 A bag contains 9 red balls and 4 white balls. Two balls are taken out at random, one at a time, without replacement.

(a) Copy and complete the tree diagram.

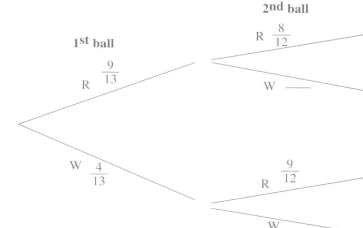

Find the probability that:

(b) both balls are white

(c) exactly one ball is white

2 A box contains 6 packets of plain crisps and 5 packets of cheese and onion crisps. Two packets of crisps are removed at random, one at a time, without replacement.

(a) Using 'P' for plain crisps and 'C' for cheese and onion crisps, draw a tree diagram to show all outcomes.

Find the probability that:

(b) both packets are plain.

(c) there is one packet of each flavour.

3 A packet contains 10 toffees (T) and 5 mints (M). Two sweets are removed at random.

(a) Draw a tree diagram to show all outcomes.

Find the probability that:

(b) both sweets are mints.

(c) there is one toffee and one mint.

4 Lewis has 6 black socks and 10 blue socks in a bag. He takes out two socks randomly.

Find the probability that:

(a) both socks are blue.

(b) both socks are the same colour.

(c) there is one sock of each colour.

220

5 A box contains 6 blue balls and 4 white balls. Three balls are taken out at random, one at a time, without replacement.

(a) Copy and complete the tree diagram.

Find the probability that:

(b) all three balls are white

(c) *at least* one ball is blue

(d) exactly two balls are blue and one ball is white

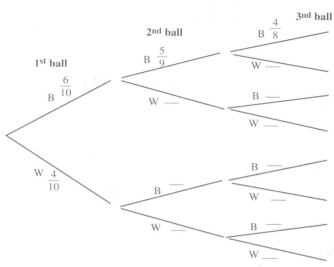

6 There are 10 boys and 15 girls in a class. Three children are chosen at random.

(a) Draw a tree diagram to show all outcomes.

Find the probability that:

(b) all three children are girls.

(c) exactly one child is a girl.

(d) *at least* one child is a boy.

7 Joshua buys a box of 12 eggs. Three of the eggs are cracked (C) and nine are good (G). Three eggs are chosen at random.

(a) Draw a tree diagram to show all outcomes.

Find the probability that:

(b) all three eggs are good.

(c) exactly two eggs are good.

(d) *at least* one egg is good.

8 Three cards are taken at random from a pack of cards. Find the probability that:

(a) all three cards are red.

(b) *at least* one card is red.

(c) exactly two cards are red.

9 15 counters are in a bag of which 5 are green, 4 are blue and 6 are red. Two counters are taken out, one after the other, without replacement.

(a) Draw a tree diagram to show all outcomes.

Find the probability that:

(b) *at least* one counter is green.

(c) the two counters are different colours.

10 A group of 2 women and 4 men are going to travel in two taxis. Each taxi can only take three people. What is the probability that the first taxi will take 2 women and 1 man?

11 A bag contains 20 balls. n balls are red and the remainder are green. Two balls are removed at random. What is the probability, in terms of n, of removing:

(a) two red balls?

(b) at least one green ball?

12 A basket of fruit contains x peaches and y nectarines. Two pieces of fruit are taken at random. What is the probability, in terms of x and y, of taking:

(a) two peaches

(b) one peach and one nectarine

60% of the population of a certain town are vaccinated against flu. The probability of someone getting the flu given that they have had the vaccination is 0.2 but the probability of someone getting flu given that they have not had the vaccination is 0.7.

(a) Draw a tree diagram to represent the above information.

(b) Find the probability that a person chosen at random gets flu.

(a)

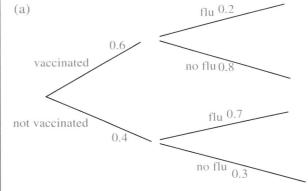

(b) p (flu)

     = p(vaccinated, flu) or p(not vaccinated, flu)

     = $(0.6 \times 0.2) + (0.4 \times 0.7)$

     = $0.12 + 0.28 = 0.4$

E8.2

1 Jack is late 60% of the time when it is raining and 30% of the time when it is dry. It rains on 25% of days.

(a) Draw a tree diagram to represent the above information.

Find the probability that:

(b) It is raining and he is late.

(c) He is late.

2 The probability of a speed camera being on is 0.75. If the camera is on, the probability that a speeding driver will be caught is 0.4. If the camera is off then the probability of a speeding driver being caught is 0.1.

(a) Copy and complete the tree diagram.

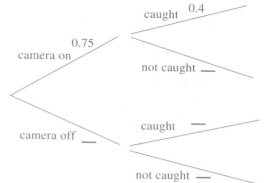

(b) Find the probability that a speeding driver does not get caught.

3 A football team plays 45% of its matches at home. The probability of winning a match given that it is at home is 0.7. The probability of winning a match given that it is away is 0.6.

(a) Draw a tree diagram to represent the above information.

(b) Find the probability that the team does not win a match.

4 The probability of there being road works on Ronnie's way to work is 15%. If there are road works then the probability of Ronnie being late to work is 80%, otherwise it is 40%.

(a) Draw a tree diagram to represent the above information (with road works first).

(b) Find the probability that, on a day chosen at random, he was late.

5 The probability of a motorist being in an accident on a Saturday night given that he is over the legal alcohol limit is 0.1. The probability of being involved in an accident on a Saturday night given that he is not over the legal limit is 0.02. In a certain town it is estimated that 5% of the motorists on the road on a Saturday night are over the limit.

(a) Draw a tree diagram to represent the above information.

(b) Find the probability that a randomly chosen motorist will be involved in an accident.

6 30% of items in an antique shop are fakes. The probability of an expert declaring an item to be fake given that it is genuine is 0.1 and the probability of him declaring an item to be genuine given that it is a fake is 0.05.

(a) Draw a tree diagram to represent the above information.

(b) Find the probability that an item will be declared genuine.

7 The probability that a woman misses her train to work in the morning if she does not get at least 6 hours sleep the night before is $\frac{3}{5}$, otherwise the probability that she misses it is only $\frac{1}{5}$. The probability that she does not get at least 6 hours sleep the night before is $\frac{1}{9}$.

(a) Use a tree diagram to represent this information.

(b) Find the probability that she misses the train.

8 The probability that Mindy forgets her calculator on Monday is $\frac{1}{4}$. If she forgets her calculator on Monday then the probability that she forgets it on Tuesday is $\frac{1}{5}$. If she does *not* forget it on Monday, the probability that she forgets it on Tuesday is $\frac{1}{2}$.

Find the probability that she forgets her calculator on just one of these days.

9 Wes and Gill shoot at a target. Wes fires first and the probability that he hits the target is $\frac{3}{4}$. Gill fires next and the probability of her hitting the target given that Wes hit the target is $\frac{2}{5}$. The probability of Gill hitting the target given that Wes missed the target is $\frac{4}{5}$.

Find the probability that of least one of them hits the target.

10 Box A contains 4 blue counters and 3 white counters. Box B contains 3 blue counters and 5 white counters.

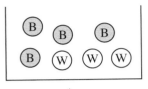

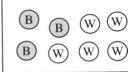

A   B

Lauren takes a counter randomly from box A and puts it in box B. She then takes a counter randomly from box B and puts it in box A. What is the probability that each box then has the original number of counters of each colour?

11 The probability of a pupil from a certain school getting an A* in Maths is 0.8. 56% of pupils get an A* in both Maths and French.

(a) Draw a tree diagram (with Maths before French) with as much information as possible on it.

(b) Find the probability that the pupil gets an A* in Maths but not in French.

It is also known that 68% of pupils get an A* in French.

(c) Find the probability of getting an A* in French but not in Maths.

(d) Complete the tree diagram fully.

12 A box contains n chocolates. 6 of the chocolates are soft-centred. Two chocolates are chosen at random. The probability that the two chocolates are soft-centred is $\frac{1}{3}$.

(a) Form an equation involving n and show that it simplifies to $n^2 - n - 90 = 0$.

(b) Find how many chocolates were in the box originally.

13 A bag contains n red beads and 5 blue beads. Two beads are taken randomly from the bag. The probability that the two beads are both red is $\frac{1}{6}$.

(a) Form an equation involving n and show that it simplifies to $n^2 - 3n - 4 = 0$.

(b) Find how many red beads were originally in the bag?

14 A bag contains 9 counters. n counters are yellow and the rest of the counters are blue. Two counters are taken randomly from the bag. The probability of the first counter removed being yellow and the second counter being blue is $\frac{5}{18}$.

(a) Form an equation involving n and show that it simplifies to $n^2 - 9n + 20 = 0$.

(b) Given that there are more yellow counters than blue, how many yellow counters were there originally?

Some people say 'you don't get 'owt for n'owt in this life'. Most things have to be paid for and that includes the electricity, gas and water you use in your home.

The amount of electricity, gas (and water in some homes) used is recorded on a **meter**. The meter is read every 3 months and a bill is sent. An electricity bill could look like the one below.

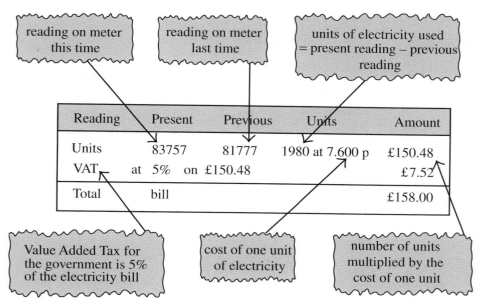

Reading	Present	Previous	Units	Amount
Units	83757	81777	1980 at 7.600 p	£150.48
VAT	at 5% on £150.48			£7.52
Total	bill			£158.00

reading on meter this time

reading on meter last time

units of electricity used = present reading – previous reading

Value Added Tax for the government is 5% of the electricity bill

cost of one unit of electricity

number of units multiplied by the cost of one unit

Payment

Some people simply pay their bill when it arrives, other people arrange to pay part of their bill each month. They are often given a small discount if they arrange to pay the bill each month.

Ally has received his electricity bill:

present reading = 61982   previous reading = 60732

cost of one unit of electricity = 7.6 p.

VAT is 5%.

How much does Ally have to pay?

units used = present – previous = 61982 – 60732 = 1250

cost of units = 1250 × 7.6 p = 9500 p = £ 95.00

$VAT = 5\% \text{ of } £ 95.00 = \dfrac{5}{100} × 95.00 = £ 4.75$

Total bill = £ 99.75

1 Nerys has received her electricity bill:

present reading = 53164   previous reading = 51083

cost of one unit of electricity = 9.3 p.

Copy and complete the bill below:

units used = present – previous = 53164 – ☐ = ☐

cost of units = ☐ × 9.3 p = ☐ p = £ ☐

VAT = 5% of £ ☐ = $\frac{5}{100}$ × ☐ = £ ☐

Total bill   = £

Work out the cost of each electricity bill below. VAT is payable at 5% each time.

Bill	present reading	previous reading	cost of one unit of electricity
2	81659	80292	8.3 p
3	23748	22095	7.6 p
4	5186	4417	7.6 p
5	63746	62640	9.4 p
6	9187	8089	8.2 p
7	5613	4688	11.4 p
8	71248	69325	7.9 p

9 During one year Marvin has bills of £138.17, £168.24, £171.38 and £138.21. He pays the bills in 12 *equal* monthly instalments. He is given a £40 discount *each year* for paying monthly. How much does Marvin have to pay *each month?*

10 How much is paid for electricity, gas and water in your home? Find out. Get a 'feel' for how much these bills are before its your turn to pay!

TEST YOURSELF ON UNIT 8

1. Working out 'expectation'

(a) This pointer is spun 60 times. How many times would you expect it to point to:

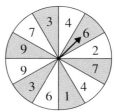

   (i) 2

   (ii) an even number

   (iii) a square number

(b) A dice is thrown 270 times. How many times would you expect to get a:

   (i) 2   (ii) a multiple of 2   (iii) a 5 or 6

226

Ravi keeps throwing a button in the air to see which way up it will land the most. The table below shows the total number of times the button landed with its most curved surface showing after every 50 throws.

number of throws	50	100	150	200	250	300	350	400	450	500	550	600	650	700
number of times the curved surface is showing	23	58	93	136	170	186	210	252	288	310	352	378	416	448

(a) Work out the relative frequency of the button landing with its most curved surface showing after every 50 throws.

(b) Plot a graph of the relative frequency of 'curved surface showing' against the total number of throws.

(c) Write down the number around which the relative frequency of 'curved surface showing' is settling.

(d) If the button was thrown 2000 times, estimate how many times the button would land with its most curved surface showing.

3. Finding probabilities

(a) Fiona has 8 cards as shown below:

Fiona picks a card at random.

What is the probability that she picks the letter:

(i) B   (ii) E   (iii) R   (iv) a vowel

(b) 12 discs numbered 1, 2, 3, 3, 5, 6, 6, 8, 9, 9, 10, 15 are placed in a bag. One disc is selected at random. Find the probability that it is:

(i) a prime number   (ii) 6   (iii) a multiple of 3

4. Listing possible outcomes

(a) Cath has to choose some of her school subjects from the option blocks below:

A	B	C
French	History	Art
Latin	Geography	Dt
Spanish		

(i) She must choose one subject from column A, one from column B and one from column C. List all the different groups of choices she could make (combinations).

(ii) How many combinations are there?

(b) Kyron throws a dice and spins the spinner shown opposite. He adds up the numbers to get a total.

(i) Copy and complete this grid to show *all* the possible outcomes and totals.

(ii) Find the probability of getting a total of 8.

(iii) Find the probability of getting a total which is a prime number.

+	1	2	3	4
1				
2				
3			5	
4				
5	6			
6				

5. Dealing with mutually exclusive events including the 'OR' rule

(a) A bag contains balls which are either white, green or blue.

The probability of selecting a white ball is $\frac{1}{3}$.

The probability of selecting a green ball is $\frac{1}{2}$.

(i) What is the probability of selecting a white *or* green ball?

(ii) What is the probability of selecting a blue ball?

(b) Gwen likes a wide range of music. The table below shows the probability of Gwen listening to a particular type of music.

rock	opera	jazz	classical
0.5	0.15	x	0.05

(i) What is the probability of Gwen listening to opera *or* classical music?

(ii) What is the probability of Gwen listening to jazz?

(iii) For the next 50 times that Gwen listens to music, how many times would you expect her to listen to rock music?

6. Dealing with independent events – the 'AND' rule

(a) A dice is thrown and a card is taken from a pack of playing cards. What is the probability of obtaining:

(i) a '3' on the dice and a black card?

(ii) an even number on the dice and a Queen?

(b) A coin is thrown five times. What is the probability that the coin will land on 'heads' each time?

7. Using probability trees

(a) A bag contains 8 strawberry chews (S) and 3 blackcurrant chews (B). One chew is taken at random then replaced. Another chew is then removed.

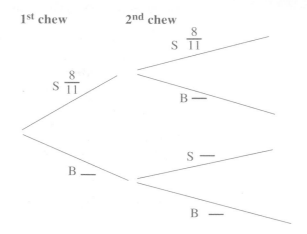

1st chew   2nd chew

(i) Copy and complete the tree diagram to show all the outcomes.

Find the probability that:

(ii) both chews are blackcurrant.

(iii) one chew is strawberry and one chew is blackcurrant

(b) The probability of Alan eating meat on any day is 0.6.

(i) Draw a tree diagram to show the probabilities of Alan eating meat on Tuesday, Wednesday and Thursday.

Find the probability that:

(ii) Alan eats meat on all three days

(iii) he does not eat meat on *at least* one day

(iv) he eats meat on exactly two days

8. Dealing with conditional probability

(a) Five yellow balls and three red balls are placed in a bag and two balls are removed, one at a time, without replacement.

(i) Draw a tree diagram to represent the above information.

Find the probability that:

(ii) both balls are red.

(iii) both balls are the same colour.

(iv) *at least* one ball is red.

(b) A hockey team play 45% of its matches at home. It wins 30% of its away matches and 60% of its home matches.

(i) Draw a tree diagram to represent the above information.

(ii) Find the probability that a match chosen randomly from the results sheet at the end of the season was won.

1 Year 9 students can choose some subjects to take in Year 10.
They must choose **either** French **or** Spanish.
They must also choose **either** Geography **or** History.

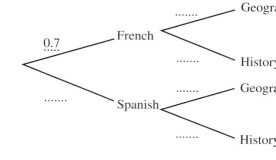

In 2002 70% of the students chose French and 60% of the students chose Geography.

(a) Complete this tree diagram.

(b) Work out the probability that a student picked at random chose

  (i) French and Geography

  (ii) French and Geography **or** Spanish and History.

In 2003 there will be 200 Year 9 students.

(c) Use the information for 2002 to work out an estimate for the number of Year 9 students who will **not** chose French and Geography in 2003.   (EDEXCEL)

2 On his route to work Robin drives through two sets of traffic lights.
The traffic lights operate independently.
The probability that he has to stop at the first set of lights is 0.4.
The probability that he has to stop at the second set of lights is 0.7.

(a) Find the probability that on the given day Robin stops at just one set of lights on his route to work.

(b) The operation of the traffic lights is changed so that they are NOT independent.
The probability that Robin has to stop at the first set of lights is now 0.3.
If he has to stop at the first set of lights the probability that he has to stop at the second is 0.9.
If he does not have to stop at the first set of lights the probability that he stops at the second is 0.2.

Find the probability that on the given day Robin has to stop at just one set of lights on his route to work.   (OCR)

3 A bag contains 2 red, 4 green and 6 white sweets.
The sweets are identical apart from colour and flavour. Jill randomly chooses a sweet from the bag, then Jack randomly chooses a sweet from those remaining in the bag.

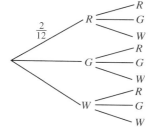

(a) Complete the tree diagram below.

(b) Find the probability that they chose sweets of the same colour.   (WJEC)

4 Jack has two fair dice.

One of the dice has 6 faces numbered from 1 to 6.
The other dice has 4 faces numbered from 1 to 4.

Jack is going to throw the two dice.
He will add the scores on the two dice to get the total.

Work out the probability that he will get

(i) a total of 7,

(ii) a total of less than 5.

(EDEXCEL)

5 The cards used in a game each have either a square, a triangle, a circle or a diamond printed on them.

(a) The table shows the probabilities of choosing some of these shapes.

Outcome	Square	Triangle	Circle	Diamond
Probabiltiy	0.3	0.2	0.35	

Complete the table.

(b) The cards are either blue or red.
There are three times as many blue cards as red cards.
What is the probability that the card drawn is blue?

(OCR)

6 A bag contains ten counters.
Four of the counters are red.
In an experiment, three counters are taken from the bag at random and put in a box.

(a) Calculate the probability that there are **exactly two** red counters in the box.

The same experiment is carried out 600 times.

(b) How many times would your expect there to be **at least two** red counters in the box?

(AQA)

7 A bag of sweets contains 5 toffees, 3 chocolates and 2 mints.
Emma and Sophie each pick one sweet at random.
What is the probability that they pick sweets of the same kind?

(AQA)

8

The letters of the word PROTRACTOR are written on ten cards, one letter on each card. The cards are shuffled and placed face down.

(a) One card is chosen at random.
What is the probability that the letter on the card is
(i) T, (ii) a vowel, (vowels are A, E, I, O, U, the rest are consonants) (iii) M?

The card is replaced and all the cards reshuffled.

(b) Two cards are now chosen at random, one after the other without replacement. What is the probability that the letters on the two cards are

   (i) a vowel and a consonant?

(c) Another word contains five vowels. As before, the letters of the word are written on cards and two cards are chosen at random without replacement from this new set.

   The probability of obtaining two consonants is $\frac{1}{6}$.

   (i) Letting x equal the number of consonants in the word, form an equation involving x and show that it simplifies to $x^2 - 3x - 4 = 0$.

   (ii) Hence calculate the number of letters in the word.   (CCEA)

9   (a) (i) Factorise $2x^2 - 35x + 98$ (ii) Solve the equation $2x^2 - 35x + 98 = 0$

A bag contains $(n + 7)$ tennis balls.
n of the balls are yellow.
The other 7 balls are white.

John will take at random a ball from the bag.
He will look at its colour and then put it back in the bag.

(b) (i) Write down an expression, in terms of n, for the probability that John will take a white ball.

Bill states that the probability that John will take a white ball is $\frac{2}{5}$

   (ii) Prove that Bill's statement cannot be correct.

After John has put the ball back into the bag, Mary will take at random a ball from the bag.
She will note its colour.

(c) Given that the probability that John and Mary will take balls with **different** colours is $\frac{4}{9}$,

   prove that $2n^2 - 35n + 98 = 0$

(d) Using your answer to part (a) (ii) or otherwise, calculate the probability that John and Mary will both take white balls.   (EDEXCEL)

In the 'M' sections (mainly grades B, C, D) you will learn how to:

- use reflection symmetry and rotational symmetry
- identify planes of symmetry
- translate shapes
- reflect shapes in mirror lines
- rotate shapes
- enlarge shapes

In the 'E' sections (mainly grades A*, A) you will learn how to:

- enlarge with negative scale factors
- prove that triangles are congruent

Also you will learn how to:

- – credit 1 – hire purchase

M **Symmetry**

🔑 Key Facts

Rotational symmetry

A shape has rotational symmetry if it fits onto itself when rotated (turned) before it gets back to its starting position.

This shape fits onto itself three times when rotated through a complete turn. It has rotational symmetry of **order three**.

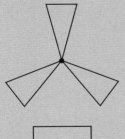

If a shape can only fit onto itself in its starting position, it has rotational symmetry of **order one**.

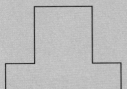

1 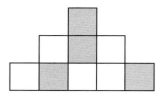 Copy this shape and shade two more squares so that it has a line of symmetry.

2 Sketch these shapes and draw on all the lines of symmetry.

(a) 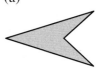 (b) 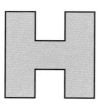 (c) 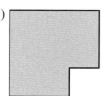 (d)

(e) (f) 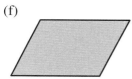 (g) (h)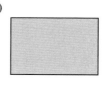

3 For each shape below write down the order of rotational symmetry (use tracing paper if you wish).

(a) (b) (c)  (d)

(e) (f) (g) (h)

(i) (j) (k) (l)

(m) (n) (o) (p)

234

Key Facts

A plane of symmetry divides a 3-D shape into two identical halves. One half must be a mirror image of the other half.

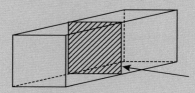

A plane of symmetry must be shown fully as a clear slice through the 3-D shape. Each half of the cuboid on each side of the plane of symmetry is symmetrical.

Note: A 3-D shape may have more than one plane of symmetry.

M9.2

1 Draw each shape below and show one plane of symmetry.

(a)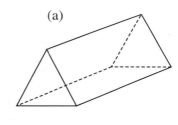

(b)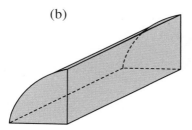

(c)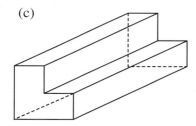

2 Write down how many planes of symmetry each shape below has.

(a)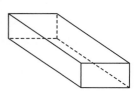

(b)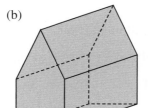

(c)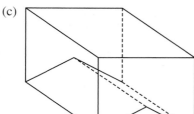

3 Name a 3D-shape which has 9 planes of symmetry.

4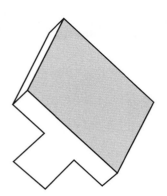

The plane of symmetry of a 3D-shape is shown shaded. Half of the 3D-shape is also shown.

Draw the complete 3D-shape.

5 Draw a solid of your own design which has 3 planes of symmetry *only*.

Can you still?

9A **Use products of prime factors (see Unit 5)**

Can you still?

Copy and complete the boxes below:

1.

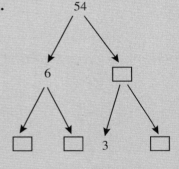

$54 = \boxed{} \times \boxed{} \times \boxed{} \times \boxed{}$

2.
```
   □)220
   □)110
   5)55
   □)□
      1
```

$220 = \boxed{} \times \boxed{} \times \boxed{} \times \boxed{}$

3. $1400 = 2^p \times 5^q \times r$. Find the values of p, q and r.

4. Express 210 as the product of its prime factors.

5. Express 336 as the product of its prime factors.

6. Use your answers to questions **4** and **5** to find the Highest Common Factor of 210 and 336.

7. Use your answers to questions **4** and **5** to find the Lowest Common Multiple of 210 and 336.

8. Use products of prime factors to find the HCF and LCM of 165 and 345.

9. Use prime factor decomposition to find the HCF and LCM of 252 and 468.

Key Facts

A 'translation' means 'movement in a straight line' (no turning)

To describe a translation, we do not have to use the words 'left', 'right', 'up' and 'down'. We use a vertical bracket like this:

$\begin{pmatrix} 4 \\ 6 \end{pmatrix}$ The top number '4' means 'move 4 units to the right'   ('−4' means 4 to the left)

The bottom number '6' means 'move 6 units up'   ('−6' means '6 down')

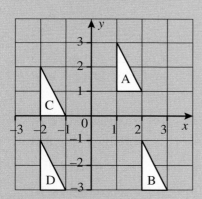

Use translation vectors to describe the following translations.

(a) A to B   (b) A to C   (c) A to D   (d) B to C

(a) $\begin{pmatrix} 1 \\ -4 \end{pmatrix}$ (b) $\begin{pmatrix} -3 \\ -1 \end{pmatrix}$ (c) $\begin{pmatrix} -3 \\ -4 \end{pmatrix}$ (d) $\begin{pmatrix} -4 \\ 3 \end{pmatrix}$

M9.3

1

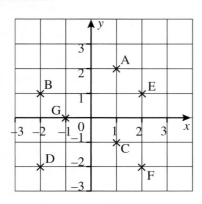

Use translation vectors to describe the following translations.

(a) A to B   (b) A to F

(c) A to G   (d) B to C

(e) F to G   (f) D to G

(g) E to B   (h) B to F

2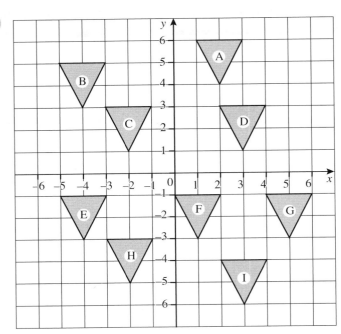

Use translation vectors to describe the following translations.

(a) A to D   (b) A to G

(c) A to H   (d) A to I

(e) B to E   (f) B to H

(g) C to D   (h) C to A

(i) C to E   (j) D to B

(k) D to H   (l) E to G

(m) E to D   (n) F to C

(o) G to I   (p) G to B

(q) H to D   (r) I to C

3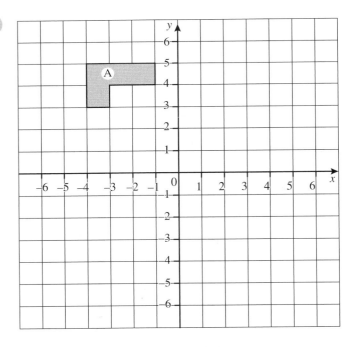

Copy the grid opposite and draw shape A as shown.

(a) Translate shape A through $\binom{5}{1}$. Label the new shape B.

(b) Translate shape B through $\binom{2}{-3}$. Label the new shape C.

(c) Translate shape C through $\binom{-2}{-5}$. Label the new shape D.

(d) Translate shape D through $\binom{-4}{4}$. Label the new shape E.

(e) Translate shape E through $\binom{-3}{-5}$. Label the new shape F.

(f) Use a translation vector to describe the translation that moves shape E to shape B.

(g) Use a translation vector to describe the translation that moves shape A to shape F.

(h) Use a translation vector to describe the translation that moves shape D to shape B.

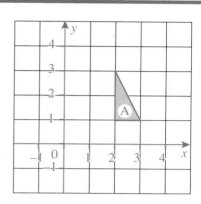

(a) Reflect triangle A in the line $x = 1$. Label the image (new triangle) B.

(b) Reflect triangle A in the line $y = x + 1$. Label the image C.

(a)

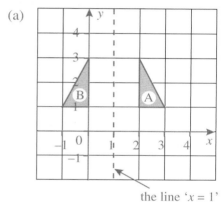

the line '$x = 1$'

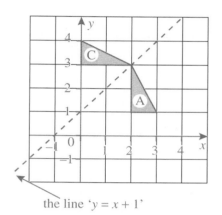

the line '$y = x + 1$'

M9.4

Draw each shape below and reflect in the mirror line.

1
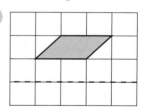

2
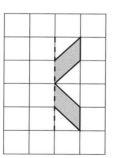

3
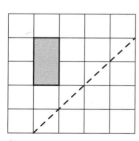

4
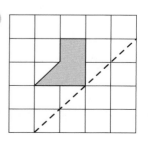

5
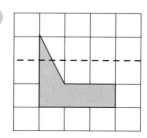

6
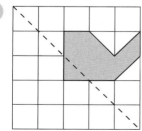

239

7

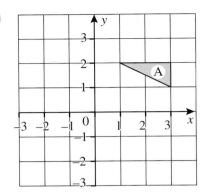

Copy the grid and shape opposite.

(a) Reflect triangle A in the y-axis. Label the image (new triangle) B.

(b) Reflect triangle A in the x-axis. Label the image C.

(c) Reflect triangle C in the y-axis. Label the image D.

(d) Describe how you could *transform* (change) triangle D into triangle B.

8

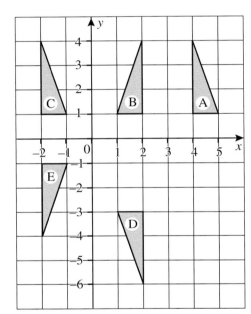

For each pair of triangles below, write down the equation of the *line of reflection*.

(a) A to B

(b) B to C

(c) B to D

(d) C to E

9 (a) Draw an x-axis from −5 to 4 and a y-axis from −7 to 6.

(b) Draw a triangle P with vertices (−1, −5), (−1, −7) and (−2, −5).

(c) Reflect rectangle P in the line $y = x - 2$. Label the image Q.

(d) Translate shape Q through $\begin{pmatrix} 0 \\ 7 \end{pmatrix}$. Label the image R.

(e) Reflect shape R in the line $x + y = 1$. Label the image S. Write down the co-ordinates of the vertices of triangle S.

10 (a) Draw an x-axis from −3 to 5 and a y-axis from −1 to 7.

(b) Draw a rectangle A with vertices (−2, 2), (−2, 4), (−3, 4) and (−3, 2).

(c) Reflect rectangle A in the line $x + y = 4$. Label the image B.

(d) Reflect shape B in the line $y = x + 2$. Label the image C.

(e) Shape C is reflected back onto rectangle A. Write down the equation of the *line of reflection*.

240

11 (a) Draw an x-axis from -5 to 6 and a y-axis from -6 to 5.

(b) Draw a rectangle A with vertices (corners) at $(3, 1)$, $(3, 3)$, $(4, 3)$ and $(4, 1)$.

(c) Reflect rectangle A in the line $y = x$. Label the image B.

(d) Reflect shape B in the y-axis. Label the image C.

(e) Reflect shape C in the line $y = -x$. Label the image D.

(f) Describe the transformation which maps (sends) shape D back onto shape A.

(g) Draw a rectangle E with vertices at $(3, -1)$, $(3, -2)$, $(6, -2)$ and $(6, -1)$.

(h) Reflect shape E in the line $y = -x$. Label the image F.

9B **Solve linear equations (see Unit 6)**

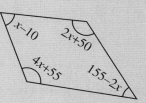

Solve the following equations:

1. $5n + 6 = 51$

2. $\dfrac{x}{7} = 3$

3. $4(2m - 1) = 12$

4. $7b + 3 = 43 - 3b$

5. $7p = 5$

6. $\dfrac{a}{6} - 4 = 3$

7. $\dfrac{x}{-4} = -8$

8. $3(2n + 5) - 4(n + 2) = 19$

9. $4 = \dfrac{3w - 2}{7}$

10. $\dfrac{20}{y} = -5$

11. $5(x - 1) = 2(4x + 5)$

12. $6 - \dfrac{2a}{5} = 10$

13.

3 cm

(3x – 1) cm

The area of this rectangle is 24 cm². Set up an equation to find x then write down the actual width of the rectangle.

14. Four consecutive even numbers add up to 164. Set up an equation then find the four numbers.

15. (a) Write down an equation using the angles.

(b) Find x.

(c) Write down the actual value of each angle in this quadrilateral.

$x - 10$ $2x + 50$ $4x + 55$ $155 - 2x$

16. £760 is divided between Rose, Imran and Megan. Imran gets £75 more than Rose and Megan gets £40 more than Imran. How much does each person get?

Key Facts

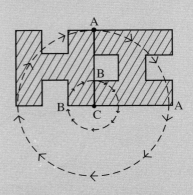

This shape has turned clockwise through a right angle $\left(90° \text{ turn or } \frac{1}{4} \text{ turn}\right)$.

Each point in the shape rotates around a circle with its centre at the dot (C).

The dot (C) is called the **centre of rotation**.

For 90° rotations, horizontal lines become vertical and vice-versa.

Describing a rotation fully

3 things must be stated:

1. the angle

2. the direction (clockwise or anticlockwise)

3. the centre of rotation

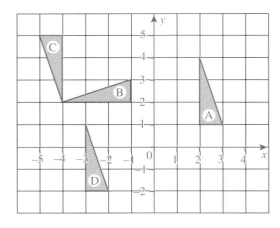

Describe *fully* the rotation which transforms:

(a) triangle A onto triangle B

(b) triangle B onto triangle C

(c) triangle B onto triangle D

For each answer, we must write down the angle, direction and centre of rotation.

(a) rotates 90° anticlockwise about (0, 0).

(b) rotates 90° anticlockwise about (−4, 2).

(c) rotates 90° clockwise about (−4, 1).

242

You may use tracing paper

1 Draw each shape and centre of rotation (C) below.
Rotate the shape as indicated and draw the image.

(a)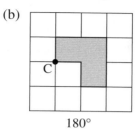

90° clockwise

(b)

180°

(c)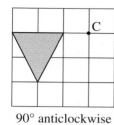

90° anticlockwise

(d)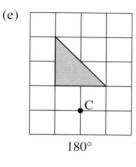

90° clockwise

(e)

180°

(f)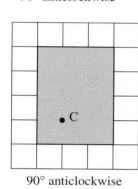

90° anticlockwise

2 In each Question below the shaded shape rotates onto the other shape. Copy each diagram and mark the centre of rotation.

(a)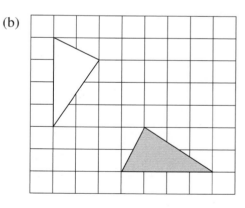

(b)

(c)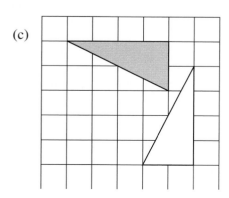

(d)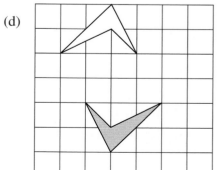

243

3 Find the co-ordinates of the centres of the following rotations:

(a) triangle A onto triangle B

(b) triangle A onto triangle C

(c) triangle A onto triangle D

(d) triangle C onto triangle E

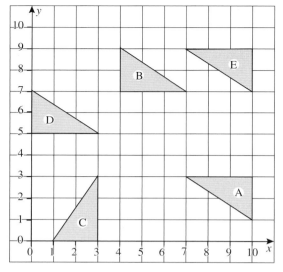

4 (a) Draw x and y axes with values from -6 to 6. Draw triangle A with vertices at $(-5, 2)$, $(-5, 6)$ and $(-3, 5)$.

(b) Rotate triangle A $90°$ clockwise about $(-4, -2)$. Label the image B.

(c) Rotate triangle B $90°$ clockwise about $(6, 0)$. Label the image C.

(d) Rotate triangle C $180°$ about $(1, 1)$. Label the image D.

(e) Rotate triangle D $90°$ anticlockwise about $(-5, 1)$. Label the image E.

(f) Describe *fully* the rotation which transforms triangle E onto triangle A.

5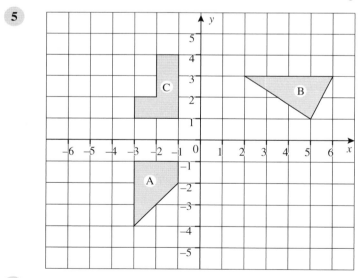

Copy the grid and shapes opposite.

(a) Rotate shape A $90°$ anticlockwise about $(-3, -4)$. Label the image P.

(b) Rotate shape B $90°$ clockwise about $(1, 0)$. Label the image Q.

(c) Rotate shape C $90°$ clockwise about $(2, 1)$. Label the image R.

6 (a) Draw x and y axes with values from -5 to 5. Draw rectangle A with vertices at $(0, 2)$, $(0, 5)$, $(-2, 5)$ and $(-2, 2)$.

(b) Rotate rectangle A $180°$ about $(-2, 2)$. Label the image B.

(c) Rotate rectangle B $90°$ clockwise about $(0, -1)$. Label the image C.

(d) Rotate rectangle C $180°$ about $(2, 0)$. Label the image D.

(e) Rotate rectangle D $90°$ clockwise about $(3, -2)$. Label the image E.

7

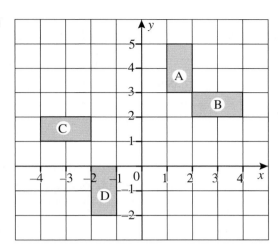

Describe *fully* the rotation which transforms:

(a) shape A onto shape B

(b) B onto C

(c) C onto D

8 (a) Draw an *x*-axis from −4 to 4 and a *y*-axis from −3 to 3.
   Draw triangle A with vertices at (−1, −2), (−2, −2) and (−2, 0).

(b) Rotate triangle A 90° clockwise about (0, −1). Label the image B.

(c) Rotate triangle B 180° about (1, 1). Label the image C.

(d) Reflect triangle C in the *x*-axis. Label the image D.

(e) Reflect triangle D in the line *y* = −2. Label the image E.

(f) Translate triangle E through $\binom{-5}{1}$. Label the image F.

(g) Describe *fully* the rotation which transforms triangle F onto triangle A.

M Enlargement

A mathematical enlargement has a **centre of enlargement** and a **scale factor**.

Every length in the original shape must be multiplied by the scale factor.

This shaded rectangle is enlarged by a scale factor 3 (each length is multiplied by 3).

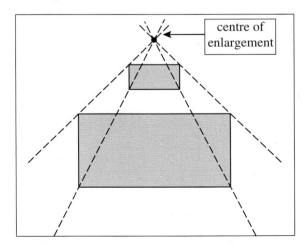

The centre of enlargement is found by drawing a broken line through a corner of the new shape and the same corner of the old shape.

Do this for each pair of points as shown in the diagram. The centre of enlargement is the point where all the broken lines meet (intersect).

Drawing an enlargement

Draw an enlargement of triangle A with scale factor 3 about the centre of enlargement C.

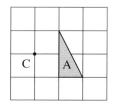

Join the centre C to one vertex with a dotted line

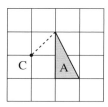

Multiply the length of the dotted line by the scale factor (do this by measuring or counting squares) then draw the longer dotted line from C

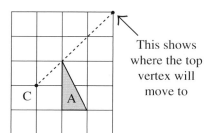

This shows where the top vertex will move to

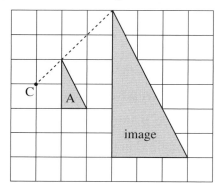

The rest of the enlarged shape can be drawn from this new vertex

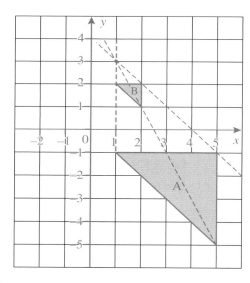

Describe fully the enlargement which transforms shape A onto shape B.

Draw broken lines through each corner of the new shape and the same corner of the old shape.

The centre of enlargement is where the broken lines meet (intersect).

Answer:

Enlargement by scale factor $\frac{1}{4}$ about (1, 3)

Note

Fractional scale factor

If a shape is *reduced in size*, the scale factor will be a fraction between 0 and 1. It is still known as an enlargement.

For Questions ① to ⑤ , draw the grid and the 2 shapes than draw broken lines through pairs of points in the new shape and the old shape. Describe fully the enlargement which transforms shape A onto shape B.

1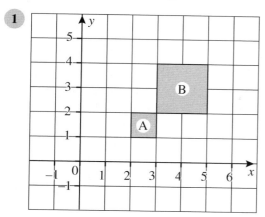

2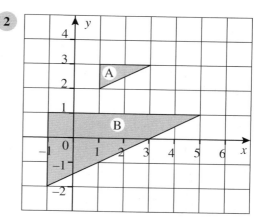

3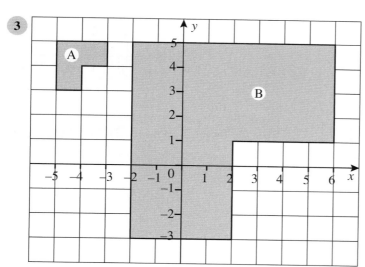

4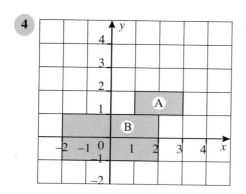

5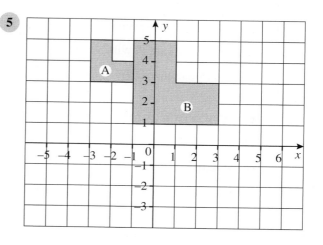

For Questions ⑥ to ⑪ , copy the diagram and then draw an enlargement using the scale factor and centre of enlargement (C) given. Leave room for the enlargement!

6

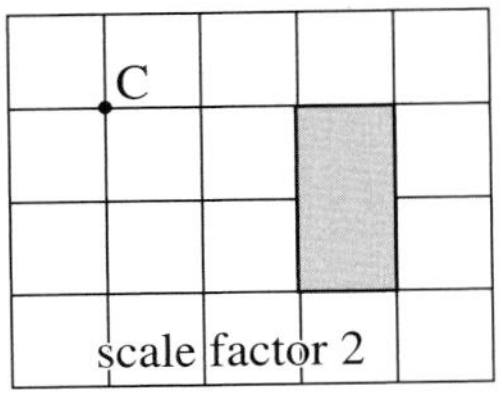

scale factor 2

7

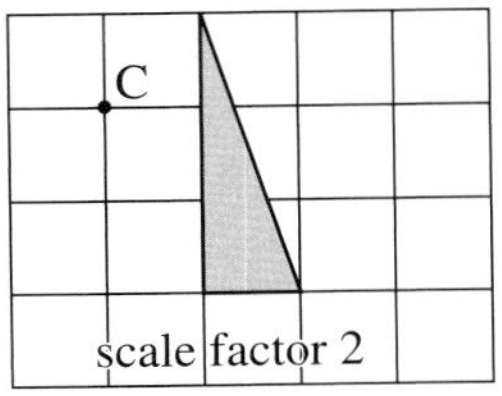

scale factor 2

8

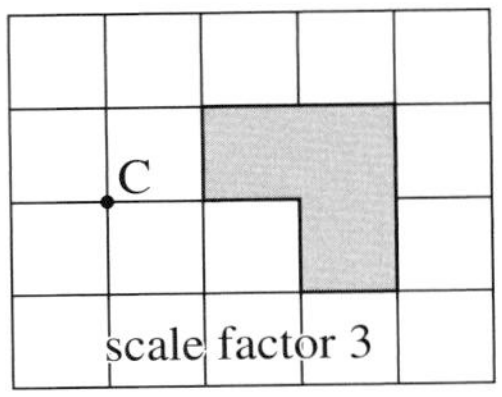

scale factor 3

9

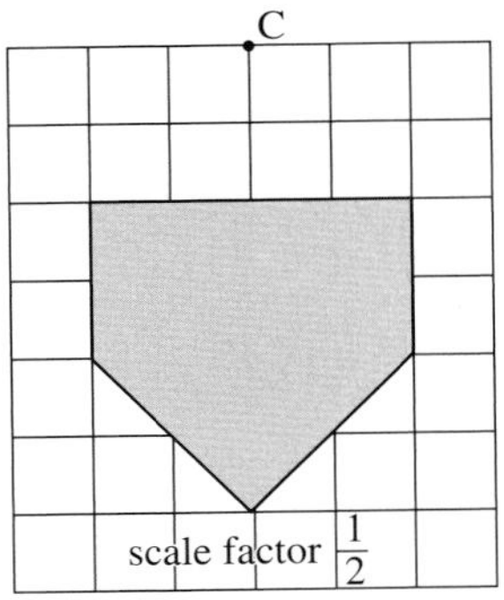

scale factor $\frac{1}{2}$

10

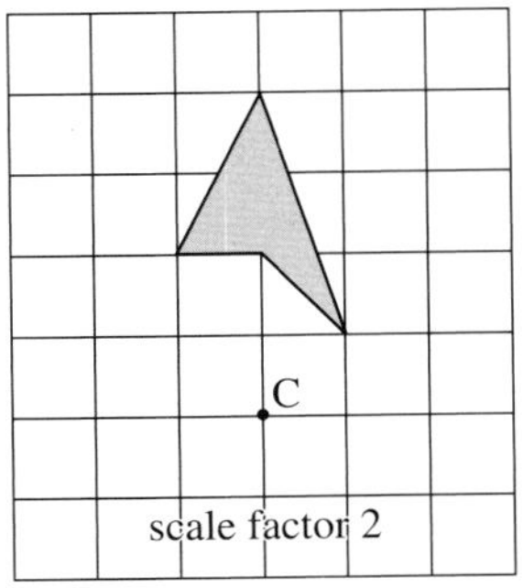

scale factor 2

11

scale factor $\frac{1}{3}$

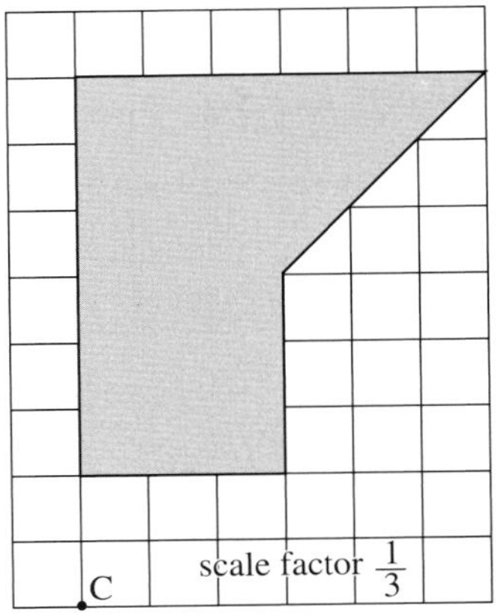

12

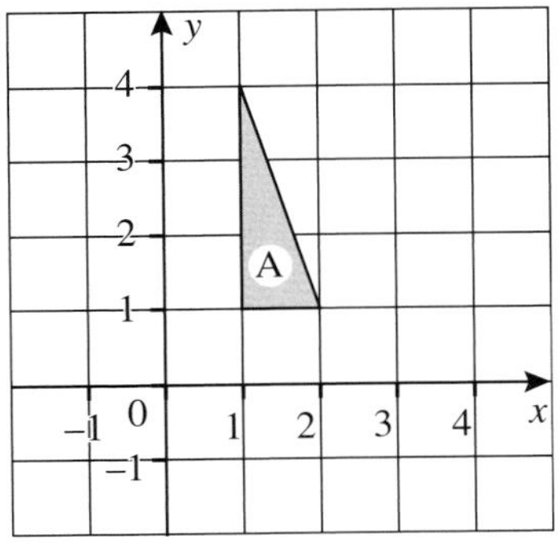

Copy the grid and triangle A. Enlarge triangle A by scale factor 2 about (0, 2). Label the image B.

13 (a) Draw an x-axis from −2 to 5 and a y-axis from −5 to 2.

(b) Draw a square A with vertices (2, −2), (4, −2), (4, −4) and (2, −4).

(c) Enlarge square A by scale factor $\frac{1}{2}$ about (0, 0). Label the image B.

14 (a) Draw an x-axis from −4 to 8 and a y-axis from −4 to 6.

(b) Draw a triangle A with vertices at (1, 3) (1, 4) and (3, 4).

(c) Enlarge triangle A by scale factor 2 about (1, 5). Label the image B.

(d) Enlarge triangle B by scale factor $\frac{1}{2}$ about (−3, 1). Label the image C.

(e) Enlarge triangle C by scale factor 3 about (−2, 3). Label the image D.

248

15 Copy the grid and rectangle A. Enlarge rectangle A by scale factor 2 about (0, 0). Label the image B.

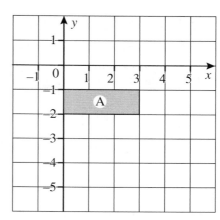

16 (a) Draw an *x*-axis from –6 to 10 and a *y*-axis from –3 to 5.

(b) Draw a shape A with vertices of (–2, 2), (–2, 3), (–1, 3), (–1, 4), (–4, 4), (–4, 3), (–3, 3) and (–3, 2).

(c) Enlarge shape A by scale factor 3 about (–6, 4). Label the image B.

(d) Enlarge shape B by scale factor $\frac{1}{3}$ about (–3, –2). Label the image C.

(e) Enlarge shape C by scale factor $\frac{1}{2}$ about (0, 0). Label the image D.

17 (a) Draw an *x*-axis from –6 to 6 and a *y*- axis from –7 to 7.

(b) Draw a triangle A with vertices of (2, 2), (2, 6) and (4, 6).

(c) Enlarge triangle A by scale factor $\frac{1}{2}$ about (0,0). Label the image B.

(d) Reflect triangle B in the *y*-axis. Label the image C.

(e) Enlarge triangle C by scale factor 3 about (–1, 4). Label the image D.

(f) Rotate triangle D 90° clockwise about (–1, –5). Label the image E.

(g) Enlarge triangle E by scale factor $\frac{1}{2}$ about (5, 1). Label the image F.

E   Negative scale factors

Draw an enlargement of triangle A with scale factor –2 about centre of enlargement at the origin.

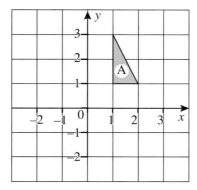

Join the centre of enlargement (in this case the origin) to one vertex with a dotted line.

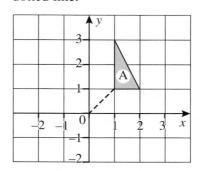

Multiply the length of the dotted line by the scale factor (i.e. 1 diagonal unit multiplied by –2 gives –2 diagonal units). The negative sign indicates that the longer dotted line should be drawn from the centre in the *opposite direction*.

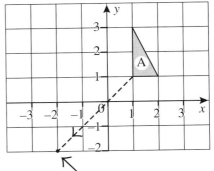

This shows where the new vertex will move to

The rest of the enlarged shape can be drawn from this new vertex (more dotted lines can be drawn if necessary).

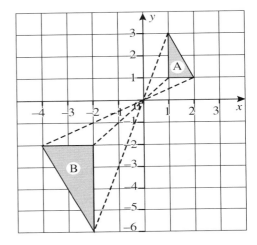

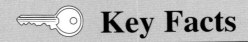 **Key Facts**

A negative scale factor leads to an image on the opposite side of the centre of enlargement to the original shape (the original shape is turned 'upside down').

E9.1

1 (a) Draw an x-axis from –1 to 6 and a y-axis from –9 to 5.

(b) Draw a rectangle A with vertices at (1, 2), (1, 4), (2, 4) and (2, 2).

(c) Enlarge rectangle A by a scale factor of –3 about (2, 1). Label the image B.

2 (a) Draw an x-axis from –4 to 4 and y-axis from –5 to 3.

(b) Draw a triangle A with vertices at (–1, 1), (–1, 2) and (–3, 1).

(c) Enlarge triangle A by a scale factor of –2 about (–1, 0). Label the image B.

(d) Write down the translation vector which describes the movement of the vertex of (–3, 1) in triangle A to its new position in triangle B.

3 (a) Draw an *x*-axis from −4 to 6 and a *y*-axis from −3 to 4.

(b) Draw a triangle A with vertices of (−2, −1), (−2, −2) and (−3, −1).

(c) Enlarge triangle A by a scale factor of −2 about (0, 0). Label the image B.

(d) Enlarge triangle B by a scale factor of $-\frac{1}{2}$ about (2, 0). Label the image C.

(e) Write down the translation vector which will translate triangle C back onto triangle A.

For Questions **4** and **5**, describe fully the enlargement which transforms shape A onto shape B (draw the grid and shape if necessary).

4

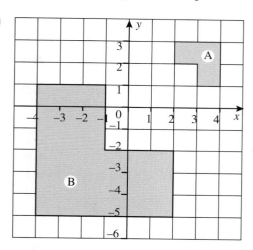

5

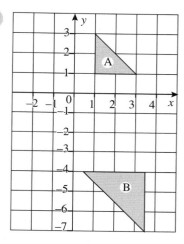

6 (a) Draw an *x*-axis from −5 to 5 and a *y*-axis from −6 to 3.

(b) Draw a triangle A with vertices at (−2, 2), (−4, 2) and (−3, 1).

(c) Enlarge triangle A by a scale factor of −3 about (−2, 1). Label the image B.

(d) Enlarge triangle B by a scale factor of $\frac{1}{3}$ about (1, −5). Label the image C.

(e) Reflect triangle C in the line *x* = −1. Label the image D.

(f) Describe where triangle D would move to if it was enlarged by a scale factor of −1 about (−3, −1).

7 (a) Draw an *x*-axis from −7 to 4 and a *y*-axis from −5 to 9.

(b) Draw a shape A with vertices at (4, 1), (4, 3), (2, 3), (2, 5), (0, 5) and (0, 1).

(c) Enlarge shape A by a scale factor of $\frac{-1}{2}$ about (−2, −1). Label the image B.

(d) Enlarge shape B by a scale factor of −3 about (−4, −1). Label the image C.

(e) Enlarge shape C by a scale factor of $\frac{2}{3}$ about (−4, −1). Label the image D.

(f) Write down the translation vector with will return shape D to shape A.

251

The questions in this Exercise use a mixture of transformations.

You may use tracing paper.

1

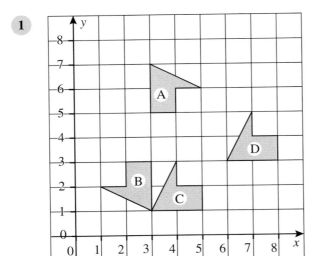

Describe *fully* the transformation which maps (sends):

(a) A onto B

(b) B onto C

(c) C onto D

2 Copy the grid and shape opposite.

(a) Rotate shape A 90° clockwise about (2, 3). Label the image B.

(b) Rotate shape B 90° anticlockwise about (6, 4). Label the image C.

(c) Describe *fully* the translation which maps shape C onto shape A.

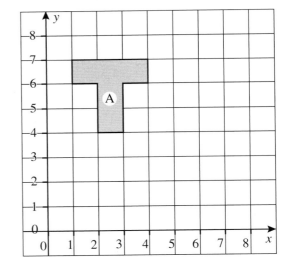

3 Describe *fully* the transformation which maps:

(a) A onto B

(b) B onto C

(c) C onto D

(d) D onto A

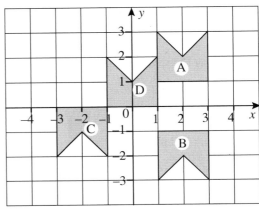

4 (a) Draw an *x*-axis from –5 to 10 and a *y*-axis from –8 to 5.

(b) Draw a shape A with vertices at (2, 2), (2, 4) (3, 3), (5, 3) and (5, 2).

(c) Rotate shape A 180° about (3, 1). Label the image B.

(d) Enlarge shape B by scale factor 3 about (1, 1). Label the image C.

(e) Reflect shape B in the *y*-axis. Label the image D.

(f) Reflect shape D in the line *y* = 1. Label the image E.

(g) Describe *fully* the transformation which maps shape E onto shape A.

5 (a) Draw an *x*-axis from –6 to 8 and a *y*-axis from –6 to 10.

(b) Draw a triangle P with vertices at (0, –1), (2, –1) and (1, 2).

(c) Translate triangle P through $\begin{pmatrix} 4 \\ -2 \end{pmatrix}$. Label the image Q.

(d) Enlarge triangle P by scale factor 2 about (–1, –2). Label the image R.

(e) Reflect triangle R in the line *y* = *x* + 3. Label the image S.

(f) Rotate triangle S 90° clockwise about (–2, –1). Label the image T.

6

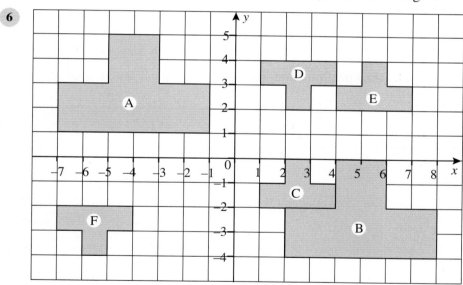

Describe *fully* the transformation which maps:

(a) A onto B

(b) B onto C

(c) C onto D

(d) D onto E

(e) E onto F

7 (a) Draw *x* and *y*-axes from –8 to 8.

(b) Draw a rectangle A with vertices at (2, 2), (6, 2), (6, 4) and (2, 4).

(c) Draw a rectangle B with vertices at (–4, 4), (–4, 0), (–2, 0) and (–2, 4)

(d) Describe *fully* the transformation which maps A onto B

(e) Reflect rectangle A in the line $y = -x$. Label the image C.

(f) Draw a rectangle D with vertices at (8, –4), (0, –4), (0, –8) and (8, –8).

(g) Describe *fully* the transformation which maps A onto D (the vertex (2, 2) in rectangle A is now at (8, –4) in rectangle B).

(h) Rotate rectangle C 90° anticlockwise about (–5, 5). Label the image E.

(i) What is the equation of the line of reflection which maps rectangle E onto rectangle A?

8 (a) Draw an x-axis from –8 to 8 and a y-axis from –8 to 12.

(b) Draw a triangle P with vertices at (5, 3), (7, 4) and (6, 6).

(c) Enlarge triangle P by a scale factor of –1 about (3, 5). Label the image Q.

(d) Enlarge triangle P by a scale factor of –2 about (4, 3). Label the image R.

(e) Describe *fully* the transformation which maps triangle R onto triangle Q.

(f) Rotate triangle P 90° clockwise about (2, 0). Label the image S.

(g) Draw a triangle T with vertices at (–2, –6), (–1, –8) and (1, –7).

(h) Describe *fully* the rotation which maps triangle P onto triangle T.

(i) Describe *fully* the transformation which maps triangle T onto triangle S.

Can you still?

(9C) **Use function notation (see Unit 6)**

Can you still?

1. If $f(x) = 9x - 5$, find the value of   (a) f(4)   (b) f(–2)

2. If $g(x) = x^3 - x$, find the value of   (a) g(4)   (b) g(–1)

3. If $p(x) = (2x + 1)^2$, find the value of   (a) p(5)   (b) $p\left(\frac{-1}{2}\right)$

4. If $s(x) = \dfrac{x^2 + x}{5x - 2}$, find the value of   (a) s(1)   (b) s(–2)

5. If $h(x) = 7(x - 3)$, find the value of x when h(x) = 21.

6. If $g(x) = x^2 - 5x + 6$, find the values of x when g(x) = 0.

7. If $f(x) = x^2 - 8x$, find the value of z when f(z) = 2z.

8. If $g(x) = \dfrac{5 - 2x}{3x}$, find the value of w when g(w) = 1.

9. Write down the expression for f(2x) if $f(x) = x^2$.

10. Write down the expression for f(x – 3) if $f(x) = 5x + 4$.

Key Facts

Two shapes are congruent if they are exactly the same size and shape.

There are four ways of proving that two triangles are congruent:

1. SSS (side, side, side)
   All 3 sides are equal.

2. SAS (side, angle, side)
   Two sides and the angle between them are equal.

3. AAS (angle, angle, side)
   Two angles and a corresponding side are equal.

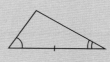

4. RHS (right angle, hypotenuse, side)
   Each triangle has a right angle. The hypotenuse and one other side are equal.

Example

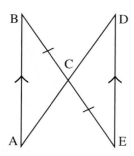

AB is parallel to ED. C is the midpoint of BE.

Prove that AC = CD.

255

A$\hat{\text{B}}$C = C$\hat{\text{E}}$D   (alternate angles)

B$\hat{\text{C}}$A = E$\hat{\text{C}}$D   (vertically opposite angles)

BC = CE   (C is midpoint of BE)

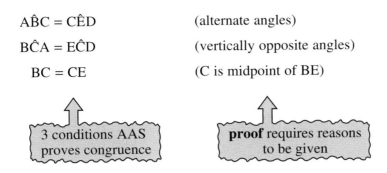

3 conditions AAS proves congruence

proof requires reasons to be given

so   Δ's   ABC / DEC   are congruent (AAS)

write the triangles underneath each other so that each angle corresponds to its equal angle in the other triangle

so AC = CD because the triangles are congruent (we can see that the letters A and C correspond to the letters D and C in the 'congruent triangles' statement above).

E9.3

In Questions **1** to **4** , state whether the pair of triangles are congruent. Give the reason (eg. SAS) if they are congruent.

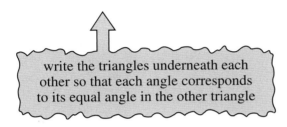

1

7 cm, 4 cm, 8 cm

4 cm, 8 cm, 7 cm

2

3.5 cm, 80°, 9 cm

3.5 cm, 80°, 9 cm

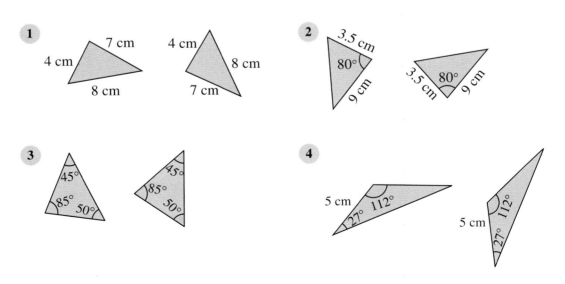

3

45°, 85°, 50°

45°, 85°, 50°

4

5 cm, 27°, 112°

5 cm, 27°, 112°

5

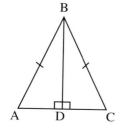

ABC is an isosceles triangle.

(a) Prove that $\triangle$ABD is congruent to $\triangle$CBD.

(b) Explain why AB̂D = CB̂D (this proves that the perpendicular bisector BD cuts AB̂C in half).

6 Draw a quadrilateral ABCD in which AB = AD and BC = CD (ie. a kite). Draw the line AC and state which two triangles are congruent. Hence prove that the angle at B is equal to the angle at D.

7

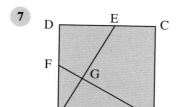

ABCD is a square. E is the midpoint of DC and F is the midpoint of AD. Prove that triangles ADE and BAF are congruent.

8 ABCD is a rectangle.

(a) Prove that triangles ABX and DCX are congruent.

(b) Hence prove that DXA is an isosceles triangle.

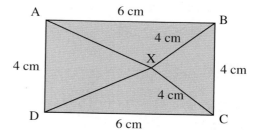

9 Draw a quadrilateral ABCD (not a rectangle) such that AB is parallel to CD and AD is parallel to CB. Draw the line AC. Use congruent triangles to prove that opposite sides of this shape are equal.

10

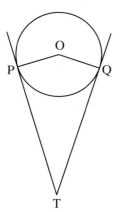

PT and QT are tangents to the circle with centre O.

(a) Find OQ̂T and OP̂T.

(b) Explain why OP is equal to OQ.

(c) Hence state, with reasons, a triangle which is congruent to triangle PTO.

257

11 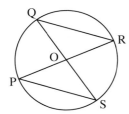 Prove that Δs OQR and OPS are congruent.

12 In the diagram below ABCD is a rhombus, E is the midpoint of DC and F is the midpoint of AD. Show that triangles AFB and ECB are congruent.

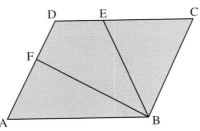

13 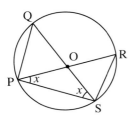 O is the centre of the circle. State, with reasons, which triangle is congruent to PRS.

14 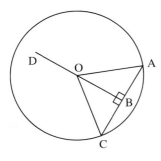 O is the centre of the circle. Use congruent triangles to prove that the perpendicular line (DB) to the chord (AC) bisects the chord AC.

15 In the diagram, PK = QK, PF = QG and the lines PQ and SR are parallel. The angle PQS is x.

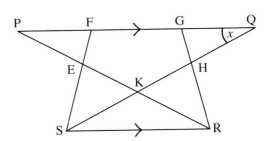

(a) Find, with reasons, the following angles:

(i) QP̂R

(ii) QŜR

(iii) PR̂S

(b) Explain why SK = RK.

(c) Hence show that PR = QS.

(d) State, with reasons, which triangle is congruent to QSF.

If you do not have enough money to buy an item, you might buy *on credit*. There are different ways of doing this such as hire purchase, credit cards, store cards, bank overdrafts and personal loans.

Make sure you know the true cost of buying on credit.

This section deals with hire purchase.

Hire purchase allows you to buy items straight away but you pay for them in instalments (usually monthly).

You probably will not own the items until all the instalments have been paid. If you stop paying the instalments, the items could be taken back.

Music Centre £650
(or a 20% deposit plus 24 monthly payments of £27.50 each month)

If you buy the music centre on credit:

deposit = 20% of £650 = £130

24 monthly payments = 24 × £27.50 = £660

total credit price = £130 + £660 = £790

How much extra does the hire purchase cost you?

extra cost = £790 – £650 = £140

Credit price Cash price

You would have to decide if you do not mind paying this *extra money* to be able to get this music centre.

GET WISE

If shops and other places offer interest-free periods, find out exactly what you have to pay in the end. It may *cost* you a lot of *extra money*.

1 A washing machine costs £420. You can buy it for a 10% deposit plus 36 equal monthly payments of £14.

(a) How much is the deposit?

(b) How much are the 36 monthly payments?

(c) What is the total credit price?

(d) How much extra does the hire purchase cost?

2 A TV costs £560. You can buy it for a 15% deposit plus 36 equal monthly payments of £15.50.

(a) How much is the deposit?

(b) How much are the 36 monthly payments?

(c) What is the total credit price?

(d) How much extra does the hire purchase cost?

3 Copy and complete the table below:

	item	cash price (£)	deposit (£)	number of monthly instalments	each monthly (£) instalment	total credit price (£)	extra cost of hire (£) purchase
(a)	cooker	735	100	24	30		
(b)	bike	390	80	24	15		
(c)	car	12400	3000	48	224		
(d)	phone	230	40	12	17.50		
(e)	dishwasher	465	55	36	14.99		

4

New windows £3250	Pay a 20% deposit then *nothing for 2 years*. Followed by 12 equal monthly payments of £299.

How much extra does the hire purchase cost?

5

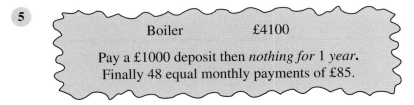

Boiler   £4100

Pay a £1000 deposit then *nothing for* 1 *year*.
Finally 48 equal monthly payments of £85.

How much is saved by paying the cash price?

1. Using reflection symmetry and rotational symmetry

For each shape below, write down (i) how many lines of symmetry it has and
(ii) the order of rotational symmetry.

(a) 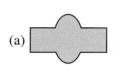   (b) 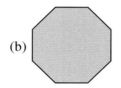   (c) 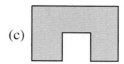   (d)

2. Identifying planes of symmetry

(a) 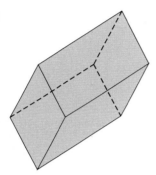   How many planes of symmetry does this
3D-shape have?

(b) This 3D-shape has two planes of symmetry,
Make two copies of the shape and
show each plane of symmetry clearly.

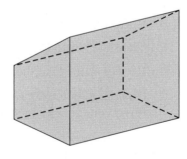

3. Translating shapes

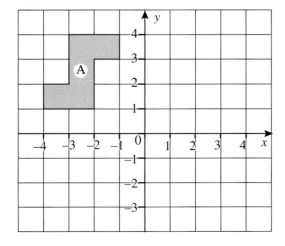

Copy the grid opposite and
draw shape A as shown.

(a) Translate shape A through $\binom{2}{-3}$.
Label the image (new shape) B.

(b) Translate shape B through $\binom{3}{2}$.
Label the image C.

(c) Describe *fully* the translation
which moves shape C onto
shape A.

4. Reflecting shapes in mirror lines

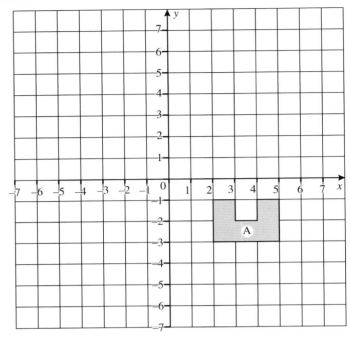

Copy the grid and shape above.

(a) Reflect shape A in the line $y = -4$. Label the image B.

(b) Reflect shape B in the y-axis. Label the image C.

(c) Reflect shape C in the line $y = -1$. Label the image D.

(d) Translate shape D through $\begin{pmatrix} 3 \\ -2 \end{pmatrix}$. Label the image E.

(e) Reflect shape E in the line $y = x$. Label the image F.

(f) How large is the area of overlap between shape F and Shape A (give your answer in square units)?

5. Rotating shapes

(a)

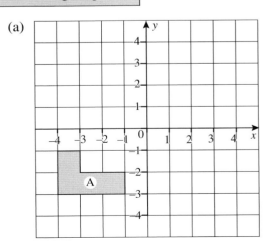

Copy the grid and shape A opposite.

(i) Rotate shape A 90° anticlockwise about (0, 0). Label the image B.

(ii) Rotate shape A 180° about (−1, −2). Label the image C.

262

(b) Describe fully the rotation which transforms:

  (i) shape A onto B

  (ii) shape A onto C

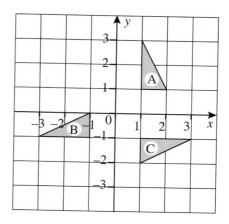

6. Enlarging shapes

(a)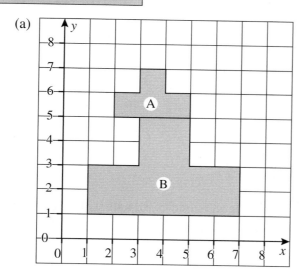

Describe fully the enlargement which transforms shape A onto shape B.

(draw the grid and 2 shapes if you need to)

(b)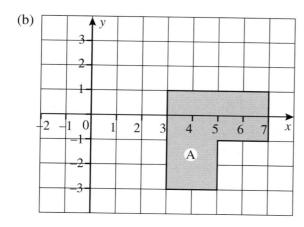

Copy the grid and shape A.

Enlarge shape A by scale factor $\frac{1}{2}$ about $(-1, -3)$. Label the image B.

263

7. Enlarging with negative scale factors

(a)

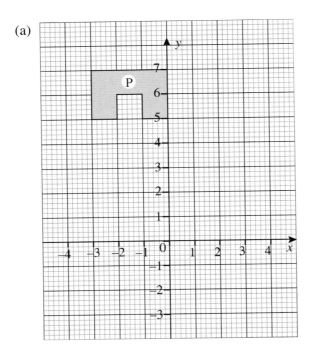

Copy this grid and shape P.

Enlarge shape P by a
scale factor of –2 about (–1, 4).
Label the image Q.

8. Proving that triangles are congruent

(a)

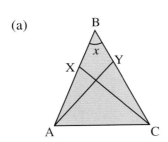

ABC is an isosceles triangle with AB = BC.
X and Y lie on AB and BC respectively so that
AX = CY.

Label the angle ABC as x.

(a) Show, with reasons, which triangle is
congruent to ABY.

(b) Hence prove that CX = AY.

(b)

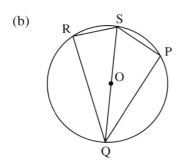

O is the centre of the circle.
RS = PS.

State, with reasons, which triangle is
congruent to QSP

264

1

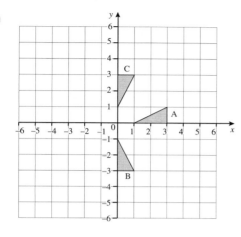

(a) Describe fully the single transformation, which maps triangle A onto triangle B.

(b) Describe fully the single transformation that maps triangle A onto triangle C.

(c) Copy the grid and triangle C. Translate the triangle by the vector $\left(\begin{smallmatrix} -3 \\ 2 \end{smallmatrix}\right)$. Label your answer D. (OCR)

2

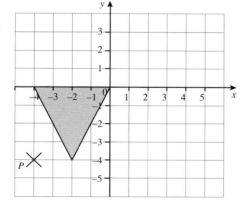

Copy the grid and shape.

Enlarge the shaded triangle by a scale factor $1\frac{1}{2}$, centre P. (EDEXCEL)

3

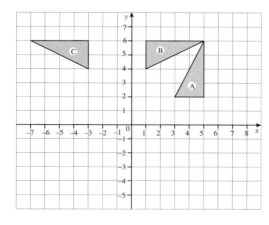

(a) Copy the grid and triangles.
Triangle B is a reflection of triangle A.

 (i) Draw the line of reflection.

 (ii) Write down the equation of the line of reflection.

(b) Describe fully the single transformation that maps triangle A onto triangle C.

(c) On the grid, enlarge triangle C by a scale factor – 1½ from the centre (–1, 2). Label the enlargement D. (EDEXCEL)

265

4 In the diagram, the lines AC and BD intersect at E.

AB and DC are parallel and AB = DC.

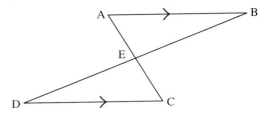

Prove that triangles ABE and CDE are congruent. (AQA)

5 (a) Describe the transformation which maps shape A onto shape B.

(b) Describe the transformation which maps shape A onto shape C.

(c) Copy the grid and shape A. Rotate shape A through 90° clockwise about the origin. Label the image R.

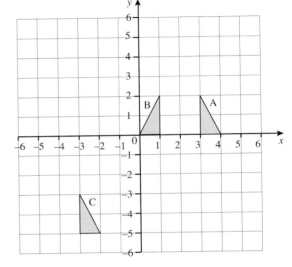

(OCR)

6 A, B and C are three points on the circumference of a circle.
Angle ABC = Angle ACB.
PB and PC are tangents to the circle from the point P.
Prove that triangle APB and triangle APC are congruent.

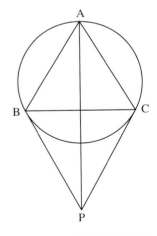

(EDEXCEL)

266

In the 'M' sections (mainly grades B, C, D) you will learn how to:

– use metric and imperial units

– calculate with speed, density and other compound measures

– use Pythagoras' theorem

– use trigonometry in right-angled triangles

In the 'E' sections (mainly grades A*, A) you will learn how to:

– deal with vectors

– use vectors in geometry

Also you will learn how to:

– ⟨WATCH YOUR MONEY!⟩ – credit 2 – credit cards and store cards

---

M | **Metric and imperial units**

🔑 Key Facts

length	mass	volume
10 mm = 1 cm	1000 g = 1 kg	1000 ml = 1 litre
100 cm = 1 m	1000 kg = 1 tonne	1 ml = 1 cm^3
1000 m = 1 km		1 m^3 = 1000 litres

Many people still 'think' using the old imperial units. 'Jack is 6 feet tall', 'Wendy weighs 10 stone'.

Below are some imperial units.

pound

pint   ounce

gallon   stone   inch

ton   mile

foot   yard

length	volume	mass
length	**volume**	**mass**
12 inches = 1 foot	8 pints = 1 gallon	16 ounces = 1 pound
3 feet = 1 yard		14 pounds = 1 stone
1760 yards = 1 mile		2240 pounds = 1 ton

M10.1

1 Copy each sentence below and choose the most sensible estimate.

(a) A baby weighs   (400 g / 4 kg).

(b) A bottle of wine contains   (7 ml / 0.7 litres).

(c) The height of the door is   (100 cm / 2 m).

(d) A can of lemonade contains   (330 ml / 33 litres).

2 Copy and complete the following:

(a) 8 mm = ☐ cm (b) 350 m = ☐ km (c) 9.5 kg = ☐ g

(d) 0.375 kg = ☐ g (e) 575 g = ☐ kg (f) 6.2 tonnes = ☐ kg

(g) 1832 ml = ☐ litres (h) 4.5 litres = ☐ ml (i) 248 cm = ☐ m

(j) 5.83 m^3 = ☐ litres (k) 7.3 litres = ☐ cm^3 (l) 872 litres = ☐ m^3

3 One tin of baked beans weighs 270 g. How many *kilograms* do 9 tins weigh?

4 How many 400 ml plastic beakers can be filled from an 88 litre barrel of beer?

5 Al has a 5.4 m piece of wood. He cuts it into small lengths of 45 cm. How many small pieces of wood will he have?

6 Copy each sentence below and choose the most sensible estimate.

(a) A bag of sugar weighs   (2 pounds / 2 ounces).

(b) A teapot contains   (2 pints / 5 gallons).

(c) A baby weighs   (7 stone / 7 pounds).

(d) The length of a cricket pitch is   (22 inches / 22 yards).

7 Copy and complete the following:

(a) 4 pounds = ☐ ounces (b) 3 tons = ☐ pounds

(c) 2 stone 6 pounds = ☐ pounds (d) 4 feet 10 inches = ☐ inches

(e) 2 miles = ☐ yards (f) 9.5 gallons = ☐ pints

(g) 70 pounds = ☐ stone (h) 7040 yards = ☐ miles

(i) 3 pounds 6 ounces = ☐ ounces (j) 2½ tons = ☐ pounds

(k) 68 pints = ☐ gallons (l) 3 stone 12 pounds = ☐ pounds

8 Henry weighs 15 stone 3 pounds. He goes on a diet and loses 1 stone 9 pounds. How much does Henry weigh now?

9 During her lifetime Jackie gives 54 pints of blood. How many gallons is this?

10 Copy and complete the clues that go across.
What word is shown going down the shaded boxes?

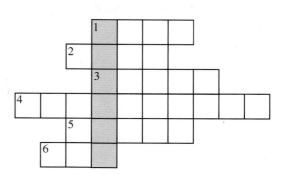

Clues

1. One thousand of these make a kilogram

2. 3 feet

3. 1000 millilitres

4. Ten of these make a centimetre

5. 16 ounces

6. 2240 pounds

🔑 Key Facts

Converting between metric and imperial units

We sometimes need to convert imperial units into metric units or metric units into imperial units.

(The '≈' sign means 'is approximately equal to'.)

We have

length	mass	capacity
1 inch ≈ 2.5 cm	1 ounce ≈ 30 g	1 litre ≈ 1.8 pints
1 foot ≈ 30 cm	1 kg ≈ 2.2 pounds	1 gallon ≈ 4.5 litres
1 yard ≈ 90 cm		
1 mile ≈ 1.6 km		

To *change units*, use the values above and *multiply* or *divide*.

Examples

(a) 3 gallons into litres ⇨ ×4.5 ⇨ 13.5 litres
(b) 33 pounds into kg ⇨ ÷2.2 ⇨ 15 kg

1 Write each length in cm.

(a) 4 inches   (b) 3 feet   (c) 5 yards   (d) 2.5 yards   (e) 1.5 feet

2 Write each mass in pounds.

(a) 3 kg   (b) 5 kg   (c) 3.5 kg   (d) 8.5 kg   (e) 6.2 kg

3 Write each capacity in litres.

(a) 2 gallons   (b) 9 gallons   (c) 20 gallons   (d) 5.5 gallons   (e) 4.6 gallons

4 On a journey, Tom's car used 6 gallons of petrol and Sarah's car used 26 litres of petrol. Which car used more petrol?

5 On a hiking holiday, Maggie walked 32 miles and Ed walked 53 km. Who walked further?

6 Copy and complete:

(a) 10 ounces ≈ ☐ g   (b) 5 litres ≈ ☐ pints   (c) 5 miles ≈ ☐ km

(d) 32 km ≈ ☐ miles   (e) 27 pints ≈ ☐ litres   (f) 4 kg ≈ ☐ pounds

(g) 66 pounds ≈ ☐ kg   (h) 31.5 litres ≈ ☐ gallons   (i) 19.2 km ≈ ☐ miles

(j) 7 yards ≈ ☐ cm   (k) 60 kg ≈ ☐ pounds   (l) 150 g ≈ ☐ ounces

(m) 6 feet ≈ ☐ cm   (n) 14 miles ≈ ☐ km   (o) 72 litres ≈ ☐ gallons

7 Which weighs more? A or B?

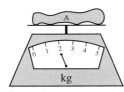 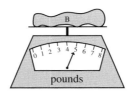

8 Which weighs more? C or D?

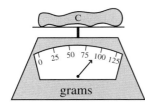 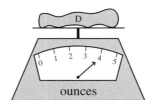

9 Sandra fills up her car with 8 gallons of petrol. How much will it cost if petrol costs 90 p per litre?

10 The distance from Leeds to York is about 24 miles. How many km is this?

11 Jamie needs 6 ounces of bacon to put in a stew. He buys 170 g of bacon. Will he have enough?

12 Which is larger – a yard or a metre?

13 An exercise machine is only strong enough to take weights up to 16 stone. Arnie weighs 100 kg. Should he use the exercise machine?

14 On a building site, 50 kg of soil is moved every minute. How many tonnes of soil will be moved in 1 hour?

10A **Find gradients of straight lines and use $y = mx + c$ (see Unit 6)**

1. Find the gradient of the line joining (2, 1) to (5, 13).

2. Write down the gradient and y-intercept of each of the following lines:

   (a) $y = 3x + 7$ (b) $y = 3 - 2x$

   (c) $2x + 5y = 1$ (d) $3y - 7x = 6$

3.

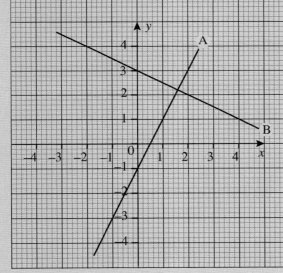

   (a) Write down the equation of line A in the form $y = mx + c$.

   (b) Write down the equation of line B in the form $y = mx + c$ then rearrange it into the form $ax + by = c$.

4. Find the equation of the line with a gradient of 4 which passes through (1, 7).

5. Find the equation of this straight line.

(3, 13)

(−2, 3)

271

Key Facts

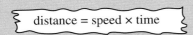

distance = speed × time

speed can be measured in km per hour

so $\left\{ \text{speed} = \dfrac{\text{distance}}{\text{time}} \right\}$ we also have $\left\{ \text{time} = \dfrac{\text{distance}}{\text{speed}} \right\}$

These three important formulas can be remembered using a triangle as shown.

To find S: cover S and you have $\dfrac{D}{T}$

To find T: cover T and you have $\dfrac{D}{S}$

To find D: cover D and you have $S \times T$

(a) A car travels 100 miles in 2 hours 30 minutes. Find the speed in m.p.h.

Time must be in hours only: 2 hours 30 minutes = 2.5 hours

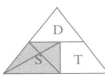

$S = \dfrac{D}{T} = \dfrac{100}{2.5} = 40$ mph.

(b) Hazel runs at a steady speed of 8 m/s.

(i) How far does she travel in 4.3 s?   (ii) How long does it take her to run 100 m?

(iii) What is her speed in km/h?

(i)

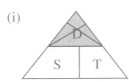

$D = S \times T$

$= 8 \times 4.3 = 34.4$ m

(ii)

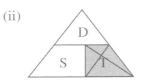

$T = \dfrac{D}{S} = \dfrac{100}{8} = 12.5$ s

(iii)   speed = 8 m/s = 8 × 60 × 60 metres per hour

$= \dfrac{8 \times 60 \times 60}{1000}$ km/h

$= 28.8$ km/h

1 A plane flies 480 km at 320 km/h. How long does the journey take?

2 Eurostar travels 420 km from London to Paris in 3 hours. Find the average speed of the train.

3 Charlie drives from Wells to Bristol at 40 mph in 30 minutes. How far is it from Wells to Bristol?

4 A hiker walks 28.5 miles at 3 mph. How long does the hiker walk for?

5 Find the speed in mph for each of the following.

distance	time	speed (mph)
30 miles	30 minutes	
9 miles	15 minutes	
15 miles	20 minutes	
6 miles	5 minutes	
30 miles	45 minutes	

6 Terry cycles at 16 mph for 30 minutes then slows down to 12 mph for 15 minutes. How far does he travel in total?

7 Janine walks at 6 km/h for 1 hour 30 minutes then 4 km/h for 2 hours 15 minutes. How far does she walk in total?

8 Sima drives 50 miles from Leeds to Manchester at an average speed of 40 mph. If she left Leeds at 10:20, when did she arrive at Manchester?

9 The speed of light is 300,000,000 m/s. How long will it take light to travel 6,000,000 km?

10 Convert the following speeds into km/h:

   (a) 3 m/s   (b) 20 m/s   (c) 35 km/min   (d) 78 cm/s

11 Convert the following speeds into m/s:

   (a) 18 km/h   (b) 115.2 km/h   (c) 61200 m/h   (d) 0.408 km/min

12 Two cyclists, Nerys and Ben, complete a race. Nerys has an average speed of 14.5 km/h and Ben has an average speed of 4 m/s. Who wins the race?

13 A car travels 80 km at an average speed of 50 km/h then travels 64 km at an average speed of 80 km/h. Find the average speed for the whole journey.

14 A plane travels 920 km at an average speed of 800 km/h. It then increases its speed by 50% and travels another 1020 km. Find the average speed for the whole journey.

15 In a marathon race, Candice is 40 m behind Jess. Candice is running at 0.7 m/s but Jess is only running at 0.5 m/s. How long will it take Candice to catch up Jess?

16 For each graph below find the speed of the journey from A to B. Give the answer
(i) in km/h and (ii) in m/s.

(a)

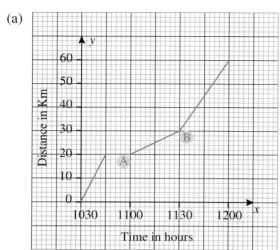

(b)

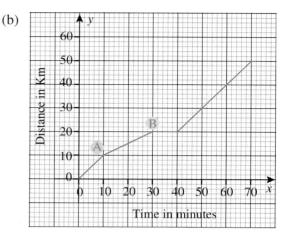

17 The graph below shows a car journey from Manchester.

(a) How far from Manchester is the car at 1030?

(b) When is the car half way between C and D?

(c) At what time is the car 30 km from Manchester?

(d) Find the speed of the car from B to C in km/h.

(e) Find the speed of the car from C to D in m/s.

(f) Find the average speed of the car from A to E in m/s.

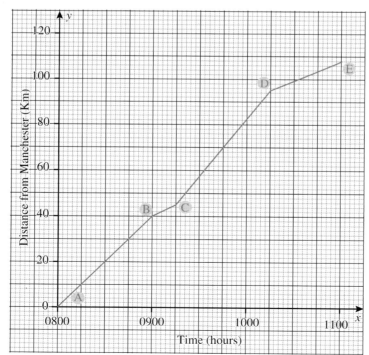

274

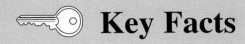

Key Facts

If the density of a substance is 30 g/cm³, it means that 1 cm³ of the substance has a mass of 30 g.

Density = Mass per unit Volume so Density = $\dfrac{\text{Mass}}{\text{Volume}}$

We can use a triangle again to remember the formulas.

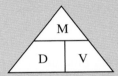

To find M: cover M and you have D × V

To find D: cover D and you have $\dfrac{M}{V}$

To find V: cover V and you have $\dfrac{M}{D}$

Note

There is a difference between 'mass' and 'weight' but in this book you may assume they have the same meaning.

(a) The density of silk is 1.3 g/cm³. What is the mass of 8 cm³ of silk?

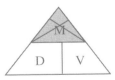

$$M = D \times V = 1.3 \times 8 = 10.4 \text{ g.}$$

(b) The density of copper is 8.9 g/cm³. The mass of a copper bar is 106.8 g. Find the volume of the copper bar.

$$V = \frac{M}{D} = \frac{106.8}{8.9} = 12 \text{ cm}^3$$

1 Copy and complete the table below:

Density (g/cm³)	Mass (g)	Volume (cm³)
	200	50
	80	5
13		8
24		36
10	150	
60		0.5
	36	9
16	320	
0.1	19	
	42	10
200		0.08

2 The density of brass is 8.2 g/cm³. The volume of a brass ring is 20 cm³. Find the mass of the brass ring.

3 A gold bar has a volume of 80 cm³ and a mass of 1544 g. Find the density of the gold.

4 A piece of cotton has a volume of 250 cm³ and a mass of 385 g. Find the density of the cotton.

5 A liquid weighs 500 g and has a density of 2.5 g/cm³. Find the volume of the liquid.

6 Which has a greater mass: A, 30 cm³ of cast iron with density 7.4 g/cm³ or B, 25 cm³ of pure nickel with density 8.9 g/cm³? Write down by how much.

7 Find the volume of some lead weighing 3 kg. The density of lead is 11.4 g/cm³. Give your answer to the nearest whole number.

8 High alloy steel has a density of 8.3 g/cm³. Find the weight of some steel with a volume of 50 cm³.

9 Brass has a density of 8.2 g/cm³. Find the volume of a brass fitting which weighs 0.574 kg.

10 Find the volume of a piece of zinc alloy weighing 2 kg. The density of zinc alloy is 6 g/cm³. Give your answer to the nearest whole number.

11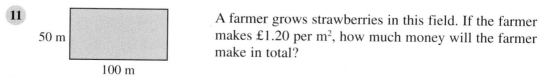

50 m

100 m

A farmer grows strawberries in this field. If the farmer makes £1.20 per m², how much money will the farmer make in total?

12 A curtain material costs £38 per metre. How much will 4.5 m cost?

13 40 m² of carpet costs £878. What is the cost per m² of the carpet?

14 The population of a country is 35 million and the area of the country is 160,000 km². What is the population density of the country (number of people per km²)?

10B **Use trial and improvement (see Unit 6)**

1.

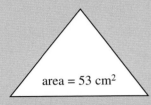

area = 53 cm²

The height of this triangle is 7 cm longer than its base. Use trial and improvement to find the base and height to 1 decimal place.

2. Use trial and improvement to solve $x^2 - x = 40$, giving your answer to 1 decimal place. Try $x = 7$ first and show all your working out.

3. Solve these equations by trial and improvement. Give each answer to 2 decimal places and show all your working out.

(a) $x^2 + 2x = 200$ (b) $x^2 (x - 1) = 85$

M | **Pythagoras' theorem**

🔑 **Key Facts**

Pythagoras' theorem

In a *right angled* triangle, the square on the hypotenuse is equal to the sum of the squares on the other two sides.

$a^2 + b^2 = c^2$

The 'hypotenuse' is the *longest* side in a right angled triangle. (ie. side c)

The theorem can be used to calculate the third side of a right angled triangle when two sides are known.

(a) Find the length x.

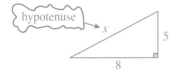

$x^2 = 5^2 + 8^2$

$x^2 = 25 + 64$

$x^2 = 89$

$x = \sqrt{89}$

$x = 9.43$ (to 2 decimal places)

(b) Find the length y.

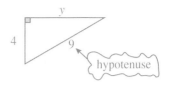

$y^2 + 4^2 = 9^2$

$y^2 + 16 = 81$

$y^2 = 81 - 16$

$y^2 = 65$

$y = \sqrt{65}$

$y = 8.06$ (to 2 decimal places)

To find the *hypotenuse*, square the known sides, *add* then square root.
To find one of the *shorter sides*, square the known sides, *subtract* then square root.

M10.5

You will need a calculator. Give your answers correct to 2 decimal places where necessary. The units are cm.

1 Copy the statements below and fill the empty boxes.

(a)

(b)

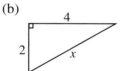

(c)

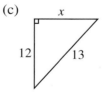

(d)

(a)
$x^2 = \boxed{}^2 + \boxed{}^2$
$x^2 = 25 + \boxed{}$
$x^2 = \boxed{}$
$x = \sqrt{\boxed{}}$
$x = \boxed{}$

(b)
$x^2 = \boxed{}^2 + \boxed{}^2$
$x^2 = 4 + \boxed{}$
$x^2 = \boxed{}$
$x^2 = \sqrt{\boxed{}}$
$x = \boxed{}$

(c)
$x^2 + \boxed{}^2 = 13^2$
$x^2 + \boxed{} = 169$
$x^2 = 169 - \boxed{}$
$x^2 = \boxed{}$
$x = \sqrt{\boxed{}}$
$x = \boxed{}$

(d)
$x^2 + 9^2 = \boxed{}^2$
$x^2 + 81 = \boxed{}$
$x^2 = \boxed{} - 81$
$x^2 = \boxed{}$
$x = \sqrt{\boxed{}}$
$x = \boxed{}$

2 Find the length x.

(a)
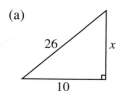

(b)
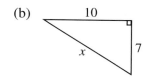

(c)
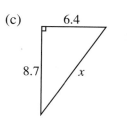

(d)
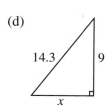

(e)
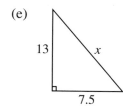

(f)
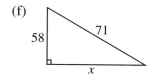

(g)
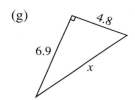

(h)
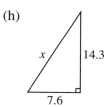

3 Find the length AB.

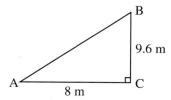

4 Find the length PQ.

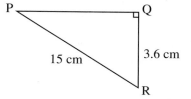

5 Find the length MN.

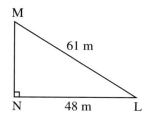

6 Find the length YZ.

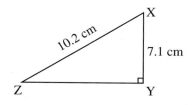

(a) A ladder of length 6 m reaches 4.8 m up a vertical wall.
How far is the foot of the ladder from the wall?

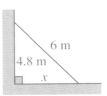

x is one of the shorter sides in a right angled triangle.

Use Pythagoras' theorem.

$x^2 + 4.8^2 = 6^2$

$x^2 + 23.04 = 36$

$x^2 = 12.96$

$x = \sqrt{12.96}$

$x = 3.6$ m

(b) Find the length of the line joining $(1, 2)$ to $(5, 4)$.

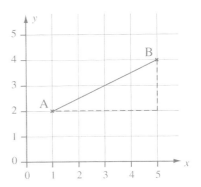

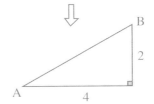

Use Pythagoras' theorem to find length AB.

$AB^2 = 2^2 + 4^2$

$AB^2 = 4 + 16$

$AB^2 = 20$

$AB = \sqrt{20}$

$AB = 4.47$ (to 2 decimal places)

M10.6

You may use a calculator. Give your answers to 2 decimal places.

1 A ladder of length 6 m rests against a vertical wall, with its foot 2.4 m from the wall. How far up the wall does the ladder reach?

2

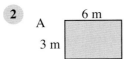

Which rectangle has the longer diagonal and by how much?

B

7 m

2 m

280

3 A ladder of length 7 m reaches 5 m up a vertical wall. How far is the foot of the ladder from the wall?

4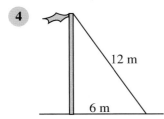

A rope attached to a flagpole is 12 m long. The rope is fixed to the ground 6 m from the foot of the flagpole.

How tall is the flagpole?

5 Towley is 8 km due east of Hapton. Castleton is 12 km due south of Hapton.

How far is Towley from Castleton?

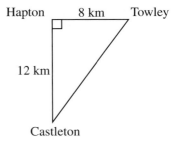

6 Redford is 9 km due north of Hagshed. Peltsham is 7 km due west of Hagshed. How far is Redford from Peltsham?

7 A rectangular TV screen is 21 inches long and 11 inches wide. What is the length of the diagonal of the TV screen?

8 A ship sails 50 km due north and then a further 62 km due east. How far is the ship from its starting point?

9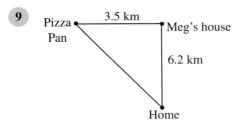

Kat and Holly are sisters. They are meeting friends at Pizza Pan. Kat drives *directly* to Pizza Pan. Holly has to pick up Meg on the way to Pizza Pan. How much further does Holly drive than Kat?

10 A clothes line is attached to 2 vertical walls as shown. How long is the clothes line?

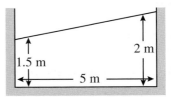

11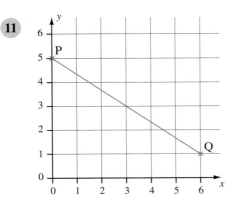

Calculate the length PQ.

12 Calculate the length of the line joining (2, 1) to (8, 9).

13 Calculate the length of the line joining (–3, 2) to (3, –4).

14 PQRS is a parallelogram. P is (4, 1), Q is (2, –2) and R is (6, –2).

(a) Draw the parallelogram using appropriate axes.

(b) Write down the co-ordinates of S.

(c) Write down the co-ordinates of the midpoint of diagonal QS.

(d) Calculate the length of the diagonal QS.

15 ABCD is a rhombus. A is (–4, 2), B is (1, 2) and C is (4, –2).

(a) Draw the rhombus using appropriate axes.

(b) Write down the co-ordinates of D.

(c) Write down the co-ordinates of the midpoint of diagonal BD.

(d) Calculate the length of the diagonal AC.

16

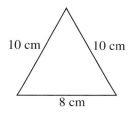

An *isosceles* triangle has a line of symmetry which divides the triangle into two right-angled triangles as shown.

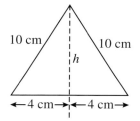

Use Pythagoras' theorem to find the height h of the triangle.

17 Find the height of each isosceles triangle below.

(a)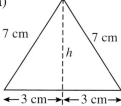

(b)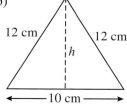

(c)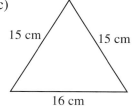

18 Find the area of this isosceles triangle.

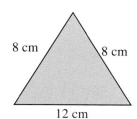

19 Calculate the vertical height and hence the area of an equilateral triangle of side 16 cm.

282

20 Find the length x. The units are cm.

(a)

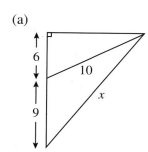

(b)

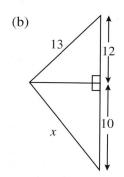

(c)

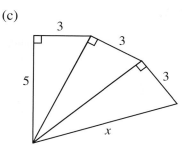

Can you still?

Can you still?

10C   **Change the subject of a formula (see Unit 6)**

Make x the subject of each formula given below:

1. $y = ax$ **2.** $y = ax + c$ **3.** $c(x - q) = y$

4. $r = ct - x$ **5.** $\dfrac{mx + c}{y} = z$ **6.** $\dfrac{x}{p} - b = m$

7. $z = \dfrac{n + bx}{5}$ **8.** $p - cx = q + r$ **9.** $x^2 + m = p$

10. $v^2 - q = \sqrt{x}$ **11.** $px^3 + w = y$ **12.** $\sqrt{(ax - b)} = w$

13. Copy and complete the following:

$$nx - p = mx + qr$$

$$nx - \boxed{} = qr + \boxed{}$$

$$x\left(n - \boxed{}\right) = qr + \boxed{}$$

$$x = \dfrac{qr + \boxed{}}{n - \boxed{}}$$

Make y the subject of each formula given below:

14. $ay - z = b - my$ **15.** $q(3x + y) = ky + 4h$

16. $\dfrac{ay + bx}{y} = c$ **17.** $m = \dfrac{hy + k}{y - n}$

18. $\sqrt[3]{\dfrac{py + zx}{y}} = m$ **19.** $\dfrac{3a}{c} = \sqrt{\dfrac{by}{m - y}}$

283

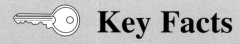 **Key Facts**

Trigonometry is used to find angles and sides in triangles. All work in this section refers to right angled triangles.

Naming the sides

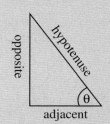

The longest side is the **'hypotenuse'**.

The side opposite an angle being used (θ) is the **'opposite'**.

The other side (touching both θ and the right angle) is the **'adjacent'**.

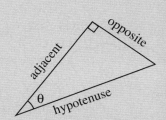

M10.7

In each triangle below, note the angle given and state whether side x is the opposite, adjacent or hypotenuse.

1

2

3

4

5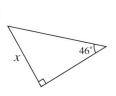

6

7

8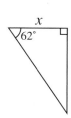

Ratios of sides

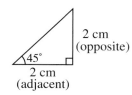

The ratio of the opposite side and the adjacent side is the same for any right-angled triangle if the angle is the same.

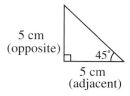

$$\frac{\text{opposite}}{\text{adjacent}} = \frac{2}{2} = 1$$

$$\frac{\text{opposite}}{\text{adjacent}} = \frac{5}{5} = 1$$

The ratio of the opposite and adjacent sides for an angle θ is known as the **'tangent'** of angle θ. We say that

$$\tan\theta = \frac{\text{opp}}{\text{adj}}$$

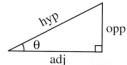

There are two more important ratios:

$$\sin\theta = \frac{\text{opp}}{\text{hyp}}$$

$$\cos\theta = \frac{\text{adj}}{\text{hyp}}$$

(sin θ means the **'sine'** of angle θ)

(cos θ means the **'cosine'** of angle θ)

You **must** learn these three formulas. Some people memorise the word

or

Some people learn a sentence:

eg. **S**ome **O**fficers **H**ave **C**oaches **A**nd **H**orses **T**o **O**rder **A**bout

Make up your own?

tan 45° is simply a number, ie. 1. For example, sin 30° = 0.5. The values of sines, cosines and tangents are stored on calculators. Check you can find them on your calculator.

Warning! Most calculators have 3 trigonometry modes: 'Deg', 'Rad' and 'Gra'. Make sure you work in 'Deg' mode.

Depending on your calculator, the value of sin 30° is found by either pressing [sin] [30] [=] or [30] [sin] [=]

 # Key Facts

Finding a side in a right-angled triangle

1. Draw a diagram.

2. Label the sides opp, hyp, adj according to the angle being used.

3. Decide whether to use the formula for sin, cos or tan.

4. Write down the formula from , or

   then cover up the quantity you wish to find and substitute the numbers (alternatively write down the formula, substitute the numbers then rearrange the formula).

5. Use a calculator to evaluate the answer.

(a) Find x

24 cm
17°
x

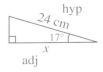

hyp
24 cm
17°
x
adj

Adj = cos θ × Hyp

$x = \cos 17° \times 24$

$x = 23.0$ cm (3 sig. figs)

(b) Find y

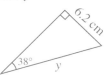

6.2 cm
38°
y

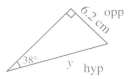

6.2 cm   opp
38°
y hyp

$\text{Hyp} = \dfrac{\text{Opp}}{\sin θ}$

$y = \dfrac{6.2}{\sin 38°}$

$y = 10.1$ cm (3 sig. figs)

M10.8

Copy and complete the following:

1

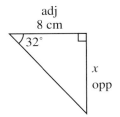

adj
8 cm
32°
x
opp

Opp = tan θ × ☐

$x = \tan$ ☐ × ☐

$x =$ ☐ cm (3 sig. figs)

2

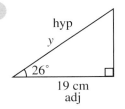

hyp
y
26°
19 cm
adj

$\text{Hyp} = \dfrac{☐}{☐}$

$y = \dfrac{☐}{☐}$

$y =$ ☐ cm (3 sig. figs)

For each triangle below, find the sides marked with letters, correct to 3 significant figures.
All lengths are in cm.

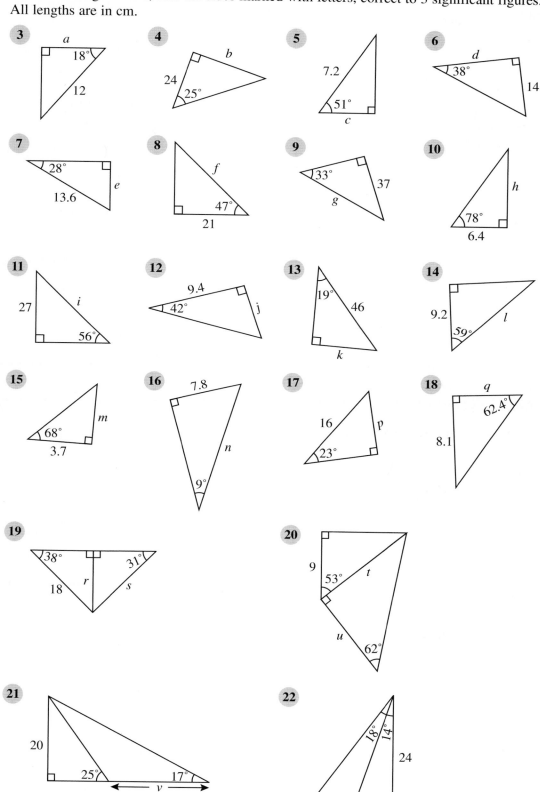

3 a, 18°, 12

4 b, 24, 25°

5 7.2, 51°, c

6 d, 38°, 14

7 28°, 13.6, e

8 f, 47°, 21

9 33°, 37, g

10 h, 78°, 6.4

11 27, i, 56°

12 9.4, 42°, j

13 19°, 46, k

14 9.2, 59°, l

15 68°, 3.7, m

16 7.8, n, 9°

17 16, 23°, p

18 q, 62.4°, 8.1

19 38°, 31°, 18, r, s

20 9, 53°, t, u, 62°

21 20, 25°, 17°, v

22 18°, 14°, 24, w

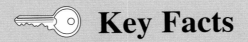

Key Facts

Finding an angle in a right-angled triangle

Follow the same method as for finding a side until you have sin θ, cos θ or tan θ equal to a number.

For example,

 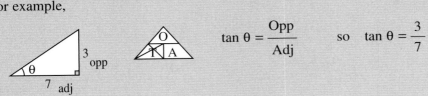

$$\tan \theta = \frac{\text{Opp}}{\text{Adj}} \qquad \text{so} \quad \tan \theta = \frac{3}{7}$$

Since $\tan \theta = \frac{3}{7}$, we need to go backwards on the calculator to find out what angle gives a tangent equal to $\frac{3}{7}$.

We do this by pressing the [INV] button before the tan button (either [INV] [tan] [(] [3] [÷] [7] [)] [=]

or [3] [÷] [4] [=] [INV] [tan]).

The [INV] button is called the 'inverse' button.

Note

On some calculators the 'inverse' button is [SHIFT] or [2ndF]

If $\tan \theta = \frac{3}{7}$ then $\theta = 23.2°$ (to 1 decimal place)

(We say that 23.2° is the *inverse* tangent of $\frac{3}{7}$, sometimes written as $\tan^{-1}\left(\frac{3}{7}\right)$)

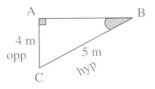 Find AB̂C

$$\sin \theta = \frac{\text{Opp}}{\text{Hyp}}$$

$$\sin \text{AB̂C} = \frac{4}{5} = 0.8$$

use [INV] [sin]

AB̂C = 53.1° (to 1 decimal place)

288

A quantity which has **both magnitude** (size) and **direction** is called a **vector**.

A vector quantity may be represented by a line because a line has a length (magnitude) and a direction.

The vector begins at A and ends at B. We can write this vector as $\overrightarrow{AB}$. The arrow above the AB indicates that the vector begins at A and finishes at B.

A vector can be identified with a single lower-case letter with a line underneath it. In books this is shown by using a bold letter (the line is omitted).

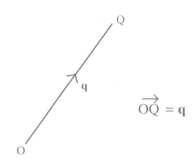

$$\overrightarrow{OQ} = \mathbf{q}$$

If the vector is on a grid, it can be represented by a **column vector**.

$$\mathbf{a} = \begin{pmatrix} 2 \\ 3 \end{pmatrix}$$

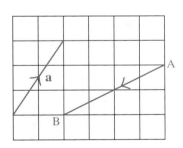

The top number shows how far left or right from the start to the finish of the vector (left indicated by a negative sign).

The bottom number shows how far up or down from the start to the finish of the vector (down indicated by a negative sign).

$$\overrightarrow{AB} = \begin{pmatrix} -4 \\ -2 \end{pmatrix}$$

Common vectors

Force, velocity, acceleration and displacement (eg. 9 km due south).

Scalar quantities

A quantity which has magnitude (size) only.

Finding the length (magnitude) of a column vector

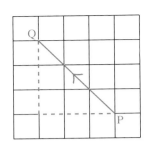

Find the length of $\overrightarrow{PQ}$

if $\overrightarrow{PQ} = \begin{pmatrix} -3 \\ 3 \end{pmatrix}$.

Use Pythagoras

$PQ^2 = 3^2 + 3^2 = 18$

$PQ = \sqrt{18}$

$\left(\text{length of } \overrightarrow{PQ} \right)$

Note

The magnitude of a vector is known as the **modulus** of the vector. The modulus of $\overrightarrow{PQ}$ can be denoted by $\left| \overrightarrow{PQ} \right|$.

E10.1

1 Write each vector as a column vector, eg. $\mathbf{a} = \begin{pmatrix} 1 \\ 3 \end{pmatrix}$ or $\overrightarrow{AB} = \begin{pmatrix} -1 \\ 2 \end{pmatrix}$.

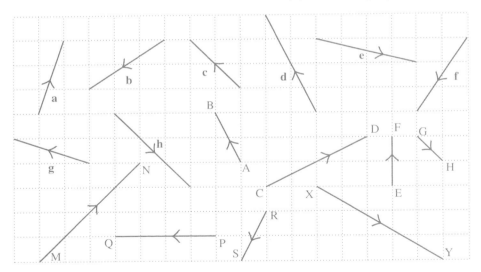

2 Draw and label each vector below on squared paper.

$\mathbf{a} = \begin{pmatrix} 2 \\ 1 \end{pmatrix}$ $\mathbf{b} = \begin{pmatrix} -3 \\ 1 \end{pmatrix}$ $\mathbf{c} = \begin{pmatrix} 5 \\ -2 \end{pmatrix}$ $\mathbf{d} = \begin{pmatrix} 0 \\ 3 \end{pmatrix}$ $\mathbf{e} = \begin{pmatrix} -1 \\ -1 \end{pmatrix}$

$\overrightarrow{AB} = \begin{pmatrix} -4 \\ 2 \end{pmatrix}$ $\overrightarrow{CD} = \begin{pmatrix} 6 \\ -1 \end{pmatrix}$ $\overrightarrow{EF} = \begin{pmatrix} 3 \\ -4 \end{pmatrix}$ $\overrightarrow{GH} = \begin{pmatrix} -2 \\ 0 \end{pmatrix}$ $\overrightarrow{MN} = \begin{pmatrix} 4 \\ -5 \end{pmatrix}$

3 Calculate the length (modulus) of each vector given in Question **2**. Leave your answers in surd form where appropriate.

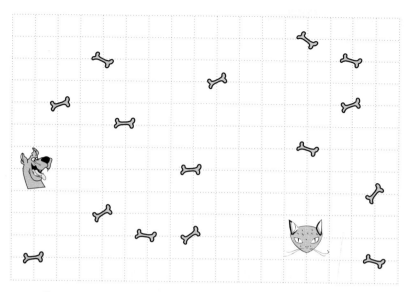

(a) Minnie is searching for bones. She follows a route described by these vectors:

$$\begin{pmatrix} 2 \\ -3 \end{pmatrix} \text{ then } \begin{pmatrix} 3 \\ 0 \end{pmatrix} \text{ then } \begin{pmatrix} 1 \\ 5 \end{pmatrix} \text{ then } \begin{pmatrix} 2 \\ 2 \end{pmatrix} \text{ then } \begin{pmatrix} 5 \\ -4 \end{pmatrix} \text{ then } \begin{pmatrix} 2 \\ -1 \end{pmatrix} \text{ then } \begin{pmatrix} -1 \\ -4 \end{pmatrix}.$$

How many bones might Minnie have found?

(b) Meg also wants bones. She follows this route:

$$\begin{pmatrix} -3 \\ 2 \end{pmatrix} \text{ then } \begin{pmatrix} -2 \\ 1 \end{pmatrix} \text{ then } \begin{pmatrix} -7 \\ -4 \end{pmatrix} \text{ then } \begin{pmatrix} 1 \\ 7 \end{pmatrix} \text{ then } \begin{pmatrix} 7 \\ 1 \end{pmatrix} \text{ then } \begin{pmatrix} 3 \\ 2 \end{pmatrix} \text{ then } \begin{pmatrix} 1 \\ -5 \end{pmatrix} \text{ then } \begin{pmatrix} 3 \\ -2 \end{pmatrix}.$$

How many bones might Meg have found?

Equal vectors

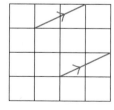

Both vectors shown are equal to $\begin{pmatrix} 2 \\ 1 \end{pmatrix}$.

Two vectors are equal if they have the same length and the same direction (the position on the diagram is not important).

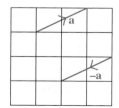

−**a** is a vector equal in length to **a** but in the opposite direction.

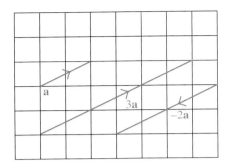

3**a** is a vector in the same direction as **a** but three times the length of **a**.

−2**a** is a vector in the opposite direction to **a** but twice the length of **a**.

Note

If $\mathbf{a} = \begin{pmatrix} 2 \\ 1 \end{pmatrix}$ then $3\mathbf{a} = 3\begin{pmatrix} 2 \\ 1 \end{pmatrix} = \begin{pmatrix} 6 \\ 3 \end{pmatrix}$

Adding vectors

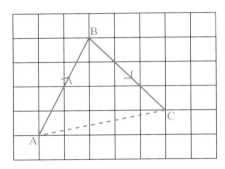

$\overrightarrow{AB} = \begin{pmatrix} 2 \\ 4 \end{pmatrix}$ and $\overrightarrow{BC} = \begin{pmatrix} 3 \\ -3 \end{pmatrix}$

Movement from A to B then B to C is the same result as movement from A to C.

We have $\overrightarrow{AC} = \begin{pmatrix} 5 \\ 1 \end{pmatrix}$

$\overrightarrow{AB} + \overrightarrow{BC} = \begin{pmatrix} 2 \\ 4 \end{pmatrix} + \begin{pmatrix} 3 \\ -3 \end{pmatrix} = \begin{pmatrix} 5 \\ 1 \end{pmatrix}$

so $\overrightarrow{AB} + \overrightarrow{BC} = \overrightarrow{AC}$

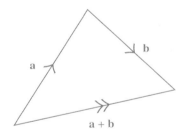

In general, adding 2 vectors shows the result of moving along one vector followed by the other. **a** + **b** is known as the resultant vector.

To add two vectors which are not already joined together, do the following:

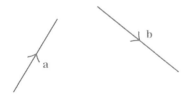

Starting from the end of **a**, draw a vector equal and parallel to **b** (ie. another **b**).

Complete the triangle to show **a** + **b**.

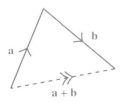

298

8 The length of a rectangle is twice the width of the rectangle. The length of a diagonal of the rectangle is 25 cm.

Work out the area of the rectangle.
Give your answer as an integer.

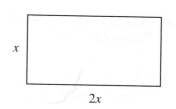

(EDEXCEL)

9

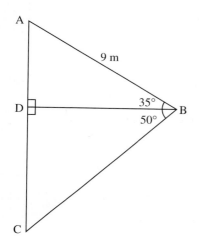

ABD and DBC are two right-angled triangles.
AB = 9 m.

Angle ABD = 35°.

Angle DBC = 50°.

Calculate the length of DC.
Give your answer correct to 3 significant figures.

(EDEXCEL)

10 OABC is a quadrilateral.
P is a point on MB.

$\overrightarrow{OM} = \mathbf{x}$, $\overrightarrow{OC} = \mathbf{y}$ and $\overrightarrow{CB} = 3\mathbf{x}$.
PB = 3MP.

(a) Find in terms of $\mathbf{x}$ and $\mathbf{y}$

   (i) $\overrightarrow{MB}$ (ii) $\overrightarrow{PB}$ (iii) $\overrightarrow{CP}$

   M is the midpoint of OA.

(b) (i) Find $\overrightarrow{CA}$ in terms of $\mathbf{x}$ and $\mathbf{y}$.

   (ii) What do $\overrightarrow{CP}$ and $\overrightarrow{CA}$ indicate about the points A, P and C?

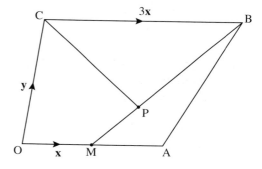

(AQA)

DATA 2

1

In the 'M' sections (mainly grades B, C, D) you will learn how to:
- use two-way tables
- use pie charts
- use scatter diagrams and lines of best fit
- find and use a moving average

In the 'E' sections (mainly grades A*, A) you will learn how to:
- take samples

Also you will learn how to:
- WATCH YOUR MONEY! – credit 3 – personal loans

M **Two-way tables**

70 students from years 10 and 11 were asked what sport they played in their last Games lesson. The information is shown in the table below.

	Football	Rugby	Badminton	Total
Year 10	18	14	B	34
Year 11	14	E	6	C
Total	A	F	D	70

(a) The 'Football' column total is 18 + 14 = 32

(b) The year 10 row total is 34 so 'Badminton' must be 2

(c) The 'Total' column adds up to 70 so the Year 11 total must be 36

(d) The 'Badminton' column total is B + 6 = 2 + 6 = 8

(e) The Year 11 row total is C = 36 so the 'Rugby' must be 16

(f) The 'Rugby' column total is 14 + E = 14 + 16 = 30

	Football	Rugby	Badminton	Total
Year 10	18	14	2	34
Year 11	14	16	6	36
Total	32	30	8	70

We can check our answers by adding the totals along the bottom row to make sure they add up to 70 (32 + 30 + 8 = 70✓)

1 100 people were asked what their favourite kind of chocolate was.
The two-way table gives some information about the results.

	plain chocolate	milk chocolate	white chocolate	Total
Female			5	43
Male	21			
Total		46	14	100

(a) Copy and complete the two-way table.

(b) How many people liked plain chocolate in total?

2 80 children were asked if they went to the cinema, swimming or cycling one day in the Easter holidays. The information is shown in the two-way table below.

	cinema	swimming	cycling	Total
Boys	18	17		47
Girls	15		8	
Total				80

How many children went swimming in total?

3 200 pupils were asked what their favourite school subjects were. The information is shown in the two-way table below.

	Art	PE	Maths	Science	Total
Boys		53	28		119
Girls		28		14	
Total	51			32	200

(a) Copy and complete the two-way table.

(b) One of these pupils is picked at random. Write down the *probability* that the pupil likes Maths best.

4 400 students in Years 10 and 11 were asked if they smoked or drank alcohol on a regular basis. The information is shown in the two-way table below.

	smoke	drink alcohol	neither	smoke and drink alcohol	Total
Year 10	21	40			
Year 11	23			38	227
Total			198	62	400

(a) Copy and complete the two-way table.

(b) One of these students is picked at random. Write down the *probability* that the student will not smoke or drink alcohol.

(c) What percentage of students in Year 11 claim to drink alcohol but not smoke? Give the answer to one decimal place.

315

5 1800 people were asked if they had been in a car accident. The information is shown in the two-way table according to different age groups.

	car accident	no car accident	Total
17 to 25	123	481	
26 to 60	65		702
over 60			
Total	286		1800

(a) Copy and complete the two-way table.

(b) What percentage of the people asked had been in a car accident?

(c) What percentage of each age group had been in a car accident? Comment on your answers.

 Can you still?

 Can you still?

11A **Find probabilities (see Unit 8)**

1. A box contains 17 packets of crisps. 6 packets are plain, 4 are cheese and onion and the remainder are roast chicken. A packet is removed at random. What is the probability that the packet is roast chicken flavour?

2. One card is picked at random from a pack of 52. Find the probability that it is:

(a) a jack (b) a club

3. There are 4 taxi firms in a town: 'abbey', 'pronto', 'slim' and 'catcha'. The table shows the probability of each taxi firm being chosen.

abbey	pronto	slim	catcha
0.25	0.4	x	0.2

(a) What is the probability of 'slim' taxis being chosen?

(b) What is the probability of 'abbey' or 'catcha' taxis being chosen?

(c) For every 40 times a taxi is chosen, how many times would you expect 'pronto' taxis to be chosen?

4. What is the probability of getting 'heads' and a square number if a coin and dice are thrown?

5. What is the probability of getting 3 'tails' if 3 coins are tossed?

6. A dice is thrown and a spinner is spun. What is the probability that the total score on the dice and spinner is:

(a) 8 (b) less than 5

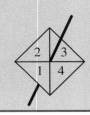

Drawing pie charts

Some people were asked what they had for breakfast. The data is recorded below:

Breakfast	Frequency (number of people)
cereal	18
toast	8
egg	4
nothing	15

To draw a pie chart:

(a) Add up the number of people. Total frequency = 18 + 8 + 4 + 15 = 45

(b) Whole angle in a pie chart = 360°.
   This must be split between 45 people.
   Angle for each person = 360° ÷ 45 = 8°

(c) Angle for 'cereal'   = 18 × 8° = 144°
   Angle for 'toast'   =   8 × 8° = 64°
   Angle for 'egg'   =   4 × 8° = 32°
   Angle for 'nothing' = 15 × 8° = 120°

Remember

Always find the total frequency then divide it into 360° to find out what angle is needed for each item in the pie chart.

Alternatively, express each frequency value as a percentage of the total frequency then find percentages of 360°.

M11.2

In Questions **1**, **2** and **3**, work out the angle for each item and draw a pie chart.

1 Favourite football team

team	frequency
Arsenal	15
Liverpool	15
Chelsea	20
Manchester Utd	25
Everton	6
Aston Villa	9

2 Most popular Briton

Briton	frequency
Shakespeare	15
Churchill	18
Newton	7
Elizabeth I	12
Brunel	8

3 Favourite snack

snack	frequency
crisps	60
fruit	35
nuts	10
biscuits	18
chocolate	34
other	23

4 Hal carries out a survey of 120 Year 10 students. He asks them their favourite cartoon. Measure the angles and complete the table.

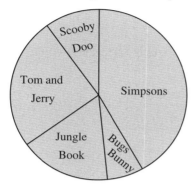

Cartoon	Frequency	Angle
Simpsons	50	
Bugs Bunny		
Jungle Book	20	60°
Tom and Jerry		
Scooby Doo		
Total	120	

5 Jack Jones runs a pub.
He makes his money from 3 main things:
food, drink and hiring out rooms.
The pie chart shows what fraction of his money
he gets from each of these things.
If Jack makes £900 one week,
how much did he make from:

(a) food   (b) hiring out a room   (c) drink

6

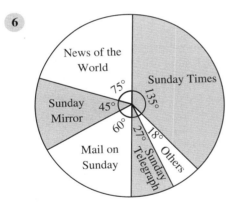

Penny delivers 240 newspapers each Sunday.

The pie chart shows the different newspapers which Penny delivers.

How many of the newspapers were:

(a) News of the World   (b) Sunday Mirror

(c) Sunday Telegraph   (d) Sunday Times

(e) Mail on Sunday   (f) Others

7 Donna asks 180 people who their favourite 'Simpsons' character is. She draws this accurate pie chart. Measure the angles and complete the table.

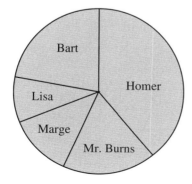

Simpsons character	Frequency	Angle
Homer		
Mr. Burns		64°
Marge		
Lisa		
Bart		
Total	180	

8 The students at
2 different schools were
asked to state their
favourite children's film.
Here are the results.

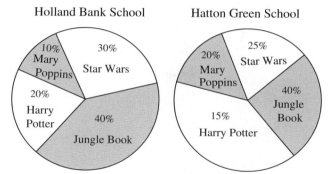

Holland Bank School

Hatton Green School

There were 800 students.   There were 1000 students.

(a) Carl says 'more students in Holland Bank School like Star Wars than the students
in Hatton Green School.'
Use both charts to explain whether or not Carl is right.

(b) Yasmin says 'less students in Holland Bank School like Harry Potter than the
students in Hatton Green School'.
Use both charts to explain whether or not Yasmin is right.

9 People in the North and South of England were asked how many hours of exercise
they took each week. The information is shown in the pie charts below.

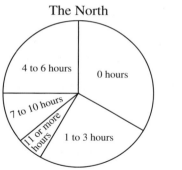

The North

The South

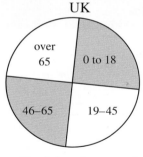

Which of the statements below is correct?

A) 'Less people in the North do some exercise than people in the South'

B) 'A smaller percentage of people in the North do some exercise than people in the South'.

C) 'More people in the North do some exercise than people in the South'.

Explain why you chose your answer.

10 The pie charts below show the ages (in years) of people in the UK and Kenya.

UK

Which of the statements below are correct

A) 'There are more 0 to 18 year-olds in
Kenya than in the UK'.

B) 'There are less 0 to 18 year-olds in Kenya
than in the UK'.

C) 'A greater percentage of the people in
Kenya are 0 to 18 year-olds than in the UK'.

Kenya

Explain why you chose your answer.

(11B) **Mixed number work (see Units 1, 2 and 5)**

1. Write these numbers in order of size (smallest first):

    0.595 $\frac{3}{5}$ $\frac{11}{20}$ 58.2% $\frac{112}{200}$ 0.563

2. How many *complete* small ribbons of length $5\frac{1}{4}$ cm can be cut from a piece of ribbon 2.8 m long?

3. John buys an antique table for £1100. The value of the table increases by 4% of its value at the start of the year. How much will the table be worth after 3 years? (give your answer to the nearest penny)

4. Write 2.83×10^{-3} as an ordinary number.

5. Evaluate $(8.4 \times 10^{12}) \div (4 \times 10^{-3})$

6. Tina earns £19688 after a 7% pay rise. How much did she earn before the increase?

7. $2600 = 2^a \times 5^b \times c$. Find the values of a, b and c.

8. Simplify $\sqrt{48} - \sqrt{12}$

9. Expand and simplify $(\sqrt{5} - 2)(\sqrt{5} + 2)$

10. If $m = 7.2$ and $n = 4.8$ (correct to two significant figures), find the largest possible value of $\frac{3m}{n^2}$

11. Express $0.3\dot{8}$ as a fraction in its lowest terms.

12. Rationalise the denominator in $\frac{4}{\sqrt{5}}$

13. M is directly proportional to the square of N. M = 200 when N = 10.
    Find (a) the value of M when N = 3, (b) the value of N when M = 128.

14. P is inversely proportional to the square root of Q. P = 2 when Q = 36.

    (a) Express P in terms of Q

    (b) Find P when Q = 16

    (c) Find Q when P = 8

M | Scatter graphs

- Here is a scatter diagram showing the number of hours without sleep for a group of people and their reaction time.

- We can see a connection. The longer people went without sleep, the greater their reaction time (ie. people reacted more slowly as they went without sleep).

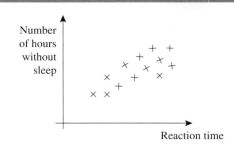

Number of hours without sleep

Reaction time

Correlation

The word 'correlation' describes how things *co-relate*. There is 'correlation' between 2 sets of data if there is a connection or relationship. The correlation between 2 sets of data can be positive or negative and it can be strong or weak.

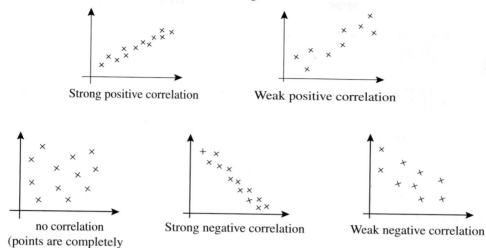

Strong positive correlation   Weak positive correlation

no correlation
(points are completely
spread out)   Strong negative correlation   Weak negative correlation

Line of best fit

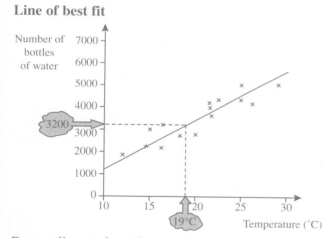

This scatter diagram shows the number of bottles of water sold by a supermarket each week and the average weekly temperature.

(a) A line of best fit is drawn (try to get the same number of points above the line as below).

(b) How many bottles of water are likely to be sold if the average weekly temperature is 19°C?

Draw a line up from the temperature axis to the line of best fit and then across to the vertical axis (as shown). We can estimate that 3200 bottles of water will be sold if the average weekly temperature is 19°C.

M11.3

1 Describe the correlation, if any, in the scatter graphs.

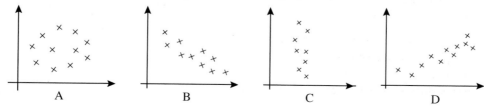

A   B   C   D

321

2 The table below shows the marks of 10 students in a Maths exam and a Science exam.

Maths	74	60	40	80	52	66	50	84	58	70
Science	70	62	44	76	54	56	46	70	56	64

(a) Copy and complete the scatter graph to show the data in the table.

(b) Draw the line of best fit.

(c) A student scored 72% in the Maths test but missed the Science test. Use your line of best fit to find out the Science mark that the student would have been most likely to get.

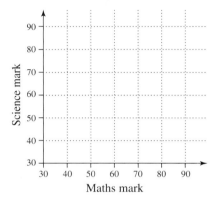

3 15 people were given a short term memory test where they could achieve a maximum score of 20. The table below shows their ages and marks.

Age	55	65	75	50	45	64	70	59	67	50	72	48	80	57	60
Score	17	12	10	16	18	13	15	15	15	17	12	19	10	15	12

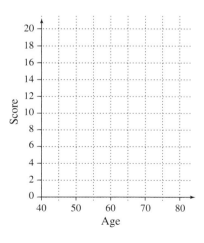

(a) Copy and complete the scatter diagram to show the data in the table.

(b) Draw the line of best fit.

(c) What score would you expect a 63 year-old to get?

4 Describe the type of correlation you would expect if you drew a scatter graph for each pair of variables below:

(a) 'adult ages' against 'time to run 100 m'

(b) 'neck size' against 'height'

(c) 'amount of snow' against 'sales of sledges'

(d) 'weekly income' against 'number of cups of tea drunk each week'

5 Information was recorded about 12 smokers. The table shows how many cigarettes they smoked each day and their age when they died.

age	65	51	58	80	46	72	61	80	75	48	52	68
number of cigarettes per day	37	42	40	10	44	23	35	20	26	49	44	32

(a) Draw a scatter graph to show this data. Use the *x*-axis for ages from 40 to 90. Use the *y*-axis for the number of cigarettes per day from 0 to 50.

(b) Describe the correlation in this scatter graph.

(c) Draw the line of best fit.

(d) If a person smoked 38 cigarettes each day, what age would you expect that person to live to?

6 **WHOLE CLASS ACTIVITY**

(a) *If your teacher allows*, each person in your class must do as many step-ups onto a chair as possible in one minute. When a person finishes, that person must find his/her pulse rate by counting how many beats in one minute. Also each person needs to find out his/her height (to the nearest cm) and record his/her shoe size.

Enter all the data in a table, either on the board or on a sheet of paper.

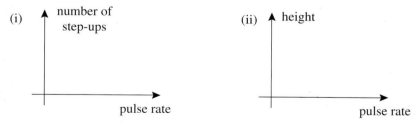

height	shoe size	number of step-ups	pulse rate

(b) Draw the scatter graphs shown below.

(i) number of step-ups (vertical axis) against pulse rate (horizontal axis)

(ii) height (vertical axis) against pulse rate (horizontal axis)

(c) Describe the correlation, if any, in the scatter graphs you drew in part (b).

(d) (i) Draw a scatter graph of 2 sets of data where you think there might be positive correlation.

(ii) Was there indeed a positive correlation?

323

11C   Use probability trees (see Unit 8)

1. Harry passes through two sets of traffic lights on his way to work. The probability of the first set of lights being red is $\frac{2}{5}$. If the first set of lights is red, the probability of the second set of lights being red is $\frac{1}{4}$. If the first set of lights is not red, the probability of the second set of lights being red is $\frac{3}{8}$. Copy and complete the tree diagram.

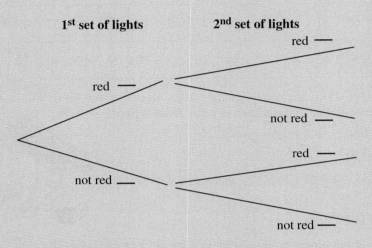

   (a) Find the probability that both lights will be red.

   (b) Find the probability that only one set of lights will be red.

2. A box contains 7 creme eggs and 8 caramel eggs. One egg is removed at random from the box followed by another egg. Use a probability tree to find the probability that

   (a) both eggs will be caramel

   (b) one egg of each type is removed

3. The probability of Joe eating an apple or an orange or a peach is equal. Joe eats one of these pieces of fruit on each of Tuesday, Wednesday and Thursday. Find the probability that

   (a) Joe will eat 3 peaches

   (b) Joe will eat the same fruit each day

   (c) Joe will eat at least one apple

4. There are 11 red cards and 8 black cards remaining in a pile of playing cards. Beth has to take 3 cards. What is the probability that

   (a) all 3 cards are red

   (b) at least one card is black

   (c) exactly 2 cards are red

The table below shows how many DVDs were hired out in each month of a year by a video shop.

month	Apr	May	Jun	Jul	Aug	Sep	Oct	Nov	Dec	Jan	Feb	Mar
number of DVDs	860	700	640	680	920	640	780	1000	1060	840	640	540

This information is shown in the graph below.

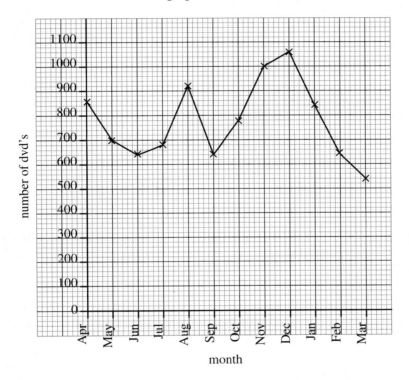

The line graph shows the monthly figures. The general *trend* can be shown more clearly by *using mean averages*.

Choose at least the first 3 months. We will in fact choose the first 4 months. Find the mean average for these 4 months.

Apr, May, Jun, Jul: mean = (860 + 700 + 640 + 680) ÷ 4 = 720

Plot this on the same graph at the midpoint of the 4 months: (See point A on next graph).

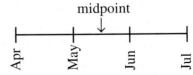

Now **move** on one month and find the mean average for these 4 months.

May, Jun, Jul, Aug: mean = (700 + 640 + 680 + 920) ÷ 4 = 735

Plot this on the graph at the midpoint of the 4 months.

Now **move** on one month and find the mean average for the 4 months Jun, Jul, Aug, Sep (i.e. 720). Plot the point then keep **moving** on one month and repeating the process (i.e. 755, 835, 870, 920, 885 and 770). We call these averages the **moving average**.

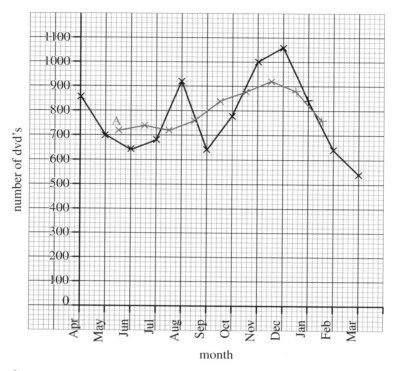

The **moving average** (joined by the blue line) gives a better idea of the trend. We can see that there is a steady rise in the number of dvd's hired out towards December then a steady fall after December.

Note

The moving average gives a clearer idea of the trend for a set of data. It deals with short-term differences.

Groups of 4 months were used in the example but 3, 5, 6 or more months could also have been used. We say a group of 4 months gives a '4-*point moving average*'.

M11.4

1 The table below shows how many cars a garage sells during one year.

month	Jan	Feb	Mar	Apr	May	Jun	Jul	Aug	Sep	Oct	Nov	Dec
number of cars	8	9	7	20	8	29	27	28	12	29	27	28

(a) Draw a line graph for the information in this table.

(b) Find the 4-point moving average (ie. use groups of 4 months). Plot the new moving average on the graph each time.

(c) Join up the moving average points with a dotted line. Comment on the trend of car sales.

2 The table below shows how many computers were sold by a store during an 18 month period.

month	Jan	Feb	Mar	Apr	May	Jun	Jul	Aug	Sep	Oct	Nov	Dec	Jan	Feb	Mar	Apr	May	Jun
number of computers	35	10	30	40	35	40	15	35	10	15	40	35	35	5	40	35	30	35

(a) Copy the axes below and draw a line graph for the information in the table.

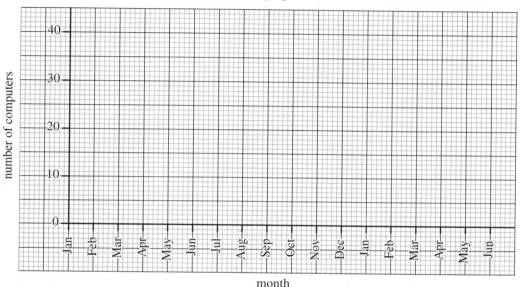

(b) Find the mean average for the first 5 months: Jan, Feb, Mar, Apr, May. Plot this average on the graph at the midpoint of the 5 months (i.e. Mar).

(c) Move along one month and find the mean average for the 5 months: Feb, Mar, Apr, May, Jun. Plot this average on the graph at the midpoint of the 5 months (ie. Apr).

(d) Keep moving along one month and finding the 5-point moving average (ie. use a group of 5 months). Plot the new moving average on the graph each time.

(e) Join up the moving average points with a dotted line. Comment on the trend of computer sales during this 18 month period.

3 The table below shows the weekly wage bill for a centre forward at a Premiership football team during the years shown.

year	1994	1995	1996	1997	1998	1999	2000	2001	2002	2003	2004	2005
wage (£1000's)	50	52	55	31	34	60	63	67	30	52	59	67

(a) Draw a line graph for the information in this table.

(b) Find the 4-point moving average.

(c) Plot the moving average points on the graph and join them up with a dotted line.

(d) Comment on the trend shown. Can you suggest any reasons for the lower wage bill in 1997, 1998 and 2002?

4 A company announces its profits every quarter (ie. every 3 months). Profits (in £ million's) over a 4-year period are shown in the table below.

	First quarter	Second quarter	Third quarter	Fourth quarter
2002	4.5	4.6	1.4	4.7
2003	4.3	4.5	4.1	0.9
2004	4.2	2.3	1.5	1.6
2005	1.4	3.2	4.3	4.5

(a) Draw a line graph for the information in this table.

(b) Find the 5-point moving average (ie. use groups of 5 quarters). Plot the new moving average on the graph each time.

(c) Join up the moving average points with a dotted line. Comment on the profits trend for this company.

5 The table below shows how many people went to a nightclub on a Friday night over a 15-week period.

week	1	2	3	4	5	6	7	8	9	10	11	12	13	14
number of people	800	680	1720	760	840	720	1640	800	1720	880	1080	1920	1520	1400

(a) Draw a line graph for the information in this table.

(b) Find the 6-point moving average (ie. use groups of 6 weeks).

(c) Plot the moving average points on the graph and join them up with a dotted line.

(d) Comment on the trend shown.

11D **Solve equations (see Units 4 and 6)**

Solve the following equations:

1. $8n - 13 = 3n + 22$

2. $5(2a - 3) = 25$

3. $11 = \dfrac{m}{4} - 3$

4. $y^2 + 6y + 8 = 0$

5. $x^2 - 9x + 20 = 0$

6. $\dfrac{5b - 4}{2} = 13$

7. $n^2 - 6n = 0$

8. $a^2 - 6a = 16$

9. $2(3x - 1) = 4(2x + 4)$

10. $m^2 = m$

11. $10x^2 - 13x - 3 = 0$

12. $12y^2 - 23y + 10 = 0$

13.

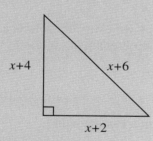

All units are in cm.

(a) Write down a quadratic equation involving x.

(b) Solve this equation to find x and state the length of each side of the triangle.

14. All units are in cm.

(a) Write down an expression for the shaded area in terms of n.

(b) Given that the shaded area is 65 cm², write down a quadratic equation involving n.

(c) Solve this equation to find the value of n.

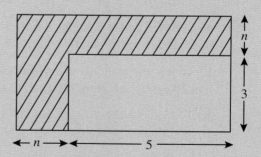

E | **Sampling**

Surveys often have to be undertaken to gather information, for example: a supermarket wants to improve the services it offers, a person wants to start a business and needs to find out the likely sales or the Government wants to discover the eating habits of people so that it can advise.

Key Facts

The whole group of whatever is under investigation is called the *population*.

The whole population is often very large so not every member of the population can always be surveyed. A *sample* of the population is surveyed (a small part of the population). This sample must be *representative* of the whole population.

The *sample size* is affected by the cost of collecting the data and the precision of the findings required. If a larger sample size is taken, the precision of the findings should be greater.

Every effort should be made to avoid *bias*. It is not likely to be very reliable to survey people entering Old Trafford (Manchester United's ground) to find out what percentage of people like each football club in the whole country!

E11.1

1. Tom wants to find out how much each person in his town earns. He selects a sample of people. Which methods below are likely to give representative samples?

   (a) asking every 5th adult at the local swimming pool

   (b) asking people at random on the High Street

   (c) asking each person in the 'Dog and Duck' pub on a Friday night

   (d) selecting people at random from the electoral register

   (e) asking people in every 10th house on every street

2. Write down which samples below are likely to be representative. For any sample which is not representative, give a reason why it is not.

   (a) To test the contents of tins of baked beans made in a factory. The sample is chosen by selecting the first 30 tins made each day and the last 30 tins.

   (b) To find out the average amount of homework given in a secondary school. The sample is chosen by selecting at random 20 pupils from each year group.

   (c) To find out the average amount of time people spend gardening each week. The sample is chosen by asking people as they enter a local garden centre.

   (d) To survey people about the local train services. The sample is chosen by selecting at random 8% of the town's population from the town's telephone directory.

   (e) To survey the nation's favourite food. The sample is chosen by sending questionnaires to randomly selected Indian restaurants throughout the country.

   (f) To investigate the level of pollution on Britain's beaches. The sample is chosen by selecting at random 5% of the beaches from a complete list of Britain's beaches.

(g) To check the contents in boxes of 'Quality Street' chocolates in a supermarket. The sample is chosen by selecting every 15th box of 'Quality Street'.

(h) To find out the most popular television programmes. The sample is chosen by selecting at random 10% of over-60s on the electoral register.

3 Describe how you would select a representative sample for each of the following:

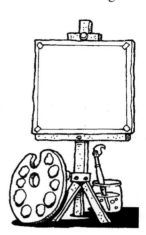

(a) To investigate the most popular colour of sock owned by people in Cheltenham town.

(b) To find out the most popular cars owned by people in Wales.

(c) To investigate the smoking habits of students in a secondary school.

(d) To survey people about their favourite pastimes.

(e) To survey opinion about a new TV comedy programme.

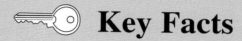 **Key Facts**

Sampling methods

Simple random sampling – every member of the population has the same chance of being chosen.

For example, we could assign each member of the population a number, write each number on an identical disc then put all the discs in a container. We could then take out a disc from the container to select a member of the population at random.

We could also use a *random number table* (your teacher may wish to illustrate this).

When tackling data handling coursework you may wish to use a *random number generator* such as a *computer* or a *calculator*.

On some calculators $\boxed{\text{SHIFT}}$ $\boxed{\text{RAN \#}}$ will generate random three-digit numbers between 0.001 and 0.999. The decimal point can then be ignored (This calculator program does not produce truly random numbers but is good enough for use in school coursework).

Systematic sampling – every n^{th} item is chosen (for example, every 5th item or every 100th item).

Stratified random sampling – the population is divided into groups where the groups have something in common. Every member of the population should belong to one and only one group. Simple random samples are then taken from each group. The numbers in each sample must be proportional to the numbers in each group making up the population.

800 people attend an athletics match. 210 people are Scottish, 328 are English, 149 are Irish and 113 are Welsh.

Sabby wants to survey 50 people on the sports provision in their home towns. She decides to take a stratified sample of 50 people.

What should be the sample size for each of the Scottish, English, Irish and Welsh people?

There are 800 people in total.

Fraction of Scottish people to be chosen $= \dfrac{210}{800}$

So Scottish sample size $= \dfrac{210}{800} \times 50 = 13$ (rounded off)

Total sample size

English sample size $= \dfrac{328}{800} \times 50 = 21$ (rounded off)

Irish sample size $= \dfrac{149}{800} \times 50 = 9$ (rounded off)

Welsh sample size $= \dfrac{113}{800} \times 50 = 7$ (rounded off)

An appropriate method would then be used to take each random sample. The total sample chosen should then be representative of all the people attending the athletics match.

E11.2

1 347 people work for a finance company called 'Loothold'. 138 people are male.
A survey is to be undertaken to find out about the working conditions at 'Loothold'.
A stratified sample of 40 people is to be taken from the male and female workers.
How many females will be chosen in the sample?

2 The list below shows the numbers of students in each year group in a certain school.
It is wanted to take a sample of 50 students from the school to question them about their attitudes to exams.

Year	Number of students
9	137
10	121
11	118
12	95
13	89

(a) Explain why you would want to use a stratified sample.

(b) Work out how many students you would want from each year group.

3 A restaurant wants detailed feedback from its customers. The owner decides to ask every 10th person.

(a) Name this type of sampling.

(b) Will the owner's sample provide a representative view?

4 Marcus needs to survey people who go to the local cinema. Explain how Marcus could take a simple random sample.

5 Students in a certain school were asked to list their favourite sports. Their choices are shown below. A sample of 100 students is to be taken from the school to question them about their attitudes to sport.

Sport	Number of students
Football	302
Rugby	128
Hockey	95
Basketball	45
Cricket	140
Netball	62
None	59

(a) Explain why you would want to use a stratified sample.

(b) Work out how many students you would want in your sample from each category.

6 A breakdown of the people attending a rock concert is shown opposite.

Mel wants to find out about the musical backgrounds of the people at the rock concert.

Age group	Male	Female	Total
12–18	32	18	50
19–25	71	70	141
26–45	93	112	205
46–55	62	93	155
over 55	24	27	51
			602

She takes a sample of 60 people.

(a) How many people should she have sampled in the 19–25 age group?

(b) Explain whether Mel should sample the same number of males and females in the 26–45 age group.

(c) How many people in the over 55 age group should she have sampled?

The height of one hundred trees is shown below (in cm) in the position in which they were planted.

55	84	91	86	76	67	88	89	97	47	43	58	57	49	57	45	51	28	65	90	82	91	83
81	80	70	81	75	39	91	57	80	78	96	88	92	87	79	62	69	72	60	50	41	50	35
71	82	45	37	41	45	56	47	38	37	80	63	77	70	63	75	79	68	95	60	54	83	77
47	42	42	95	87	92	91	80	91	76	91	80	71	66	87	83	40	92	87	85	82	95	92

(a) Use a systematic sample to find an estimate for the mean height of the trees (use the 1st, 6th, 11th etc. value), writing down the 20 values that you use.

(b) Now use only the 1st, 11th, 21st etc. to find another estimate for the mean height of the tree.

(c) Which estimate is more reliable?

(d) What other method of sampling might be more reliable?

8 Mehm wants to investigate the health history of common pets in his town. There are 328 dogs, 336 cats, 218 rabbits and 188 hamsters. He wants to take a total stratified sample of 10% of all the pets.

(a) How many of each type of pet will he use in his sample?

(b) Describe how he will ensure he gets a random sample for each category of pet.

WATCH YOUR MONEY! – Credit 3 – personal loans

If you do not have enough money to buy an item, you might buy *on credit*. There are different ways of doing this such as hire purchase, credit cards, store cards, bank overdrafts and personal loans.

Make sure you know the true cost of buying on credit.

This section deals with personal loans.

Personal loans

- An amount of money borrowed from a bank or another organisation.
  The loan is paid back in fixed amounts, usually each month.

- The fixed amount must be paid each month. You cannot pay a little less one month then a little more the following month.

- The interest rate is usually a lot less than the interest rate on a credit card.

Payment protection

People are advised to take out insurance with their loan so that loan repayments will be made if people become ill, unemployed or have an accident. Payment protection increases the cost of a loan.

The table below shows the monthly repayments on loans over 1 year up to 5 years, with and without payment protection.

Loan (£)	12 months (£)		24 months (£)		36 months (£)		48 months (£)		60 months (£)	
	With protection	Without protection	With protection	Without protection	With protection	Without protection	With protection	Without protection	With protection	Without protection
1000	90.12	88.75	47.91	46.63	33.82	32.70	26.38	25.65	22.06	21.52
3000	269.09	265.31	142.38	139.65	100.83	98.12	79.18	77.36	66.32	64.91
5000	441.18	436.12	230.36	227.49	160.01	157.24	125.31	123.32	102.75	101.48
10000	879.83	873.51	458.31	453.62	318.09	314.21	248.03	245.72	204.89	202.27
15000	1316.42	1308.65	684.37	678.63	475.18	470.53	369.23	366.14	305.92	303.86
25000	2187.38	2177.28	1138.46	1130.36	788.41	782.08	611.74	607.83	506.99	504.69

1   What is the monthly repayment on a £5000 loan over 36 months with protection?

2   What is the monthly repayment on a £3000 loan over 24 months without protection?

3   What is the monthly repayment on a £15000 loan over 60 months without protection?

4   What is the monthly repayment on a £10000 loan over 12 months with protection?

5   How much *more* will the monthly repayment on a £3000 loan with protection over 36 months cost than without protection?

6   How much *more* will the monthly repayment on a £25000 loan with protection over 48 months cost than without protection?

7   If Carl borrows £5000 over 60 months with protection for a holiday to Italy, how much money will he pay back *in total*? How much *interest* will he pay *in total*?

8   If Sunita borrows £15000 for a new car over 36 months without protection, how much money will she pay back *in total*? How much *interest* will she pay *in total*?

9   If you borrow £1000 over 24 months without protection, how much money will you pay back *in total*? How much *interest* will you pay *in total*?

10   If you borrow £10000 over 60 months with protection, how much *more* will it cost you *in total* than borrowing the money without protection?

335

1. Using two-way tables

120 people were given the chance to go to Australia, India or the USA. The information showing their choices is in the two-way table below.

	Australia	India	U.S.A	Total
Female		32		71
Male	24			
Total	47		33	120

(a) Copy and complete the two-way table.

(b) One of these people is picked at random. Write down the *probability* that the person has chosen India.

(c) What percentage of the females chose the U.S.A?

2. Using pie charts

(a) In a list of the 120 richest people in the country, their backgrounds are listed below.

background	number of people
inherited	23
business	38
music	28
sport	19
other	12

Draw a pie chart to show this information.

(b)

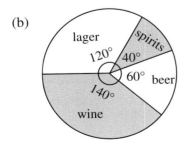

108 people were asked what their favourite drink is. The results are shown in the pie chart. How many people said:

(i) beer   (ii) lager

(iii) spirits   (iv) wine?

3. Using scatter diagrams and lines of best fit

The table below shows the engine sizes of 12 cars and how many miles per gallon they operate at.

engine size (litres)	1.8	1.1	2	1.6	1	1.8	1.5	2.8	1.2	2	1.6	1.4	2.4	2.1
miles per gallon	35	53	24	33	47	31	33	16	46	30	40	42	20	22

(a) Copy and complete the scatter diagram to show the data in the table.

(b) Describe the correlation.

(c) Draw the line of best fit.

(d) Use the line of best fit to estimate how many miles per gallon a 1.3 litre car would do.

(e) Roughly with what engine size would you expect the car to do 23 miles per gallon?

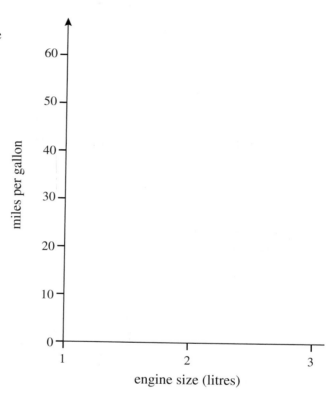

4. Finding and using a moving average

The table below shows how many umbrellas are sold by a store during one year.

month	Jan	Feb	Mar	Apr	May	Jun	Jul	Aug	Sep	Oct	Nov	Dec
number of umbrellas sold	420	440	400	380	200	360	100	120	300	420	460	480

(a) Draw a line graph for the information in this table.

(b) Find the 4-point moving average.

(c) Plot the moving average points on the graph and join them up with a dotted line.

(d) Comment on the trend shown. Suggest reasons for this trend.

337

(a) Calli wants to find out what leisure facilities the people in her town would like. She stands outside the main supermarket in the town one Thursday morning and asks the first 100 people she sees. Criticise this method of taking a sample of the people who live in her town.

(b) People who work for a certain firm were asked to list their favourite holiday destinations. Their choices are shown below. A sample of 80 people is to be taken from the firm to question them about their requirements for a satisfying holiday.

Holiday destination	Number of people
Spain	61
Greece	49
USA	82
Australia	37
Thailand	28
France	79
India	21
China	17

(i) Explain why you would want to use a stratified sample.

(ii) How many people would you want in your sample from each category?

(c) A local council wishes to survey the students in three different secondary schools about their attitudes to education. Suggest how the council should obtain a representative sample.

Mixed examination questions

1 The table shows information about a group of adults.

	Can drive	Cannot drive
Male	32	8
Female	38	12

(a) A man in the group is chosen at random.

What is the probability that he can drive?

(b) A man in the group is chosen at random and a woman in the group is chosen at random.

What is the probability that both the man and the woman **cannot** drive?   (AQA)

2 A scientist weighs some chicks. She records their weights in grams and their ages in days. The table below shows her results.

Age (days)	3	8	1	10	5	8	11	2
Weight (grams)	12	20	7	23	18	24	30	10

(a) Draw a scatter diagram to show these results.

(b) The mean weight is 18g. Calculate the mean age.

(c) Draw a line of best fit on your scatter diagram.

(d) Use your scatter diagram to estimate the weight of a chick 9 days old. (WJEC)

3 (a) Here is a scatter graph. One axis is labelled "weight".

Weight

(i) For this graph state the type of correlation.

(ii) From this list choose an appropriate label for the other axis.

shoe size, length of hair, height, hat size, length of arm

(b) Here is another scatter graph with one axis labelled "weight".

Weight

(i) For this graph state the type of correlation.

(ii) From this list choose an appropriate label for the other axis.

shoe size, distance around neck, waist measurement, GCSE Maths mark

(EDEXCEL)

4 The table shows the number of computer games sold in a supermarket each month from January to June.

Jan	Feb	Mar	Apr	May	Jun
147	161	238	135	167	250

(a) Work out the three month moving averages for this information. (EDEXCEL)

5 The table shows the number of students in a school.

Boys	241
Girls	258

A stratified random sample of 50 students were asked some questions about school dinners.

How many boys were included in the sample? (AQA)

6 Sam was making a survey of pupils in his school.

He wanted to find out their opinions on noise pollution by motor bikes.

The size of each year group in the school is shown below.

Year Group	Boys	Girls	Total
8	85	65	150
9	72	75	147
10	74	78	152
11	77	72	149
6th Form	93	107	200
			798

Sam took a sample of 80 pupils.

(a) Explain whether or not he should have sampled equal numbers of boys and girls in year 8.

(b) Calculate the number of pupils he should have sampled in year 8.   (EDEXCEL)

7 720 students were asked how they travelled to school.

The pie chart shows the results of this survey.

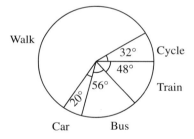

Work out how many of the students travelled to school by bus.

8 The table shows the number of people in each age group who watched a school sports day.

Age group	0–16	17–29	30–44	45–59	60+
Number of people	177	111	86	82	21

Martin did a survey of these people.

He used a stratified sample of exactly 50 people according to age group.

Work out the number of people from each age group that should have been in his sample of 50.

Complete the table.

Age group	0–16	17–29	30–44	45–59	60+	Total
Number of people in sample						

(EDEXCEL)

Answer these questions by forming a pair of simultaneous equations then solving them.

1 Ted buys three ties and two shirts which cost him £132. Keanan buys four ties and three shirts for £190. Find the cost of a tie and the cost of a shirt.

2 A shop sells 'Gello' pens and 'Inko' pens. A 'Gello' pen costs £5 and an 'Inko' pen costs £7. One day the shop sold 17 pens and received £109. How many of each type of pen were sold?

3 The Smith family buys 3 tickets for adults and 5 tickets for children at Legoland for £34. The Green family buys 5 tickets for adults and 7 tickets for children which cost a total of £52. Find the cost of one adult ticket and one child's ticket.

4 A man had £1.75 in his pocket made up of 2 p and 5 p coins. If he had 50 coins in his pocket then find the number of 2 p coins he had.

5 Three times one number plus the other number adds up to 45. The difference between the two numbers is 7. Find the values of the two numbers.

6 Nasser buys 3 first class tickets and 5 second class tickets for a plane journey. These cost him £1264.
Mary buys 7 first class tickets and 3 second class tickets for the same journey. These cost her £1827.
Find the cost of one first class ticket and one second class ticket.

7 Sinead buys 4 tickets in stand A and 5 tickets in stand B for a football match which cost her £144. Terri buys 6 tickets in stand A and 7 tickets in stand B and these cost her £207. Find the cost of one stand A ticket and one stand B ticket.

8 A straight line has an equation $y = mx + c$. It passes through the point (1, 2). It also passes through the point (5, 14). Find the values of m and c.

9 A mother is six times as old as her daughter. Let the mother's age be m and the daughter's age be d.

(a) Write down an equation involving m and d.

(b) Write down an expression for the mother's age in two years' time.

(c) Write down an expression for the daughter's age in two years' time.

(d) In two years' time, the mother is five times as old as her daughter. Write down a second equation involving m and d.

(e) Solve the equations of (a) and (d) to find the present age of the mother and daughter.

347

10 A curve has an equation $y = ax^2 + bx + c$. The curve passes through the points (0, 2), (1, 10) and (2, 24). Find the values of a, b and c.

11 A hotel sold twice as many 'standard' rooms as it sold 'luxury' suites for a certain week. The 'standard' rooms cost £125 and the 'luxury' suites cost £220. The total cost of the rooms and suites was £17390.
Find how many 'standard' rooms and how many 'luxury' suites were sold.

Can you still?

Can you still

12A **Transform shapes (see Unit 9)**

1.

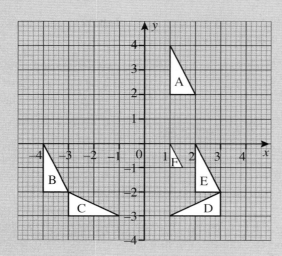

Describe *fully* the transformation that maps the triangles as shown below:

(a) A onto B   (b) B onto C

(c) C onto D   (d) D onto E

(e) E onto F   (f) F onto A

2. (a) Draw an x-axis from –5 to 10 and a y-axis from –3 to 10.

(b) Draw a triangle A with vertices at (–2, 4), (–6, 4) and (–6, 2).

(c) Enlarge triangle A by a scale factor of $-\frac{1}{2}$ about the origin. Label the image B.

(d) Translate triangle B through $\begin{pmatrix} 5 \\ -1 \end{pmatrix}$. Label the image C.

(e) Enlarge triangle C by a scale factor of 3 about (–4, –4). Label the image D.

(f) Reflect triangle D in the line $x = 3$. Label the image E

(g) Rotate triangle E 90° anticlockwise about (3, 2). Label the image F.

(h) Write down the co-ordinates of all the vertices of triangle F.

M   Sequences

M12.6

In Questions **1** to **6**, write down the *next 2 numbers*. What is the rule for each sequence?

1 2, 6, 18, 54, ...

2 $\frac{1}{2}$, 1, $1\frac{1}{2}$, 2, ...

3 150, 140, 120, 90, ...

4 1.3, 1.7, 2.1, 2.5, ...

5 300, 30, 3, 0.3, ...

6 $\frac{1}{2}$, $\frac{1}{10}$, $\frac{1}{50}$, $\frac{1}{250}$, ...

7   shape 1   shape 2   shape 3   shape 4

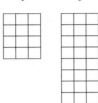

How many small squares are needed for (a) shape 5

(b) shape 6

In Questions **8** to **15** find the next 2 numbers in each sequence (it may help you to work out the 2nd differences).

8 6, 7, 10, 15, 22, ...

9 3, 5, 12, 24, 41, ...

10 1, 4, 10, 19, 31, ...

11 2, 3, 7, 14, 24, ...

12 1, 9, 25, 49, 81, ...

13 5, 6, 11, 20, 33, ...

14 4, 9, 19, 34, 54, ...

15 7, 8, 11, 16, 23, ...

16 Find the next 2 numbers in the sequence below. Try to explain the pattern.

1, 1, 2, 3, 5, 8, 13, ...

17 Find the next 2 numbers in the sequence below.

0, 0, 1, 1, 2, 4, 7, 13, ...

18 This is Pascal's triangle.

```
            1
          1   1
        1   2   1
      1   3   3   1
    1   4   6   4   1
  1   5  10  10   5   1
1   6  15  20  15   6   1
```

(a) Look carefully at how the triangle is made. Write down the next row. It starts: 1 7...

(b) Work out the sum of the numbers in each row of Pascal's triangle. What do you notice?

19 Each term in a sequence may be called the nth term. If the nth term $= 3n + 4$ then

1st term $= (3 \times 1) + 4 = 7$ (using $n = 1$)

2nd term $= (3 \times 2) + 4 = 10$ (using $n = 2$)

10th term $= (3 \times 10) + 4 = 34$ (using $n = 10$)

Write down the first 6 terms of the sequence which has n^{th} term $= n^2 + 5$

20 Write down the first four terms of the sequence which has an nth term equal to:

(a) $4n - 3$ (b) $n^2 - 1$ (c) $n^2 + 8$

(d) 2^n (e) $\dfrac{2n - 1}{2n + 1}$ (f) $\dfrac{1}{2}n(n - 1)$

M **Linear sequence rules**

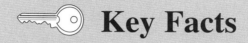 **Key Facts**

The *term-to-term* rule explains how one term in a sequence is connected to the next term.

3, 5, 9, 17, ... the term-to-term rule is 'double then subtract 1'.

The *position-to-term* rule explains how a term in a sequence is connected to its position in the sequence.

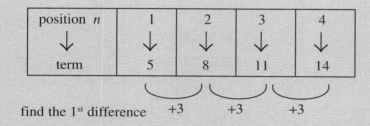

find the 1st difference +3 +3 +3

If the 1st difference is the same, the rule will involve the '1st difference' *multiplied* by the 'position n' ie. $3 \times n$ (we write $3n$)

Work out the '$3n$' numbers and write them beneath the terms.

position n	1	2	3	4
term	5	8	11	14
$3n$	3	6	9	12

We can see that we need to add 2 onto each '$3n$' value to get the term so each term = $3n + 2$

We call this the formula for the 'n^{th} *term*'

n^{th} term = $3n + 2$

We can check this formula by substituting a value of n, for example $n = 2$

n^{th} term = $3n + 2 = (3 \times 2) + 2 = 8$ so the formula appears to work.

Find the nth term for the sequence 30, 26, 22, 18, ...

Draw a table showing positions and terms.

position n	1	2	3	4
term	30	26	22	18
$-4n$	-4	-8	-12	-16

1st difference = -4
so work out $-4n$ values

Need to add 34 to each '$-4n$' value to get each term

so n^{th} term $= -4n + 34$

this is better written as n^{th} term $= 34 - 4n$

(check with n values of your choice)

M12.7

1 Use the tables below to help you find the nth term of each sequence.

(a) Sequence 8, 10, 12, 14, ...

position n	1	2	3	4
term	8	10	12	14
$2n$	2	4	6	8

n^{th} term $= 2n +$ ☐

(b) Sequence 3, 7, 11, 15, ...

position n	1	2	3	4
term	3	7	11	15
$4n$	4	8	12	16

n^{th} term $=$ ☐

(c) Sequence 5, 9, 13, 17, ...

n	1	2	3	4
term	5	9	13	17
$4n$				

n^{th} term $=$ ☐

(d) Sequence 2, 5, 8, 11, ...

n	1	2	3	4
term	2	5	8	11
$3n$				

n^{th} term $=$ ☐

2 For each sequence below, make tables if necessary and find the nth term.

(a) 3, 9, 15, 21, ...

(b) 4, 11, 18, 25, ...

(c) 13, 23, 33, 43, ...

(d) 8, 13, 18, 23, ...

(e) 1, 9, 17, 25, ...

(f) 7, 16, 25, 34, ...

(g) 12, 10, 8, 6, ...

(h) 17, 13, 9, 5, ...

(i) 2.5, 3, 3.5, 4, ...

(j) 40, 31, 22, 13, ...

3 (a) Find the nth term of 5, 11, 17, 23, ...

(b) Find the 40th term of 5, 11, 17, 23, ...

(c) Which term of 5, 11, 17, 23, ... is equal to 479?

4   (a) Find the nth term of 3, 10, 17, 24, ...

     (b) Find the 71st term of 3, 10, 17, 24, ...

     (c) Which term of 3, 10, 17, 24, ... is equal to 710?

5   (a) Find the nth term of 8, 19, 30, 41, ...

     (b) Find the 12th term of 8, 19, 30, 41, ...

     (c) Which term of 8, 19, 30, 41, ... is equal to 250?

6   Here is a sequence of shapes made from sticks.

let n = shape number and s = number of sticks

    $n = 1$ $n = 2$ $n = 3$

    $s = 5$ $s = 9$ $s = 13$

     (a) Draw the next shape in the sequence.

     (b) Find a formula for the number of sticks(s) for the shape number n.

     (c) Use your formula to find out how many sticks are in shape number 50.

For each of the sequences in Questions **7** to **9**,

     (a) Draw the next shape in the sequence.

     (b) Use a table and 1st difference to find a formula for the number of sticks(s) for the shape number n.

       Use values of n to *check* if each formula is correct.

     (c) Use the formula to find out how many sticks are in shape number 50.

7

    $n = 1$ $n = 2$ $n = 3$

8

    $n = 1$ $n = 2$ $n = 3$

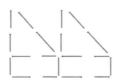   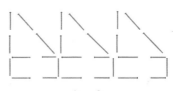

9

    $n = 1$ $n = 2$ $n = 3$

10 A French teacher gives his class a set of words to learn each week. On the first week of the term he asked them to learn 25 words and then increased this by 5 words each week.

(a) How many words would the class have to learn in the nth week of the term?

(b) How many words would the class have to learn in the 9th week of the term?

(c) In which week would the class have to learn 90 words?

11 Ponds are surrounded by paving slabs as shown below:

$n = 1$

$n = 2$

$n = 3$

(a) Draw the next shape in the sequence.

(b) How many white paving slabs surround each pond shown above?

(c) Find a formula for the number of white slabs (w) surrounding each pond n.

(d) How many white slabs surround pond number 40?

12 A football club had 35,000 supporters at its first home match. The attendance increased by 250 at each home game.

(a) How many supporters would be at its nth home game?

(b) If there were 40,750 at its last home game of the season then how many home games did it play?

13 (a) Find the nth term of 4, 7, 10, 13, ...

(b) Which is the first term of this sequence to be greater than 1000?

14 (a) Find the nth term of 38, 30, 22, 14, ...

(b) Find the nth term of 93, 82, 71, 60, ...

(c) After how many terms will the nth term of 93, 82, 71, 60, ... be smaller than the nth term of 38, 30, 22, 14, ...?

E ▌ Quadratic sequence rules

If the nth term $= n^2 + 5$

then 1st term $= 1^2 + 5 = 6$ 2nd term $= 2^2 + 5 = 9$ 3rd term $= 3^2 + 5 = 14$

4th term $= 4^2 + 5 = 21$ 5th term $= 5^2 + 5 = 30$

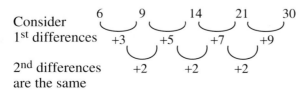

353

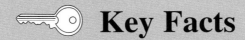

Key Facts

If you can find the second differences for a pattern and all the second differences are equal, the rule is quadratic (ie. contains a highest power of n^2).

The coefficient of n^2 (the number in front of n^2) is in fact half the second difference.

In the sequence on the last page, half the second difference is +1 and from the nth term $= n^2 + 5$ we can see that the coefficient of n^2 is +1.

The following two examples will illustrate a method for finding quadratic sequence rules.

(a) Find the nth term of the sequence $-1, 5, 15, 29, 47$

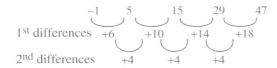

The second differences are the same so we have a quadratic rule with $2n^2$ in the formula because the coefficient of n^2 is half the second difference.

Now write down values for $2n^2$ underneath each corresponding term from the sequence (remember: $2n^2$ means $n^2 \times 2$).

term	-1	5	15	29	47
$2n^2$	2	8	18	32	50
SUBTRACT	-3	-3	-3	-3	-3

We can see that the $2n^2$ value is 3 too many for each term so

$$n^{th} \text{ term} = 2n^2 - 3$$

(check by testing n values to see if the formula works)

(b) Find the nth term of the sequence $2, 7, 14, 23, 34$

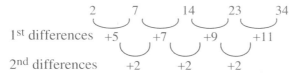

The second differences are the same so we have a quadratic rule with n^2 in the formula because the coefficient of n^2 is half the second difference.

Now write down values for n^2 underneath each corresponding term from the sequence.

term	2	7	14	23	34
n^2	1	4	9	16	25
SUBTRACT	1	3	5	7	9

We need to add '1 3 5 7 9' onto n^2 to find each term.

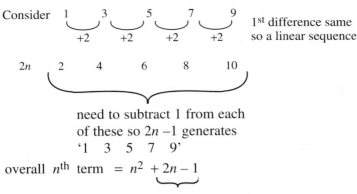

Consider 1 3 5 7 9   1st difference same
so a linear sequence

$2n$ 2 4 6 8 10

need to subtract 1 from each
of these so $2n - 1$ generates
'1 3 5 7 9'

overall n^{th} term $= n^2 + 2n - 1$

last part of the formula found above

(check by testing n values to see if the formula works)

Note

If sequence rules are neither linear nor quadratic, possibilities will include n as a power or formulas containing n^3.

For example, n^{th} term $= 3^n - 1$ gives 2, 8, 26, 80, ... and n^{th} term $= n^3 + n$ gives 2, 10, 30, 68, ...

E12.1

Find the nth term of each sequence below:

1 3, 6, 11, 18, 27, ...

2 0, 3, 8, 15, 24, ...

3 –3, 0, 5, 12, 21, ...

4 11, 14, 19, 26, 35, ...

5 Find the nth term of 2, 6, 12, 20, 30, ...

6 Find the nth term of –1, 0, 3, 8, 15, ...

7 For the sequence 4, 10, 18, 28, 40, ...

Find (a) the nth term   (b) the 20th term

8 Here is a sequence of shapes made from dots.

let n = shape number   and d = number of dots

$n = 1$ $n = 2$ $n = 3$ $n = 4$

(a) Find a formula for d in terms of n.

(b) How many dots in shape number 30?

9 Find the nth term of each sequence below:

(a) 5, 9, 15, 23, 33, ...   (b) 2, 8, 16, 26, 38, ...

(c) 3, 10, 21, 36, 55, ...   (d) 8, 21, 40, 65, 96, ...

10 Here is a sequence of shapes made from paving slabs.

let n = shape number and s = number of slabs

$n = 1$

$n = 2$

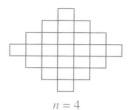
$n = 3$

$n = 4$

(a) Find a formula for s in terms of n.

(b) How many slabs in shape number 20?

11

$n = 1$ $n = 2$

$n = 3$

$n = 4$

$n = 5$

Find a formula for the nth term of the triangular numbers above.

12 Find the nth term of each sequence below:

(a) 4, 16, 64, 256, ...

(b) 1, 3, 7, 15, 31, ...

(c) 0, 7, 26, 63, 124, ...

(d) 1, 3, 9, 27, 81, ...

Can you still?

Can you still?

12B **Find angles (see Unit 3)**

Find the angles marked with letters. In circle Questions, O is always the centre of the circle.

1.
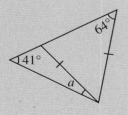

2.
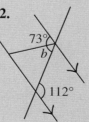

3.

4.
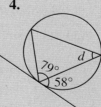

5.

6.
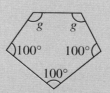

7.
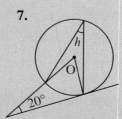

8.
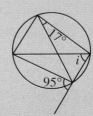

356

$(x - 3)^2$ and $(x + 5)^2$ are examples of 'perfect squares'.

$(x + 5)^2 = (x + 5)(x + 5) = x^2 + 10x + 25$

so $(x + 5)^2 - 25 = x^2 + 10x$

If we rewrite $x^2 + 10x$ as $(x + 5)^2 - 25$, we say we are 'completing the square'.

Key Facts

Consider $x^2 + 8x$.   Complete the square.

Method

1. *Halve the coefficient of x*, ie. '+4'

   This indicates that the perfect square will be $(x + 4)^2$

2. *Subtract the square of '+4' from above, ie. '16'*

   So $x^2 + 8x = (x + 4)^2 - 16$ This has completed the square.

   (check: $(x + 4)^2 - 16 = (x + 4)(x + 4) - 16 = x^2 + 8x + 16 - 16 = x^2 + 8x$)

   Quadratic equations – these can be solved by completing the square.

   Solve $x^2 - 4x + 1 = 0$

   This does not factorise so we try completing the square for the part of the equation which contains the x's.

$$x^2 - 4x + 1 = 0$$

$$(x - 2)^2 - 4 + 1 = 0$$

−2 is half the coefficent of x | $(-2)^2$

$$(x - 2)^2 = 3$$ remember the negative square root

$$x - 2 = \sqrt{3} \quad \text{or} \quad -\sqrt{3}$$
$$x = 2 + \sqrt{3} \quad \text{or} \quad 2 - \sqrt{3}$$

The answers can be left as 'exact' surds or worked out if a calculator is available.

Note

If the coefficient of x^2 in the quadratic equation is greater than 1, divide the whole equation to make the coefficient of x^2 equal 1. It is then easier for you to solve by completing the square.

(a) $x^2 - 5x$

$$= \left(x - \frac{5}{2}\right)^2 - \frac{25}{4}$$

(b) $x^2 - 6x - 10$

$$= (x - 3)^2 - 9 - 10$$

$$= (x - 3)^2 - 19$$

(c) $3x^2 + 12x + 1$

$$= 3\left(x^2 + 4x + \frac{1}{3}\right)$$

$$= 3\left((x + 2)^2 - 4 + \frac{1}{3}\right)$$

$$= 3\left((x + 2)^2 - \frac{11}{3}\right)$$

(d) Solve $x^2 + 2x - 4 = 0$ by completing the square, leaving the answer in the form $a \pm \sqrt{b}$.

$$x^2 + 2x - 4 = 0$$

$$(x + 1)^2 - 1 - 4 = 0$$

$$(x + 1)^2 = 5$$

$$x + 1 = \sqrt{5} \text{ or } -\sqrt{5}$$

$$x = -1 + \sqrt{5} \text{ or } -1 - \sqrt{5}$$

E12.2

Write the following in the form $(x + p)^2 + r$ where p and r are numbers to be determined:

1 $x^2 + 8x + 7$

2 $x^2 - 12x + 25$

3 $x^2 + 18x + 75$

4 $x^2 - 6x + 5$

5 $x^2 - 10x - 17$

6 $x^2 + 12x + 3$

7 $x^2 + 3x + 1$

8 $x^2 + 7x + 3$

9 $x^2 + x + 1$

10 Copy and complete below:

$$x^2 + 8x - 9 = 0$$

$$(x + 4)^2 - \boxed{} - 9 = 0$$

$$(x + 4)^2 = \boxed{}$$

$$x + 4 = \sqrt{\boxed{}} \text{ or } -\sqrt{\boxed{}}$$

$$x = \boxed{} \text{ or } \boxed{}$$

11 Copy and complete below:

$$x^2 - 2x - 7 = 0$$

$$(x - 1)^2 - \boxed{} - 7 = 0$$

$$(x - 1)^2 = \boxed{}$$

$$x - 1 = \sqrt{\boxed{}} \text{ or } -\sqrt{\boxed{}}$$

$$x = 1 + \sqrt{\boxed{}} \text{ or } 1 - \sqrt{\boxed{}}$$

Solve the following quadratic equations by completing the square (leave your answers in the form $p \pm \sqrt{q}$ where appropriate):

12 $x^2 + 4x + 1 = 0$

13 $x^2 - 6x + 7 = 0$

14 $x^2 - 10x + 20 = 0$

15 $x^2 + 8x + 11 = 0$

16 $x^2 + 2x - 7 = 0$

17 $x^2 + 12x + 25 = 0$

18 $x^2 + 11x + 1 = 0$

19 $x^2 + 7x - 3 = 0$

20 $x^2 + x - 3 = 0$

21 $2x^2 - 12x + 28 = a\left((x - b)^2 + c\right)$. Find the values of a, b and c.

22 $3x^2 - 12x - 9 = p\left((x - q)^2 + r\right)$. Find the values of p, q and r.

23 $5x^2 + 10x - 35 = a\left((x + b)^2 + c\right)$. Find the values of a, b and c.

Solve the following equations by completing the square. First write them in the form $x^2 + bx + c = 0$ (leave your answers in the form $p \pm \sqrt{q}$ where appropriate).

24 $3x^2 + 6x - 12 = 0$ **25** $2x^2 + 10x + 1 = 0$ **26** $7x^2 - 3x - 1 = 0$

By completing the square, find the co-ordinates of the turning points of the following functions:

27 $g(x) = x^2 - 10x + 3$ **28** $h(x) = x^2 - 4x + 1$

29 (a) Find the minimum value of the function $f(x) = x^2 + 4x + 5$.

    (b) How many solutions are there to the equation $x^2 + 4x + 5 = 0$?

    (c) Explain what happens when you try to solve the equation $x^2 + 4x + 5 = 0$ by completing the square.

E   Quadratic equations – solving with the formula

Solve $ax^2 + bx + c = 0$ by completing the square.

$$x^2 + \frac{bx}{a} + \frac{c}{a} = 0$$

$$x^2 + \frac{bx}{a} = -\frac{c}{a}$$

$$\left(x + \frac{b}{2a}\right)^2 - \left(\frac{b}{2a}\right)^2 = -\frac{c}{a} \quad \text{(completing the square)}$$

$$\left(x + \frac{b}{2a}\right)^2 = \left(\frac{b}{2a}\right)^2 - \frac{c}{a}$$

$$\left(x + \frac{b}{2a}\right)^2 = \frac{b^2}{4a^2} - \frac{c}{a}$$

$$\left(x + \frac{b}{2a}\right)^2 = \frac{b^2}{4a^2} - \frac{4ac}{4a^2}$$

$$x + \frac{b}{2a} = \pm\sqrt{\frac{b^2 - 4ac}{4a^2}}$$

$$x + \frac{b}{2a} = \frac{\pm\sqrt{b^2 - 4ac}}{2a}$$

$$x = \frac{-b}{2a} \pm \frac{\sqrt{b^2 - 4ac}}{2a} = \frac{-b \pm \sqrt{b^2 - 4ac}}{2a}$$

 **Key Facts**

The quadratic equation $ax^2 + bx + c = 0$ can be solved by using the formula $x = \dfrac{-b \pm \sqrt{b^2 - 4ac}}{2a}$

Solve $2x^2 - 5x - 8 = 0$ by using the formula. Give your answer to 3 significant figures.

$$2x^2 - 5x - 8 = 0$$

(match to $ax^2 + bx + c = 0$)

$a = 2 \quad b = -5 \quad c = -8$

$$x = \frac{-b \pm \sqrt{b^2 - 4ac}}{2a} = \frac{-(-5) \pm \sqrt{\{(-5)^2 - (4 \times 2 \times -8)\}}}{2 \times 2}$$

$$x = \frac{5 \pm \sqrt{\{25 + 64\}}}{4} = \frac{5 \pm \sqrt{89}}{4}$$

$$x = \frac{5 \pm 9.434}{4}$$

require answer to 3 sig. figs so work to 4 sig. figs to ensure appropriate accuracy in the final answer

$$x = \frac{5 + 9.434}{4} \qquad \text{or} \qquad \frac{5 - 9.434}{4}$$

$$x = \frac{14.434}{4} \qquad \text{or} \qquad \frac{-4.434}{4}$$

$$x = 3.61 \qquad \text{or} \qquad -1.11 \quad \text{(to 3 sig. figs)}$$

Note

If an 'exact' answer is needed, it can be left in surd form, ie. $x = \frac{5 \pm \sqrt{89}}{4}$ or $\frac{5}{4} \pm \frac{\sqrt{89}}{4}$.

The quadratic formula is usually used if you cannot solve the equation by factorising.

In a calculator exam, you can be sure you need to use the formula if the question wants a quadratic equation solved to one or two decimal places.

E12.3

Use the formula to solve the following quadratic equations, giving each answer to 3 significant figures.

1 $x^2 + 7x + 5 = 0$ **2** $x^2 + 2x - 1 = 0$ **3** $x^2 - 3x - 7 = 0$

4 $5x^2 + x - 2 = 0$ **5** $4x^2 - 3x - 11 = 0$ **6** $3x^2 + 5x + 1 = 0$

7 $7x^2 + 10x - 1 = 0$ **8** $5x^2 - 2x - 3 = 0$ **9** $2x^2 + x - 4 = 0$

10 $4x^2 + 9x + 3 = 0$ **11** $13x^2 + 20x + 5 = 0$ **12** $9x^2 + 7x - 8 = 0$

13 $5x^2 + 12x - 33 = 0$ **14** $11x^2 = 7x + 10$ **15** $x(7x + 1) = 5$

16 $(x + 1)(x + 3) = 7$ **17** $5 - 7x - 2x^2 = 0$ **18** $5 + \frac{2}{x} = x$

Find the solutions to the following quadratic equations, leaving your answers in the form $\dfrac{p \pm \sqrt{q}}{r}$.

19 $x^2 + 5x + 1 = 0$

20 $x^2 + 3x - 2 = 0$

21 $5x^2 - 3x - 11 = 0$

22 $3x^2 + x - 1 = 0$

23 $7x^2 + 5x - 7 = 0$

24 $11 - 8x - x^2 = 0$

E More problems leading to quadratic equations

E12.4

In this exercise you will formulate quadratic equations then solve them by any appropriate method (factorising, using the formula or completing the square).

1 A right angled triangle is such that its hypotenuse is 3 metres longer than twice its shortest side.

(a) If the length of the shortest side is x metres and the other side (ie. not the hypotenuse) is 4 metres then, by using Pythagoras' Theorem, write down an equation involving x.

(b) Show that this can be written as $3x^2 + 12x - 7 = 0$.

(c) Use the formula to find x to 3 significant figures.

2 The shortest side of a right angled triangle is 2 cm shorter than its next shortest side. If its area is 7 cm² then find the shortest side of the triangle (give your answer to 3 significant figures).

3 A field is 25 m longer than it is wide. The diagonal of the field is 85 m. What is the width of the field?

4 The diagonal of a rectangle is 1 cm longer than twice its length. Its width is 7 cm. Let x be the length of the rectangle.

(a) Write down an expression for the diagonal involving x.

(b) Write down an equation involving x.

(c) Solve this to find the length of the rectangle.

5 The difference between a positive number and its reciprocal is 4. What is the number (give your answer to 3 significant figures)?

6 A rectangular box is 23 cm longer than it is wide. Its diagonal is 65 cm. If x is the width of the box then:

(a) Find an expression for the length of the box in terms of x.

(b) Show that $x^2 + 23x - 1848 = 0$.

(c) Solve this equation to find the exact value of x.

7 The rectangular base of a box is such that its length is 17 mm longer than its width. The diagonal is 305 mm. Let x be the width of the box.

(a) Find an equation involving x.

(b) Solve this equation to find x.

8 A rectangle is 7 cm longer than it is wide. The largest possible circle is cut out of the rectangle and the remaining area is 40 cm². What are the dimensions of the rectangle, giving your answers to 3 significant figures? (**hint**: call the width of the rectangle 2x)

9 (a) Given that the unshaded area in the diagram opposite is 50 cm², write down an equation involving d (leave π in your equation).
   (b) Solve this quadratic equation to find d, giving your answer to 3 significant figures.

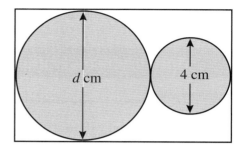

10 A garage is 4 m longer than it is wide and 1m higher than it is wide. The longest pole which can fit inside the garage is 7.5 m long. How wide is the garage (to 3 significant figures)?

E | Linear and quadratic simultaneous equations

Earlier in this unit we solved linear simultaneous equations by '*elimination*'. Another method involves '*substitution*'.

Solve the simultaneous equations $u - 2v = -5$
$$5u + 3v = 14$$

Rearrange the first equation to isolate 'u'.

$$u = -5 + 2v$$

Substitute for u in the second equation using this expression

$$5(-5 + 2v) + 3v = 14$$
$$-25 + 10v + 3v = 14$$
$$13v = 39$$
$$v = 3$$

Substitute $v = 3$ in the first equation

$$u - (2 \times 3) = -5$$
$$u - 6 = -5$$
$$u = 1 \quad \text{Solution: } u = 1, v = 3$$

Use the method of substitution to solve simultaneous equations involving one linear and one quadratic equation. Always *rearrange the linear equation first.*

Solve the simultaneous equations $x - y = 1$
$$x^2 + y^2 = 13$$

$x - y = 1$ ... (1)

$x^2 + y^2 = 13$ ... (2)

From (1)

$x = y + 1$

Substitute for x in (2)

$(y + 1)^2 + y^2 = 13$

$(y + 1)(y + 1) + y^2 = 13$ (remember: $(y + 1)^2$ is *not* $y^2 + 1^2$)

$y^2 + 2y + 1 + y^2 = 13$

$2y^2 + 2y - 12 = 0$

$y^2 + y - 6 = 0$

$(y + 3)(y - 2) = 0$

$y = -3$ or 2

These are simultaneous equations so for each y-value we must give the corresponding x-value.

We know $x = y + 1$

When $y = -3$, $x = -3 + 1 = -2$

When $y = 2$, $x = 2 + 1 = 3$

Solution: $x = 3$, $y = 2$ and $x = -2$, $y = -3$

 Key Facts

$x^2 + y^2 = r^2$ is the equation of a circle of radius r with its centre at $(0, 0)$

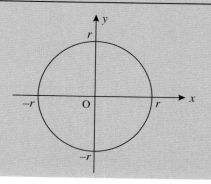

In the previous example, $x^2 + y^2 = 13$ is a circle with its centre at $(0, 0)$.

$r^2 = 13$ so radius $r = \sqrt{13} = 3.6$ approximately.

$x - y = 1$ is a straight line as shown opposite
$(x - 1 = y)$

The solution to the simultaneous equations shows where the line meets the circle, ie. at $(3, 2)$ and $(-2, -3)$

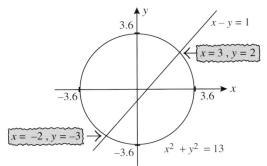

E12.5

Solve the following linear simultaneous equations by using the method of '*substitution*':

1 $2x + 3y = 30$

$y = 3x - 1$

2 $a = 3b + 1$

$7a + 2b = 53$

3 $10p + 11q = 21$

$p = 5q - 4$

4 $2a + 3b = 123$

$a = 3 + 5b$

5 $c = 7d - 2$

$3c - 4d = 28$

6 $2w + 7x = 41$

$w = 3x + 1$

Solve the following simultaneous equations, leaving your answers as fractions where necessary (all the quadratics can be solved by factorising):

7 $xy = 2$

$y = x + 1$

8 $y(x + 1) = 10$

$y = 2x + 3$

9 $xy + x + y = -1$

$y = 3x + 1$

10 $xy - 2y - x = 2$

$x + y = 7$

Solve the following simultaneous equations:

11 $y = 3x^2$

$y - 3x = 6$

12 $x^2 + y^2 = 169$

$y = x + 7$

13 $y^2 - x^2 = 60$

$y = 3x + 2$

14 $x^2 - 2xy + y^2 = 1$

$x + y = 9$

15 Find the points of intersection of the circle and the line shown below:

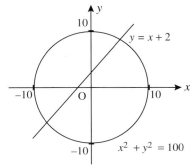

16 Find the points of intersection of the line $2x + y = 10$ and the circle $x^2 + y^2 = 25$.

364

(12C) **Use Pythagoras' theorem and trigonometry (see Unit 10)**

Give each answer in this section to one decimal place.

Find the value of x in Questions ① to ⑥.

1.

2.

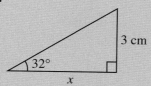

3.

4.

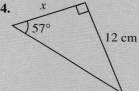

5.

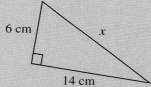

6.

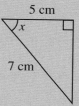

7. A ladder leans against a vertical wall so that its base is 1.6 m from the wall and the top of the ladder is 4.3 m up the wall. What angle does the ladder make with the vertical wall?

8.

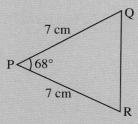

Find the length QR

9. Calculate the length of the line joining (2, 5) to (4, 10)

10.

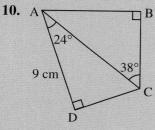

Find the length AB

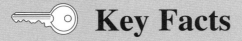

🔑 Key Facts

Exponential growth – the rate of *increase* of a quantity is proportional to the amount of the quantity currently present.

$y = a^x$ is an exponential function where a is a positive number.

Exponential decay – the rate of *decrease* of a quantity is proportional to the amount of the quantity currently present.

$y = a^{-x}$ is an exponential function where a is a positive number. This generates a 'decay' curve.

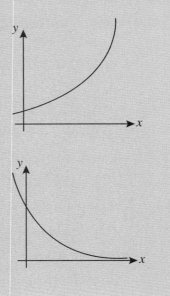

E12.6

1 Some bacteria grew so that after t minutes, the number of bacteria, N, was given by the formula

$$N = 2^t$$

(a) Copy and complete the table below.

t	0	1	2	3	4	5
N						

(b) Using appropriate axes, draw the graph of $N = 2^t$

(c) Use your graph to find the value of t when $N = 25$

(d) Explain what will happen to the curve as t continues to increase.

2 (a) Using a table of values, plot the graph of $y = 4^x$ for x-values from –3 to 3.

(b) From your graph find the value of x when $y = 30$

(c) From your graph find the value of y when $x = 1.5$

3 A radioactive substance decays so that the amount of radioactive substance present, y, after t centuries is given by the formula

$$y = 10 \, (2^{-t})$$

> this means 2^{-t} then multiply by 10

(a) Copy and complete the table below.

t	0	1	2	3	4	5
y						

(b) Using appropriate axes, draw the graph of $y = 10 \, (2^{-t})$.

(c) Use your graph to find the value of t when y = 4.

(d) Will the curve ever drop below the horizontal axis? Explain why you are giving your answer.

4 £100 is invested in a bank. The amount of money, M, in the account after t years is given by the formula

$$M = 100 \, (1.06)^t$$

Find the amount of money (to the nearest penny) in the account after:

(a) 3 years   (b) 4 years   (c) 10 years

(d) Plot a graph showing the amount of money in the account over the first 10 years.

(e) After how many years will there be £140 in the account (give your answer to 1 decimal place).

5 A population, P, grows in such a way that after t years,

$$P = 8(1.04)^t \quad \text{(P is measured in 1000's)}$$

Find the population P after:

(a) 2 years   (b) 10 years   (c) 20 years

(d) Plot a graph showing the population over the first 20 years.

(e) After how many years will the population have reached 12,000 (give your answer to 1 decimal place)?

6 (a) Using a table of values, plot the graph of $y = 3^{-x}$ for x-values from –2 to 3.

(b) From your graph find the approximate solution of $3^{-x} = 5$.

7 The value, V (in £'s), of a house in Henton after t years is given by the formula

$$V = 90000 \, (1.05^t)$$

The value, W (in £'s), of a house in Rowton after t years is given by the formula

$$W = 120000 \, (0.96^t)$$

Using the same axes, draw a graph for each equation and use them to find out after how many years the houses have the same value.

8

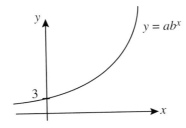

The curve $y = ab^x$ passes through $(0, 3)$ and $(1, 15)$. Find the values of a and b.

Key Facts

An equation such as $x^2 - 3x = 5x + 1$ can be solved by drawing the graph of $y = x^2 - 3x$ and the graph of $y = 5x + 1$ then finding the points at which the two graphs intersect. At the point of intersection, the x-value fits both equations hence the value of $x^2 - 3x$ must equal the value of $5x + 1$. Graphical solutions are often *approximate* because it is difficult to draw graphs to perfection or to read off values accurately.

Draw the graph of $y = x^2 - 3x - 1$ using x-values from -2 to 4.

Use the graph to solve (a) $x^2 - 3x - 1 = 0$ (b) $x^2 - 2x - 2 = 0$

$y = x^2 - 3x - 1$

x	-2	-1	0	1	2	3	4
y	9	3	-1	-3	-3	-1	3

(a) To solve $\qquad x^2 - 3x - 1 = 0$ $\Big\}$ We need to

compare the graph $x^2 - 3x - 1 = y$ find out where $y = 0$ on the curve

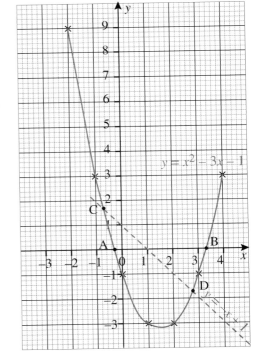

Read off the x-values at A and B where $y = 0$

$x = -0.3$ and 3.3

$x = -0.3$ and 3.3

These are the two approximate solutions of $x^2 - 3x - 1 = 0$

(b) To solve $x^2 - 2x - 2 = 0$, we need to rearrange the equation into the form of the graph $x^2 - 3x - 1 = y$

$$x^2 - 2x - 2 = 0 \implies x^2 - 2x \; \boxed{-x} \; -2 \; \boxed{+1} = \boxed{-x} \; \boxed{+1}$$

$$x^2 - 3x - 1 = -x + 1$$

compare the graph $x^2 - 3x - 1 = y$ $\left.\begin{array}{c} \\ \\ \end{array}\right\}$ we need to draw the line $y = -x + 1$ to find out where the curve meets this line

Read off the x-values at C and D where $y = x^2 - 3x - 1$ meets the line $y = -x + 1$,

$$x = -0.7 \text{ and } 2.8$$

$x = -0.7$ and 2.8

These are the two approximate solutions of $x^2 - 2x - 2 = 0$

E12.7

1 (a) Copy and complete the table below for $y = x^2 - 2x - 4$.

x	−3	−2	−1	0	1	2	3	4	5
y								4	

(b) Using appropriate axes, draw the curve $y = x^2 - 2x - 4$

(c) Use the graph to solve $x^2 - 2x - 4 = 0$ (to 1 decimal place)

(d) Use the graph to solve $x^2 - 2x - 4 = 5$ (to 1 decimal place)

2 (a) Copy and complete the table below for $y = x^2 + 4x + 3$.

x	−6	−5	−4	−3	−2	−1	0	1	2
y								8	

(b) Using appropriate axes, draw the curve $y = x^2 + 4x + 3$

Use the graph to solve

(c) $x^2 + 4x + 3 = 0$

(d) $x^2 + 4x + 3 = 5$ (to 1 dec. pl.)

(e) $x^2 + 4x - 7 = 0$ (to 1 dec. pl.)

3

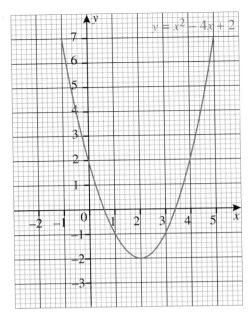

Use this graph to solve (to 1 dec. pl.)

(a) $x^2 - 4x + 2 = 0$

(b) $x^2 - 4x + 2 = 4$

(c) $x^2 - 4x + 1 = 0$

4 If we have the graph of $y = 2x^2 + 5x - 1$, work out what line needs to be drawn to solve each of the following equations:

(a) $2x^2 + 4x - 1 = 0$ (b) $2x^2 + 4x - 5 = 0$

(c) $2x^2 + 2x + 3 = 0$ (d) $2x^2 + 7x - 4 = 0$

5 Use this graph to solve (to 1 dec. pl.)

(a) $x^2 + x - 4 = 0$

(b) $x^2 + x - 4 = 3$

(c) $x^2 - 6 = 0$

(d) $x^2 + x - 1 = 0$

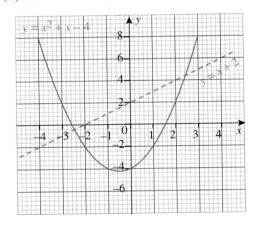

6

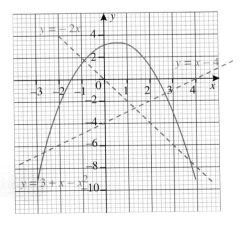

Use this graph to solve (to 1 dec. pl.)

(a) $3 + x - x^2 = 0$

(b) $7 - x^2 = 0$

(c) $x - x^2 = 0$

(d) $3 + 3x - x^2 = 0$

(e) $6 + 2x - 2x^2 = 0$

7 Using x-values from -4 to 4 draw $y = x^2 - 5$ and $y = 2x - 4$ on the same axes.

Use the graph to solve (to 1 dec. pl.)

(a) $x^2 - 1 = 2x$ (b) $x^2 - 7 = 0$

8 Using x-values from -2 to 4 draw $y = x^2 - 2x + 3$ and $y = 6 - x$ on the same axes.

Use the graph to solve (to 1 dec. pl.)

(a) $x^2 - 2x - 4 = 0$ (b) $x^2 - x - 3 = 0$

9 Draw the graph of $y = x^2 - 3x + 6$ for x-values from -2 to 5. By drawing suitable straight lines, solve each of the following equations (to 1 dec. pl.)

(a) $x^2 - 2x - 1 = 0$ (b) $x^2 - 5x + 4 = 0$

10 Draw the graph of $y = x^2 + 5x + 3$ for x-values from -6 to 1. By drawing suitable straight lines, solve each of the following equations (to 1 dec. pl.)

(a) $x^2 + 6x + 1 = 0$ (b) $x^2 + 3x - 1 = 0$

WATCH YOUR MONEY! – Which is better value?

How do you spot the best value in a shop?

A pack of 2 kitchen rolls £1.20		A pack of 3 kitchen rolls £1.71

To compare the cost, find the cost of 1 kitchen roll (the *unit* cost) for each pack.

2 rolls for £1.20 gives 60 p per roll

3 rolls for £1.71 gives 57 p per roll

The pack of 3 rolls is the *best value*.

(Obviously you would only buy the pack of 3 kitchen rolls if you do not mind having that many rolls or have enough money to buy that pack at that particular moment)

Flakes £2.25 750 g	Which packet of flakes is the best value?	Flakes £1.60 500 g

750 g costs 225 p so 1 g costs $\frac{225}{750} = 0.3$ p

500 g costs 160 p so 1 g costs $\frac{160}{500} = 0.32$ p

so the 750 g box is the best value.

OR

500 g costs 160 p so 250 g costs 80 p

At this price, 3×250 g $= 750$ g costs 3×80 p $= £2.40$

This is more expensive than the 750 g box.

For each of Questions **1** to **5**, decide which is the better value.

1

A | A pack of 2 light bulbs 92 p | or | B | A pack of 5 light bulbs £2.40

2

A | 1 can of cola 45 p | or | B | A pack of 6 cans of cola £2.34

3

A | 1 tin of baked beans 33 p 150 g | or | B | 1 tin of baked beans 56 p 400 g

4

A | 1 pack of 4 galia melons £3.16 | or | B | Galia melon £1.14 each BUY TWO AND GET ONE FREE

5

A | 1 punnet of strawberries £1.89 500 g BUY ONE AND GET ONE FREE | or | B | 1 punnet of strawberries £3.82 1 kg

6 Carl is buying paper plates and plastic cups for a party. Paper plates cost 80 p for a pack of 20 or £1.50 for a pack of 50.

Plastic cups cost 78 p for a pack of 12 or £1.80 for a pack of 30.

Carl needs 60 plates and 75 cups. What is the cheapest way of buying them?

7 Jordan buys some tomato ketchup from the local supermarket. There are 3 different sized bottles.

A | 600 g PLUS 20% EXTRA £1.26 | B | 750 g £1.50 | C | 1 kg £1.90

Which bottle gives the best value for money?

8 Which box of washing powder below is the best value?

A | 650 g £2.47 | B | 925 g £3.33 | C | 1.2 kg £4.50

1. Using the 'cover–up' method for drawing straight lines

(a) (i) Draw x and y axes from 0 to 6

(ii) Use $x = 0$ then $y = 0$ to find 2 points for $x + 3y = 6$

(iii) Draw the straight line $x + 3y = 6$

(b) On the same axes as above, use the 'cover-up' method to draw $4x + 5y = 20$

2. Solving simultaneous equations on a graph

(a) Use the graph to solve the simultaneous equations

$$2y - x = 4$$

$$x + y = 5$$

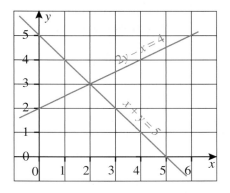

(b) Draw x and y axes from 0 to 6

Solve graphically the simultaneous equations $3x + y = 6$

$$x + y = 4$$

(c) Draw x and y axes from 0 to 8

Solve graphically the simultaneous equations $2x + y = 8$

$$2x + 3y = 12$$

3. Solving simultaneous equations algebraically

Solve the simultaneous equations

(a) $3x - 2y = 8$ (b) $2a + 3b = 15$ (c) $3m - 4n = 13$

  $x - 2y = 0$ $5a - 2b = -29$ $7m + 2n = 36$

(d) A cinema has 30 rows of seating. Some of the rows have 25 seats and the rest have only 18 seats. If the cinema holds 659 people then find out how many rows have 25 seats and how many have 18 seats.

4. Finding rules for linear sequences

(a) Find the nth term of the sequence 5, 8, 11, 14, ...

(b) Find the 37th term of the sequence 7, 13, 19, 25, ...

(c) A farmer has to put fence posts in a straight line. The fence posts are initially in a pile. The first fence post is put into a hole 50 m from the pile and there is a gap of 3 m between the posts so the second post is 53 m away from the pile, the third is 56 m away, etc.

   (i) How far from the pile will the nth post be?

   (ii) Which post is 83 m from the pile?

5. Finding rules for quadratic sequences

   (a) Find the nth term of the sequence –3, –4, –3, 0, 5,…

   (b) Find the 50th term of the sequence –1, 4, 11, 20, 31,…

   (c) Here is a sequence of shapes made from triangles

      let n = shape number and t = number of triangles

$n = 1$ $n = 2$ $n = 3$ $n = 4$

   Find a formula for t in terms of n.

6. Solving quadratic equations by completing the square

Solve the following quadratic equations by completing the square (leave your answers in the form $a \pm \sqrt{b}$):

(a) $x^2 + 6x - 1 = 0$ (b) $x^2 - 8x + 9 = 0$

(c) $2x^2 - 20x + 56 = p((x - q)^2 + r)$. Find the values of p, q and r.

7. Solving quadratic equations by using the formula

Solve the following equations, giving your answers to 2 decimal places:

(a) $5x^2 + 2x - 4 = 0$ (b) $x(3x - 1) = 1$

(c) A rectangle is 3 m longer than it is wide. The diagonal is 11m. If x is the width of the rectangle then.

   (i) Write down the length of the rectangle in terms of x.

   (ii) Use Pythagoras' theorem to find an equation involving x and show that it simplifies to $x^2 + 3x - 56 = 0$.

   (iii) Solve this equation to find the value of x, giving your answer to 3 significant figures.

8. Solving linear and quadratic simultaneous equations

(a) Solve the simultaneous equations $x^2 + 2y = 12$

$$y = 3x - 2$$

(b)

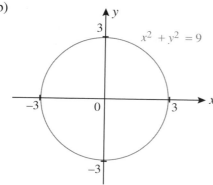

Solve the simultaneous equations $x^2 + y^2 = 9$

$$x - y = 3$$

to find the points of intersection of the circle $x^2 + y^2 = 9$ and the line $x - y = 3$.

9. Recognising exponential growth and decay

A car is bought for £16000. Its value, V (in £'s), after t years is given by the formula

$$V = 16000 \, (0.9)^t$$

Find the value of the car (to the nearest £10) after:

(a) 2 years   (b) 5 years   (c) 10 years

(d) Plot a graph showing the value of the car over the first 10 years.

(e) After how many years is the car worth £10000 (give your answer to 1 decimal place)?

10. Solving equations graphically

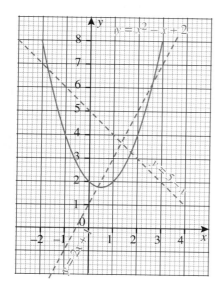

Use this graph to solve (to 1 decimal place)

(a) $x^2 - x + 2 = 5$

(b) $x^2 - x - 4 = 0$

(c) $x^2 - x + 2 = 5 - x$

(d) $x^2 - 3x + 1 = 0$

1 Solve the simultaneous equations.

$$6x - 2y = 33$$
$$4x + 3y = 9$$

(EDEXCEL)

2 Solve algebraically these simultaneous equations.

$$2x + 6y = 11$$
$$3x - 4y = 10$$

(OCR)

3 A sequence begins 2, 5, 8, 11,...

(i) One number in the sequence is x.

Write, in terms of x, the next number in the sequence.

(ii) Write, in terms of n, the nth term of the sequence. (AQA)

4 The diagram shows a sketch of the line $2y + x = 10$.

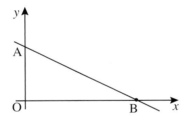

(a) Find the co-ordinates of points A and B.

(b) (i) On the same diagram, sketch the graph of $y = 2$

(ii) Solve the simultaneous equations

$$2y + x = 10$$
$$y = 2x$$

(OCR)

5 Solve the simultaneous equations.

$$4x + y = 8$$
$$2x - 3y = 11$$

(EDEXCEL)

6 Find the values of a and b such that

$$x^2 - 10x + 18 = (x - a)^2 + b$$

(AQA)

7 Solve $x^2 + 7x + 5 = 0$ giving the roots correct to 2 decimal places. (OCR)

8 The expression $x^2 - 10x + 14 + a$, where a is an integer, can be written in the form $(x - b)^2$, where b is an integer.

(a) Calculate the values of a and b.

(b) Solve the equation $x^2 - 10x + 14 = 0$. (OCR)

9 Write down an expression in terms of n for the nth term of the sequence

$$0, 3, 8, 15, 24, \ldots$$

(AQA)

10 (a) On a grid, draw the graph of $y = x^2 - x - 4$

Use values of x between -2 and $+3$.

(b) Use your graph to write down an estimate for

(i) the minimum value of y.

(ii) the solutions of the equation $x^2 - x - 4 = 0$ (EDEXCEL)

11 (a) Draw the graph of $y = 2^x$ for values of x from -2 to 3.

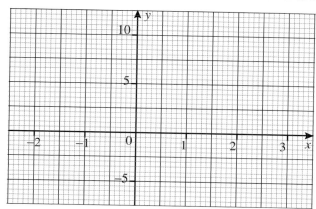

(b) Use your graph to solve $2^x = 6$.

(OCR)

12 Members of a youth club can either pay a nightly fee or buy a season ticket.

When 8 members paid nightly fees and 3 members bought season tickets, the treasurer collected £50.50.

When 5 members paid nightly fees and 2 members bought season tickets, the treasurer collected £33.

Use simultaneous equations, solving them algebraically, to calculate the nightly fee and the cost of a season ticket. Show your working.   (CCEA)

13 This diagram shows a graph with equation of the form $y = kx^n$.

The graph passes through the points $(1, 10)$ and $(8, 20)$.

Find the values of k and n.

(AQA)

14 The first five terms of a sequence are $0, 2, 6, 12, 20, \ldots$

Write down the nth term of this sequence.

(AQA)

15 Solve algebraically.

$$x^2 + y^2 = 34$$
$$y = x + 8$$

(OCR)

16 (a) Draw the graph of $y = 10 - x - 2x^2$ for values of x from -3 to 3.

(b) Use the graph to solve the equation $10 - x - 2x^2 = 1 - 2x$.

(c) Emma wants to use the graph to solve the equation $4x^2 + 2x = 15$.

What is the equation of the line she needs to draw? (AQA)

17 This sketch shows part of the graph with equation

$$y = pq^x,$$

where p and q are constants.

The points with coordinates $(0, 8), (1, 18)$ and $(1.5, k)$ lie on the graph.

Calculate the values of p, q and k.

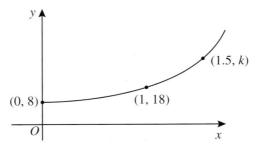

(EDEXCEL)

18 (a) Expand and simplify $(x + 4)^2$

(b) The diagram shows the circle $x^2 + y^2 = 36$ and the line $y = x + 4$.

The line and the circle intersect at the points A and B.

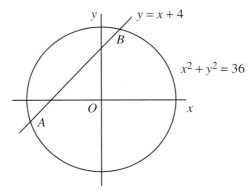

Show that the x-coordinates of A and B are given by the solutions to the equation

$$x^2 + 4x - 10 = 0$$

(c) Solve the equation $x^2 + 4x - 10 = 0$.

Give your answers to 2 decimal places.

You must show your working. (AQA)

In the 'M' sections (mainly grades B, C, D) you will learn how to:
 – find areas
 – find volumes of prisms and convert between units of area and volume
 – use similar shapes, particularly triangles

In the 'E' sections (mainly grades A*, A) you will learn how to:
 – find lengths of arcs
 – find areas of sectors and segments
 – find volumes of spheres, pyramids and cones
 – find surface areas of cylinders, spheres and cones
 – find lengths, areas and volumes of similar shapes

Also you will learn how to:
 – WATCH YOUR MONEY! – car insurance

M   Areas

🔑 Key Facts

 Area of triangle $= \frac{1}{2} bh$

Area of trapezium $= \frac{1}{2} h(a + b)$

 Area of circle $= \pi r^2$

Area of parallelogram $= bh$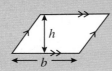

M13.1

Give answers to one decimal place if necessary.

1 Find the shaded area. All lengths are in cm.

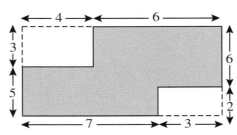

379

Find the area of each shape below. All lengths are in cm.

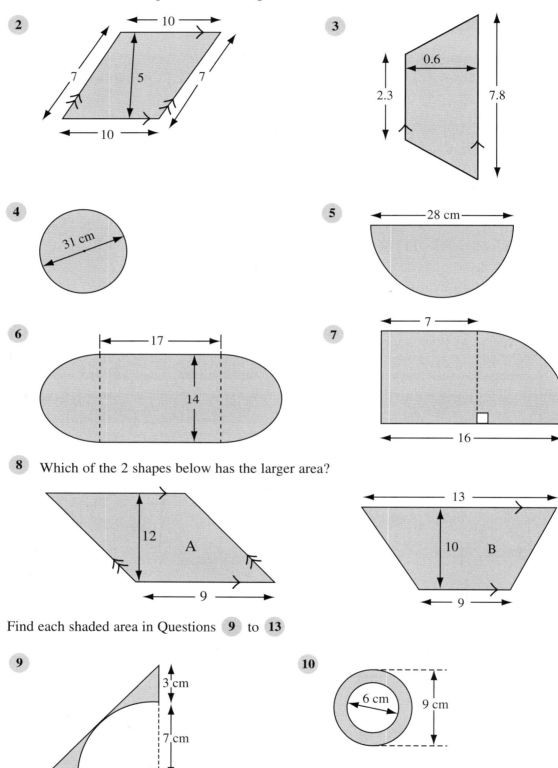

2

10

7   5   7

10

3

0.6

2.3   7.8

4

31 cm

5

28 cm

6

17

14

7

7

16

8 Which of the 2 shapes below has the larger area?

12   A

9

13

10   B

9

Find each shaded area in Questions **9** to **13**

9

3 cm

7 cm

2 cm

10

6 cm   9 cm

380

11

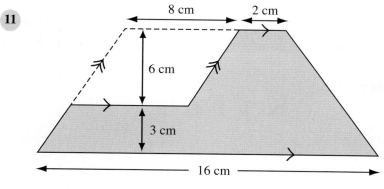

12

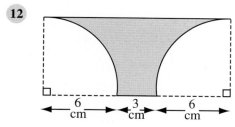

13

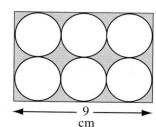

14 A triangle has an area of 102 cm². What is the height of the triangle if the base is 17 cm?

15 One parallel side in a trapezium is twice as long as the other parallel side. If the distance between the two parallel sides is 9 cm and its area is 135 cm², what are the lengths of the two parallel sides?

16 Find the area of this parallelogram.

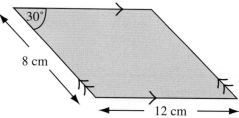

17

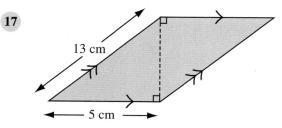

Find the area of this parallelogram.

18 ABCD is a square. Find the shaded area.

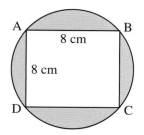

19 Find the area of this regular octagon.

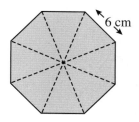

Key Facts

$$\sin \hat{C} = \frac{h}{a} \quad \text{so } h = a \sin \hat{C}$$

$$\text{area of triangle ABC} = \frac{1}{2} \, bh$$

$$= \frac{1}{2} \, b \, a \sin \hat{C}$$

$$\boxed{\text{area of triangle} \ = \frac{1}{2} \, ab \sin \hat{C}}$$

(the angle C must be between two sides a and b)

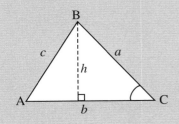

47° is between the two sides 8 cm and 14 cm.

$$\text{area of triangle} = \frac{1}{2} \times 8 \times 14 \sin 47°$$

$$= 41.0 \text{ cm}^2 \qquad \text{(to 1 decimal place)}$$

E13.1

Find the area of each triangle below, giving the answer to one decimal place.

1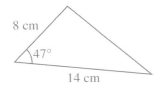

2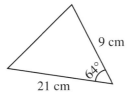

3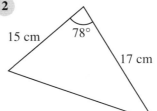

4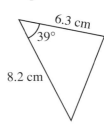

5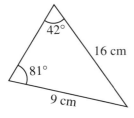

6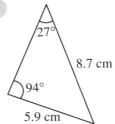

7 Find the value of θ (to 1 decimal place) in each triangle below.

(a)

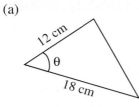

12 cm
θ
18 cm
area = 50 cm²

(b)

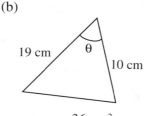

19 cm
θ
10 cm
area = 36 cm²

(c)

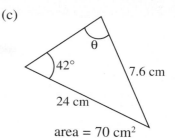

θ
42°
7.6 cm
24 cm
area = 70 cm²

8

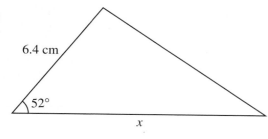

6.4 cm
52°
x

Find x if the area of this triangle is 51 cm². Give your answer to 1 decimal place.

Can you still?

Can you still?

13A **Use metric and imperial units (see Unit 10)**

1. Floyd has 15.2 litres of petrol in his car. On a short journey he uses 1740 ml of petrol. How much petrol is left in his car?

2. Naomi is 5 feet 4 inches tall. Ivan is 6 feet 1 inch tall. How much taller is Ivan than Naomi?

3. Which is heavier – 1 pound or 0.5 kg?

4. Tom weighs 12 stone 5 pounds, Mary weighs 8 stone 7 pounds and Emilie weighs 9 stone 1 pound. Is their combined weight more or less than 30 stone?

5. Which is cheaper – 5 gallons of petrol at £1.03 per litre or 23 litres at the same price per litre?

6. Copy and complete:

(a) 4 feet ≈ ☐ cm   (b) 20 miles ≈ ☐ km   (c) 33 pounds ≈ ☐ kg

(d) 9 inches ≈ ☐ cm   (e) 12 gallons ≈ ☐ litres   (f) 8 litres ≈ ☐ pints

7. Beth travels 58 km and Ollie travels 36 miles. Who travels the furthest and by how much?

8. Carla has 1 gallon of water. She uses 3.4 pints. How much water has she got left?

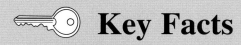

Key Facts

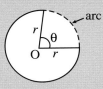

O is centre circle

An arc is part of the circumference

circumference = πd where d = diameter

360° in a whole circle

so arc length is $\dfrac{\theta}{360}$ of the circumference

$$\text{arc length} = \dfrac{\theta}{360} \times \pi d$$

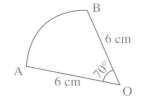

Find the perimeter of this shape, leaving the answer in terms of π.

arc AB = $\dfrac{70}{360} \times \pi \times 12$ (diameter = 12 cm)

$= \dfrac{\cancel{70}}{\cancel{360}} \times \dfrac{\pi}{1} \times \dfrac{\cancel{12}}{1}$

$= \dfrac{7\pi}{3}$ cm

perimeter = arc AB + AO + OB

$= \dfrac{7\pi}{3} + 6 + 6$

$= \left(\dfrac{7\pi}{3} + 12 \right)$ cm

This is an 'exact' answer in terms of π. If a calculator is used, the answer is 19.3 cm (to one decimal place).

E13.2

In Questions **1** to **3** use a calculator to work out the length of arc MN to one decimal place.

1
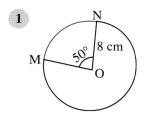

2
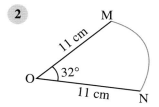

3
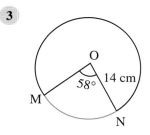

384

In Questions **4** to **6** use a calculator to work out the perimeter of each shape to one decimal place.

4

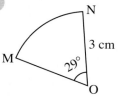

5

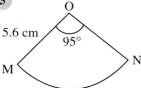

6

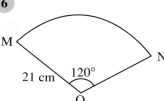

7

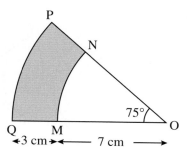

Find the perimeter of the shaded area.

8

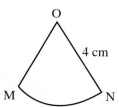

The arc MN = 11cm.

Find MÔN to 1 decimal place.

9 The arc PQ = 15 cm. Find the length OP to 1 decimal place.

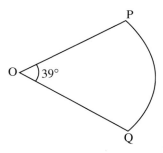

10

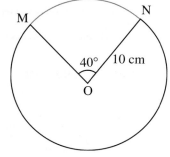

Show that arc MN = $\dfrac{20\pi}{9}$ cm

11

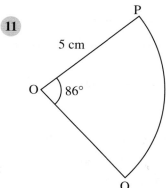

Show that arc PQ = $\dfrac{43\pi}{18}$ cm

385

12

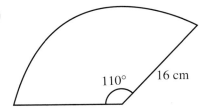

Find the perimeter of this shape,
leaving the answer in terms of π.

13

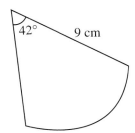

Find the perimeter of this shape,
leaving the answer in terms of π.

14 Find the perimeter of the shaded area below,
giving the answer to 1 decimal place.

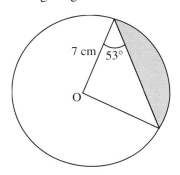

15

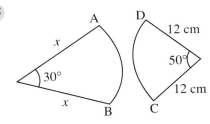

Arc AB is equal to arc CD. Find x.

E | **Areas of sectors and segments**

🔑 **Key Facts**

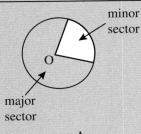

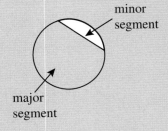

area of circle = πr^2

$$\text{area of sector AOB} = \frac{\theta}{360} \times \pi r^2$$

area of minor segment = area of sector AOB – area of triangle AOB

so area of minor segment = $\frac{\theta}{360} \times \pi r^2$ – area $\triangle$ AOB

area $\triangle$ AOB = $\frac{1}{2} r^2 \sin \theta$ (from area $\triangle = \frac{1}{2} ab \sin \hat{C}$)

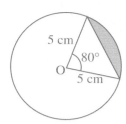

Find the area of the shaded segment, giving your answer to 1 decimal place.

area sector $= \dfrac{80}{360} \times \pi 5^2$

area $\Delta = \dfrac{1}{2} \times 5^2 \sin 80°$ (from area $\Delta = \dfrac{1}{2} a b \sin \hat{C}$)

area segment $= \dfrac{80}{360} \times \pi 5^2 - \dfrac{1}{2} \times 5^2 \sin 80° = 5.1 \text{ cm}^2$

E13.3

In this Exercise, give the answer to one decimal place when necessary. In Questions **1** to **3**, find the area of each sector.

1

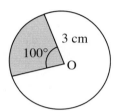

2

3

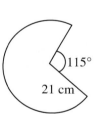

4 Find the shaded area

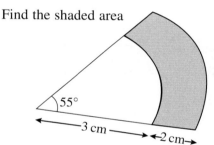

5

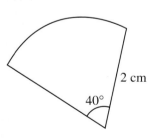

Show that the sector area is $\dfrac{4\pi}{9}$ cm²

6

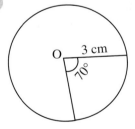

Show that the sector area is $\dfrac{7\pi}{4}$ cm²

7 Find the shaded area, leaving your answer in terms of π.

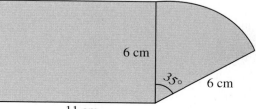

8 A circle has radius 6 cm with centre O. A and B are points on the circumference such that the angle AOB is 30°. Show that the area of the sector AOB is exactly 3π.

9

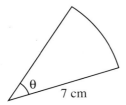

Find the value of θ if the sector area is 10.7 cm².

10

Find the value of r if the sector area is 32 cm².

11 Find the area of each triangle.

(a)

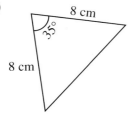

(b)

12

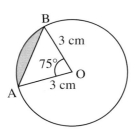

(a) Find the area of triangle AOB.

(b) Find the area of the sector AOB.

(c) Use the answers from (a) and (b) above to find the area of the shaded segment.

13 Find the area of each shaded segment below.

(a)

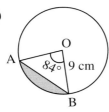

(b)

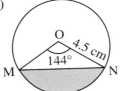

(c)

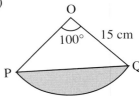

14

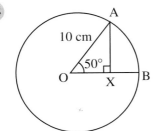

(a) Find OX and AX.

(b) Find the area of triangle AOX.

(c) Find the area of the sector AOB.

(d) Find the area enclosed between the lines AX, XB and the circle.

15 (a) Find the radius of the circle.

(b) Find the area of the shaded segment.

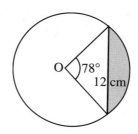

16

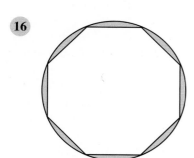

A regular octagon fits inside the circle of radius 7 cm as shown. Find the shaded area.

17 Two circles of radius 10 cm have centres P and Q where PQ is horizontal and has length 16 cm. The two circles intersect at A and B. The line AB intersects the line PQ at a point X. Y is the point on the circle with centre P which lies on the line PQ.

(a) Find the angle APX.

(b) Find the area of the triangle APX.

(c) Find the area of the sector APY.

(d) Hence show that the area enclosed between the two circles and which *lies above the line PQ* is 16.4 cm².

18 Two circles of radius 13 cm have centres P and Q where PQ is horizontal and has length 24 cm. Show that the area which is common to both circles is 13.4 cm².

19

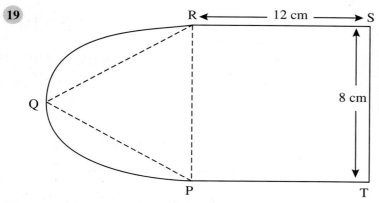

This diagram shows the base of an iron. Arc PQ has the centre of its circle at R and arc QR has the centre of its circle at P.

Find the area of the iron base PQRST.

389

13B   **Mixed algebra (see Units 2, 4, 6)**

1. Factorise
   (a) $x^2 + 5x$
   (b) $4x^2 - 1$
   (c) $x^2 - 7x + 10$
   (d) $a^2 - ax + ay - xy$
   (e) $6x^2 + 11x - 10$

2. Simplify
   (a) $\dfrac{x^4 \times x^5}{(x^3)^2}$
   (b) $x^{\frac{1}{3}} \times x^{-4}$
   (c) $\sqrt{(16x^{10}y^4)}$

3. Solve
   (a) $3^x = \dfrac{1}{27}$
   (b) $2^{3x-1} = \dfrac{1}{8^x}$
   (c) $27^{2x} = 9^{x+1}$

4. Solve
   (a) $5(2x + 1) = 3(3x + 4)$
   (b) $8 = \dfrac{x}{3} + 4$
   (c) $x^2 - 5x = 24$

5. Find the value of f(3) if $f(x) = 5x^2$.

6. If $g(x) = x^2 - 7x$, find the value of x when $g(x) = 3x$.

7. Simplify
   (a) $5(x - 3) - 4(x+5)$
   (b) $(x + y)^2$
   (c) $(x - 1)^2$

8. Make x the subject of each formula given below:
   (a) $\dfrac{x}{p} - q = 2r$
   (b) $\sqrt{(x + 3y)} = z - 3$
   (c) $fx + g = 2x + 3h$

9. A rectangular field is 7m longer than it is wide. If x is the width of the field then:

   (a) Find the length of the field (in terms of x).

   (b) Find an equation involving x.

   (c) Solve this equation to find the *exact* value of x.

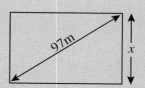

🔑 Key Facts

Length: 1 m = 100 cm

area: 1 m × 1 m = 100 cm × 100 cm

1 m ☐ 1 m² = 10000 cm² ☐ 100 cm
    1 m   100 cm

volume: 1 m × 1 m × 1 m = 100 cm × 100 cm × 100 cm

1 m ▱ 1 m³ = 1000000 cm³ ▱ 100 cm
1 m   100 cm
  1 m   100 cm

Capacity

1 litre = 1000 ml

1 ml is the same as 1 cm³

we have 1 m³ = 1000000 cm³

so 1 m³ = 1000000 ml

so 1 m³ = 1000 litres

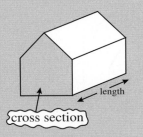

cross section ⟍ length

A prism has the same cross section throughout its length.

Volume of prism = (area of cross section) × (length)

$$V = A\,l$$

In particular,

Volume of cylinder = $\pi r^2 h$

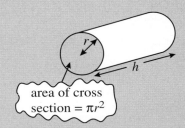

area of cross
section = πr^2

391

(a)

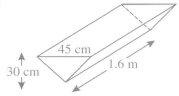

45 cm
30 cm
1.6 m

How many litres of water will
fill this trough?

$V = A\,l$

$V = \left(\dfrac{1}{2} \times 45 \times 30\right) \times 160$

1.6 m changed into
160 cm so all units
are the same

$V = 108000 \text{ cm}^3$

$V = 108$ litres   (because 1000 cm³ are same
as 1000 ml so divide by
1000 to convert into litres)

(b)

0.8 m

The capacity of this
container is 226 litres.
Find the radius to one
decimal place.

Let radius be r

$226\,l = 0.226 \text{ m}^3$ (1 m³ = 1000 ml)

$\pi r^2 \times 0.8 = 0.226$

$r^2 = \dfrac{0.226}{\pi \times 0.8}$

$r^2 = 0.0899$

$r = 0.3$ m (1 decimal place)

M13.2

In this Exercise give answers to 1 decimal place where necessary.

1   (a) Work out the volume of this
solid in m³.

(b) What is the volume of this
solid in cm³?

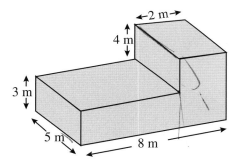

2 m
4 m
3 m
5 m
8 m

2

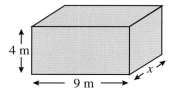

4 m
9 m
x

The capacity of this rectangular tank is
72000 litres.

Find the missing value x.

3   Copy and complete

(a) 1 m³ = ☐ cm³

(b) 2 m³ = ☐ cm³

(c) 4.7 m³ = ☐ cm³

(d) 1 m² = ☐ cm²

(e) 3 m² = ☐ cm²

(f) 80000 cm² = ☐ m²

(g) 35000 cm² = ☐ m²

(h) 9.25 m² = ☐ cm²

(i) 1 m³ = ☐ litres

(j) 7 m³ = ☐ litres

(k) 5600 litres = ☐ m³

(l) 3.9 m³ = ☐ cm³

4 Find the volume of each prism.

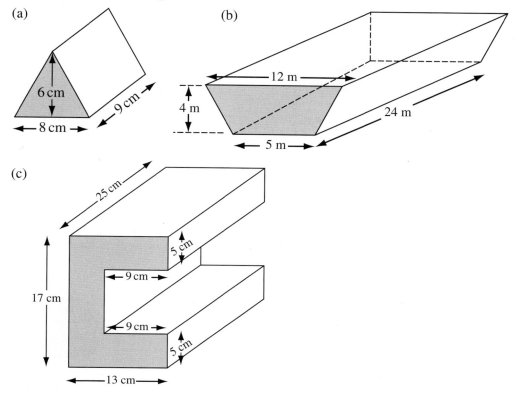

(a)

6 cm
9 cm
8 cm

(b)

12 m
4 m
24 m
5 m

(c)

25 cm
5 cm
9 cm
17 cm
9 cm
5 cm
13 cm

5 Find the *total surface area* of each prism

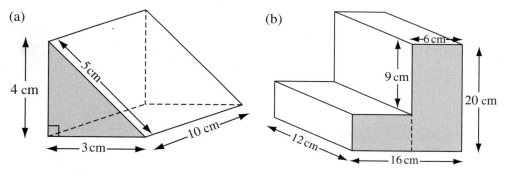

(a)

4 cm
5 cm
3 cm
10 cm

(b)

6 cm
9 cm
20 cm
12 cm
16 cm

6 A piece of metal is in the shape of a prism. It has a volume of 6400 cm³. If the area of the cross section is 32 cm², how long is the piece of metal?

7 Find the volume of each prism.

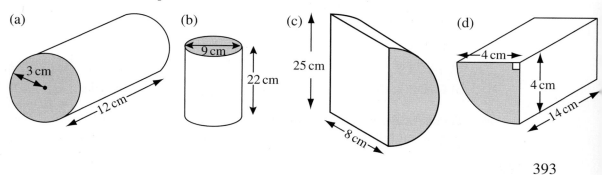

(a)

3 cm
12 cm

(b)

9 cm
22 cm

(c)

25 cm
8 cm

(d)

4 cm
4 cm
14 cm

393

8 Find the volume, in *litres* of a cylindrical container of radius 0.8 m and height 0.95 m.

9 Which of the cylinders below has the larger volume?

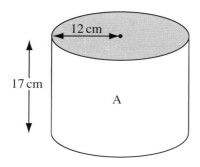
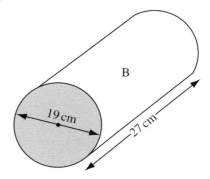

10 A cylindrical can of dog meat has a radius of 3.5 cm and a height of 11 cm. If the can contains 400 cm³ of dog meat, how much empty space is there inside the can?

11

How many glasses of radius 2.5 cm and height 10 cm can be completely filled from the bottle of lemonade?

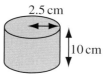

12

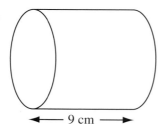

The volume of this cylinder is 450 cm³. Find the radius.

13 A cylindrical container has a capacity of 1.8 litres and a length of 14 cm. Find the diameter.

14 A cylindrical drum has a capacity of 1350 litres and a radius of 0.6 m. Find the height of the drum.

15 A 300 m tunnel is dug. It forms a prism with the cross section shown.

(a) Calculate the area of the cross section.

(b) Calculate the volume of earth which is dug out for the tunnel.

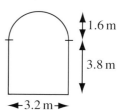

16 A cylindrical glass has a radius of 3 cm and holds 360 cm³ of water when full. Find the height of the glass.

394

17 Find the weight of a lead cylinder of radius 4 cm and length 16 cm. The density of lead is 11.4 g/cm³.

18

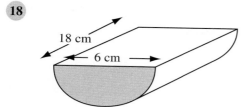

Find the 'exact' volume of this prism, leaving your answer in terms of π.

19

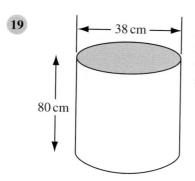

A cylindrical barrel is full of water. The water is poured into a trough as shown.

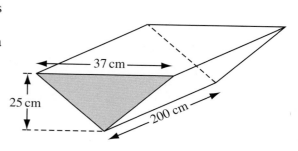

(a) Will all the water go in without the trough overflowing?

(b) What is the difference in the volumes of the two containers?

20 A cylindrical tank is fully covered with an insulating foam which is 15 cm thick. If the tank has height 1 m and base radius 0.8 m before it is covered then what is the volume of the foam used?

21

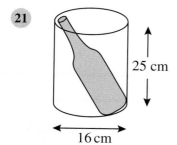

A 1.5 litre bottle of champagne is placed in a cylindrical ice bucket whose diameter is 16 cm and whose height is 25 cm. The bucket is then completely filled with cold water so that the bottle stays completely immersed. Ignoring the volume of the *glass* of the bottle, what is the volume of water used to fill the bucket?

22 A cylindrical pipe lies on its side. The pipe is 2 m long and has an internal radius of 13 cm. It has some water lying in the pipe such that the maximum depth of the water is 5 cm.

(a) Draw a diagram of this pipe and the water.

(b) Find the cross sectional area of the water in the pipe.

(c) Find the volume of water in the pipe.

Key Facts

sphere

volume = $\frac{4}{3}\pi r^3$

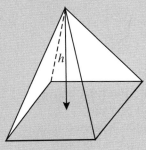

pyramid

volume = $\frac{1}{3} \times$ (base area) $\times h$

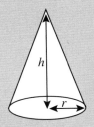

cone

volume = $\frac{1}{3}\pi r^2 h$

A metal cone is melted down and made into 100 ball bearings. If the cone has a base diameter of 8 cm and height of 7 cm, what is the radius of one ball bearing?

volume of cone = $\frac{1}{3}\pi 4^2 \times 7$

volume of bearing (sphere) = $\frac{4}{3}\pi r^3$

volume of 100 bearings = $100 \times \frac{4}{3}\pi r^3$

$$\frac{1}{3}\pi 4^2 \times 7 = 100 \times \frac{4}{3}\pi r^3$$

$$112 = 400 \, r^3$$

$$r^3 = \frac{112}{400} = 0.28$$

$$r = \sqrt[3]{0.28}$$

radius of one ball bearing = 0.65 cm (to 1 dec. place)

E13.4

In this Exercise give answers to 3 significant figures where necessary.

1 Find the volume of each solid.

(a)

9 cm

(b)

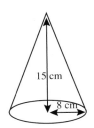

15 cm

8 cm

(c)

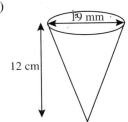

19 mm

12 cm

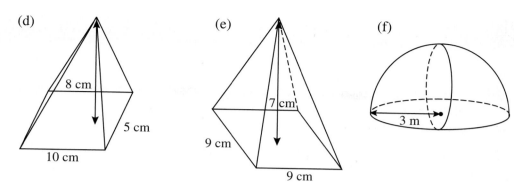

(d) 8 cm 5 cm 10 cm

(e) 7 cm 9 cm 9 cm

(f) 3 m

2 Work out the volume of a hemisphere of diameter 18 cm.

3 A square based pyramid is made from gold. The density of gold is 19.3 g/cm³. What does the pyramid weigh if the base length is 5 cm and the pyramid height is 11 cm?

4 A sphere of radius 2.1 cm is made from a zinc alloy of density 6 g/cm³. Find the mass of the sphere.

5 Find the height of a cone of radius 3 cm and volume 170 cm³.

6 Find the 'exact' volume of each solid, *leaving your answers in terms of π.*

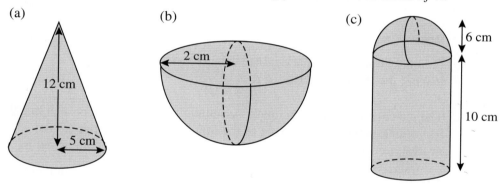

(a) 12 cm 5 cm

(b) 2 cm

(c) 6 cm 10 cm

7 A golf ball is covered in a coating of width 3 mm. If it has a radius of 2 cm before it is covered then find the volume of the coating.

8 Find the volume of each solid, *leaving your answer in terms of π.*

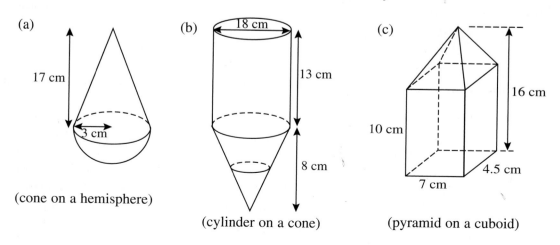

(a) 17 cm 3 cm
(cone on a hemisphere)

(b) 18 cm 13 cm 8 cm
(cylinder on a cone)

(c) 16 cm 10 cm 7 cm 4.5 cm
(pyramid on a cuboid)

9 A cylinder of radius 5 cm and height 12 cm is filled up with water. The water is then poured into a cone with height 4 cm so that it fills the cone exactly. What is the base radius of the cone?

10 A company makes spherical and cubical ice holders. When frozen, both holders are full. What is the diameter of the spherical container if it holds as much as the cubical container of side length 13 mm?

11 A cone of height 45 cm has to hold 3 litres of water. What is the least possible value of the base radius?

12 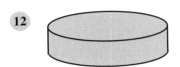 A cake has diameter 35 cm and height 8 cm. A slice of cake is cut so that the angle of the slice is 40°. Calculate the volume of this piece of cake.

13 A cylindrical container has a base radius of 10 cm. Water is poured into the cylinder to a height of 8 cm. A heavy solid sphere of radius 3 cm is placed into the water so that it rests on the bottom of the cylinder. By how much does the height of the water increase?

14 Some wine is poured into the conical glass shown opposite.

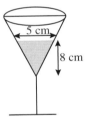

(a) Find the volume of the wine, leaving the answer in terms of π.

(b) Find the volume of a spherical ice cube of radius 1 cm, leaving the answer in terms of π.

(c) The ice cube is put into the glass. Assuming that the ice floats such that 25% of its volume is above the surface of the liquid, calculate the rise (to the nearest mm) in level of the drink in the glass after the ice cube is put in.

15 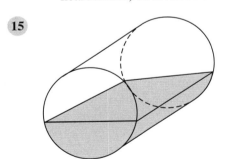 A cylindrical pipe is 3 m long and has a radius of 10 cm. Some water is lying in the pipe such that the maximum depth of the water is 16 cm.

(a) Find the cross sectional area of the water in the pipe.

(b) Find the volume of the water in the pipe.

16 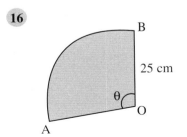 A circle has radius 25 cm. A sector AOB is cut out where O is the centre and A and B are points on the circle such that the angle AOB is θ.

(a) Show that the length of the arc AB is $\frac{5\pi\theta}{36}$.

(b) The sides OA and OB are then joined together to form a cone. If the height of the cone is 24 cm then find the base radius (Hint: use Pythagoras' theorem).

(c) Hence (i) find the perimeter of the base of the cone and (ii) use this to find θ.

17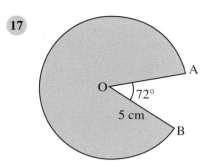

(a) Find the length of the major arc AB.

(b) OA is joined to OB so that a cone shape is formed. Use your answer to part (a) to find the exact value of the radius of the circular base of this cone.

(c) What is the height of this cone?

18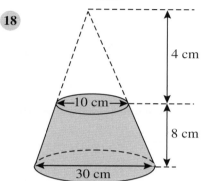

The shaded *frustum* is made by cutting off a small cone from the large cone. Find the volume of the *frustum*.

E | Surface areas of cylinders, spheres and cones

🔑 Key Facts

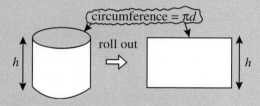

cylinder

curved surface area = πdh or $2\pi rh$
total surface area = $\pi dh + 2\pi r^2$
(including two ends)
                  or $2\pi rh + 2\pi r^2$

sphere

surface area = $4\pi r^2$

cone

curved surface area = πrl

l is called the 'slant' height.

Note

The perpendicular height h, the radius r and the slant height l are connected by Pythagoras' theorem

$h^2 + r^2 = l^2$

Find the total surface area of this cone (to 3 sig. figs).

We need the slant height.

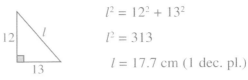

$l^2 = 12^2 + 13^2$

$l^2 = 313$

$l = 17.7$ cm (1 dec. pl.)

total surface area = curved surface area + base

$= \pi r l + \pi r^2$

$= (\pi \times 13 \times 17.7) + (\pi \times 13^2)$

$= 1253.8 = 1250$ cm^2 (3 sig. figs)

E13.5

In this Exercise give answers to 3 significant figures where necessary.

1 Find the *curved* surface area of each solid.

(a)

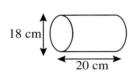

(b)

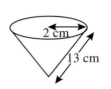

(c)

2 Find the 'exact' *total* surface area of each solid, leaving answers in terms of π.

(a)

(b)

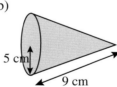

(c)

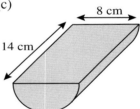

3 (a) Which of these two cylinders has the larger total surface area and by how much?

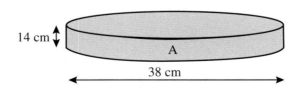

4 What is the surface area of a cricket ball if its diameter is 10 cm?

5 A cone has curved surface area 6 cm^2 and radius 1 cm. What is the slant height of the cone?

6 A 3 litre pot of paint is used to paint the surface of a large sphere and the instructions say that one litre will cover 5 m². What is the maximum radius of the sphere?

7

The surface area of a closed cylinder is 175 cm² and its radius is 4 cm.

Find the height of this cylinder.

8 An apple (assume that it is spherical) of radius 4 cm is cut in half. What area of cling film will be needed to cover completely one half of the apple?

9 Find the total surface area of each cone.

(a)

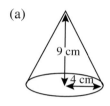

(b)

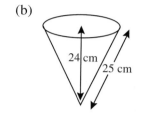

(c)

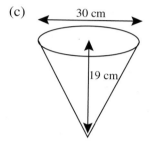

10 A cone has curved surface area 16 cm² and radius 2 cm. What is the *perpendicular* height of the cone?

11 A cone has curved surface area 60π cm² and radius 6 cm. What is the *perpendicular* height of the cone?

12

A circle has radius 12 cm. A sector AOB is cut out where O is the centre and A and B are points on the circle such that angle AOB = 60°.

(a) Find the area of the sector.

(b) Find the perimeter of the arc AB.

(c) The sides OA and OB are then joined together to form a cone. Use your answer to part (b) to find the base radius of the cone.

(d) Verify that the formula πrl for the curved surface area of a cone does give the correct area from part (a).

(e) Find the height of the cone.

13

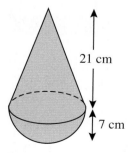

A cone is joined to a hemisphere as shown. The solid is to be protected by using a spray which costs 29p per cm².

How much will it cost to spray the whole solid?

14 A sphere has a volume of 250 cm³. Find the surface area of the sphere.

Two triangles are *similar* if they have the same angles.

Any two shapes are *similar* if one shape is an enlargement of the other. Corresponding sides must be in the same proportion.

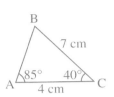 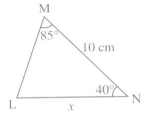

Find *x*.

The triangles are similar because all 3 angles are the same.

Redraw the triangles so that the angles correspond more clearly.

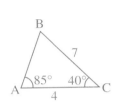 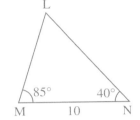

Sides AC and MN correspond.

MN is $\frac{10}{4}$ times longer, ie. 2.5 times longer.

Each side in the larger triangle is 2.5 times longer than the corresponding side in the smaller triangle. Sides LN and BC correspond so $x = 2.5 \times 7 = 17.5$ cm.

M13.3

1 For each part of the Question below, the shapes are similar. Find *x*.

(a)

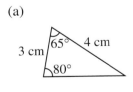 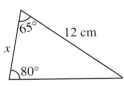

(b)

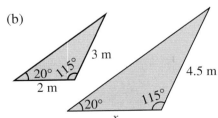

(c)

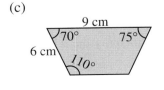

(d)

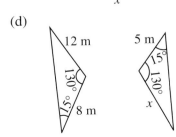

2

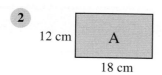

12 cm, A, 18 cm

Picture A is enlarged to make picture B. Find *x*.

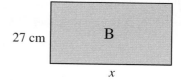

27 cm, B, *x*

3

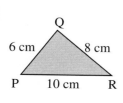

Explain why these triangles are similar.

4

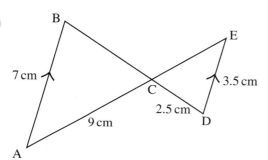

(a) Prove that triangles ABC and CDE are similar.

(b) Find BC.

(c) Find CE.

5 (a) Prove that triangles PQT and PRS are similar.

(b) Find PS.

(c) Find PQ.

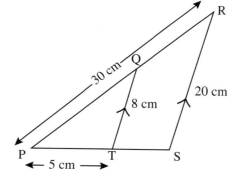

6 Use similar triangles to find *x* in each diagram below.

(a)

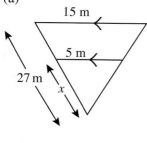

(b)

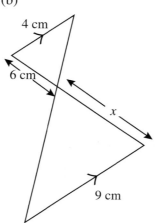

(c)

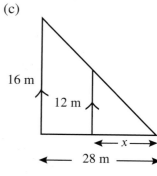

(a)
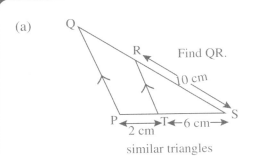
Find QR.

similar triangles

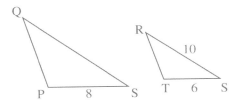

$$\frac{PS}{TS} = \frac{8}{6} = \frac{4}{3}$$

$$QS = \frac{4}{3} \times 10 = \frac{40}{3} = 13\frac{1}{3}$$

$$QR = QS - RS = 13\frac{1}{3} - 10 = 3\frac{1}{3} \text{ cm.}$$

(b)
 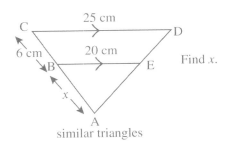
Find x.

similar triangles

 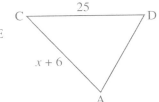

$$\frac{CD}{BE} = \frac{25}{20} = \frac{5}{4}$$

$$x + 6 = \frac{5}{4} x$$

$$4x + 24 = 5x$$

$$x = 24 \text{ cm}$$

M13.4

In Questions ① to ⑥ , find x.

1
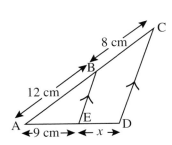

2
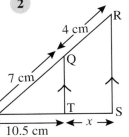

3
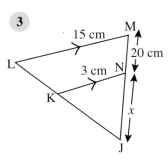

4
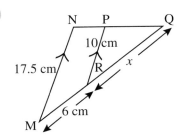

5
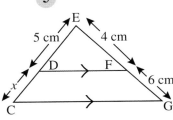

6
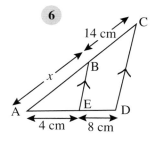

7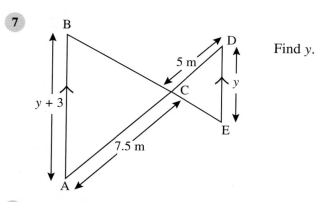

Find y.

8 A man of height 2 m casts a shadow of 3.75 m. At the same moment a tower of height 47 m casts a shadow. How long is the shadow?

9 Find PQ and PT.

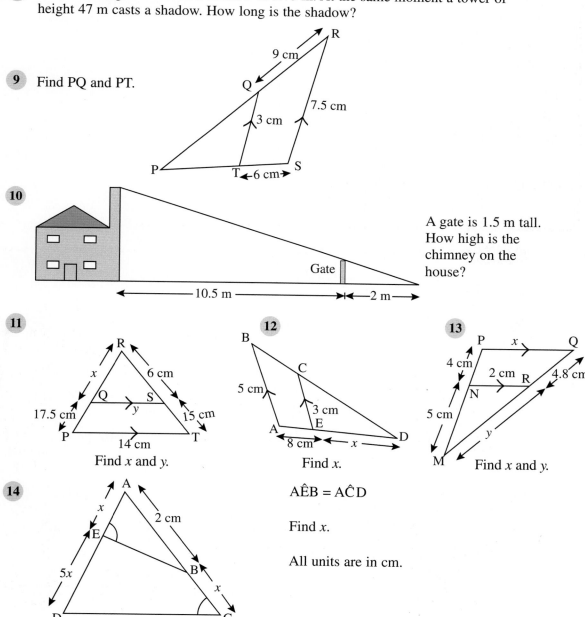

10

A gate is 1.5 m tall. How high is the chimney on the house?

Gate

10.5 m   2 m

11

Find x and y.

12

Find x.

13

Find x and y.

14

$\hat{AEB} = \hat{ACD}$

Find x.

All units are in cm.

405

15 PQSU is a parallelogram.

P$\hat{Q}$V = R$\hat{T}$S

Find PV.

All units are in cm.

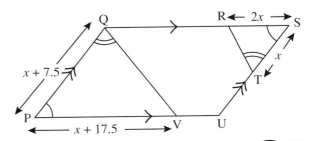

Can you still?

13C **Use vectors (see Unit 10)**

Can you still?

1. If $\mathbf{m} = \begin{pmatrix} -2 \\ -6 \end{pmatrix}$ and $\mathbf{n} = \begin{pmatrix} -3 \\ 9 \end{pmatrix}$, find:

  (a) $3\mathbf{m}$ (b) $\mathbf{m} + \mathbf{n}$ (c) the *magnitude* of $\mathbf{m} + \mathbf{n}$

2.

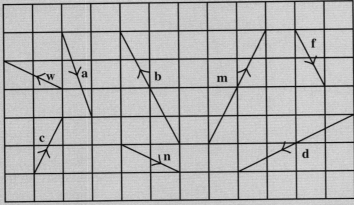

Name a vector equal to   (a) $2\mathbf{c}$ (b) $-\mathbf{n}$ (c) $-\frac{1}{2}\mathbf{b}$

3.

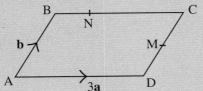

QP is parallel to RS and twice as long. Express each vector below in terms of $\mathbf{a}$ and $\mathbf{b}$:

  (a) $\overrightarrow{RS}$ (b) $\overrightarrow{SQ}$ (c) $\overrightarrow{RQ}$

4. State the geometrical relationship between $3\mathbf{a} - 2\mathbf{b}$ and $12\mathbf{a} - 8\mathbf{b}$.

5. ABCD is a parallelogram. M is the midpoint of CD. N is such that BN : NC = 1:2. Express the following vectors in terms of $\mathbf{a}$ and $\mathbf{b}$:

  (a) $\overrightarrow{CM}$ (b) $\overrightarrow{NC}$ (c) $\overrightarrow{NM}$

The lines AB and MN are extended so that they meet at point P.

  (d) Express $\overrightarrow{NP}$ in terms of $\mathbf{a}$ and $\mathbf{b}$.

  (e) Express $\overrightarrow{AP}$ in terms of $\mathbf{b}$.

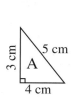

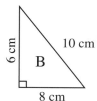

These two triangles are similar.

length of a side in triangle B is *2 times* the length of a side in triangle A, ie. scale factor = 2.

area A = $\frac{1}{2}$ × 4 × 3 = 6 cm² area B = $\frac{1}{2}$ × 8 × 6 = 24 cm²

area of triangle B is *4 times* area of triangle A

ie. 2^2 times area A (this is (scale factor)²)

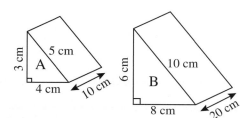

These two prisms are similar.

volume A = area × length = 6 × 10 = 60 cm³

volume B = area × length = 24 × 20 = 480 cm³

volume B is *8 times* volume A

ie. 2^3 times volume A (this is (scale factor)³)

🔑 Key Facts

For two similar shapes,

if the ratio of corresponding lengths   = k

then the ratio of the areas   = k^2

and the ratio of the volumes   = k^3

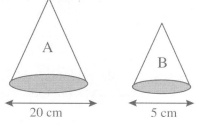

These cones are similar. The total surface area of B is 13 cm².

Find the total surface area of A.

ratio of corresponding lengths = 20 ÷ 5 = 4
so ratio of areas   = 4^2 = 16
total surface area of A   = 16 × area of B
                = 16 × 13
                = 208 cm²

Note: that no 'area of cone' formulas were needed.

407

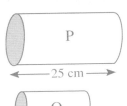

These cylinders are similar.

The capacity of P is 4.8 *l*

The capacity of Q is 1.9 *l*

Find *h*.

ratio of volumes = 4.8 ÷ 1.9 = 2.526 (4 sig. figs)

if ratio of lengths is k then k^3 = 2.526

$$k = \sqrt[3]{2.526}$$

so ratio of lengths is 1.362 (4 sig. figs)

h = 25 ÷ length ratio = 25 ÷ 1.362

h = 18.4 cm (3 sig. figs)

E13.6

1 Find the ratio of the volumes for each pair of similar shapes below.

(a)

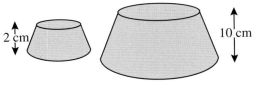

2 cm   10 cm

(b)

0.2 m

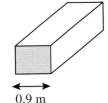

0.9 m

2 Find the ratio of the lengths for each pair of similar shapes below.

(a)

area = 6 m²   area = 294 m²

(b)

surface
area = 11 cm²

surface
area = 63.36 cm²

(c)

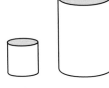

volume
= 8 m³

volume
= 216 m³

(d)

volume
= 28 cm²

volume
= 5463.136 cm²

3

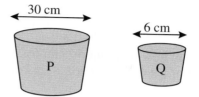

These prisms are similar. The total surface area of prism A is 42 m². Find the total surface area of prism B.

4 These containers are similar.
The volume of P is 2000 cm³.
Find the volume of Q.

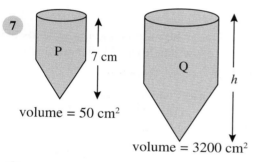

5 A fabric shop sells similar rugs. A customer buys a rug which is 2 m from one corner to the opposite corner and which has an area of 3.6 m². What will the area be of a similar rug which is 3 m from one corner to the opposite corner?

6 A certain vase is 25 cm high and holds 1500 cm³ of water. How much water (to 3 sig. figs.) will a similar vase hold if it is 18 cm high?

7

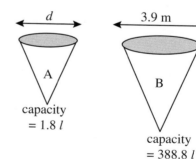

P and Q are similar shapes.

Find h.

8 These cones are similar.

Find d.

capacity = 1.8 l

capacity = 388.8 l

9

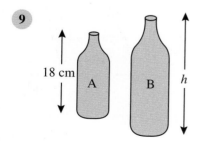

These two bottles are similar.

The total surface area of A is 415 cm².

The total surface area of B is 10375 cm².

Find h.

10 Two pictures are similar. The area of one is 54 cm² and the other is 216 cm². If the length of the larger one is 18 cm then find the length of the smaller one.

11 Two round cakes are similar. One has a radius of 10 cm and weighs 1.5 kg. What is the radius (to 3 sig. figs) of the other cake if it weighs 2 kg?

12 Two milk bottles are similar. The larger one is 20 cm tall and has a volume of 1.5 litres. How much (to 3 sig. figs.) will the smaller bottle hold if it is 15 cm tall?

13

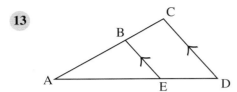

In this diagram, AB = 5 cm and BC = 4 cm. The area of triangle ABE is 23 cm². Find the area of triangle ACD.

14 An egg box of height 54 mm has a volume of 300 cm³. What is the height (to 3 sig. figs) of a similar egg box if its volume is 550 cm³?

15 Two spheres have surface areas in the ratio 9:64. If the diameter of the smaller sphere is 57 cm, find the diameter of the larger sphere.

16 Two similar containers have heights in the ratio 2:5. Find the capacity of the smaller container if the capacity of the larger container is 26 litres.

17 An art shop charges £10 for the area of glass that is needed to cover a painting of length 50 cm. How much would it charge to cover a similar painting of length 70 cm with the same sort of glass?

18 Two football pitches are similar to each other. One is 80 m long and the groundsman needs 15 litres of weed killer to cover the pitch. How much weed killer (to 3 sig. figs) is required for the pitch which is 60 m long?

19 A shop sells two sizes of plastic cylindrical containers which are similar to each other. The larger container has a diameter of 28 cm and a volume of 20 litres. What is the diameter (to 3 sig. figs) of the container which holds 15 litres?

20

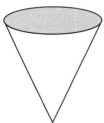

When 216 cm³ of water is poured into the cone shown below, it reaches height h cm. When a further 1512 cm³ of water is poured in, the level of water rises by 8 cm.

(a) Draw two diagrams, marking on the volumes and heights of the water.

(b) Write down an equation involving $h + 8$ and h.

(c) Solve this equation to find the value of h.

 # Key Facts

Connecting the area ratio and volume ratio

If you have the area ratio and need the volume ratio, *find the length ratio first.*

area ratio $\Rightarrow \sqrt{} \Rightarrow$ length ratio $\Rightarrow$ cube $\Rightarrow$ volume ratio

Similarly,

volume ratio $\Rightarrow \sqrt[3]{} \Rightarrow$ length ratio $\Rightarrow$ square $\Rightarrow$ area ratio

Two bottles of wine are similar. One bottle contains 0.7 *l* and the other bottle contains 1 litre. If the surface area of the smaller bottle is 475 cm², find the surface area of the larger bottle.

ratio of volumes $= \dfrac{1}{0.7}$ (it is better to calculate this at the end)

ratio of lengths $= \sqrt[3]{\dfrac{1}{0.7}}$

ratio of areas $= \left(\sqrt[3]{\dfrac{1}{0.7}}\right)^2$

surface area of larger bottle $= \left(\sqrt[3]{\dfrac{1}{0.7}}\right)^2 \times 475$

$= 603$ cm² (to 3 sig. figs)

E13.7

1

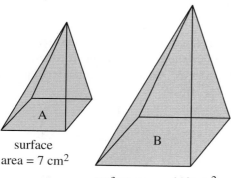

surface area = 7 cm²

surface area = 112 cm²

These two pyramids are similar.
If the volume of A is 36 cm³, find:

(a) the area ratio

(b) the length ratio

(c) the volume ratio

(d) the volume of B

2

capacity = 0.2 *l*

capacity = 68.6 *l*

These two containers are similar.
If the surface area of N is 1421 cm², find

(a) the volume ratio

(b) the length ratio

(c) the area ratio

(d) the surface area of M.

3 Two cuboids are similar. One has volume 6 m³ and the other has volume 11 m³. If the surface area of the smaller one is 22 m², what is the surface area (to 3 sig. figs) of the larger one?

4 A plant pot has a volume of 3.5 litres and a surface area of 850 cm². What is the volume (to 3 sig. figs) of a similar plant pot whose surface area is 1200 cm²?

5 Three layers of wedding cake are similar. The middle layer has a surface area of 3600 cm² and a mass of 5 kg.

(a) What is the mass (to 3 sig. figs) of the bottom layer if its surface area is 8000 cm²?

(b) What is the surface area (to 3 sig. figs) of the top layer if its mass is 3 kg?

6 Two cylinders are similar. The smaller cylinder has a volume of 240 cm³ and surface area 236 cm². What is the volume (to 3 sig. figs) of the larger cylinder whose surface area is 432 cm²?

7

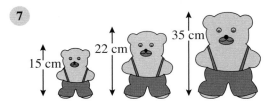

In a shop, teddy bears can be bought in 3 different sizes. The teddy bears are similar. The teddy bears cost the same amount of money per cubic centimetre to make.

If the medium sized bear costs £7 to make, find (to the nearest penny) the cost of making (a) the smaller bear and (b) the larger bear.

8 Two milk churns are similar. One has a surface area of 3600 cm² and a volume of 8 litres. The smaller one has a surface area of 900 cm². Find the volume of the smaller churn.

9

A and B are similar metal components, made with the same density throughout. If the surface area of A is 0.8 m², what is the surface area of B (to 3 sig. figs)?

mass = 5 kg   mass = 11.4 kg

10 A balloon has a length of 18 cm. One day later it has lost 9% of the air in it. Assuming its shape is similar to the previous day, what is its new length (to 3 sig. figs)?

11 Two cones are similar. Their volumes are in the ratio 3:7. The surface area of the smaller cone is 235 cm². Find the surface area of the larger cone (to 3 sig. figs).

12 50 similar metal toys are melted down to make one large toy of a similar shape. If the length of a small toy is 7 cm, what is the length of the large toy (to 3 sig. figs)?

WATCH YOUR MONEY! – Car insurance

The law says you must have car insurance if you drive on public roads.

The car insurance will pay out money if you injure or kill somebody or damage another person's property.

The two main types of car insurance are:

Third party, fire and theft

This does not provide much cover for your own vehicle but will deal with the other person if you are responsible for the damage.

Fully comprehensive

This provides full cover for your own vehicle and any other vehicle involved.

Cost

The amount you pay for car insurance depends on several factors:

- the value of your car

- where you live

- your age

- if you have made a claim on the car insurance in recent years.

No claims bonus

The amount you pay is reduced by 10% each year you do not claim on your car insurance. The biggest discount you can usually have is 60% which is a considerable saving. This percentage reduction is called the 'no claims bonus'.

The bonus is lost if you make a claim on your car insurance then you build up the bonus again over the next few years. Some people pay extra to protect their 'no claims bonus'.

Payments

Some people pay the annual (yearly) cost of their car insurance in one payment but many people spread the cost over 12 equal monthly instalments.

This year Karen's fully comprehensive car insurance quote is £700. She gets a 60% no claims bonus and wants to pay 12 equal monthly instalments. How much is each monthly payment (to the nearest penny)?

no claims bonus	= 60% of £700 = £420
amount to pay	= £700 – £420 = £280
monthly payment	= £280 ÷ 12 = £23.33	(to the nearest penny)

WYM 13

1 Warren is given a quote of £620 this year for third party, fire and theft insurance on his Nissan Micra. He gets a 60% no claims bonus and wants to pay 12 equal monthly instalments. How much is each monthly payment (to the nearest penny)?

2 Helen's fully comprehensive car insurance quote this year for her Astra is £1154. She has a 40% no claims bonus. If she pays 12 equal monthly instalments, how much is each payment (to the nearest penny)?

Copy and complete the table below.

	car	annual car insurance(£)	no claims bonus	annual insurance to pay (£)	monthly payment (£)
3	Corsa	950	60%	380	
4	Lexus	1260	60%		
5	Shogun	1530	30%		
6	Ford Escort	1125	50%		
7	Saab 900S	935	20%		
8	Ford Fiesta	870	60%		
9	VW Golf	1060	20%		

10 Sally bumps her car and has to claim on her car insurance. Her annual insurance is £1280. Before her claim she had a 60% no claims bonus. After the claim, her no claims bonus is reduced *by* 20% (ie. she has a 40% no claims bonus).

(a) What was her monthly payment before the claim?

(b) What is her monthly payment after the claim?

(c) How much more does she have to pay each month?

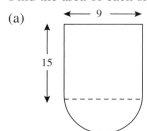

11 David is involved in a car accident and puts in a claim on his car insurance. His annual insurance is £1370. Before the accident he had a 50% no claims bonus. After the claim, his no claims bonus is reduced to 20%. How much more will he have to pay each month for his car insurance?

12 There are many other insurances that people are advised to take out, for example: life insurance, medical insurance, buildings insurance, contents insurance, critical illness insurance and income protection insurance.

(a) Find out what these insurances cover you for.

(b) **Discuss with your teacher** the advantages and disadvantages of taking out these types of insurance.

TEST YOURSELF ON UNIT 13

In all sections below, give answers to one decimal place if necessary.

1. Finding areas

Find the area of each shape below. All lengths are in cm.

(a)

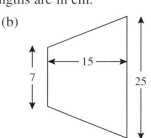

(b)

414

(c)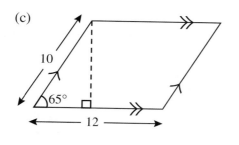

(d)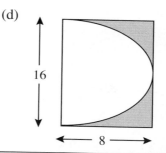

A semi-circle is drawn inside a rectangle.

Find the shaded area.

(a)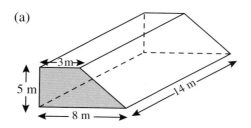

Find the volume of the prism.

(b) Copy and complete

(i) $5 \text{ m}^3 = \boxed{} \text{ cm}^3$

(ii) $7.2 \text{ m}^2 = \boxed{} \text{ cm}^2$

(iii) $2600 \text{ cm}^2 = \boxed{} \text{ m}^2$

(c) A large cylindrical water tank has a radius of 2 m and a height of 3 m. How much water (in litres) will it hold?

(d) A tank in the shape of a triangular prism has a capacity of 360000 litres. Its length is 18 m and the base of the triangular cross section is 8 m. What is the height of the triangular cross section?

(a)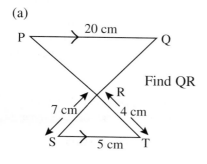

Find QR

(b)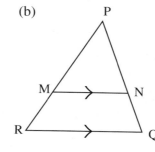

MN = 5 cm
RQ = 12 cm
MR = 5.6 cm

Find PM

(c)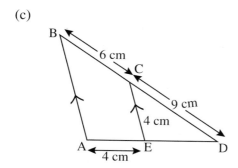

Find AB and DE

415

(a)

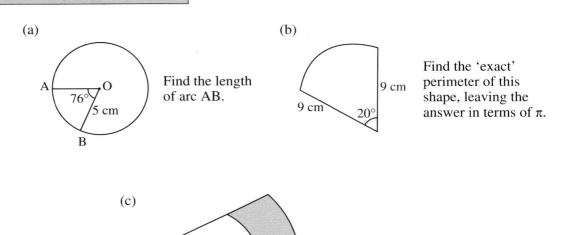

Find the length
of arc AB.

(b)

Find the 'exact'
perimeter of this
shape, leaving the
answer in terms of π.

(c)

Find the perimeter of
the shaded area.

5. Finding areas of sectors and segments

(a)

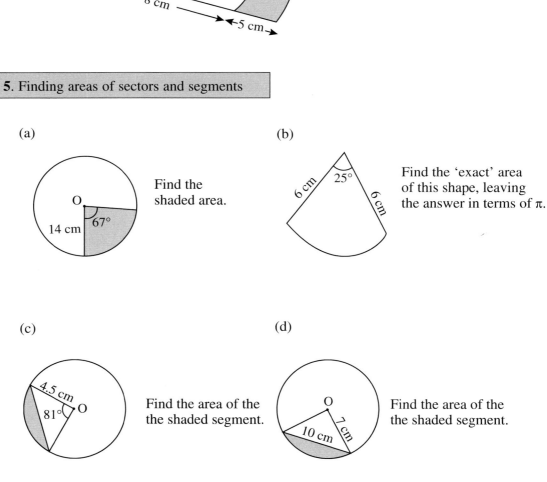

Find the
shaded area.

(b)

Find the 'exact' area
of this shape, leaving
the answer in terms of π.

(c)

Find the area of the
the shaded segment.

(d)

Find the area of the
the shaded segment.

(a)

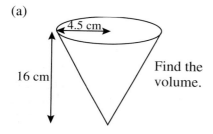

Find the volume.

(b)

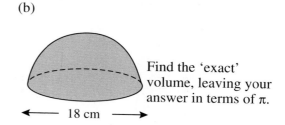

Find the 'exact' volume, leaving your answer in terms of π.

(c)

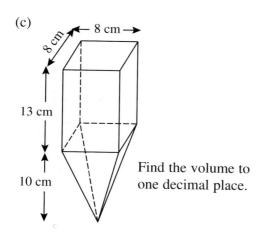

Find the volume to one decimal place.

(d) 1.5 litres of champagne is mixed with an equal volume of orange juice in a hemispherical bowl which is exactly filled by the drink. Find the radius of the bowl.

(a)

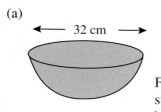

Find the curved surface area of this hemisphere.

(b)

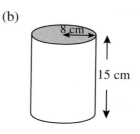

Find the 'exact' total surface area of this cylinder, leaving the answer in terms of π.

(c)

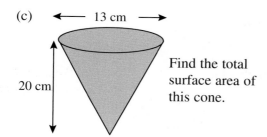

Find the total surface area of this cone.

(d) A cylinder has a height of 3 cm. If its total surface area is 20π cm², find its radius.

8. Finding lengths, areas and volumes of similar shapes

(a)

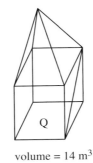

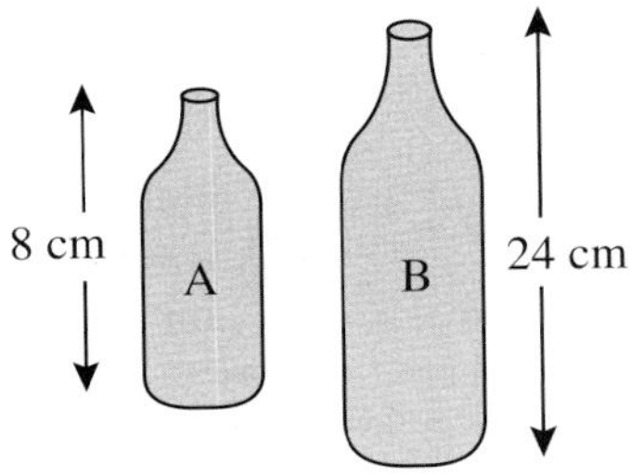

These bottles are similar. The capacity of A is 0.15 litres. Find the capacity of B.

(b) Two books are similar. The smaller one has a surface area of 64 cm² and a width of 7 cm. What is the width of the larger book if its surface area is 106 cm²?

(c)

P and Q are similar solids. The total surface area of Q is 35 m².
Find the total surface area of P.

volume = 2.3 m³   volume = 14 m³

Mixed examination questions

1 ABCD is a trapezium.

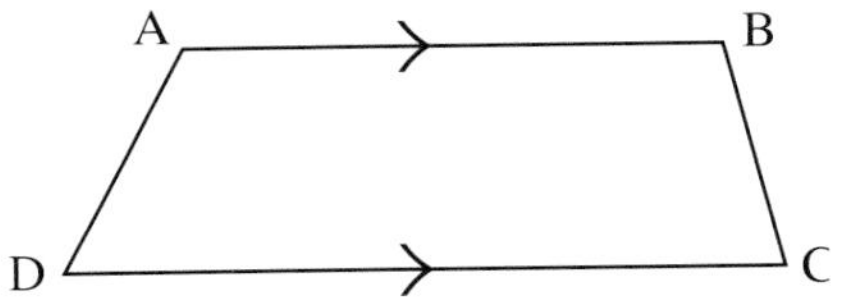

AB = 24cm. DC = 35 cm. The perpendicular distance between AB and DC is 5 cm.

Find the area of the trapezium ABCD.   (OCR)

2 Find the total perimeter of a semicircle with diameter 15 cm.   (WJEC)

3

A 20 Euro note is a rectangle 133 mm long and 72 mm wide.
A 500 Euro note is a rectangle 160 m long and 82 mm wide.

Show that the two rectangles are **not** mathematically similar.   (EDEXCEL)

418

4 The diagram shows glass sectors in a wooden door. The angles of the sectors are 40°, 60°, 40° and the radius of each sector is 24 cm.

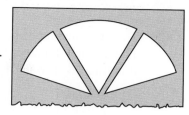

(a) Calculate the total area of glass used in the sectors. You may take $\pi = 3.14$.

(b) Thin strips of wooden framing (which can be curved) are to be placed along the perimeter of each sector.

Calculate the total length of framing required, giving the answer in metres correct to 1 decimal place.

(CCEA)

5 A and B are two similar cylinders.

The height of cylinder A is 10 cm and its volume is 625 cm³
The volume of cylinder B is 5000 cm³

Calculate the height of cylinder B.

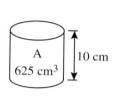
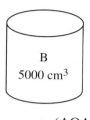

(AQA)

6 Shapes ABCD and EFGH are mathematically similar.

(i) Calculate the length of BC.

(ii) Calculate the length of EF.

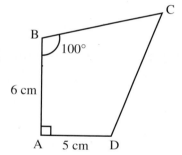
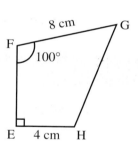

(EDEXCEL)

7

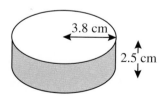

An ice hockey puck is in the shape of a cylinder with a radius of 3.8 cm, and a thickness of 2.5 cm.

It is made out of rubber with a density of 1.5 grams per cm³.

Work out the mass of the ice hockey puck.
Give your answer correct to 3 significant figures.

(EDEXCEL)

419

8 Change 6 m³ to cm³.

9 The glass test tube shown is cylindrical with a hemispherical base.
The internal diameter is 2.6 cm.
It is filled with water to a depth of 11.3 cm.

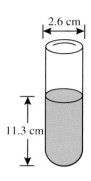

(a) Calculate

    (i) the volume of water in the test tube.

    (ii) the area of glass in contact with the water.

(b) A stone sinks into the water in the test tube, causing the water
level to rise by 24 mm. Calculate the volume of the stone.

$$\text{Volume of sphere, radius } r, = \frac{4}{3}\pi r^3.$$

Surface area of sphere, radius r, $= 4\pi r^2$.
(You may take $\pi = 3.14$)   (CCEA)

10 A building block is in the form of a prism of
length 6 cm.

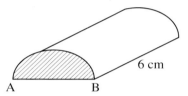

The cross-section of the prism is the segment of a circle.

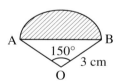

The segment is the shaded part of sector AOB.
The sector has centre O and radius 3 cm.
Angle AOB = 150°.

Calculate the volume of the building block.   (AQA)

11 BC is parallel to DE.
AB is twice as long as BD.

AD = 36 cm and AC = 27 cm.

(a) Work out the length of AB.

(b) Work out the length of AE.

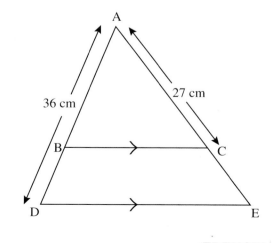

(EDEXCEL)

420

12 The diagram shows a cone.

The cone has a height of 12 cm and a base radius of 3 cm.

(a) Calculate the volume of the cone.

A sphere has the same volume as the cone.

(b) Calculate the radius of the sphere.

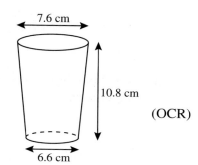

x ml of paint are needed to paint the surface area of the cone.
nx ml of paint are needed to paint the surface area of a similar cone of radius 4.5 cm.

(c) What is the value of n?

(AQA)

13 A can of tinned fish is in the shape of a frustum of a right cone.

The diameter of the top is 7.6 cm.
The diameter of the base is 6.8 cm.
The vertical height is 10.8 cm.
Calculate the capacity of the can.

(OCR)

14 A solid cylinder has diameter d cm.

The height of the cylinder is equal to its diameter.

The total surface area of the cylinder is the same as the surface area of a sphere radius r cm.

Show that $d^2 = \frac{8}{3} r^2$.

In the 'M' sections (mainly grades B, C, D) you will learn how to:
- find the mean, median, mode and range for sets of numbers
- find the median and mode from tables of information
- find mean averages from tables of information (including grouped data)
- use stem and leaf diagrams
- find the interquartile range from a list of numbers
- draw and use cumulative frequency graphs
- draw and use box plots

In the 'E' sections (mainly grades A*, A) you will learn how to:
- draw and interpret histograms
- compare sets of data

Also you will learn how to:

- WATCH YOUR MONEY! – income tax

M | Averages and range

The shoe sizes of 6 people were: 6, 2, 8, 5, 8, 7

(a) *mean* shoe size = $\dfrac{6+2+8+5+8+7}{6}$ ← add up all the numbers

the total number of people

$= \dfrac{36}{6} = 6$

(b) arrange the shoe sizes in order: 2 5 6 7 8 8

the median is the $\frac{1}{2}$-way number

$median = \dfrac{6+7}{2} = 6.5$

(c) *mode* = 8 because there are more 8's than any other number

(d) *Range* = highest number – lowest number

$= 8 - 2 = 6$

The box plots below show the Science test marks for two classes.

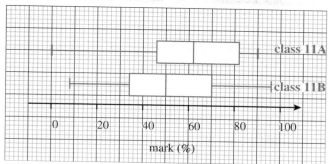

Compare the two sets of marks. Class 11A has a higher median than class 11B. The upper and lower quartiles for class 11A are both higher than those for class 11B. This suggests that in general pupils in class 11A did better than those in class 11B although the highest mark achieved was by a child in class 11B.

M14.8

1 Many pet-owning families were asked how old their dogs were. The information is shown in the box plot below:

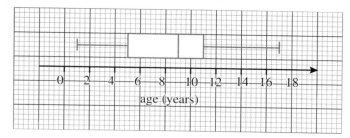

Find   (a) the median   (b) the range   (c) the lower quartile

(d) the upper quartile   (e) the interquartile range

2 Various people were asked how many pieces of fruit they eat in one week. The values in the table opposite were obtained.

Draw a box plot to show this data.

	pieces of fruit
lowest value	0
highest value	37
median	14
lower quartile	10
upper quartile	21

3 A group of people were given a memory test. The values below were obtained:

minimum value = 7   maximum value = 26   median = 15

lower quartile = 13   upper quartile = 19

Draw a box plot to show this data.

4 The box plots below show the annual salaries of workers for two firms, Sibcorn and Naylor's.

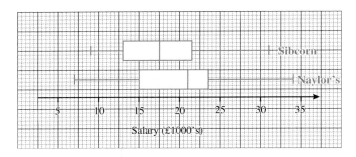

Compare the salaries for the two firms.

5 Two groups of people were asked how many soaps they watched on TV in one month. The values for the over–65 group and the under–25 group are shown below:

	number of soaps (over–65's)	number of soaps (under–25's)
lowest value	3	0
highest value	60	54
median	39	24
lower quartile	32	18
upper quartile	44	45

(a) Draw a box plot for each group of people.

(b) Compare the number of soaps watched by the two groups.

6 The marks obtained by some girls in a history exam are shown in the box plot below:

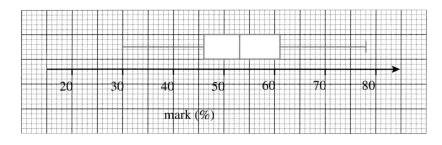

The values below sum up the boys' performance in the same history exam:

lowest value = 38　　　　highest value = 71　　　　median = 54

lower quartile = 50　　　upper quartile = 57

(a) Draw a box plot for the boys' performance.

(b) Compare the performance of the boys and girls.

(14B) Take samples (see Unit 11)

1. Explain what is meant by a *simple random sample*.

2.

	Boy	Girl	Total
Year 10	140	120	260
Year 11	110	130	240
Total	250	250	500

Carol is doing a project on participation in sports in her school. She decides to take a stratified sample of 50 students from Years 10 and 11. How many boys and girls from each Year group will she have in her sample?

3. To find out opinion on the building of a new large supermarket in a town, Ronan decides to look at the local phone book and to take a simple random sample of people. Will this give a representative sample? Give reasons why it does or does not?

4. Give a situation when systematic sampling would be a sensible method to use.

5. A large company owns the cars shown in the table opposite. A stratified sample of 60 cars is to be taken to analyse the overall performance of these vehicles. How many cars of each make will be included in the sample?

make of car	number of cars
Audi	142
Peugeot	208
Vauxhall	320
Mitsubishi	101

6. A magazine wishes to survey young people aged 16 to 21 about their musical tastes. Suggest how the magazine should obtain a representative sample.

E | Histograms

 # Key Facts

A histogram resembles a bar chart. There are no gaps between the bars and the horizontal axis has a continuous scale.

The area of each bar represents the frequency so the height of each bar is known as the frequency density (*not* the frequency).

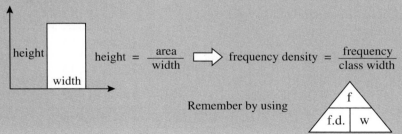

441

Drawing histograms

The ages of the workers in a factory are shown in the table opposite. Draw a histogram to illustrate the distribution of ages. The height (frequency density) of each bar must be calculated first.

ages A (years)	frequency
$20 \leq A < 30$	30
$30 \leq A < 35$	25
$35 \leq A < 40$	35
$40 \leq A < 50$	40
$50 \leq A < 70$	20

ages A (years)	frequency	frequency density
$20 \leq A < 30$	30	$30 \div 10 = 3$
$30 \leq A < 35$	25	$25 \div 5 = 5$
$35 \leq A < 40$	35	$35 \div 5 = 7$
$40 \leq A < 50$	40	$40 \div 10 = 4$
$50 \leq A < 70$	20	$20 \div 20 = 1$

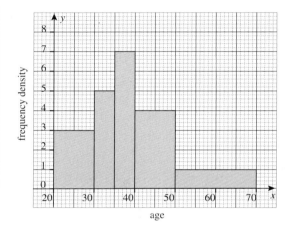

Note – the true lower and upper bounds for each class interval must be clearly established.

If weights are rounded off to the nearest kg, an interval of 5 to 10 does *not* have a width of 5. The true interval is 4.5 to 10.5 so the width is 6. The bar on the histogram would run from 4.5 to 10.5 and the width of 6 would be used to calculate the frequency density (remember there are no gaps between the bars).

E14.1

1 Some commuters were asked how long they spent in their cars during one week. The information is shown in the table opposite.

(a) Work out the frequency density for each class interval.

(b) Draw a histogram to illustrate this data.

time t (hours)	frequency
$0 \leq t < 5$	20
$5 \leq t < 10$	25
$10 \leq t < 12.5$	20
$12.5 \leq t < 15$	15
$15 \leq t < 17.5$	10
$17.5 \leq t < 30$	25

2 (a) Copy and complete the following table which shows the time taken by a group of candidates to finish an exam.

time t (minutes)	$45 \leq t < 50$	$50 \leq t < 55$	$55 \leq t < 60$	$60 \leq t < 70$	$70 \leq t < 90$
number of candidates	21	32	37	29	18
frequency density	$\dfrac{21}{5} = 4.2$				

(b) Draw a histogram to illustrate this data.

3

height (cm)	frequency	class width	frequency density
5–	6	5	$\dfrac{6}{5} = 1.2$
10–	9		
15–	11		
20–	5	10	$\dfrac{5}{10} = 0.5$
30–	4		
40–60	2		

The heights (in cm) of some plants is shown opposite.

(a) Copy and complete the table.

(b) Draw a histogram to illustrate this data.

4 Summarised below are the prices of the goods (to the nearest £) sold by an electrical shop on a certain day.

price of goods (£)	frequency	frequency density
20–39	20	1
40–49	37	
50–59	62	
60–69	51	
70–89	30	
90–129	8	

(a) Explain why the bar on the histogram for '20–39' should go from 19.5 to 39.5.

(b) Copy and complete the table.

(c) Draw a histogram.

5 The table below shows the ages of the people stopped by a company investigating the voting intentions of the adults in a certain town.

age (years)	18–21	22–25	26–35	36–49	50–74
frequency	14	24	39	28	25

(a) Explain why the '18–21' class when written as an inequality is $18 \leq A < 22$ where A is the age.

(b) Explain why the frequency density for the '18–21' class is 3.5.

(c) Draw a histogram to illustrate this data.

6 The height of a certain type of flower was measured (to the nearest cm) and the results are shown below:

height (cm)	6–10	11–15	16–20	21–30	31–40	41–60
frequency	34	47	49	52	32	17

(a) Explain why the '6–10' class when written as an inequality is $5.5 \leq h \leq 10.5$ where h is the height.

(b) Explain why the frequency density for the '6–10' class is 6.8.

(c) Draw a histogram.

Interpreting histograms

This histogram shows the heights of the adults living in the village of Granwych.

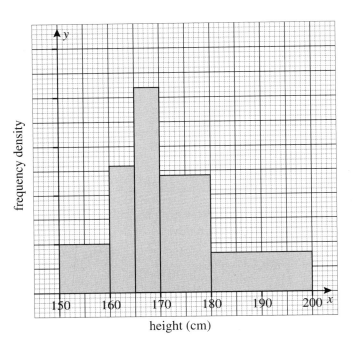

height (cm)

Copy and complete the frequency table below:

height h (cm)	frequency
$150 \leq h < 160$	
$160 \leq h < 165$	65
$165 \leq h < 170$	
$170 \leq h < 180$	
$180 \leq h < 200$	

If the 'frequency density' axis was labelled, the frequencies could be found by using
frequency = frequency density × width

remember:

To label the 'frequency density' axis we must use the information provided about the '$160 \leq h < 165$' interval, ie. frequency = 65

$$\text{frequency density} = \frac{\text{frequency}}{\text{width}} = \frac{65}{5} = 13$$

This enables us to label the 'frequency density' axis.

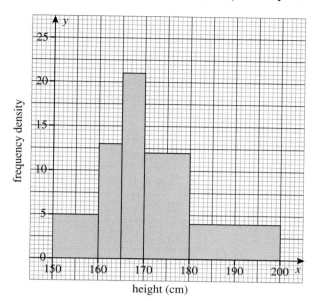

height (cm)

Now complete the frequency table using

frequency = frequency density × width

height h (cm)	frequency
$150 \leq h < 160$	$5 \times 10 = 50$
$160 \leq h < 165$	65
$165 \leq h < 170$	$21 \times 5 = 105$
$170 \leq h < 180$	$12 \times 10 = 120$
$180 \leq h < 200$	$4 \times 20 = 80$

E14.2

1

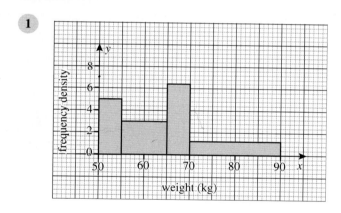

weight (kg)

(a) Copy and complete the frequency table below:

weight w (kg)	frequency
$50 \leq w < 55$	
$55 \leq w < 65$	
$65 \leq w < 70$	
$70 \leq w < 90$	

(b) What is the total frequency?

2

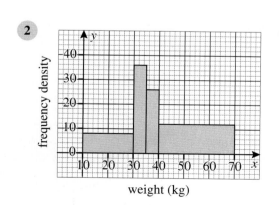

weight (kg)

What is the total frequency?

3

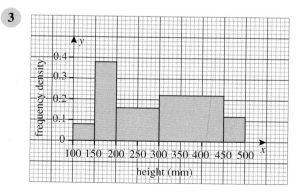

height (mm)

Find the total frequency.

445

4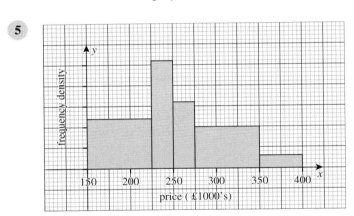

This histogram shows the ages of some people who entered a magazine competition. Copy and complete the frequency table below.

age A (years)	frequency
$10 \le A < 20$	
$20 \le A < 25$	
$25 \le A < 30$	240
$30 \le A < 35$	
$35 \le A < 50$	

5

The histogram shows the house prices around the town of Howstall.

(a) Copy and complete the frequency table below.

price p (£1000's)	frequency
$150 \le p < 225$	
$225 \le p < 250$	
$250 \le p < 275$	8
$275 \le p < 350$	
$350 \le p < 400$	

(b) What is the total frequency?

(c) What percentage of the houses cost more than £275000 (give your answer to 2 decimal places)?

6 This histogram illustrates the marks (out of 20) obtained by a class in a maths test.

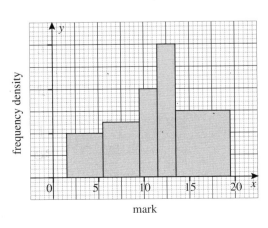

(a) Copy and complete the table below:

mark	frequency
2–5	
6–9	
10–11	
12–13	6
14–19	

446

(b) How many pupils sat the test?

(c) The pass mark was 50%. What percentage of the class passed the test (give your answer to the nearest whole number)?

7 In a survey, people were asked about the economy rate of their cars (in miles per gallon (mpg)). The information is shown in the unfinished histogram and table below.

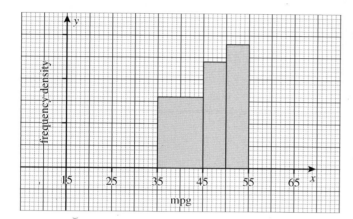

rate r (mpg)	frequency
$15 \leq r < 35$	56
$35 \leq r < 45$	
$45 \leq r < 50$	48
$50 \leq r < 55$	
$55 \leq r < 65$	48

(a) Use the information shown on the histogram to copy and complete the table.

(b) Use the information shown in the table to copy and complete the histogram.

14C **Solve quadratic equations by completing the square**
(see Unit 12)

1. $x^2 + 12x + 8 = (x + a)^2 + b$ Find the values of a and b

2. $x^2 - 4x + 7 = (x + p)^2 + q$ Find the values of p and q

3. Solve the following quadratic equations by completing the square (leave your answers in the form $a \pm \sqrt{b}$).

   (a) $x^2 - 4x - 3 = 0$ (b) $x^2 + 20x + 5 = 0$

4. $4x^2 - 24x + 44 = p((x - q)^2 + r)$ Find the values of p, q and r

5. Solve the following quadratic equations by completing the square (give your answers to 2 decimal places).

   (a) $x^2 + 5x - 8 = 0$ (b) $4x^2 + 8x - 4 = 0$

447

Key Facts

To compare 2 sets of data, always write at least 2 things:

1. Compare an *average* (ie. mean, median or mode)

2. Compare the *spread* of each set of data (this could be the range or interquartile range)

---

6 members of the Harris family weigh 40 kg, 53 kg, 71 kg, 75 kg, 79 kg and 90 kg.

5 members of the Collins family weigh 61 kg, 62 kg, 82 kg, 86 kg and 87 kg.

Compare the weights of the Harris family and the Collins family.

Harris family: median = 73 kg   range = 90 – 40 = 50 kg

Collins family: median = 84 kg   range = 87 – 61 = 26 kg

Answer: The median for the Harris family is less than the median for the Collins family but the range for the Harris family is greater than the range for the Collins family (ie. the weights are more spread out).

E14.3

1   The marks obtained by 2 classes in a maths test are shown in the back-to-back stem and leaf diagram.

```
        Class 10 A              Class 10 B
               9 6  | 4 |  3 3 7 8
         7 7 7 3 2  | 5 |  0 1 4 6 6 6 8
       9 9 8 8 4 1  | 6 |  2 5 5 8 9
           6 6 5 2  | 7 |  4 5 7 7 9 9
           8 7 4 0  | 8 |  1 3 6
               1 1  | 9 |  2 4
```

Key 4|6 = 64   Key 6|5 = 65

(a) Find the median and range for each class.

(b) Compare the test marks for the two classes.

2 The tables below show how many televisions are owned by families living in 2 streets.

Ash Lane	
number of TV's	frequency
0	3
1	5
2	7
3	4
4	1

Tibbs Drive	
number of TV's	frequency
0	1
1	2
2	4
3	1
4	2

(a) Work out the mean and range for Ash Lane.

(b) Work out the mean and range for Tibbs Drive.

(c) Compare the number of televisions owned by families in Ash Lane and Tibbs Drive.

3 80 students take a Science and Maths test. The table below shows the distribution of marks.

Mark	31–40	41–50	51–60	61–70	71–80	81–90	91–100
Science frequency	4	14	21	23	12	6	0
Maths frequency	7	26	7	17	15	5	3

(a) On the same axes draw a cumulative frequency curve for each of the Science and Maths marks.

(b) Find the median and interquartile range for each of the Science and Maths marks.

(c) Compare the distribution of the marks for the Science and Maths tests.

4 The ages at which women in the town of Hosforth passed their driving test are shown in the box plot below.

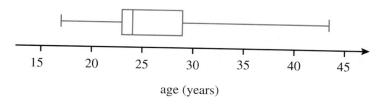

age (years)

The values below indicate the ages of the men when they passed their driving test.

lowest value = 17   highest value = 35   median = 22

lower quartile = 20   upper quartile = 27

Compare the ages of the men and the women when they passed their driving test.

5 The table below shows the ages at which people died in area A.

age A (years)	30 ≤ A < 50	50 ≤ A < 55	55 ≤ A < 60	60 ≤ A < 70	70 ≤ A < 75	75 ≤ A < 80	80 ≤
frequency	4000	3000	4500	8000	6000	7500	8

(a) Draw a histogram to illustrate this data.

(b) The histogram below shows the ages at which people died in area B.

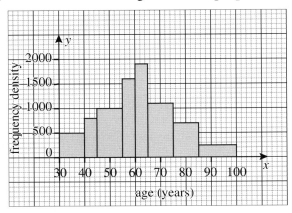

Compare the distribution of the ages at which people died in areas A and B.

WATCH YOUR MONEY! – Income tax

Tim starts a job earning £200 each week. When he gets his first pay packet, he finds £18.42 has been taken off his money already. This is *income tax*.

This does not make Tim happy but this money is used by the government to pay for things like hospitals, schools and defence.

Most people have income tax deducted from their pay *before* they receive it, by their employer, who then pays the tax to the government. This method of paying income tax is called *PAYE (Pay As You Earn)*

Tax allowance

An amount of money a person may earn before paying income tax (at the time of writing this is £4745 each year for a single person).

Taxable income

Taxable income = income – tax allowance

Income tax is worked out as a percentage of the taxable income.

Percentage rate of income tax

10% on first £1960 of taxable income.

22% on the next £28540 of taxable income.

40% on any other taxable income.

450

If Tim earns £200 each week, that will be £10,000 in one year (assuming 50 working weeks in one year).

tax allowance   = £4745

taxable income = income – tax allowance

$$= 10000 - 4745$$

$$= £5255$$

Tim pays 10% of £1960 on first £1960 of taxable income.

This leaves 5255 – 1960 = £3295 of taxable income.

Tim must then pay 22% of £3295

Income tax = 10% of 1960 = £196

and 22% of 3295 = £724.90

Total income tax for the year = £920.90   (this is £18.42 for each week if divided by 50 weeks)

WYM14

1 Sophie earns £15000 each year. She has a tax allowance of £4745. Copy and complete the statement below to find out how much income tax Sophie must pay.

Taxable income = income – tax allowance

$$= 15000 - \boxed{}$$

$$= £ \boxed{10255}$$

income tax = 10% of 1960 = £ $\boxed{}$

and 22% of $\boxed{\text{'taxable income'} - 1960}$

$$= 22\% \text{ of } \boxed{} = £ \boxed{}$$

total income tax = £ $\boxed{}$ + £ $\boxed{}$ = £ $\boxed{}$

2 Callum earns £13400 each year. He has a tax allowance of £4745. Copy and complete the statements below to find out how much income tax Callum must pay.

Taxable income = income – tax allowance

$$= \boxed{} - \boxed{}$$

$$= £ \boxed{}$$

income tax = 10% of 1960 = £ $\boxed{}$

and 22% of $\boxed{\text{'taxable income'} - 1960}$

$$= 22\% \text{ of } \boxed{} = £ \boxed{}$$

total income tax = £ $\boxed{}$ + £ $\boxed{}$ = £ $\boxed{}$

451

3 Wendy earns £28500 each year. She has a tax allowance of £4745.

(a) What is Wendy's taxable income?

(b) How much income tax will Wendy have to pay?

4 Alex earns £1450 each month. He has a tax allowance of £4745.

(a) What is his annual (yearly) taxable income?

(b) How much income tax will he pay for one year?

(c) How much income tax will he pay each month?

5 Angus earns £6000 each year. How much income tax will he pay? (He has a tax allowance of £4745)

6 Millie earns £320 each week. She has a tax allowance of £4745.

(a) Find her annual salary (assuming 52 weeks in one year).

(b) What is her taxable income?

(c) How much income tax will she pay for one year?

(d) How much income tax will she pay each week?

7 Dom earns £90 each week. His tax allowance is £4745. Assuming 52 weeks in one year, how much income tax will Dom pay each week?

8 Emma earns £896 each month from her work in a shop. She also works in a pub, earning £30 each week. Her tax allowance is £4745.
Assuming 52 weeks in one year, how much income tax will Emma pay each week?

TEST YOURSELF ON UNIT 14

1. Finding the mean, median, mode and range for sets of numbers

(a) 9, 7, 3, 7, 4, 8, 2, 7, 1, 6, 1

For the set of numbers above, find the
(i) mode   (ii) median   (iii) mean   (iv) range

(b) Seven women have a mean weight of 63 kg and eleven men have a mean weight of 74 kg. Find the mean weight (to 1 dec. place) of all 18 men and women.

2. Finding the median and mode from tables of information

Some 16 year-olds were asked how many dental fillings they had been given during their lifetimes. The table shows the information.

number of fillings	0	1	2	3	4	5
frequency	12	17	24	18	7	3

Find (a) the modal number of fillings

(b) The median number of fillings

3. Finding mean averages from tables of information (including grouped data)

(a) This table shows the number of bicycles owned by families who live in Camden Terrace.

    (i) Find the total number of bicycles.

    (ii) Find the mean average number of bicycles per family.

number of bicycles	frequency
0	8
1	4
2	17
3	24
4	16
5	6

(b) The table below shows how many hours were spent using a computer by 200 people last week.

hours using a computer (h)	$0 \leq h < 5$	$5 \leq h < 10$	$10 \leq h < 20$	$20 \leq h < 30$	$30 \leq h < 40$	$40 \leq h < 60$
frequency	49	68	36	23	17	7

Estimate the mean number of hours spent using a computer.

4. Using stem and leaf diagrams

The ages of 25 people who work for a local newspaper are recorded below.

31	42	27	50	21
26	19	19	62	35
32	23	53	27	46
48	43	28	53	58
37	51	36	47	20

(a) Draw a stem and leaf diagram to show this data.

(b) What is the median age?

(c) Find the range of the ages.

5. Drawing and using cumulative frequency graphs

The ages of customers in a large restaurant one evening are recorded in the table opposite.

(a) Draw a cumulative frequency graph.

(b) Use the graph to estimate the median age.

(c) Use the graph to estimate the interquartile range.

age A (years)	frequency
$15 \leq A < 25$	12
$25 \leq A < 35$	33
$35 \leq A < 45$	41
$45 \leq A < 55$	18
$55 \leq A < 65$	10
$65 \leq A < 75$	6

6. Finding the interquartile range from a list of numbers

7 18 9 13 7 10 14 8 13 19 9 8 16 11 6

For the list of numbers above, find   (a) the median (b) the lower quartile (c) the upper quartile (d) the interquartile range

7. Drawing and using box plots

The times taken to get from home to school by pupils from Avalon Meadow School are shown in the box plot below.

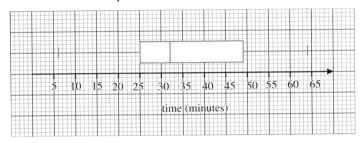

The values below sum up the times taken to get from home to school by pupils from Ellis Gate School:

    lowest value = 2 mins.   highest value = 28 mins.   median = 16 mins.

    lower quartile = 11 mins.   upper quartile = 19 mins.

(a) Draw a box plot for the Ellis Gate School information.

(b) Compare the times taken by the pupils from each school. What might account for the differences?

8. Drawing and interpreting histograms

The time spent by people in an out-of-town shopping centre one day is shown in the unfinished histogram and table below.

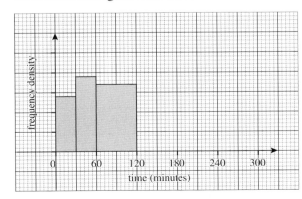

time t (minutes)	frequency
$0 \leq t < 30$	210
$30 \leq t < 60$	
$60 \leq t < 120$	
$120 \leq t < 180$	810
$180 \leq t < 210$	330
$210 \leq t < 300$	495

(a) Use the information shown on the histogram to copy and complete the table.

(b) Use the information shown in the table to copy and complete the histogram.

454

Choosing the hypotheses

A simple hypothesis – this will involve 2 factors.

Example: 'I believe boys are generally taller than girls in my school'. This involves height and the sex (boy or girl).

(If you only test a simple hypothesis, you cannot score more than a grade D/E).

The simple hypothesis must be developed to introduce another factor which leads to a new hypothesis.

A substantial task – this will involve 3 factors.

Example: 'I believe boys are generally taller than girls in year 11 but boys and girls are generally the same height in year 7.' This involves height, sex and age.

(If you only deal with a substantial task, you are unlikely to score more than a grade B).

To achieve the higher grades, more creative thinking needs to be applied. This may involve introducing more factors, possibly in the form of several hypotheses. We call this a *complex* task. It should be chosen to allow you to use a range of higher level statistical methods. You can try to discover which factors have the greatest effect and which factors can be combined to give a better comparison.

The plan

- Is there a reason why you have chosen your hypotheses?

- Where will you collect the data?

- Will the data be reliable? How do you know?

- How will you take a sample from the data?

- How will you avoid bias?

- How large will the sample size be?

- Can you think of any problems at this stage and how can you overcome them?

You must write your plan down. Do not leave it until the end. Do it early on and show it to your teacher. The plan must be detailed and you must explain why you have made the various decisions in your plan.

The sample

Sample size	– use enough sets of data or the results will not be very reliable (use at least 30 sets of data).
Sampling method	– the most likely methods would be simple random sampling or stratified sampling (refer to work in Unit 11 if necessary). Only choose a particular method if it is appropriate.
A representative sample	– think carefully about the data you are examining. You must avoid bias (refer to work in Unit 11 if necessary).

Pre-test

If you are collecting your own data, it can make sense to carry out an initial test. This gives enough information to allow you to make changes before gathering the full set of data and conducting your tests.

Process and represent the data

- Only do things which you are going to use to examine your hypotheses (do not waste time drawing charts/graphs which you are not going to use).

- Which charts/graphs will be useful?

- Which statistical measures can you work out from your data? Will they be of any use?

- How will you check your calculations?

- Have you dealt with problems such as missing data?

Remember

It is vital that you only produce charts, graphs and calculations if they are relevant and you are going to use them later.

The table below shows the typical things you might do for strand 2 to score the grades shown.

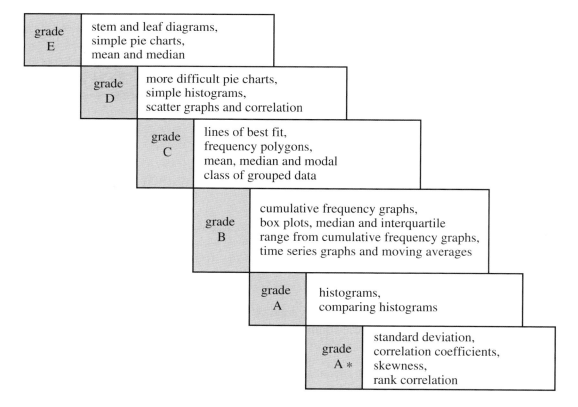

grade E	stem and leaf diagrams, simple pie charts, mean and median
grade D	more difficult pie charts, simple histograms, scatter graphs and correlation
grade C	lines of best fit, frequency polygons, mean, median and modal class of grouped data
grade B	cumulative frequency graphs, box plots, median and interquartile range from cumulative frequency graphs, time series graphs and moving averages
grade A	histograms, comparing histograms
grade A *	standard deviation, correlation coefficients, skewness, rank correlation

Using topics beyond GSCE

The topics listed in 'grade A*' on the last page are beyond GCSE. It is possible to achieve the maximum mark without using one of these topics if your overall project is tackled in a creative, complex manner. If you choose to use the topics beyond GCSE, you must research them and then apply them. You must convince your teacher that you understand them and can interpret them if you use them.

Using ICT

You are encouraged to use ICT whenever possible. Spreadsheets are particularly useful for sorting, drawing certain diagrams and performing functions such as working our means, standard deviation and correlation coefficients.

If a computer is used, it is vital that you explain clearly what you are doing and can interpret the results. You will get low marks if you fail to do this. You could choose to print out the formulae that you have used to show how efficiently you have handled the spreadsheet.

Interpret and discuss your findings

At any appropriate stage:

- you must summarise your findings from the data you collected.

- You must compare any statistical measures and *link it back to your hypotheses*.

- Example: 'The boys have a greater mean average height than the girls and the standard deviation values for their heights are almost identical. This suggests that the boys are generally taller than the girls which supports my hypothesis.'

- Are differences significant? Make use of percentages?

- What effect might the nature and size of the sample have had on the conclusions to be drawn?

- Use the vocabulary of probability, where appropriate, when making statements? Can you write down any factors which might concern you about how reliable your findings are?

- Can you suggest any real-life reasons why the results suggested your hypotheses were true or false?

The conclusion

- Write down your key findings, always linking them to your hypotheses.
- Discuss any problems/limitations in what you did.
- How might you have improved what you did?
- What else might you have looked at if you had been given the time?

In the 'M' sections (mainly grades B, C, D) you will learn how to:
- solve inequalities
- shade regions given by inequalities
- use dimensions to recognise a length, area or volume formula

In the 'E' sections (mainly grades A*, A) you will learn how to:
- cancel, multiply and divide algebraic fractions
- add and subtract algebraic fractions
- solve equations containing algebraic fractions
- tackle algebraic proof

Also you will learn how to:
- (WATCH YOUR MONEY!) – buying a house

M   **Inequalities**

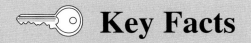

Key Facts

Solving inequalities

To solve an inequality, like $2x + 4 < 10$, find the *range of values of x* which satisfy the inequality.

To isolate x, follow the same methods as for solving equations except:

If you multiply or divide both sides by a negative number, the inequality sign must be reversed.

for example $3 > 2$ multiply both sides by -1 ⇨ $-3 > -2$ not true

reverse inequality sign

$-3 < -2$ is true!

(a) Solve $3x - 2 \le 13$

$3x \le 13 + 2$

$3x \le 15$

$x \le \dfrac{15}{3}$

$x \le 5$

(b) Solve $4 - 2x > 10$

Either $4 - 2x > 10$

$-2x > 10 - 4$

$-2x > 6$

$x < \dfrac{6}{-2}$ [reverse inequality because dividing by -2]

$x < -3$

or make the x's positive first

$4 - 2x > 10$

$4 > 10 + 2x$

$4 - 10 > 2x$

$-6 > 2x$

$\dfrac{-6}{2} > x$

$-3 > x$

we say $x < -3$

(c) Show on a number line the range of values of x for the inequalities shown.

$x > 2$

The circle at the left hand end of the range is open. This means x cannot equal 2.

$-2 \le x < 1$

x can equal -2 so the circle at -2 is filled in.

(d) Solve $1 \le 2x + 3 < 15$

Deal with each inequality separately

$1 \le 2x + 3$

$1 - 3 \le 2x$

$-2 \le 2x$

$\dfrac{-2}{2} \le x$

$-1 \le x$

$2x + 3 < 15$

$2x < 15 - 3$

$2x < 12$

$x < \dfrac{12}{2}$

$x < 6$

Answer: $-1 \le x < 6$

M16.1

1 Write down the inequalities shown below:

(a)

(b)

(c)

2 Find the range of values of x which satisfy each inequality below and *show each answer on a number line.*

(a) $5x \le 30$

(b) $9x > -27$

(c) $2 + x \ge 6$

(d) $\dfrac{x}{2} \ge 1$

(e) $4 < x + 1 \le 9$

(f) $-1 < 2x - 1 < 7$

3 Solve the inequalities below:

(a) $a - 7 > -2$

(b) $\dfrac{x}{5} < -9$

(c) $2b + 4 < 10$

(d) $3y - 1 \le 14$

(e) $14 - 3n < 5$

(f) $4c + 12 \le 28$

(g) $9 - 5x \leq 34$ (h) $3(a - 2) < 15$ (i) $\dfrac{n}{6} - 4 \geq 2$

(j) $5x + 3 \geq 2x + 21$ (k) $8n - 2 > 3n + 33$ (l) $6x + 8 < 38 - 4x$

4   Write down all the *integer* values (*whole numbers*) of x which satisfy the given inequalities.

(a) $0 < x < 4$ (b) $1 \leq x < 7$ (c) $-2 \leq x \leq 2$ (d) $-4 < x \leq 0$

5   Write down the greatest positive integer, n, which satisfies each inequality below:

(a) $\dfrac{2n - 1}{5} \leq 1$ (b) $\dfrac{3n}{8} - 2 < 1$ (c) $2 - 7n \geq -12$

(d) $3 + \dfrac{n}{7} < 9$ (e) $5 - 2n > 1$ (f) $\dfrac{4n - 3}{5} < 5$

6   Solve the inequalities below:

(a) $15 \leq 3x < 21$ (b) $9 \leq x - 3 \leq 25$ (c) $-11 < x + 1 < -8$

(d) $2 \leq \dfrac{x}{5} < 3$ (e) $3 \leq \dfrac{1 + 2x}{3} < 5$ (f) $-2 < \dfrac{2 + 5x}{4} \leq 3$

(g) $x + 1 < 3x + 2 < x + 10$ (h) $-1 \leq \dfrac{2 + 5x}{3} \leq 4$ (i) $10 - 2x < 4(x - 2) \leq 2x$

🔑 Key Facts

Solving inequalities involving x^2

Make x^2 the subject of the inequality first

If $x^2 < a$ then $-\sqrt{a} < x < \sqrt{a}$

and if $x^2 > a$ then $x > \sqrt{a}$ or $x < -\sqrt{a}$

this part of the solution is often missed

(a) Solve $x^2 \leq 9$

     $-3 \leq x \leq 3$

(b) Solve $5x^2 - 2 > 178$

         $5x^2 > 180$

           $x^2 > 36$

       $x > 6$ or $x < -6$

Solve the inequalities below:

1 $x^2 < 25$ **2** $m^2 \le 81$ **3** $y^2 > 4$ **4** $z^2 \le 400$

5 $b^2 \ge 144$ **6** $n^2 < 6.25$ **7** $4m^2 \ge 64$ **8** $3x^2 > 3$

9 $2n^2 + 5 < 23$ **10** $4a^2 - 32 \ge 68$ **11** $8x^2 + 12 > 20$ **12** $49 - x^2 > 0$

13   Find the range of values of x which satisfy each inequality below and *show each answer on a number line*.

    (a) $y^2 + 10 < 131$ (b) $5m^2 - 14 \ge 6$ (c) $3(n^2 + 4) > 120$

    (d) $22.25 - p^2 > 10$ (e) $9 + 2x^2 \le 401$ (f) $5m^2 + 28 \ge 52 - m^2$

M | Shading regions given by inequalities

🔑 Key Facts

a broken line is used for < or > boundaries to show that points on the boundary line are not included

unbroken lines are used for ≤ or ≥ boundaries to show that points on the boundary lines are included

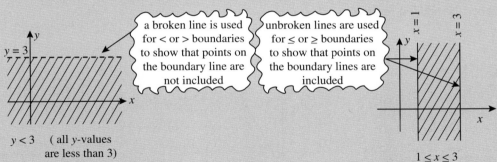

$y < 3$ (all y-values are less than 3)

$1 \le x \le 3$
(all x-values lie between and include 1 and 3)

To draw $y > 2x - 3$, draw the boundary line $y = 2x - 3$ first (unbroken for >)

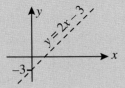

Decide on which side of the line to shade. Choose any point not on the boundary line, eg. (0, 0). Does this point satisfy $y > 2x - 3$?

Put $x = 0$, $y = 0$ into $y > 2x - 3$ ⇨ $0 > 0 - 3$ ie. $0 > -3$. This is clearly true so shade the region on the side of the boundary line which includes (0, 0).

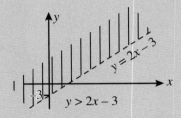

1 Write down the inequality which describes the shaded region.

(a)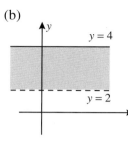

(b)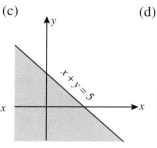

(c)

(d)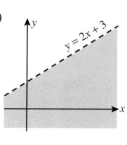

2 Draw graphs to show the regions given by the inequalities below:

(a) $y > 1$ (b) $-2 \le x < 3$ (c) $0 < y < 4$ (d) $y \le x$

(e) $y > x - 2$ (f) $y < 3x + 1$ (g) $x \le 0$ (h) $x + y \ge 7$

(i) $2x + y > 4$ (j) $x - 3y \le 9$ (k) $2x + 3y \le 6$ (l) $5x - y > 10$

3 By finding the equation of the boundary line, write down the inequality which describes the shaded region.

(a)

(b)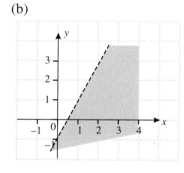

(c)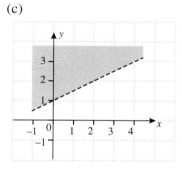

4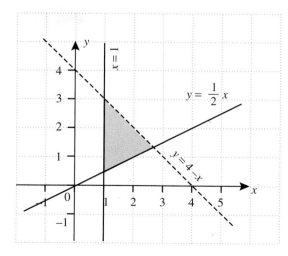

The shaded area opposite is described by 3 inequalities: $x \ge 1$, $y < 4 - x$ and one other inequality. Write down the other inequality.

5

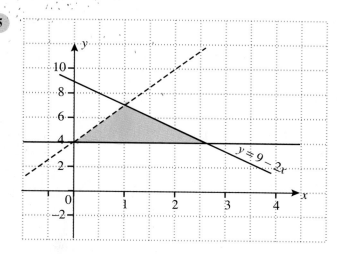

The shaded area above is described by 3 inequalities. By finding the equations of the remaining two boundary lines, write down the 3 inequalities.

6 Draw graphs to show the region given by each group of inequalities below. Use shading to make the required region clear.

(a) $1 \leq x < 5$, $2 < y < 5$

(b) $y > x - 2$, $x \geq 0$, $y \leq 3 - x$

(c) $y < 2x + 1$, $2y + x \leq 6$, $2x - 3y \leq 12$

(d) $x - 2y \leq 2$, $5x - 2y \geq -10$, $5x + 6y < 30$

(e) $3x - 2y \leq 12$, $x + 2y \leq 8$, $x > -1$

(f) $2x + 3y < 12$, $y - 2x \leq 4$, $x - 3y < 6$

(g) $y \leq 8 - 2x$, $4x - 3y > -24$, $4y - x \geq -4$, $6y + x > -6$

(h) $3x + 2y \leq 12$, $3x - 2y \leq 12$, $3x - 2y \geq -12$, $3x + 2y \geq -12$

7

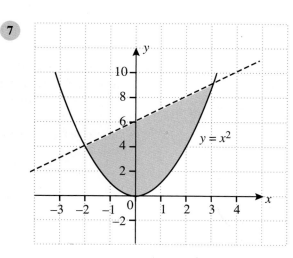

Use two inequalities to describe this shaded region.

469

16A **Areas and volumes (see Unit 13)**

Give answers to one decimal place if necessary.

1. Find the areas of these two shapes.

(a)

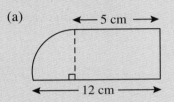

(b)

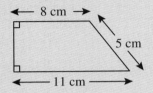

2. Find the 'exact' volumes of these two solids, *leaving your answers in terms of* π.

(a)

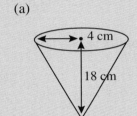

(b)

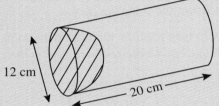

(a hemisphere is 'hollowed' out of a cylinder)

3. Find the *total* surface area of this cone.

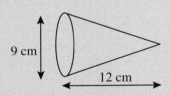

4. A metal cylinder of radius 3 cm and height 11 cm is melted down and made into 2000 hemispheres. What is the radius of one hemisphere?

5. This container has 3.5 litres of water in it. The water level is somewhere within the cylinder. How high is the water level above the bottom of the container?

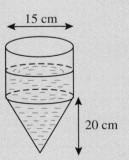

Length (one dimensional)

Perimeter of square $= x + x + x + x = 4x$

x is a length and is the only length involved in the formula.

$4x$ is said to have *one dimension* (length). The number 4 written before the letter is *not* a length so has *no* dimension.

(ie. x has one dimension, $2x$ has one dimension, $5x$ has one dimension and so on)

Area (two dimensional)

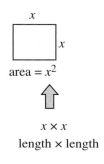

area $= x^2$

⬆

$x \times x$

length × length

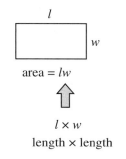

area $= lw$

⬆

$l \times w$

length × length

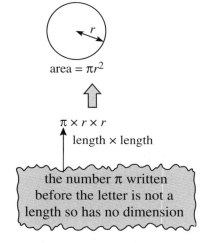

area $= \pi r^2$

⬆

$\pi \times r \times r$

length × length

the number π written before the letter is not a length so has no dimension

Volume (three dimensional)

volume $= lwh$

⬆

$l \times w \times h$

length × length × length

volume $= x^3$

⬆

$x \times x \times x$

length × length × length

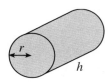

volume $= \pi r^2 h$

⬆

$\pi \times r \times r \times h$

length × length × length

the number π has no dimension

Key Facts

A formula with one length only represents a length.

A formula with 2 lengths multiplied together represents an area.

A formula with 3 lengths multiplied together represents a volume.

A number has no dimension unless it is defined as a length.

1 x and y are lengths.

$P = 4xy$ Is this a formula for a length, area or volume?

2 m and n are lengths.

$Y = 3m^2n$ Is this a formula for a length, area or volume?

3 a, b and c are all lengths.
Which of the following expressions could be a volume?

$3ab$ $4c$ πb^2 $2abc$ πac

4 Each letter below is a length. For each expression write down if it represents a length, area or volume.

(a) pq (b) $5b$ (c) $2xy$ (d) a^2 (e) $6y$

(f) abc (g) $8b^2$ (h) $5xyz$ (i) $3xz$ (j) b^2c

(k) $4a^3$ (l) $7x^2$ (m) $9x$ (n) πy (o) a^2b

(p) πy^2 (q) $4bc$ (r) πabc (s) $5\pi a$ (t) $8\pi ab$

5 Here are 5 expressions:

expression	length	area	volume	none of these
πr^2				
$4r^2l^2$				
πrl				
$2\pi r$				
πr^2l				

r and l are lengths.

Copy the table and put a tick in the correct column to show whether the expression can be used for length, area, volume or none of these.

More difficult formulas

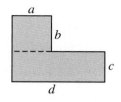

area of L-shape = *ab* + *cd*

ab is a 'term'
length × length (L × L)
area

cd is a 'term'
length × length (L × L)
area

Both terms have the same number of dimensions so when they are added together, the whole formula will give an area.

Question – does the formula V = 3*a*² + *abc* give a volume?

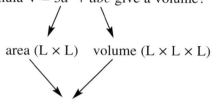

area (L × L)   volume (L × L × L)

terms with different dimensions *cannot* be added together.

We say the formula is *not consistent* (the formula is meaningless).

For each expression below, write down if it represents a length, area, volume or if it is meaningless. (each letter is a length)

(a)   π*l* + 4*r*

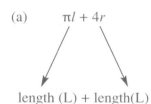

length (L) + length(L)

consistent
(L) + (L) makes another (L)
This could represent a *length*.

(b) $a(b^2 + c)$

$= ab^2 + ac$

volume (L³) + area (L²)

not consistent
This expression is *meaningless*.

(c) $\dfrac{\pi r^3 l}{2h}$

$= \dfrac{L^3 \times L}{L}$

One dimension can be cancelled to give (L³) so this could represent a *volume*.

M16.5

1 *x* and *y* are lengths.

T = 3*x*² + π*y* Is this a formula for a length, area, volume or does it have no meaning?

2 *a* and *b* are lengths.

Y = π*a* + 7*b* Is this a formula for a length, area, volume or does it have no meaning?

3 Each letter below is a length. Write down which expressions below could be meaningless.

(a) $8ab + b^2$

(b) $a + ab$

(c) $3x + 2y$

(d) $a^3 + abc$

(e) $a^2 + b^3$

(f) $5r + rh$

(g) $6pq + 2qr$

(h) $8rl + 3l^2$

(i) $\pi(r + l)$

(j) $r^3 + r^2h$

(k) $5a + \pi a^2$

(l) $4(r + \pi h)$

(m) $2\pi r + 3\pi h$

(n) $\pi rhl + 2r^2h$

(o) $\pi r(r + h)$

(p) $3\pi h(r + \pi l)$

(q) $\dfrac{3x^3}{y}$

(r) $5(\pi r^3 + 3lh)$

(s) $\dfrac{a^2 + b^2}{b}$

(t) $\dfrac{3r^3l^2}{\pi h}$

4 Here are 6 expressions

expression	length	area	volume	none of these
$5a^2b$				
$3(2a + b^2)$				
$\dfrac{\pi a^3}{4b}$				
$6ab(3a - 4)$				
$4\pi(3a + 2b)$				
$\dfrac{5(\pi a^2 + 3ab)}{\pi a}$				

a and b are lengths.

Copy the table and put a tick in the correct column to show whether the expression can be used for length, area, volume or none of these.

5 Each letter below is a length. For each expression write down if it represents a length, area, volume or if it is meaningless.

(a) $3a^2 + 4b^2$

(b) $5ab + 7bc$

(c) $\pi rl + 7rhl$

(d) $3\pi r + h$

(e) $\dfrac{\pi r^2}{4}$

(f) $\dfrac{4}{3}\pi r^3$

(g) $\dfrac{6a^2}{5b}$

(h) $\pi(r^2 - a^2)$

(i) $4h(2r - rh)$

(j) $\pi xy + 4\pi x$

(k) $\dfrac{7\pi r^2h}{2l}$

(l) $\dfrac{2a^3 + 3a^2b}{\pi b^2}$

(m) $3\pi(ab + b^2)$

(n) $4\pi(abc - 3a^2)$

(o) $\pi a^2(4b + 3a)$

(p) $\dfrac{r(4h + 2l)}{7}$

6 Janice has found a formula for a volume:

$$V = \pi r^\square h + 5r^3$$

What number belongs in the box if the formula is to be consistent?

7 Terry says that an area formula could be

$$A = \frac{3\pi r^3}{4h} + 6rh$$

Could Terry be correct?

8 Max has found a formula for an area:

$$A = \frac{4h^2 r^\square}{3h^3}$$

What number belongs in the box?

16B **Solve quadratic equations by using the formula (see Unit 12)**

1. Solve the following equations, giving your answers to 2 decimal places.

   (a) $x^2 - 5x - 3 = 0$ (b) $5x^2 + 2x - 7 = 0$ (c) $x(x + 5) = 39$

2. Solve the following equations by using the formula, leaving your answers in the form $\dfrac{p \pm \sqrt{q}}{r}$

   (a) $x^2 + 5x + 2 = 0$ (b) $3x^2 + 7x - 2 = 0$

3. A rectangular sheet of metal is such that its length is 7 cm longer than its width. A square with side length 3 cm is cut out at each corner and the remaining shape is the net of a box. If the volume of the box is 65 cm³, find the length of the metal sheet to one decimal place.

E   Algebraic fractions

Cancelling

Always factorise the numerator and denominator first.

Any common factors in the numerator and denominator can then be cancelled.

Note $\dfrac{\overset{1}{\cancel{a}} + b}{\cancel{a}c}$ ✗ not possible because a is not a common factor in the numerator.

Simplify   (a) $\dfrac{m^2 + mn}{mp}$

(b) $\dfrac{x^2 + 2x + 1}{x^2 + 4x + 3}$

(c) $\dfrac{6x + 6y}{3x^2 - 3y^2}$

$$= \frac{\cancel{m}(m + n)}{\cancel{m}p}$$

$$= \frac{(x + 1)\cancel{(x + 1)}}{(x + 3)\cancel{(x + 1)}}$$

$$= \frac{\overset{2}{\cancel{6}}(x + y)}{\underset{}{\cancel{3}}(x^2 - y^2)}$$

$$= \frac{m + n}{p}$$

$$= \frac{x + 1}{x + 3}$$

$$= \frac{2\cancel{(x + y)}}{\cancel{(x + y)}(x - y)}$$

$$= \frac{2}{x - y}$$

475

Simplify

1 $\dfrac{ab}{bc}$

2 $\dfrac{mn}{n^2}$

3 $\dfrac{4a}{10b}$

4 $\dfrac{5a^2b}{20ab^2}$

5 $\dfrac{m-n}{mn}$

6 $\dfrac{3m-3n}{6mn}$

7 $\dfrac{12ab}{4ba}$

8 $\dfrac{8p+16q}{8}$

9 $\dfrac{ab+ac}{a}$

10 $\dfrac{mn-mp}{mp}$

11 $\dfrac{4c-10d}{2c-5d}$

12 $\dfrac{5x^2}{xy+xz}$

13 Write down whether each statement is true or false.

(a) $\dfrac{9x-18y}{9xy}=-1$

(b) $\dfrac{ab+b^2}{b^2}=\dfrac{a+b}{b}$

(c) $\dfrac{x^2-y^2}{3x}=\dfrac{x-y^2}{3}$

(d) $\dfrac{x^2-4}{2x+4}=\dfrac{x-2}{2}$

(e) $\dfrac{5m^2n}{10mn-5n}=\dfrac{m^2}{2m-1}$

(f) $\dfrac{x^2+5x}{x^2+x}=3$

Cancel down the fractions as far as possible in Questions **14** to **29** .

14 $\dfrac{3x}{3x^2-9x}$

15 $\dfrac{12mn-6n^2}{10m^2-5mn}$

16 $\dfrac{6x^2+4xy}{9x^2+6xy}$

17 $\dfrac{3a^2-6ab}{3a^2+6ab}$

18 $\dfrac{12+4m^2}{3+m^2}$

19 $\dfrac{x^2-9}{2x+6}$

20 $\dfrac{x^2+5x+6}{x^2+3x}$

21 $\dfrac{x^2+3x-4}{x^2+6x+8}$

22 $\dfrac{x^2+3x+2}{x+2}$

23 $\dfrac{m^2+5m+6}{m+3}$

24 $\dfrac{a^2-1}{a-1}$

25 $\dfrac{b^2-7b+10}{b-2}$

26 $\dfrac{n^2+3n+2}{n^2+5n+4}$

27 $\dfrac{2y^2+3y+1}{y+1}$

28 $\dfrac{25x^2-1}{5x+1}$

29 $\dfrac{4m^2-8m+3}{2m-3}$

Multiplying and dividing

Always factorise numerators and denominators first. Cancel before multiplying out. It is usual to leave answers in factorised form.

Simplify

(a) $\dfrac{x}{2y}\times\dfrac{y^2}{3x}$

(b) $\dfrac{m^2-mn}{m^2-n^2}\times\dfrac{2m+2n}{3m^2}$

(c) $\dfrac{x^2+5x+4}{x^2-x-2}\div\dfrac{x^2-16}{5x-10}$

$=\dfrac{\cancel{x}}{2\cancel{y}}\times\dfrac{y^{\cancel{2}}}{3\cancel{x}}$

$=\dfrac{\cancel{m}(m\cancel{-n})}{(m\cancel{+n})\,(m\cancel{-n})}\times\dfrac{2(m\cancel{+n})}{3m^{\cancel{2}}}$

$=\dfrac{x^2+5x+4}{x^2-x-2}\times\dfrac{5x-10}{x^2-16}$

$=\dfrac{y}{6}$

$=\dfrac{2}{3m}$

$=\dfrac{(x+4)\cancel{(x+1)}}{\cancel{(x-2)}\cancel{(x+1)}}\times\dfrac{5\cancel{(x-2)}}{(x-4)\cancel{(x+4)}}$

$=\dfrac{5}{x-4}$

Simplify

1 $\dfrac{m}{3n} \times \dfrac{5m}{m^2}$

2 $\dfrac{3x}{2} \times \dfrac{4y}{6}$

3 $\dfrac{9m^2}{5n} \times \dfrac{10n}{3m}$

4 $\dfrac{x + 2}{5} \times \dfrac{10x - 15}{2x + 4}$

5 $\dfrac{3a}{a^2 - b^2} \times \dfrac{a + b}{12}$

6 $\dfrac{5m - 10}{4} \times \dfrac{8m + 24}{2m + 6}$

7 $\dfrac{5a}{6} \div \dfrac{10}{9b}$

8 $\dfrac{x}{2y} \div \dfrac{3x}{y^2}$

9 $\dfrac{6x + 6y}{5} \div \dfrac{3x + 3y}{2}$

10 $\dfrac{4(m - 5)}{2m} \div \dfrac{2m(m - 5)}{6m^2}$

11 $\dfrac{3x + 6}{5x - 15} \div \dfrac{7x + 14}{21x - 63}$

12 $\dfrac{10c}{4c + 12} \div \dfrac{5c - 15}{c^2 - 9}$

13 Show that $\dfrac{x + 1}{x - 2} \times \dfrac{x^2 - 4}{x^2 - 1}$ is equivalent to $\dfrac{x^2 + 5x + 6}{x^2 - 9} \times \dfrac{4x - 12}{4x - 4}$

14 Show that $\dfrac{5n + 10}{n^2 + 3n - 10} \div \dfrac{n^2 + 4n + 4}{n + 5}$ is equivalent to $\dfrac{5n - 20}{n^2 - 4} \div \dfrac{n^2 - 3n - 4}{n + 1}$

15 Simplify

(a) $\dfrac{n^2 - n - 6}{5n - 15} \times \dfrac{2n - 10}{n^2 - 3n - 10}$

(b) $\dfrac{m^2 + 4m - 12}{6m - 12} \times \dfrac{m^2 + 6m - 7}{m^2 + 5m - 6}$

(c) $\dfrac{x^2 + 7x + 12}{x^2 - 9} \div \dfrac{x^2 + 2x - 8}{x^2 - 2x - 3}$

(d) $\dfrac{b^2 + 5b + 6}{b^2 - b - 12} \times \dfrac{b^2 - 2b - 8}{b^2 + 3b + 2}$

(e) $\dfrac{x^2 y}{x^3 - 2x^2} \div \dfrac{x^2 - 4}{x^2 + 2x}$

(f) $\dfrac{m^2 - 8m}{m^2 + 9m} \times \dfrac{3m + 6}{m^2 - 6m - 16}$

(g) $\dfrac{c^2 - 12c + 36}{2c - 12} \div \dfrac{c^2 - 1}{c^2 + 2c + 1}$

(h) $\dfrac{n^2 - 2n - 3}{n^2 - 6n + 9} \div \dfrac{n^2 - 4n - 5}{2n - 6}$

(i) $\dfrac{9b^2 - 1}{3b^2 + 7b + 2} \times \dfrac{b^2 - 4}{3b - 1}$

(j) $\dfrac{a - 9}{4a} \div \dfrac{a^2 - 7a - 18}{4a^3 + 4a^2}$

(k) $\dfrac{6x^2 + 13x - 5}{4x^2 + 20x + 25} \times \dfrac{x^2 + 4x - 21}{3x^2 - 10x + 3}$

(l) $\dfrac{2n^2 - 5n - 3}{2n^2 + 5n + 2} \div \dfrac{n^2 - 9}{n^2 - 4}$

16C **Find rules for sequences (see Unit 12)**

1. Which formula below is the nth term of the sequence 2, 7, 12, 17, ...

   $5n - 3$ or $n + 5$?

2. Find the nth term of the sequence 4, 10, 16, 22, ...

3. Find the 87th term of the sequence 3, 12, 21, 30, ...

4. Which sequence below has an nth term equal to $n^2 - 2n$

   A $-1, 2, 7, 14, 23, ...$ or B $-1, 0, 3, 8, 15, ...$?

5. Find the nth term of the sequence 2, 6, 12, 20, 30...

6. Tables are put together to seat people at a banquet.

1 table ($n = 1$)	2 tables ($n = 2$)	3 tables ($n = 3$)
6 people	10 people	14 people

   (a) Draw the next shape in the sequence.

   (b) Find a formula for the number of people (p) in terms of the number of tables (n).

   (c) By looking at where people are sitting, can you explain each part of the formula found in part *(b)*?

7. Find the 47th term of the sequence $-1, 5, 15, 29, 47, ...$

8. Find the nth term of the sequence 1, 3, 7, 15, 31, ...

Adding and subtracting algebraic fractions

We often get the common denominator by multiplying the given denominators together.

Factorise denominators *first* because it may help you to identify the lowest common denominator.

Remember to cancel answers at the end if you can.

Simplify

(a) $\dfrac{5}{2x} + \dfrac{3}{y}$

$= \dfrac{5y}{2xy} + \dfrac{6x}{2xy}$

$= \dfrac{5y + 6x}{2xy}$

(b) $\dfrac{2}{x+3} + \dfrac{5}{x-1}$

$= \dfrac{2(x-1) + 5(x+3)}{(x+3)(x-1)}$

$= \dfrac{2x - 2 + 5x + 15}{(x+3)(x-1)}$

$= \dfrac{7x + 13}{(x+3)(x-1)}$

(c) $\dfrac{7x}{x^2-4} - \dfrac{3}{x+2}$

factorise

$= \dfrac{7x}{(x+2)(x-2)} - \dfrac{3}{x+2}$

only need to multiply this by $(x-2)$ to make denominators the same

$= \dfrac{7x}{(x+2)(x-2)} - \dfrac{3(x-2)}{(x+2)(x-2)}$

$= \dfrac{7x - 3x + 6}{(x+2)(x-2)}$

$= \dfrac{4x + 6}{(x+2)(x-2)} = \dfrac{2(2x+3)}{(x+2)(x-2)}$

E16.3

Simplify

1 $\dfrac{x}{3} + \dfrac{x}{2}$

2 $\dfrac{2x}{5} + \dfrac{3y}{4}$

3 $\dfrac{a}{b} + \dfrac{b}{a}$

4 $\dfrac{3}{2a} - \dfrac{5}{b}$

5 $\dfrac{m}{3n} + \dfrac{2n}{5}$

6 $\dfrac{x}{2y} - \dfrac{2y}{x}$

7 $\dfrac{5}{3x} - \dfrac{2}{4y}$

8 $\dfrac{3n}{2m} + \dfrac{1}{n}$

9 $\dfrac{x+2}{3} + \dfrac{x}{5}$

10 $\dfrac{x+1}{6} + \dfrac{x+3}{7}$

11 $\dfrac{m-2}{3} - \dfrac{2m}{4}$

12 $\dfrac{n+5}{8} - \dfrac{(n-1)}{5}$

13 Which two fraction expressions below are equivalent?

A $\dfrac{x+2}{3} + \dfrac{x+1}{8}$

B $\dfrac{x+6}{2} - \dfrac{(5x+10)}{12}$

C $\dfrac{2x-1}{6} + \dfrac{x+8}{4}$

D $\dfrac{x+6}{4} - \dfrac{(x-4)}{6}$

14 Write as a single fraction:

(a) $\dfrac{3}{x+1} + \dfrac{4}{x+2}$

(b) $\dfrac{6}{m+3} + \dfrac{3}{m+5}$

(c) $\dfrac{5}{n-1} - \dfrac{2}{n+3}$

479

(d) $\dfrac{6}{y+5} - \dfrac{4}{y-2}$ (e) $\dfrac{7}{2x+1} + \dfrac{3}{x+6}$ (f) $\dfrac{8}{m-3} - \dfrac{6}{3m+2}$

(g) $\dfrac{7}{a+6} - \dfrac{2}{1-4a}$ (h) $\dfrac{2}{x-2} + \dfrac{1}{2-x}$ (i) $\dfrac{6}{m-n} - \dfrac{3}{n-m}$

15 Simplify

(a) $\dfrac{4}{x^2-9} + \dfrac{5}{x-3}$ (b) $\dfrac{2}{x+1} + \dfrac{3}{x^2+4x+3}$ (c) $\dfrac{5}{x^2-1} - \dfrac{2}{x+1}$

(d) $\dfrac{6}{x^2-x-6} - \dfrac{2}{x-3}$ (e) $\dfrac{7}{m^2+m} + \dfrac{4}{m^2-m}$ (f) $\dfrac{6}{y^2-3y-4} - \dfrac{1}{y^2-2y-8}$

(g) $\dfrac{3}{m^2-mn} - \dfrac{2}{mn-m^2}$ (h) $\dfrac{4}{a^3-5a^2+6a} + \dfrac{3}{a^3+3a^2-10a}$ (i) $\dfrac{8}{x^2+7x+10} - \dfrac{5}{x^2-4}$

E   Equations containing algebraic fractions

Combine the algebraic fractions first or multiply throughout the equation first to remove the denominators.

Solve $\dfrac{2}{x+3} - \dfrac{3}{x-1} = 4$

Either combine fractions   **or**   multiply throughout to remove the denominator

$$\dfrac{2(x-1)-3(x+3)}{(x+3)(x-1)} = 4 \qquad\qquad \dfrac{2(\cancel{x+3})}{\cancel{x+3}} - \dfrac{3(x+3)}{x-1} = 4(x+3)$$

$$\dfrac{2x-2-3x-9}{(x+3)(x-1)} = 4 \qquad\qquad 2(x-1) - \dfrac{3(x+3)(\cancel{x-1})}{\cancel{x-1}} = 4(x+3)(x-1)$$

$$\dfrac{-x-11}{(x+3)(x-1)} = 4 \qquad\qquad 2x-2-3x-9 = 4(x+3)(x-1)$$

$$-x-11 = 4(x+3)(x-1) \qquad\qquad -x-11 = 4(x+3)(x-1)$$

$$-x-11 = 4(x^2+2x-3)$$

$$-x-11 = 4x^2+8x-12$$

$$0 = 4x^2+9x-1$$

This quadratic does not factorise so use the formula or complete the square.

$$x = \dfrac{-9 \pm \sqrt{81+16}}{8} = \dfrac{-9 \pm \sqrt{97}}{8} = 0.11 \text{ or } -2.36$$

(to 2 dec. places)

1 Show that

(a) $\dfrac{3}{x+2} + \dfrac{1}{x+5} = 2$ is equivalent to $2x^2 + 10x + 3 = 0$

(b) $\dfrac{6}{x-4} - \dfrac{2}{x+3} = 1$ is equivalent to $x^2 - 5x - 38 = 0$

(c) $\dfrac{3}{2x+1} + \dfrac{8}{1-3x} = 3$ is equivalent to $9x^2 + 5x + 4 = 0$

Solve the equations in Questions **2** to **13** . Give the answers to 3 significant figures when necessary.

2 $\dfrac{y+5}{2} - \dfrac{y}{7} = 5$

3 $\dfrac{n+2}{3} + \dfrac{n+1}{4} = 2$

4 $x + \dfrac{1}{x} = 4$

5 $x + \dfrac{4}{x+1} = 5$

6 $2a - \dfrac{3}{a-1} = -2$

7 $1 + \dfrac{2}{b+3} = b$

8 $\dfrac{5}{n+2} - \dfrac{6}{n+3} = 1$

9 $\dfrac{3}{2m-1} + \dfrac{4}{3m+1} = 2$

10 $\dfrac{5}{y} = \dfrac{3}{4y-1} - 4$

11 $\dfrac{8}{2x+1} + \dfrac{1}{3x-5} = 2$

12 $\dfrac{q}{2q+1} - \dfrac{3}{q-2} = 1$

13 $\dfrac{r}{4r-3} - \dfrac{r+1}{2r-1} = 2$

14

The perimeter of this isosceles triangle is 10 cm.

Write down an equation involving x and use it to find x.

15 A group of 60 people can be divided into n equally sized groups or $(n+1)$ equally sized groups. The difference between the size of these groups is 3.

(a) Write down an equation involving n.

(b) Solve this equation to find n.

16 In a relay a man runs 100 m at a speed of v m/s. He then passes to another man who runs 200 m at $(v-1)$ m/s.

(a) If the men take a total time of 36 seconds then write down an equation involving v.

(b) Use this equation to find v (to 3 sig. figs.).

17

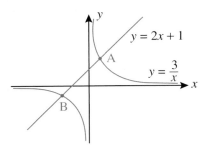

Find the *co-ordinates* of A and B, i.e. solve

$$\frac{3}{x} = 2x + 1$$

18 A man travels 300 km from home to see his cousin. On his return journey home his average speed was increased by 20 km/h and the time of his journey decreased by 1¼ hr.

(a) If v is the average speed of his outward journey then show that

$$\frac{300}{v} - \frac{300}{v + 20} = 1.25$$

(b) Solve this equation to find v.

Can you still?

Can you stir

16D **Solve linear and quadratic simultaneous equations (see Unit 12)**

1. Solve $y = x^2 + 2$
   $y = 2x + 5$

2. Solve $y = 2x^2$
   $x + y = 3$

3. Solve $3x^2 + 2y^2 = 30$
   $y = 5 - x$

4.

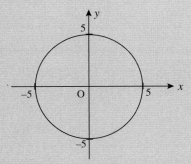

The equation of this circle with its centre at the origin and a radius of 5 units is $x^2 + y^2 = 25$

(reminder: $x^2 + y^2 = r^2$ is the equation of a circle of radius r with its centre at $(0, 0)$)

Find the points of intersection of the line $y = x + 1$ and the circle $x^2 + y^2 = 25$.

5. Solve $x^2 + 2xy + y^2 = 144$
   $x - y = 8$

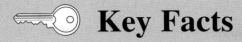

Key Facts

Algebra is often used to prove that results are true.

Note – if 2 whole numbers are consecutive, they are often referred to as n and $n + 1$

– an even number is any multiple of 2 such as $2n$ or $2(n + 3)$

– an odd number is 1 more or 1 less than an even number, eg. $2n + 1$ or $2n - 1$

(a) Prove that the difference between 2 odd numbers is even. Let one odd number $= 2n + 1$ and the other odd number $= 2m + 1$ where m and n are whole numbers.

difference $= (2n + 1) - (2m + 1)$

$= 2n + 1 - 2m - 1$

$= 2n - 2m$

$= 2(n - m)$ which is a multiple of 2

so the difference between any 2 odd numbers is even.

(b) Prove that the difference between the squares of 2 consecutive numbers is odd.

let consecutive numbers be n and $(n + 1)$

difference between the squares $= (n + 1)^2 - n^2$

$= (n + 1)(n + 1) - n^2$

$= n^2 + n + n + 1 - n^2$

$= 2n + 1$

$2n + 1$ is 1 more than a multiple of 2, ie. an odd number

so the difference between the squares of 2 consecutive numbers is odd.

E16.5

1 Use algebra to prove that the sum of an odd number and an even number is always odd.

2 Prove that the sum of two even numbers is always even.

3 Prove that the cube of an even number is divisible by 8.

4 Prove that the product of two odd numbers is odd.

5 Prove that $(n + 1)^2 - (n - 1)^2 = 4n$

6 Prove that $n^2 + (n + 4)^2 - 8 = 2(n + 2)^2$

7 Prove that $(2n + 3)^2 - (2n + 1)^2 = 8(n + 1)$

8 The terms 3, 8, 15, 24, 35... in a sequence are of the form 1×3, 2×4, 3×5, ...

    (a) Write down a formula for the nth term.

    (b) Explain why the formula for the $(n + 1)^{th}$ term is $(n + 1)(n + 3)$

    (c) Prove that the difference between two consecutive terms in the sequence is $2n + 3$

9 Prove that the sum of the squares of 2 consecutive integers is odd.

10 Prove that the sum of the squares of two consecutive *odd* numbers is even.

11 The terms 4, 18, 48, 100, 180... in a sequence are of the form 1×2^2, 2×3^2, 3×4^2, ...

    (a) Write down a formula for the nth term.

    (b) Prove that the difference between two consecutive terms in the sequence is $3n^2 + 7n + 4$.

12 (a) Find the sum of the squares of 3 consecutive *even* numbers then subtract 8.

    (b) Prove that this result is 12 times a square number.

13 The nth triangular number is given by the formula $\dfrac{n(n + 1)}{2}$.

    Prove that the sum of two consecutive triangular numbers is a square number.

14 Prove that the sum of the squares of any 7 consecutive numbers is divisible by 7.

WATCH YOUR MONEY! – Buying a house

Although house prices may seem very expensive at the moment you may one day in the future wish to buy a house.

Mortgages

Most people need to take out a mortgage which they usually pay back over 25 years. Interest has to be paid on the mortgage so it is important to shop around for the best deal.

Repayment mortgage

An amount is paid each month to pay the interest and some of the borrowed money. The monthly amount is worked out so that all the money is paid back after 25 years.

Interest – only mortgage

This costs less than a repayment mortgage because only the interest is paid back each month. This means that after 25 years you will still owe the same amount of money as you borrowed at the start.

You would have to save money to pay back the mortgage at the end or have another plan. If not, you would have to sell your home to pay back the mortgage at the end.

Deposit

If you save some money towards your new home before you buy it, your mortgage payments will be smaller. Often if you have at least a 5% deposit you will get a better deal on the mortgage interest rate.

Stamp Duty

Money paid to the government when a property is bought.

If you buy a flat for £90000, you have to pay stamp duty at 1% of £90000 to the government. That is £900.

At the time of writing, **Stamp duty**

Property worth up to £60000 – no stamp duty

£60001 to £250000 – 1% of the cost of the property

£250001 to £500000 – 3% of the cost of the property

more than £500000 – 4% of the cost of the property

WYM16

1. Dom wants to buy a house for £140,000. He earns £35,000 each year. A building society will give him a mortgage of 3.5 times his annual (yearly) salary.

    (a) How much mortgage can Dom get?

    (b) How much more money does he need to buy the house?

    (c) Stamp duty is 1% of £140,000. The solicitor and surveyor bills amount to £2000. How much money will he really need to have saved to buy this house if he takes the full mortgage?

2. Jim and Hannah have saved £40,000. They earn £30,000 between them each year. A bank will give them a mortgage of 4 times their joint annual salary.

    (a) How much mortgage can they get?

    (b) They want to buy a house for £155,000. Stamp duty is 1%. The solicitor and surveyor bills amount to £2800. Can they afford this house? How much money will be left over if they take out the full mortgage?

3. Donna sells her flat and makes £73,000 profit. She earns £27000 each year. A bank will give her a mortgage of 3.5 times her annual salary.

    (a) What is the most money she will have available to buy a new property?

    (b) If she bought a house for this amount of money, how much stamp duty would be payable at 1%?

4 Laura earns £26,000 each year and Bruce earns £19,000. They can both get a mortgage of 3.5 times their salary.

(a) How much mortgage can Laura get?

(b) How much mortgage can Bruce get?

(c) They have a joint deposit of £33,000. They buy a property costing £182,000. Stamp duty is 1%. The solicitor and surveyor bills amount to £2950. What is the *lowest* joint mortgage they would need to take out?

5 4 friends want to buy a house together. They can jointly raise a mortgage of £240,000 and have a total deposit of £41,000. They buy a house, costing £268,000. Stamp duty is 3%. The solicitor and surveyor bills amount to £3420.

How much money will they have left over if they take out the full mortgage?

6 Peter and Sonia can *rent* a flat for £560 each month. They could *buy* a similar flat and the monthly mortgage payments would be £560. *Discuss with your teacher* the advantages and disadvantages of buying the flat compared to renting the flat.

TEST YOURSELF ON UNIT 16

1. Solving inequalities

Solve the inequalities shown below:

(a) $7x - 3 \leq 18$

(b) $3 - 5x > 13$

(c) $-3 < x - 2 \leq 9$

(d) Solve $\dfrac{3 - x}{2} < 6$, showing your answer on a number line.

(e) Find the range of values of x for which $4x^2 + 7 > 43$

2. Shading regions given by inequalities

(a)

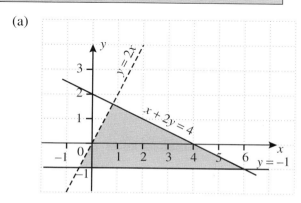

Write down the 3 inequalities which describe the shaded region.

(b) Draw the boundary lines and shade the region defined by the inequalities:
$y < x + 2$ $x \leq 5$ $2x + y > 6$

3. Using dimensions to recognise a length, area or volume formula

Each letter below is a length. For each expression write down if it represents a length, area, volume or if it is meaningless.

(a) $5ab$

(b) $6r + \pi l$

(c) $5r^3 + 3r^2l$

(d) $8xyz + 5x^2y$

(e) $2\pi(ab + b^2)$

(f) $2\pi r + 3r^2$

(g) $4h(r^2 + 5h)$

(h) $ab^2 + bc^2$

(i) $\dfrac{8a^2b}{3bc}$

(j) πa^3

(k) $3a(\pi b + a^2)$

(l) $\dfrac{6(\pi r^3 - 4rh^2)}{3\pi h}$

4. Cancelling, multiplying and dividing algebraic fractions

Simplify

(a) $\dfrac{x^2 - 1}{x^2 + 4x + 3}$

(b) $\dfrac{4x + 8}{x^2 + x - 2} \times \dfrac{x^2 + 7x - 8}{x^2 + 6x - 16}$

(c) $\dfrac{xy - 4y}{x^2 + 3x} \div \dfrac{x^2 - 2x - 8}{2x^2 + 4x}$

5. Adding and subtracting algebraic fractions

Simplify

(a) $\dfrac{x}{y} - \dfrac{y}{x}$

(b) $\dfrac{x + 2}{2} - \dfrac{(x + 1)}{3}$

(c) $\dfrac{4}{x + 3} + \dfrac{5}{x - 2}$

(d) $\dfrac{4}{x^2 - x - 12} - \dfrac{7}{x + 3}$

6. Solving equations containing algebraic fractions

Solve

(a) $\dfrac{x + 4}{3} + \dfrac{2x + 1}{4} = 5$

(b) $x - \dfrac{3}{x} = 2$

(c) $\dfrac{1}{2p + 3} + \dfrac{7}{5p + 1} = 6$

(d) One year x people applied for a Council grant worth £40000 and each person received the same amount. The year before $(x + 10)$ people applied for a grant of £35000 and each person received the same amount (£600 less for each person than the year after).

(i) Show that $3x^2 + 5x - 2000 = 0$

(ii) Find the value of x.

7. Tackling algebraic proof

(a) Prove that the sum of *any* 2 odd numbers is always even.

(b) Prove that the difference between the squares of 2 consecutive *odd* numbers is a multiple of 8.

1 (a) Write down the integer values of n for which $-3 \le 3n < 12$.

(b) Solve the inequality $4x + 3 \ge 23$. (OCR)

2 Find the whole number values of n that satisfy the inequality.

$$7 \le 3n + 5 < 20.$$ (WJEC)

3 Here are some expressions.

$\dfrac{ab}{h}$	$2\pi b^2$	$(a + b)ch$	$2\pi a^3$	πab	$2(a^2 + b^2)$	$\pi a^2 b$

The letters a, b, c and h represent lengths.

π and 2 are numbers that have no dimensions.

Write down three of the expressions which could represent areas. (EDEXCEL)

4 Find all the integer values of n that satisfy the inequality $-8 \le 3n < 6$. (WJEC)

5 (a) $-2 < x \le 1$

x is an integer.

Write down all the possible values of x.

(b) $-2 < x \le 1$ $\qquad y > -2$ $\qquad y < x + 1$

x and y are integers.

Copy the grid then mark with a cross (×) each of the six points which satisfies all these 3 inequalities.

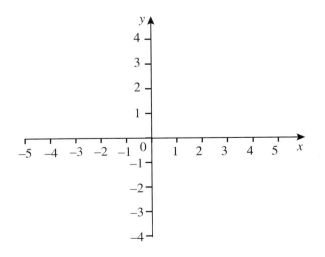

(EDEXCEL)

488

6 The expressions below can be used to calculate lengths, areas or volumes of some shapes.

The letters p, q and r represent lengths.

π and 2 are numbers and have no dimension.

$$\pi(p + q) \qquad \frac{pq}{r} \qquad rq(p + q) \qquad \pi pq \qquad \frac{p^2 r}{2}$$

$$2r \qquad \frac{qr}{2} \qquad r(p + q) \qquad \frac{p^2 \pi}{r} \qquad \frac{\pi pqr}{2}$$

Write down the three expressions that can be used to calculate an area.   (EDEXCEL)

7 Simplify the expression $\dfrac{x^2 - 2x}{x^2 - 4}$ (AQA)

8 Simplify $\dfrac{x - x^2}{x^2 + 5x - 6}$

9 Simplify $\dfrac{x^2 - 2x}{x^2 + 5x - 14}$

10 Simplify the expression $\dfrac{x}{x - 1} - \dfrac{1}{x + 1}$.

11 The table shows six expressions.

a, b and c are lengths.

2 and 3 are numbers and have no dimension.

$2a + 3b$	$3ab$	$a + b + c$	$2a^2c$	$2a^2 + bc$	$ab(b + 2c)$

(i) Write down the two expressions that could represent an area.

(ii) Write down the two expressions that could represent a volume.   (EDEXCEL)

12 $2n + 1$, $2n + 3$, $2n + 5$ are three consecutive odd numbers.

(a) Explain why

(i) these are odd numbers,

(ii) these are consecutive odd numbers.

(b) Prove that the sum of these numbers is always divisible by 3.   (OCR)

13 You are given that $\dfrac{3}{x + 2} - \dfrac{2}{2x - 5} = 1$.

Show that $2x^2 - 5x + 9 = 0$.   (AQA)

489

14 Solve $\dfrac{2}{x+1} + \dfrac{3}{x-1} = \dfrac{5}{x^2-1}$ (EDEXCEL)

15 (a) Factorise $2x^2 + 7x + 3$

(b) Write as a single fraction in its simplest form

$$\frac{1}{x+3} + \frac{x}{2x^2+7x+3}$$

16 (a) Find the prime factors of 4891 by writing 4891 as $70^2 - 3^2$.

(b) By writing the nth term of the sequence 1, 3, 5, 7, ... as $(2n-1)$, or otherwise, show that the difference between the squares of any two consecutive odd numbers is a multiple of 8. (EDEXCEL)

17 Zarig took part in a 26 mile road race.

(a) He ran the first 15 miles at an average speed of x mph. He ran the last 11 miles at an average speed of $(x-2)$ mph. Write down an expression, in terms of x, for the time he took to complete the 26 mile race.

(b) Zarig took 4 hours to complete the race. Using your answer to part **a**, form an equation in terms of x.

(c) (i) Simplify your equation and show that it can be written as $2x^2 - 17x + 15 = 0$.

(ii) Solve this equation and obtain Zarig's average speed over the first 15 miles of the race. (AQA)

18 (a) Write down an expression, in terms of n, for the nth multiple of 5.

(b) Hence or otherwise

(i) prove that the sum of two consecutive multiples of 5 is always an odd number.

(ii) prove that the product of two consecutive multiples of 5 is always an even number. (EDEXCEL)

19 (a) Show that the equation

$$\frac{2}{(x+1)} - \frac{1}{(x+2)} = \frac{1}{2}$$

can be written in the form

$$x^2 + x - 4 = 0.$$

(b) Hence, or otherwise, find the values of x, correct to 2 decimal places, that satisfy the equation

$$\frac{2}{(x+1)} - \frac{1}{(x+2)} = \frac{1}{2}.$$ (EDEXCEL)

In the 'M' sections (mainly grades B, C, D) you will learn how to:
- use map scales
- construct with a ruler and compasses only
- draw loci

In the 'E' sections (mainly grades A*, A) you will learn how to:
- draw the graphs of $y = \sin x$, $y = \cos x$ and $y = \tan x$
- solve equations using trigonometry with angles of any size
- transform curves on graphs

Also you will learn how to:
- **WATCH YOUR MONEY!** – council tax

M   Map scales

Scale as a ratio

On a map, 1 cm for every 5 m can be written as a ratio 1 cm : 5 m

Make the units the same

1 cm : 5 m = 1 cm : 500 cm = 1 : 500

The ratio 1 : 500 shows us that the real measurements are 500 times as big as the measurements on the scale drawing.

On a map of scale 1 : 3 000 000, Leeds and Manchester are 2 cm apart. What is the actual distance between the cities?

1 cm on map represents 3 000 000 cm

2 cm on map represents 6 000 000 cm

$$= 60\ 000 \text{ m}$$

$$= 60 \text{ km}$$

The actual distance between Leeds and Manchester is 60 km.

1. A model of a car is made using a scale of 1 : 50. The model is 8 cm long. How long is the real car? (give your answer in metres)

2.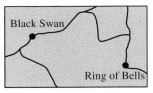

Scale is 1 : 50000

Measure the shortest distance between the Black Swan and the Ring of Bells (give your answer in km).

3. Two towns are 3 cm apart on a map whose scale is 1 : 5 000 000. Find the actual distance (in km) between the two towns.

4. The length of part of a railway track is 18 km. How long will it be on a map of scale 1 : 200 000?

5.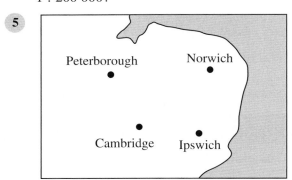

Scale is 1 : 3 000 000

Measure then write down the actual distances (in km) between:

(a) Norwich and Ipswich

(b) Peterborough and Norwich

(c) Cambridge and Ipswich

6. The distance between two cities is 110 km. How far apart will they be on a map of scale 1 : 2 000 000?

7.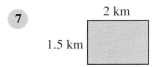

A park has an area of 3 km². A map has a scale of 1 : 50 000. What is the area of the park on the map?

8. A plan is made of this design using a scale of 1:10. How large will AB̂C be on the plan?

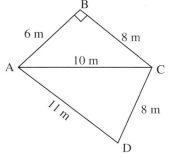

9. A map has a scale of 1 : 40 000. What is the actual area enclosed by the three roads shown?

492

17A **Find arc lengths and areas of sectors and segments (see Unit 13)**

1.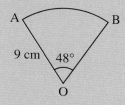

AB is an arc length on a circle whose centre is at O. Find the perimeter of the whole shape (give your answer to one decimal place).

2.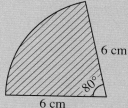

Find the 'exact' area of this sector, leaving the answer in terms of π.

3.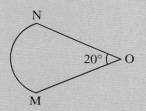

The length of the arc MN is 4π cm. Find the length of OM.

4.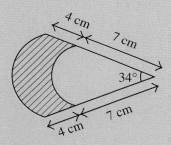

Work out the shaded area (give your answer to one decimal place).

5. (a) Find the area of the triangle OAB (to one decimal place).

   (b) Find the area of the shaded segment (to one decimal place).

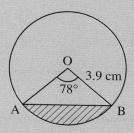

6.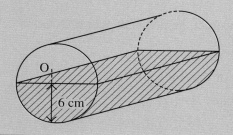

O is the centre of one end of a horizontal cylindrical pipe. The radius of the circle is 9 cm and the pipe is 5 m long. The pipe contains some water which has a maximum depth of 6 cm as shown. Calculate the volume of water in the pipe (to three significant figures).

Perpendicular bisector

Draw a line AB 8 cm long.

Set the pair of compasses to more than
4 cm (half the line AB). Put the compass
point on A and draw an arc as shown.

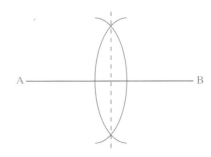

Put the compass point on B (**Do not let
the compasses slip**). Draw another arc
as shown.

This broken line cuts line AB in half (*bisects*) and is at right angles to line AB (*perpendicular*).

The broken line is called the *perpendicular bisector* of line AB.

Bisector of an angle

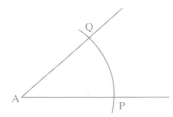

Put the compass point on A and
draw an arc as shown.

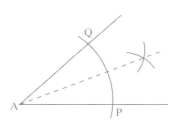

Put the compass point on P and
draw an arc as shown. Put the compass
point on Q and draw an arc as shown.

Draw a broken line as shown.

This broken line cuts the angle in half (*bisects*).

This broken line is called the *angle bisector.*

M17.2

1 Draw a *vertical* line EF of length 10 cm. Construct the perpendicular bisector
of EF.

2 Draw an angle of 50°. Construct the bisector of the angle.

3 Draw an angle of 110°. Construct the bisector
of the angle.

4 (a) Use a pencil, ruler and a pair of compasses *only* to *construct* the triangle ABC shown opposite.

(b) Construct the perpendicular bisector of line AB.

(c) Construct the perpendicular bisector of line BC.

(d) Construct the perpendicular bisector of line AC.

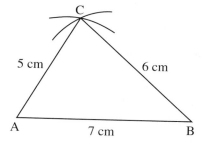

The 3 perpendicular bisectors should cross at the same point.

5 Draw any triangle XYZ and construct

(a) The perpendicular bisector of XY.

(b) The perpendicular bisector of XZ. Mark the point of intersection M.

(c) Take a pair of compasses and, with centre at M and radius MX, draw a circle through the points X, Y and Z. This is the circumcircle of triangle XYZ.

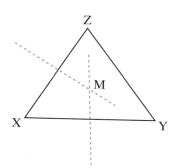

(d) Repeat this construction for another triangle with different sides.

6 Draw any triangle ABC and then construct the bisectors of angles A, B and C. If done accurately the three bisectors should all pass through one point.

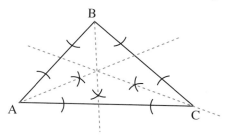

7 Draw any triangle XYZ and construct the bisectors of angles X and Y to meet at point M. With centre at M draw a circle which just touches the sides of the triangle. This is the *inscribed circle of the triangle.*

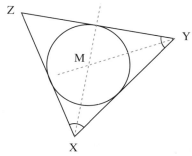

Repeat the construction for a different triangle.

Constructing a 60° angle

Draw a line 6 cm long.

Set the pair of compasses to less than 6 cm. Put the compass point on A and draw an arc as shown.

Put the compass point on B (**Do not let the compasses slip**). Draw another arc as shown.

Join C to the end of the line. The two lines make an angle of 60°. BÂC = 60°

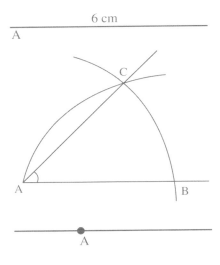

Constructing a 90° angle at a point on a line

Draw any line and mark a point on that line.

Set the pair of compasses to around 3 cm. Put the compass point on A and draw 2 small arcs which cross the line on each side of A. (If necessary, make the line longer)

Put the compass point on B and set the compasses longer than BA. Draw an arc above the line.

Put the compass point on C (**Do not let the compasses slip**). Draw another arc as shown.

Join D and A with a straight line.

The two lines make an angle of 90°.
CÂD = 90°

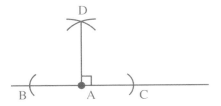

M17.3

1 (a) Draw a line 9 cm long and mark the point A on the line as shown.

4 cm   A   5 cm

(b) Construct an angle of 90° at A.

2 (a) Draw a line 7 cm long and mark the point B on the line as shown.

4 cm   B   3 cm

(b) Construct an angle of 45° at B.

3 Construct an angle of 60°.

4 Construct an angle of 30°.

5 Construct an equilateral triangle with each side equal to 5 cm.

6 Construct these triangles (only use a protractor to *check* at the end).

(a)

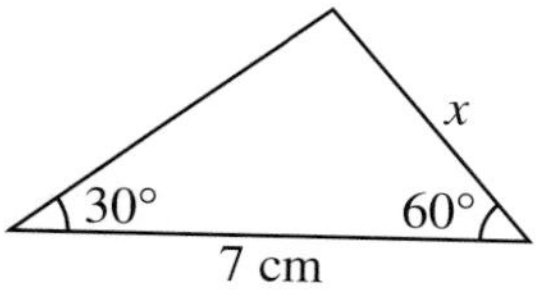

[diagram: triangle with 30° and 60° angles, base 7 cm, side x]

Measure *x*.

(b)

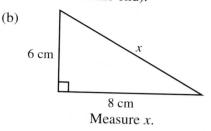

Measure *x*.

7 Construct an angle of 15°.

8 Construct a right-angled triangle ABC, where AB = 7 cm, AB̂C = 90° and BÂC = 45°. Measure the length of BC.

9 Construct an angle of 22.5°.

10 Construct each shape below and measure *x*.

(a)

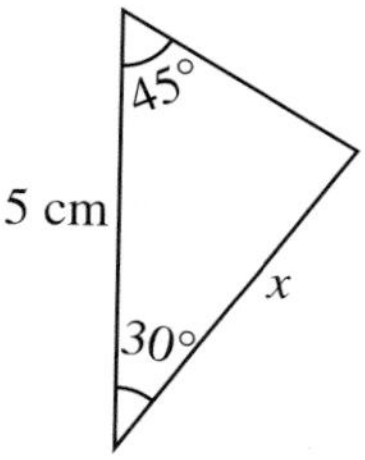

[diagram: triangle with 45° at top, 5 cm left side, 30° at bottom, x]

(b)

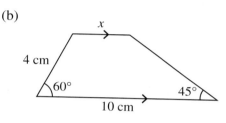

(c)

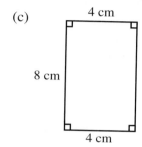

11 (a) Draw any line and any point as shown opposite.

A ●

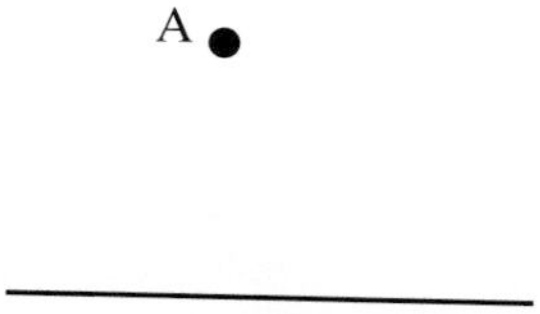

(b) Put the compass point on A and set the compasses so that an arc can be drawn as shown.

A ●

[diagram: line with B and C, arc]

B ⌣ C

(c) Now draw the perpendicular bisector of the line BC. The line AD is described as the *'perpendicular from the point A to the line'*.

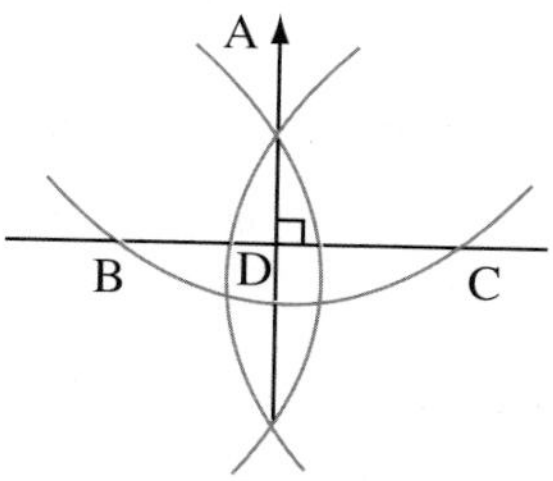

12 Draw any vertical line and any point as shown opposite.

Construct the perpendicular from the point to the line.

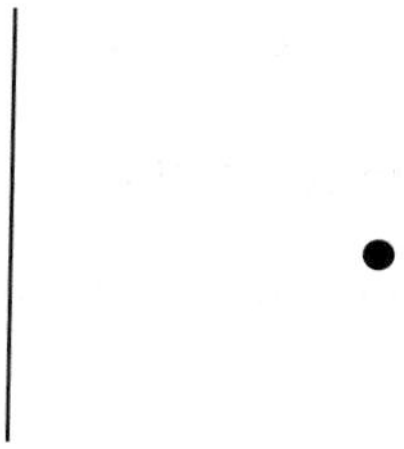

[diagram: vertical line with a point ●]

497

13 The diagram shows the *net* of a solid.
Each triangle is congruent.

(a) Use compasses and a ruler to
draw the net accurately.

(b) What is the name of the solid?

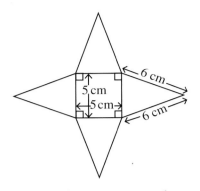

14

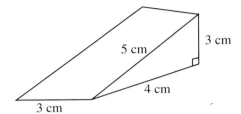

Use compasses and a ruler to construct the
net for this wedge.

15

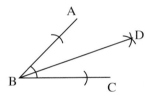

By examining a certain quadrilateral,
explain clearly why the constructed line BD
will bisect the angle ABC.

16 *Explain* clearly why the construction of the 60° angle works.

M   Locus

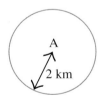

Sarah walks so that she is always 2 km from a point A.
She ends up walking in a circle.
She walks in a circle because she is following the rule that she is
always 2 km from point A.
The circle is called a 'locus'.

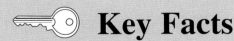 **Key Facts**

A *locus* is the *set of points* which fit a given rule.

The plural of locus is '*loci*'.

For Sarah walking above, the circle is the *locus* of points 2 km from point A.

(a) Draw the locus of all points which are 2 cm from the line AB.

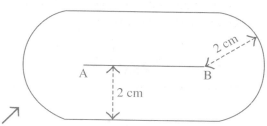

each point is 2 cm from line AB.

(b) A garden has a tree at the corner B.
A lawn is made so that it is greater than or equal to 1 m from the edge of the garden and *at least* 2 m from the tree.
Draw the lawn in the garden.

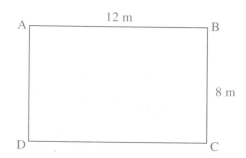

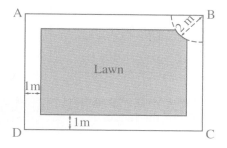

The lawn is a 'locus' even though the word 'locus' was *not* used in the question.

M17.4

You will need a ruler and a pair of compasses.

1 Draw the locus of all points which are 4 cm from a point A.

2 Draw the locus of all points which are 3 cm from the line AB.

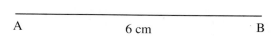

3 A goat is tied by a 5 m rope to a peg in a field. Using a scale of 1 cm for 1 m, shade the area that the goat can graze in.

4 Draw the locus of all points which are less than or equal to 1.5 cm from the line PQ.

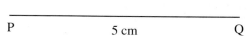

5 A wild headteacher is placed in a cage. The pupils are not allowed to be within one metre of the cage. Using a scale of 1 cm for 1 m, sketch the cage and show the locus of points where the pupils are *not* allowed.

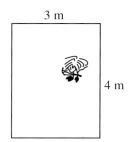

3 m

4 m

6

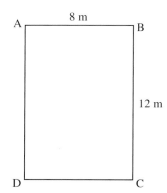

A   10 m   B

6 m

D   C

A garden has a tree at the corners C and D. The whole garden is made into a lawn except for anywhere less than or equal to 4 m from any tree. Using a scale of 1 cm for 2 m, draw the garden and shade in the lawn.

7 Another garden has a tree at the corner A. A lawn is made so that it is greater than or equal to 2 m from the edge of the garden and *at least* 5 m from the tree. Using a scale of 1 cm for 2 m, draw the garden and shade in the lawn.

A   8 m   B

12 m

D   C

8

Person

A ladder leans against a wall. A person is standing at the centre of the ladder. The ladder starts to slip! Draw the locus of the person as the ladder falls (make sure in your drawing, the ladder stays the same length!).

9

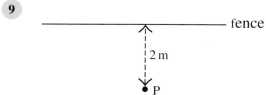

fence

2 m

P

A goat is tied by a 3 m rope to a peg P as shown. Using a scale of 1cm for 1 m, copy the diagram then shade the area that the goat can graze in.

10

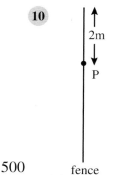

2m

P

fence

The goat is moved so that it is tied by a 3 m rope to a peg P as shown. Using a scale of 1 cm for 1 m, copy the diagram then shade the area that the goat can graze in.

You will need a ruler and a pair of compasses.

1 Draw the locus of points which are the same distance from P and Q below.

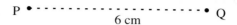

P ● · ● Q
6 cm

2

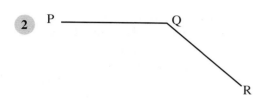

Draw the locus of points which are the same distance from the lines PQ and QR.

3 A soldier walks across a courtyard from B so that he is always the same distance from AB and BC. Using a scale of 1 cm for 20 m, draw the courtyard and construct the path taken by the soldier.

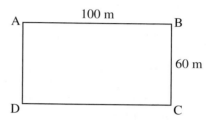

4

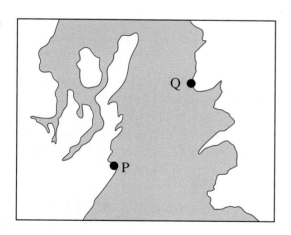

Two ports P and Q are 4 km apart. A ship sails so that it is *equidistant* from P and Q. Draw P and Q using a scale of 1 cm for 1 km. Construct the path taken by the ship.

5 Draw this square. Show the locus of points inside the square which are nearer to A than to C *and* are more than 3 cm from B.

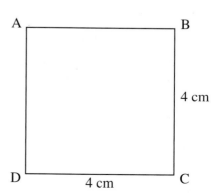

6 A transmitter at Redford has a range of 80 km and another transmitter at Hatton has a range of 60 km. The 2 transmitters are 120 km apart. Using a scale of 1 cm for 20 km, draw the 2 transmitters then shade the area where a signal can be received from both transmitters.

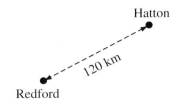

7

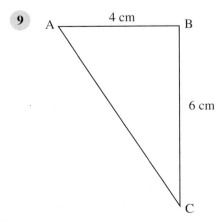

Draw this square.
Show the locus of points *inside the square* which are nearer to Q than to S.

8 A new straight section of a motorway is to be built so that it is the same distance from Horley and Cadle but also lies within 25 km of Morton.

Using a scale of 1 cm for 5 km, draw the diagram opposite then draw the new section of motorway.

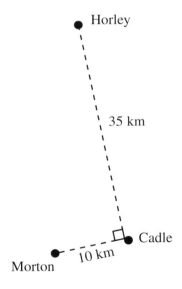

9

Draw one copy of triangle ABC and show on it:

(a) the locus of points equidistant from A and B.

(b) the locus of points equidistant from lines AB and AC.

(c) the locus of points nearer to AC than to AB.

502

10 A child's block is rolled along the floor.
Draw the locus of C as the block is
rotated about B and then about A.

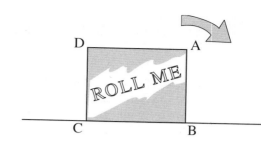

Can you still?

17B **Similar triangles and similar solids (see Unit 13)**

Can you still?

1.

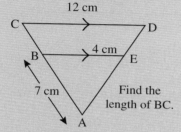

Find the
length of BC.

2.

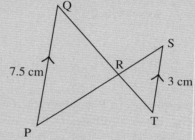

Work out the area of triangle PQR if the
area of triangle RST is 8 cm².

3.

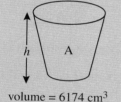

volume = 6174 cm³   volume = 18 cm³

A and B are similar containers.
Calculate the height h of container A.

4.

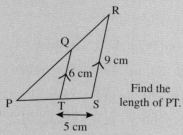

Find the
length of PT.

5. Two models are similar.
The larger model has a surface area of
112 cm² and a volume of 328 cm³.
Find the volume of the smaller model
if its surface area is 83 cm².
Give your answer to 3 significant
figures.

6.

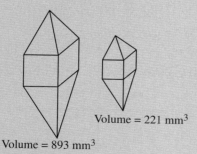

Volume = 221 mm³

Volume = 893 mm³

Two precious gems are similar. If the
surface area of the smaller gem is 197 mm²,
calculate the surface area of the larger
gem, giving your answer to 3 significant
figures.

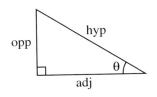

We know

$$\sin \theta = \frac{\text{opp}}{\text{hyp}} \text{ and } \cos \theta = \frac{\text{adj}}{\text{hyp}}$$

This is true for any angles less than 90° in a right-angled triangle.

We can use the following definition for angles of any size. The co-ordinates of P are (x, y).

We can see opposite that:

$$\cos \theta = \frac{x}{1} \text{ so } x = \cos \theta$$

$$\sin \theta = \frac{y}{1} \text{ so } y = \sin \theta$$

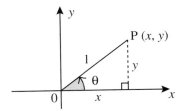

The co-ordinates of P are therefore $(\cos \theta, \sin \theta)$. The angle θ can increase to any size but we define the co-ordinates of P as always being $(\cos \theta, \sin \theta)$.

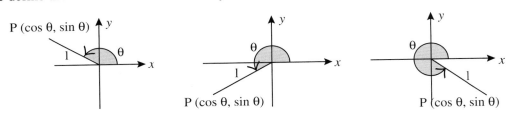

Note – if θ is measured in an anticlockwise direction, it is taken to be positive (θ will be a negative angle if it is measured in a clockwise direction).

Quadrants

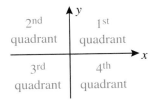

Angles between 0° and 90° lie in the 1st quadrant.

Angles between 90° and 180° lie in the 2nd quadrant.

Angles between 180° and 270° lie in the 3rd quadrant.

Angles between 270° and 360° lie in the 4th quadrant.

Consider the following point:

The co-ordinates of P are $(\cos 150°, \sin 150°)$

so $\cos 150° = -0.866$

and $\sin 150° = 0.5$

If θ is obtuse, $\cos \theta$ is always negative.

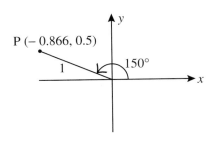

The values of sin θ and cos θ can be explored in each quadrant. These values are stored on calculators. These can be used to plot the graphs of $y = \sin θ$ and $y = \cos θ$.

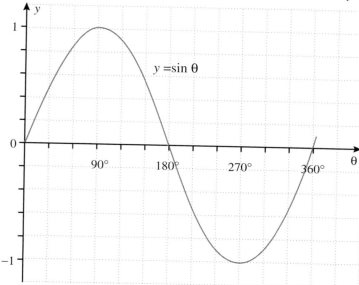

We can see that sin 150° = sin 30°

sin 135° = sin 45°

sin 165° = sin 15°

We have sin θ = sin (180° – θ)

The sine curve above the x-axis has symmetry about x = 90° and below the x-axis has symmetry about x = 270°

E17.1

1 (a) Use a calculator to find the values of cos θ for values of θ from 0° to 360° using intervals of 30°.

(b) Draw a graph of $y = \cos θ$.

(c) Find three different values of θ from your graph which illustrate that

$$\cos θ = -\cos (180° - θ)$$

This relationship is always true.

2 Which of the statements below are true?

(a) cos 300° = cos 60°

(b) cos 315° = – cos 45°

(c) cos 210° = cos 30°

(d) cos 120° = – cos 60°

(e) cos 135° = – cos 45°

3 Draw your own graph of $y = \sin\theta$ or use the graph drawn earlier to decide which of the statements below are true:

(a) $\sin 210° = \sin 30°$

(b) $\sin 120° = \sin 60°$

(c) $\sin 315° = -\sin 45°$

(d) $\sin 240° = -\sin 60°$

(e) $\sin 300° = \sin 60°$

4 (a) Use a calculator to find the values of $\tan\theta$ for values of θ from $0°$ to $360°$ using intervals of $20°$.

(b) What happens if you try to work out $\tan 90°$ and $\tan 270°$?

(c) Draw a graph of $y = \tan\theta$.

At $x = 90°$ and $x = 270°$, draw vertical dotted lines. These dotted lines are called *asymptotes*. The tangent curve will never actually cross an asymptote.

5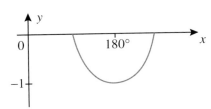

Is this part of the graph of $y = \sin x$ or $y = \cos x$?

6 Which of the following curves pass through the point (180, 0): $y = \sin x$, $y = \cos x$, $y = \tan x$?

7 Does $\cos x$ ever equal 1.5?

8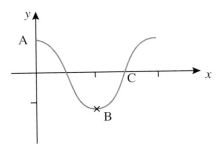

This is the graph of $y = \cos x$. Write down the co-ordinates of the points A, B and C.

9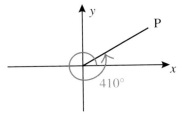

(a) Draw the graph of $y = \sin\theta$ for values of θ from $0°$ to $720°$.

(b) Find three different values of θ from your graph which illustrate that $\sin(360° + \theta) = \sin\theta$.

An angle greater than $360°$ is obtained by travelling more than one complete turn in an anticlockwise direction.

10

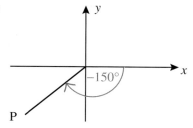

A negative angle is obtained by travelling in a clockwise direction from the x-axis.

(a) Draw the graph of $y = \cos \theta$ for values of θ from $-360°$ to $360°$.

(b) Does the relationship $\cos (360° + \theta) = \cos \theta$ seem to be true?

(c) Draw the graph of $y = \tan \theta$ for values of θ from $-360°$ to $360°$.

(d) Find three different values of θ from your graph which illustrate that $\tan (180° + \theta) = \tan \theta$.

E   Solving equations involving sin, cos or tan

(a) If $\cos 25° = 0.906$, find another angle whose cosine is 0.906.

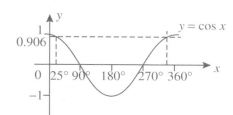

By using the symmetry of the graph of $y = \cos x$, another angle whose cosine = 0.906 is $360° - 25° = 335°$.

(b) Solve $\sin x = 0.3$ for x-values between $0°$ and $360°$.

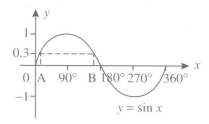

$\boxed{\text{SHIFT}}$ $\boxed{\text{sin}}$ $\boxed{0.3}$ on a calculator to find an
$\boxed{\text{INV}}$ angle whose sine is 0.3.
We find that $\sin 17.5° = 0.3$.

correct to 1 decimal place

On the graph, A = $17.5°$. By using symmetry, another angle whose sine = 0.3 is B which is $180° - 17.5° = 162.5°$

The solutions of $\sin x = 0.3$ in the range $0 \leqslant x \leqslant 360°$ are $x = 17.5°$ and $162.5°$

E17.2

Use the symmetry of the graphs of $y = \sin x$ and $y = \cos x$ to answer the following questions, giving your answers to the nearest degree.

1 If $\cos 32° = 0.848$, find another angle whose cosine is 0.848

2 If $\cos 68° = 0.375$, find another angle whose cosine is 0.375

3 If $\sin 18° = 0.309$, find another angle whose sine is 0.309

4 If $\sin 230° = -0.766$, find another angle whose sine is –0.766

5 Write down another angle which has the same sine as

(a) 75° (b) 133° (c) 158° (d) 320°

6 Solve cos x = 0.5 for x-values between 0° and 360°.

7 Solve sin x = 0.82 for x-values between 0° and 360°.

8 Solve cos x = –0.34 for x-values between 0° and 360°.

9 Solve cos x = –0.8 for 0° ⩽ x ⩽ 360°.

10 Express the following in terms of the sine or cosine of an acute angle (the first one is done for you):

(a) sin 265° = –sin85° (b) cos 290° (c) cos 115°

(d) sin 170° (e) sin 205° (f) cos 125°

(g) cos 335° (h) sin 295° (i) cos 248°

11 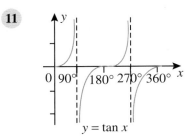 Express the following in terms of the tangent of an acute angle:

(a) tan 220°

(b) tan 254°

(c) tan 105°

(d) tan 300°

12 Solve tan x = 2 for 0° ⩽ x ⩽ 360°.

13 Solve tan x = $\dfrac{1}{\sqrt{3}}$ for 0° ⩽ x ⩽ 360°.

14 Find two solutions between 0° and 360° for each of the following:

(a) sin x = $\dfrac{1}{\sqrt{2}}$ (b) tan x = $\sqrt{3}$ (c) sin x = $\dfrac{\sqrt{3}}{2}$

(d) cos x = $\dfrac{-1}{\sqrt{2}}$ (e) tan x = 1 (f) cos x = $\dfrac{-\sqrt{3}}{2}$

15 Write down 4 values of x for which cos x = 0.5.

16 Write down 4 values of x for which :

(a) sin x = 0.71 (b) tan x = 5.7 (c) cos x = – 0.6

17 Solve 3 sin x = 1 for x-values between 0° and 360°.

18 The depth d (metres) of water in a river after t minutes is given by the formula

$$d = 16 + 12 \cos t$$

Find two values of t at which the depth will be 4 metres.

19 Solve $4(\cos x)^2 = 1$ for $0° \leqslant x \leqslant 360°$ (There are 4 solutions)

20 Solve $\sin 2x = 0.5$ for $0° \leqslant x \leqslant 360°$ (There are 4 solutions)

Can you still?

Can you still?

(**17C**)   **Use cumulative frequency graphs and histograms**
(see Unit 14)

1.

water w drunk each day (litres)	frequency
$0 \leqslant w < 0.5$	21
$0.5 \leqslant w < 1$	48
$1 \leqslant w < 1.5$	53
$1.5 \leqslant w < 2$	35
$2 \leqslant w < 2.5$	14
$2.5 \leqslant w < 3$	9

180 people are monitored to find out the average amount of water they drink each day.
The results are recorded in the table opposite.

(a) Draw a cumulative frequency graph.

(b) Use the graph to estimate the median amount of water drunk.

(c) Use the graph to estimate the interquartile range.

(d) A doctor recommends that a person should drink at least 1.8 litres of water each day. Use the graph to estimate the percentage of people who satisfy the doctor's advice.

2. The unfinished histogram and table below show the number of days various pupils were absent from school during one academic year.

days absent d	frequency
$0 \leqslant d < 10$	4
$10 \leqslant d < 15$	6
$15 \leqslant d < 18$	
$18 \leqslant d < 20$	
$20 \leqslant d < 25$	4
$25 \leqslant d < 40$	6
$40 \leqslant d < 60$	2

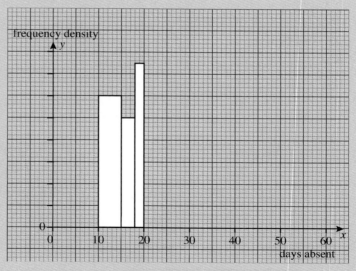

(a) Use the information shown on the histogram to copy and complete the table.

(b) Use the information shown in the table to copy and complete the histogram.

(c) If a child has more than 35 days of absence in a year, the Social Services are contacted. Use the histogram to estimate how many pupils fall into this category.

Refer to Unit 6 if you need reminding about the use of function notation, f(x).

Consider $y = x^2$.
We could write $f(x) = x^2$.

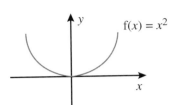

Add 2 onto all the y-values,
i.e. $f(x) + 2 = x^2 + 2$
The graph of f(x) moves up 2 units.

We say that f(x) is translated through $\begin{pmatrix} 0 \\ 2 \end{pmatrix}$

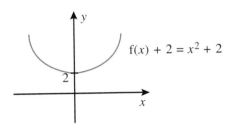

Add 2 onto all the x-values only,
i.e. $f(x + 2) = (x + 2)^2$
The graph of f(x) moves 2 units *to the left*.

We say that f(x) is translated through $\begin{pmatrix} -2 \\ 0 \end{pmatrix}$

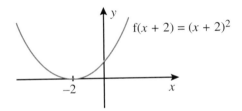

Change the sign of all the y-values,
i.e. $-f(x) = -x^2$

The graph of f(x) is reflected in the x-axis.

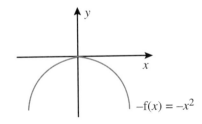

Consider $f(x) = x^3$

Change the sign of all the x-values,
i.e. $f(-x) = (-x)^3 = -x^3$

The graph is reflected in the y-axis.

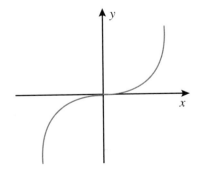

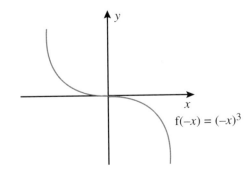

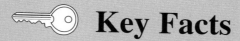

Key Facts

If you have the graph of $y = f(x)$, it can be transformed if necessary with the following rules:

$y = f(x) + k$ translation through $\begin{pmatrix} 0 \\ k \end{pmatrix}$

$y = f(x + k)$ translation through $\begin{pmatrix} -k \\ 0 \end{pmatrix}$

$y = -f(x)$ reflection in x-axis

$y = f(-x)$ reflection in y-axis

E17.3

Use a graphical calculator or computer if it is available to check your answers.

1 (a) Sketch the graph of $f(x) = x^2 - 3$.

(b) Sketch $y = f(x) + 4$, indicating where the curve crosses the y-axis.

(c) Sketch $y = -f(x)$, indicating where the curve crosses the y-axis.

(d) Sketch $y = f(x + 1)$, indicating the co-ordinates of the lowest point on the graph.

2

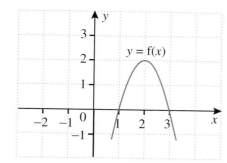

On squared paper, sketch

(a) $y = f(x + 3)$

(b) $y = f(x) - 2$

(c) $y = f(x - 1)$

(d) $y = f(-x)$

3 On squared paper, sketch

(a) $y = g(x) + 1$

(b) $y = -g(x)$

(c) $y = g(x - 2)$

(d) $y = g(-x)$

(e) $y = g(x + 1)$

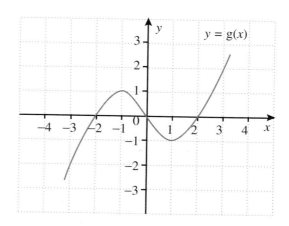

511

4 (a) Sketch the graph of $y = x^3$

(b) Sketch $y = (x - 2)^3$

(c) Sketch $y = x^3 - 4$

5 (a) Sketch $y = \sin x$ for $0 \leqslant x \leqslant 360°$

(b) Sketch $y = \sin(x + 180°)$

(c) Sketch $y = 1 + \sin x$

6 (a) Sketch $y = \cos x$ for $0 \leqslant x \leqslant 360°$

(b) Sketch $y = \cos(x - 90°)$

(c) Write down another equation for the graph you have drawn for part (b).

7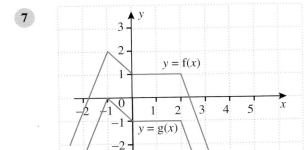

$y = g(x)$ has been sketched from the graph of $y = f(x)$.
Write $g(x)$ in terms of $f(x)$.

8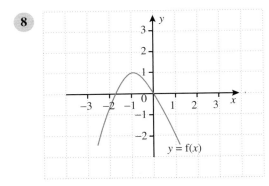

Write down the co-ordinates of the maximum point for the graph of each equation below:

(a) $y = f(x - 3)$ (b) $y = f(x + 1)$

(c) $y = f(-x)$

9 The graph of $y = \dfrac{1}{x}$ is shown opposite.

(a) Sketch $y = \dfrac{1}{x} - 1$

(b) Sketch $y = \dfrac{-1}{x}$

(c) Sketch $y = \dfrac{1}{x - 1}$

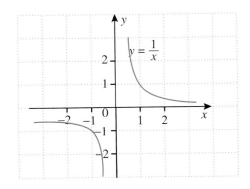

Consider $y = 2x - x^2$

We could write $f(x) = 2x - x^2$.

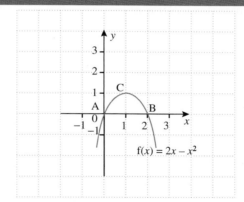

Multiply all the y-values by 3,
i.e. $3f(x) = 3(2x - x^2) = 6x - 3x^2$

$f(x)$ is stretched by a factor of 3 parallel to the y-axis

Note – all *points* on the *x-axis* remain *fixed* (points A and B)

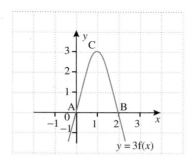

Notice the y-value of point C is now 3 times larger

Multiply all the x-values only by 2,
i.e. $f(2x) = 2(2x) - (2x)^2 = 4x - 4x^2$

The distance of each point on the curve from the y-axis is divided by 2

We say that $f(x)$ is stretched by a factor of $\frac{1}{2}$ parallel to the x-axis

Note – all *points* on the *y-axis* remain *fixed* (point A)

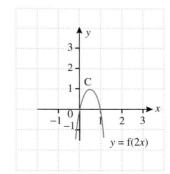

Notice the distance of point C from the y-axis has now been halved

 Key Facts

If you have the graph of $y = f(x)$, it can be transformed if necessary with the following rules:

$y = kf(x)$ stretch by a factor of k parallel to the y-axis

$y = f(kx)$ stretch by a factor of $\dfrac{1}{k}$ parallel to the x-axis

Use a graphical calculator or computer if it is available to check your answers.

1

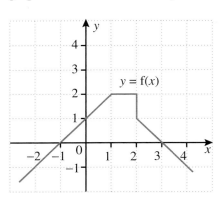

On squared paper, sketch

(a) $y = 2f(x)$

(b) $y = f(2x)$

(c) $y = \dfrac{1}{2}f(x)$

(d) $y = f\left(\dfrac{1}{2}x\right)$

2 (a) Sketch the graph of $y = x^2$.

(b) Sketch $y = 4x^2$. Describe the transformation which changes $y = x^2$ into $y = 4x^2$.

(c) Sketch $y = \dfrac{1}{3}x^2$. Describe the transformation which changes $y = x^2$ into $y = \dfrac{1}{3}x^2$.

3

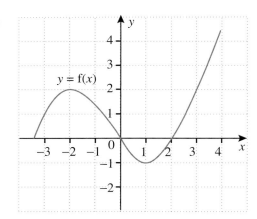

On squared paper, sketch

(a) $y = \dfrac{1}{2}f(x)$

(b) $y = f(3x)$

4

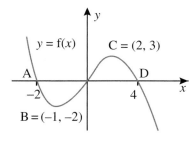

Write down the new co-ordinates of A, B, C and D for the graphs of:

(a) $y = 4f(x)$

(b) $y = f\left(\dfrac{1}{3}x\right)$

(c) $y = f(2x)$

5 (a) Sketch $y = \cos x$ for $0 \leqslant x \leqslant 360°$

(b) Sketch $y = 3\cos x$

(c) Sketch $y = \dfrac{1}{2}\cos x$

6 Sketch $y = \cos 2x$ for $0 \leqslant x \leqslant 360°$

7 (a) Sketch $y = \sin x$ for $0 \leqslant x \leqslant 360°$

(b) Sketch $y = \sin 3x$

8 Sketch $y = 5\sin x$ for $-360° \leqslant x \leqslant 360°$

9 Sketch $y = \tan \frac{1}{2}x$ for $-360° \leqslant x \leqslant 360°$

10

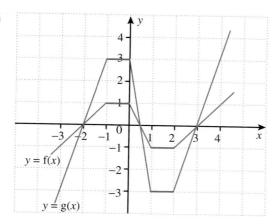

$y = g(x)$ has been sketched from the graph of $y = f(x)$.
Write $g(x)$ in terms of $f(x)$.

11 (a) Describe the transformation which changes $y = x^2 - x$ into $y = (4x)^2 - 4x$.

   (b) Describe the transformation which changes $y = \sin x$ into $y = 10 \sin x$.

12 (a) The graph $y = x^3 + 3x$ is stretched by a factor of $\frac{1}{3}$ parallel to the x-axis.
   Write down the equation of the new graph.

   (b) The graph of $y = \cos x$ is stretched by a factor of $\frac{1}{6}$ parallel to the x-axis.
   Write down the equation of the new graph.

   (c) The graph of $y = \frac{1}{x}$ is stretched by a factor of 8 parallel to the y-axis.
   Write down the equation of the new graph.

(a) Use 2 transformations to change $y = x^2$ into $y = 3x^2 + 2$.

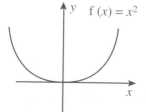

stretch by
a factor
3 parallel
to y-axis

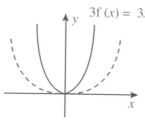

$3f(x) = 3x^2$

translate
through

$\begin{pmatrix} 0 \\ 2 \end{pmatrix}$

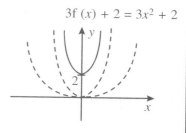

$3f(x) + 2 = 3x^2 + 2$

(b)

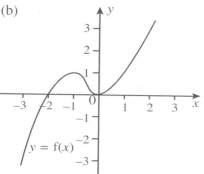

Sketch $y = f(-x) - 1$

Reflect $y = f(x)$ in
the y-axis to get
$y = f(-x)$

Translate $y = f(-x)$

through $\begin{pmatrix} 0 \\ -1 \end{pmatrix}$ to

get $y = f(-x) - 1$

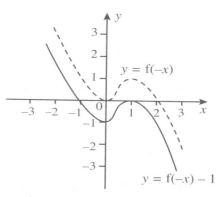

515

Use a graphical calculator or computer if it is available to check your answers.

1

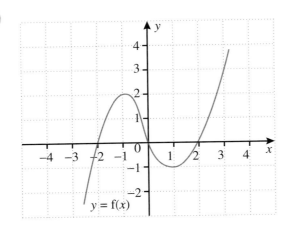

On squared paper, sketch

(a) $y = f(2x)$

(b) $y = -f(x)$

(c) $y = -f(x) + 2$

(d) $y = f(x + 2)$

2

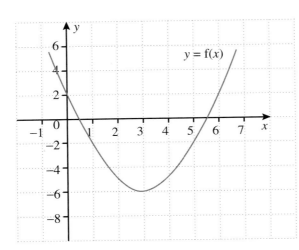

Copy the graph opposite then sketch

(a) $y = \dfrac{1}{3} f(x)$

(b) $y = \dfrac{1}{3} f(x) - 4$

(c) What are the co-ordinates of the minimum point of

$y = \dfrac{1}{3} f(x) - 4$?

3 (a) Sketch $y = x^2$.

(b) On the same graph, sketch $y = (x + 3)^2$. Write down the co-ordinates of the points where $y = (x + 3)^2$ meets the axes.

4 Sketch $y = x^3$. On the same axes sketch $y = (x + 2)^3$ and $y = (x + 2)^3 - 4$. Label each curve.

5 Write down the co-ordinates of V for each of the following graphs:

(a) $y = f(x + 4)$ (b) $y = -f(x)$

(c) $y = 5f(x)$ (d) $y = f(2x)$

(e) $y = 2f(x)$ (f) $y = 2f(-x)$

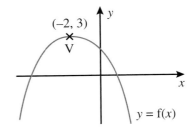

6 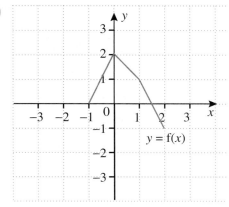 The function $y = f(x)$ is defined for $-1 \leqslant x \leqslant 2$. Using squared paper, sketch on separate axes:

(a) $y = f(x) - 2$ (b) $y = f(x + 1)$

(c) $y = \dfrac{1}{2} f(x)$ (d) $y = f\left(\dfrac{1}{2}x\right)$

$y = f(x)$

7 (a) The graph of $y = 3x - \sin 3x$ is drawn by using the graph of $y = x - \sin x$. Describe the transformation.

(b) The graph of $y = (x - 2)^2 + 5(x - 2)$ is drawn by using the graph of $y = x^2 + 5x$. Describe the transformation.

(c) The graph of $y = x - x^3$ is drawn by using the graph of $y = x^3 - x$. Describe the transformation.

8 (a) The graph of $y = x^2 - 3x$ is translated through $\begin{pmatrix} 0 \\ 4 \end{pmatrix}$. Write down the equation of the new curve drawn.

(b) The graph of $y = \sin x$ is reflected in the y-axis. Write down the equation of the new curve drawn.

(c) The graph of $y = x^3$ is reflected in the x-axis then translated through $\begin{pmatrix} 0 \\ -3 \end{pmatrix}$. Write down the equation of the new curve drawn.

9 (a) Sketch $y = \sin x$ for $0 \leqslant x \leqslant 360°$

(b) Sketch $y = 2\sin x - 2$

10 (a) Sketch $y = \cos x$ for $-360° \leqslant x \leqslant 360°$

(b) Sketch $y = 3\cos (x + 90)°$

WATCH YOUR MONEY! – Council tax

This is tax collected by local authorities. It is a tax on domestic property. In general, the bigger the property is, the more tax will be charged.

Each property is put into a *valuation band*. At the time of writing the bands are as listed below.

valuation band	range of values
A	up to £40 000
B	over £ 40 000 and up to £ 52 000
C	over £ 52 000 and up to £ 68 000
D	over £ 68 000 and up to £ 88 000
E	over £ 88 000 and up to £120 000
F	over £120 000 and up to £160 000
G	over £160 000 and up to £320 000
H	over £320 000

The council tax is used to pay for local services such as rubbish collection, schools and the fire service.

Council tax is not paid on some properties, for example any property that only students live in or a property where all the people who live in it are aged under 18.

Note

If only one person lives in a property they will get a 25% discount on the council tax bill.

Jack lives on his own in a flat worth £75000. This year's council tax rates in his area are shown in the table below:

band	A	B	C	D	E	F	G	H
annual council tax (£)	650	800	1000	1200	1350	1550	1900	2300

(a) How much council tax will Jack have to pay this year?

(b) If he spreads the council tax payment over 10 months, how much will he pay each month?

(a) Using the table at the start of this section, Jack's flat is in band D. The other table shows he must pay £1200 this year.

Jack lives on his own so gets a 25% discount

25% of £1200 = £300

Jack pays £1200 – £300 = £900

(b) If the payment is spread over 10 months, each month Jack pays £900 ÷ 10 = £90

WYM17

For this exercise use the council tax rates shown in the table below.

Use the table at the start of this section to find out which band each property belongs to.

band	A	B	C	D	E	F	G	H
annual council tax (£)	661	798	1109	1252	1420	1675	1910	2405

1 Harry and Erica Smith live in a house worth £105000. How much council tax will they have to pay?

2 Simon and Shanice live in a house worth £132000.

(a) How much council tax will they have to pay?

(b) If the council tax payment is spread over 10 months, how much will the monthly payments be?

3 Molly lives on her own in a bedsit valued at £50000. How much council tax will Molly have to pay this year?

4 The Jackson family live in a house valued at £210000. If they spread their council tax payment over 10 months, what will the monthly payments be?

5 Jenny, David and Matt are all students. They live in a house valued at £90000. How much council tax will they have to pay this year?

6 Mr. and Mrs. Pickford live in a flat valued at £102,000. They are allowed to pay their council tax in 4 equal (quarterly) payments. How much will each quarterly payment be?

7 Rhys lives on his own in a bungalow valued at £110000. If he spreads his Council tax payment over 10 months, what will his monthly payments be?

8 Find out what the council tax bill for a band D property in *your area* is this year. Do you think council tax is a fair way of collecting money for local services or not? Give reasons. Discuss with your teacher.

TEST YOURSELF ON UNIT 17

1. Using map scales

(a)

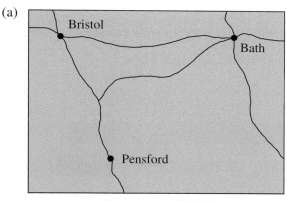

Scale is 1 : 300000

Measure then write down the actual distances (in km) between:

(i) Bristol and Bath

(ii) Bristol and Pensford

(b) The distance between two villages is 7.5 km. How far apart will they be (in cm) on a map of scale 1 : 500000?

2. Constructing with a ruler and compasses only

Construct the triangles below using a ruler and compasses only.

(a)

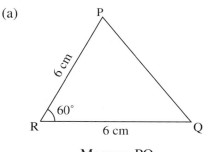

Measure PQ.

(b)

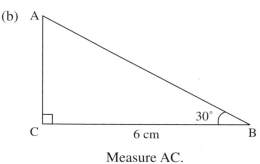

Measure AC.

519

3. Drawing loci

(a) The diagram shows a rectangular room ABCD. Draw *two* diagrams using a scale of 1 cm for every 1 m. Use one diagram to show each locus below:

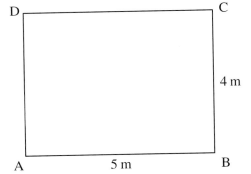

(i) Points in the room less than or equal to 3 m from D *and* nearer to A than to D.

(ii) Points in the room nearer to BC than to AB *and* equidistant from B and C.

(b) Draw the locus of all points which are 3.5 cm from the line PQ.

P ——————————————— Q
7 cm

4. Drawing graphs of $y = \sin x$, $y = \cos x$ and $y = \tan x$

(a) Draw $y = \cos x$ for x-values from 0° to 360°.

(b) Write down 3 values of x at which the graph of $\sin x$ crosses the x-axis.

(c) Write down the maximum and minimum values of $\sin x$.

(d) Draw $y = \tan x$ for $-180° \leqslant x \leqslant 180°$.

5. Solving equations using trigonometry with angles of any size

(a) $\cos 340° =$ A $\cos 20°$

B $-\cos 20°$

C $\cos 70°$

(b) $\sin 235° =$ A $\sin 55°$

B $\sin 35°$

C $-\sin 55°$

Select the correct answer.   Select the correct answer.

(c) Find two solutions for x-values between 0° and 360° if $\cos x = 0.84$.

(d) One of the solutions of $\sin x = 0.5$ is $x = 30°$. By considering the graph of $y = \sin x$, find two solutions of $\sin x = -0.5$ in the range $0° \leqslant x \leqslant 360°$.

6. Transforming curves on graphs

(a) Describe fully the transformation which would change the graph of $y = 2x - x^3$ into $y = 2(x - 4) - (x - 4)^3$

(b) Sketch the graph of $y = \cos x$ for $0 \leqslant x \leqslant 360°$ then sketch $y = \cos 3x$

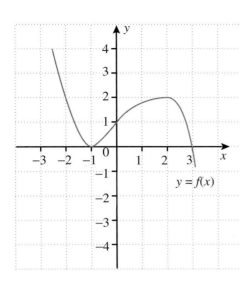

On squared paper, sketch

(c) $y = f(x + 1)$

(d) $y = 2f(x)$

(e) $y = -f(x)$

(f) $y = f(2x)$

(g) $y = f(x + 1) - 2$

Mixed examination questions

1

Copy the line AB then draw the locus of all points which are 3 cm away from the line AB. (EDEXCEL)

2 In this question, use ruler and compasses only.

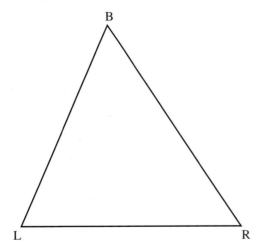

Scale: 1cm represents 1 m

Copy the diagram above.

Triangle LRB is the plan of the garden drawn to the scale of 1 cm to 1m. A lime tree (L), a rowan tree (R) and a beech tree (B) are at the corners of the garden.

(a) Construct the perpendicular bisector of LR. Show your construction lines clearly.

(b) Diana wants to put a bird table in the garden. The bird table must be nearer the rowan tree than the lime tree. It must also be within 4 metres of the beech tree.

Shade the region on the plan where the bird table may be placed. (OCR)

521

3 (a) Sketch the graph of $y = \sin x$ for $-360° < x < 360°$.

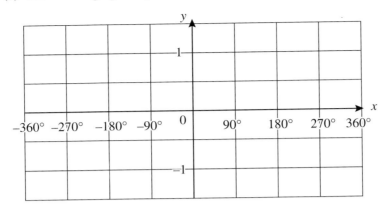

(b) One solution of the equation $\sin x = 0.4$ is $x = 24°$ to the nearest degree.

Find all the other solutions to the equation $\sin x = 0.4$ for $-360° \le x \le 360°$.

(AQA)

4 (a) Sketch the graph of $y = \tan x$ for values of x from $-90°$ to $270°$.

(b) Use your sketch together with your calculator to find all the solutions of the following equation in the range $-90°$ to $270°$. Give your answers correct to one decimal place.

$\tan x = -6.2$

(WJEC)

5 A garden sprinkler waters a circular area of radius 2 m.

To water the flower beds, a gardener moves the sprinkler along the path ABC.

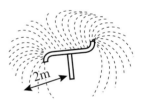

Copy the path ABC.

Indicate on the diagram the area that is watered.

Use a scale of 2 cm to represent 1 m.

(OCR)

6 This is a sketch of the curve with equation $y = f(x)$.

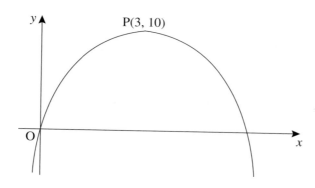

The vertex of the curve is P(3,10).

Write down the coordinates of the vertex of each of the curves having the following equations.

(a) $y = f(x) + 2$　　(b) $y = f(x + 2)$　　(c) $y = f(-x)$　　(d) $y = 2f(x)$

7 (a) The diagram shows a sketch of $y = x^3$, copy the diagram then sketch the curve $y = \frac{1}{3}x^3$.

(b) The diagram shows a sketch of $y = x^3$, copy the diagram then sketch the curve $y = -x^3$.

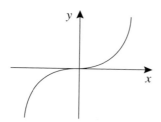

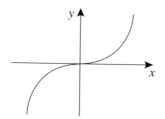

(c) The diagram shows a sketch of $y = f(x)$, copy the diagram then sketch the curve $y = f(x + b)$. Mark clearly the coordinates of the point where the curve crosses the x-axis.

(d) The diagram shows a sketch of $y = f(x)$, copy the diagram then sketch the curve $y = f(x) + c$. Mark clearly the co-ordinates of the point where the curve crosses the y-axis.

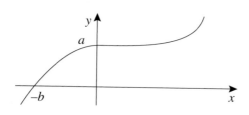

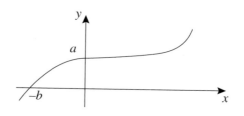

(WJEC)

523

8

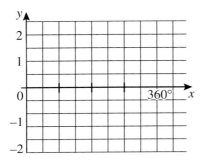

(a) Copy the grid opposite then sketch the graphs of

    (i) $y = \sin x$ (ii) $y = \sin 2x$

for values of x between $0°$ and $360°$.

Label each graph clearly.

(b) Calculate all the solutions to the equation

$$2 \sin 2x° = -1$$

between $x = 0°$ and $x = 360°$.

(EDEXCEL)

9 The diagram shows the graph of the three related functions $y = f(x)$, $y = g(x)$ and $y = h(x)$.

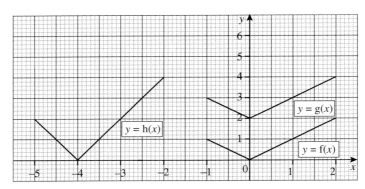

(a) Express $g(x)$ in terms of $f(x)$

(b) Express $h(x)$ in terms of $f(x)$ (AQA)

10 Copy the diagram opposite then draw the locus of the points, outside the rectangle, that are 3 centimetres from the edges of this rectangle.

(EDEXCEL)

11 (a) (i) Sketch the graph of $y = \cos x$ for $-180° < x < 180°$.

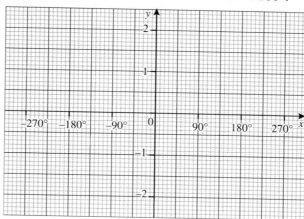

One solution of the equation $\cos x = 0.5$ is $x = 60°$.

(ii) Find the solutions of the equation $\cos x = -0.5$ for $0° < x < 180°$.

(b) You are given that $\tan x = 1$.

One solution of this equation for values of x between $0°$ and $360°$ is $x = 45°$.

What is the other solution of the equation $\tan x = 1$ for values of x between $0°$ and $360°$?

(AQA)

12 This is a sketch of the curve with equation $y = f(x)$.

It passes through the origin O.

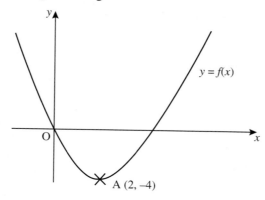

The only vertex of the curve is at A $(2, -4)$

(a) Write down the coordinates of the vertex of the curve with equation.

(i) $y = f(x - 3)$.

(ii) $y = f(x) - 5$.

(iii) $y = -f(x)$.

(iv) $y = f(2x)$.

The curve with equation $y = x^2$ has been translated to give the curve $y = f(x)$.

(b) Find $f(x)$ in terms of x.

(EDEXCEL)

In the 'M' sections (mainly grades B, C, D) you will learn how to:

- draw and use plans and elevations
- measure and calculate bearings
- use angles of elevation and depression
- use 3 co-ordinates for a point in 3-D space

In the 'E' sections (mainly grades A*, A) you will learn how to:

- use the sine and cosine rules
- solve three-dimensional problems using trigonometry

Also you will learn how to:

- WATCH YOUR MONEY! – old age pensions

M Plans and elevations

 **Key Facts**

plan view

Here is a 3-D object made from centimetre cubes.

front elevation

side elevation

A plan view is when the object is looked at from above.

plan view

A front elevation is when the object is viewed from the front.

front elevation

A side elevation is when the object is viewed from the side.

side elevation

In questions **1** to **6** draw the plan view, the front view and the side view of the object.

1

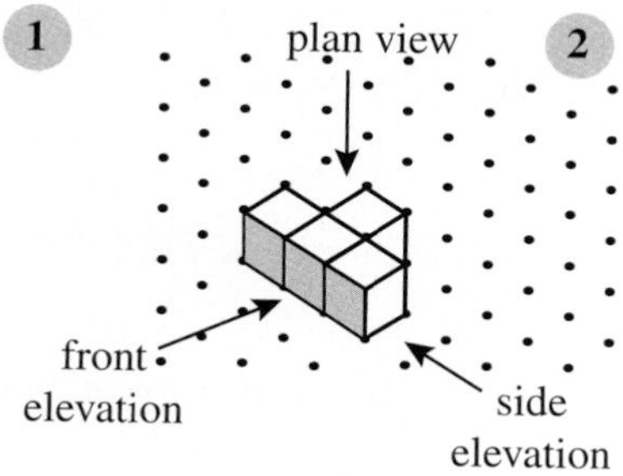

plan view

2

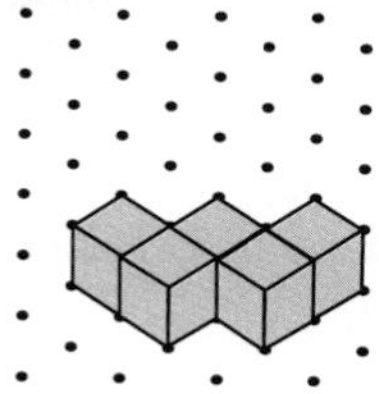

3

front
elevation

side
elevation

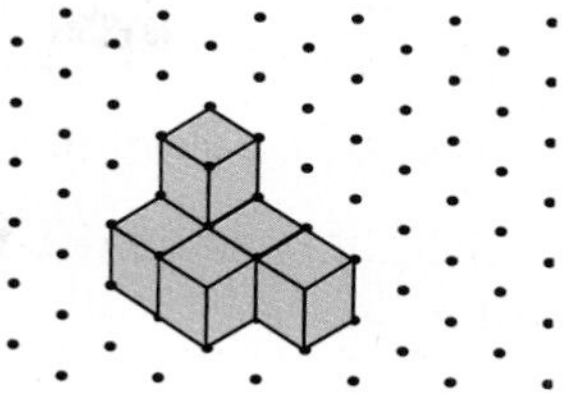

4

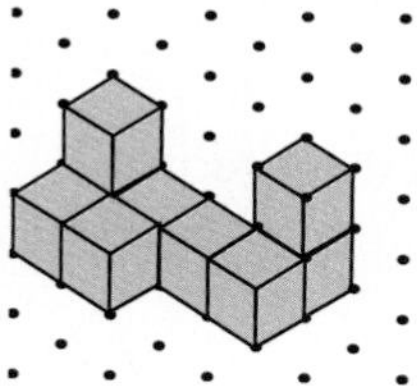

5

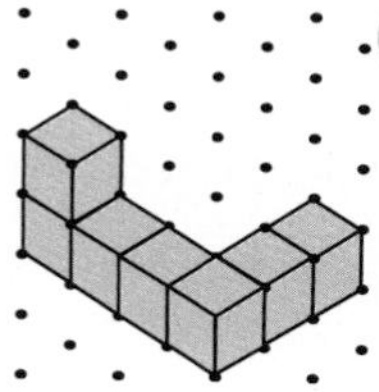

6

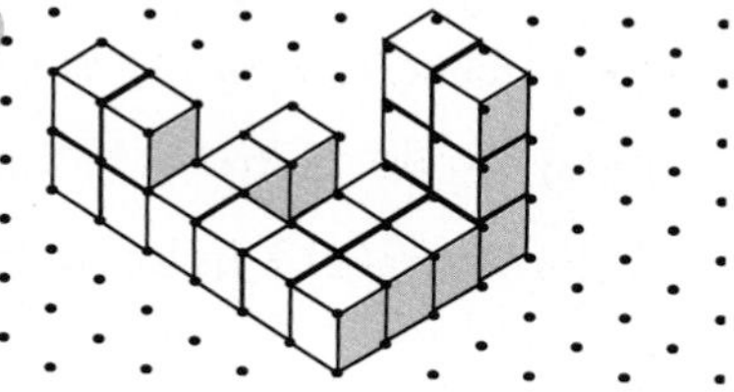

7 Draw and label the plan and a side elevation for:

(a) a cylinder   (b) a cone 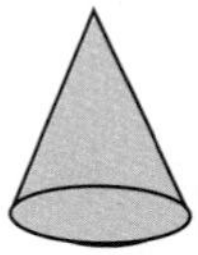   (c) a square based pyramid

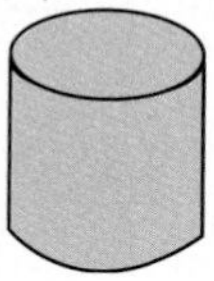

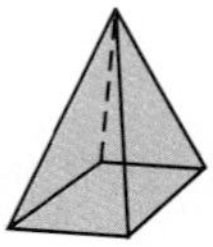

In Questions **8** to **11** you are given the plan and two elevations of an object. Use the information to make the shape using centimetre cubes. Draw the object on isometric paper if you can.

8 front elevation

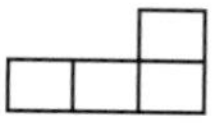

plan view

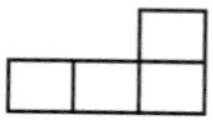

side elevation

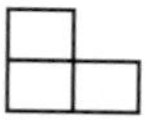

9 front elevation

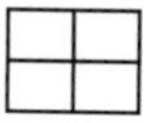

plan view

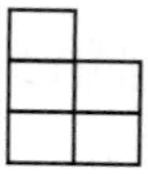

side elevation

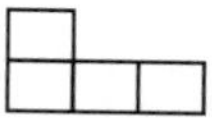

10 front elevation

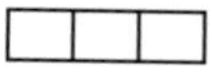

plan view

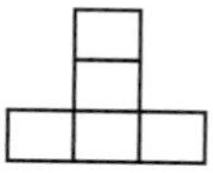

side elevation

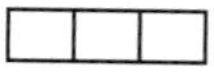

11 front elevation

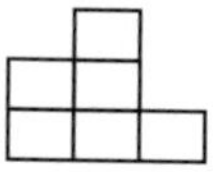

plan view

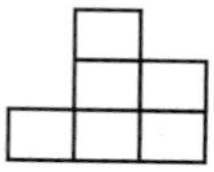

side elevation

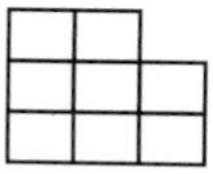

(18A) Number work

1. Write 3.4×10^{-2} as an ordinary number.

2. The number 225 can be written as $5^n \times m^2$ where m and n are prime numbers. Find the values of m and n.

3. £6000 is shared between Colin, Tariq and Arlene in the ratio 5:3:7. How much money does Arlene receive?

4. The price of a rail ticket from Bath to London was increased by 4% to £43.16. What was the price of a ticket *before* this increase?

5. Work out $(5.1 \times 10^{-8}) \times (6.4 \times 10^{-18})$, giving your answer in standard form.

6. Express $0.1\dot{8}$ as a fraction in its simplest form.

7. Evaluate   (a) 2^{-3} (b) 5^0 (c) $27^{\frac{1}{3}}$ (d) $\left(\dfrac{27}{64}\right)^{-\frac{2}{3}}$

8. $\sqrt{48} - \sqrt{12} = n\sqrt{3}$ where n is an integer. Find n.

9. V is directly proportional to the cube of L. $V = 40$ when $L = 2$. Find the value of L when $V = 320$.

10. Simplify $(\sqrt{3} - 1)(\sqrt{3} + 1)$

11. The price of a TV depreciates each year by 8% of its value at the start of the year. If the TV is worth £620, how much will it be worth 4 years later?

12. A bottle contains 130 ml of medicine measured to 2 significant figures. A medicine spoon takes 5 ml measured to the nearest ml. What is the least number of complete spoonfuls of medicine which can be obtained from this bottle?

M Bearings

Bearings are used by navigators on ships and aircraft and by people travelling in open country.

> Bearings are measured from the *North* line in a *clockwise* direction.
> A bearing is always given as a *three-figure number*.

North

58° Tom

Tom is walking on a bearing of 058°

↑
3-figures used

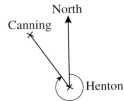

North

Canning

Henton

324°

Canning is on a bearing of 324° *from Henton*

Often bearings can be *calculated* by using trigonometry.

Sam leaves Carla and walks 6 km due north then 5 km due east. If Carla now walks directly to Sam, on what bearing must she travel?

Draw a diagram.

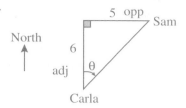

Use trigonometry to find θ

S O H C A H T O A

$$\tan θ = \frac{\text{Opp}}{\text{Adj}} \quad \text{so} \quad \tan θ = \frac{5}{6}$$

$$\left(θ = \begin{array}{c} \text{INV} \\ \text{or} \hspace{4pt} \text{SHIFT} \end{array} \quad \boxed{\tan} \quad \boxed{(} \quad \boxed{5} \quad \boxed{÷} \quad \boxed{6} \quad \boxed{)} \quad \boxed{=} \right)$$

θ = 39.8° (to 1 dec. place)

θ is the angle measured clockwise from the North line so Carla must walk on a bearing of 039.8°.

M18.2

1 Peter hits 6 golf balls, aiming north, with his usual precision.
The golf balls travel in the directions shown.
On what bearing does each golf ball fly?

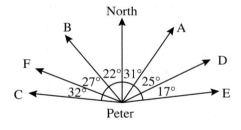

2

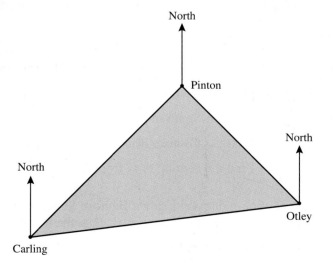

Use a protractor to measure the bearing of:

(a) Carling *from* Pinton

(b) Otley *from* Carling

(c) Pinton *from* Otley

(d) Carling *from* Otley

529

3 Yasmin goes on a sponsored walk.
Her route is shown opposite.

Work out the bearing of
the journey from:

(a) Start to Jam Hill

(b) Jam Hill to Pilling Mount

(c) Pilling Mount to the White Swan

(d) The White Swan back to the Finish

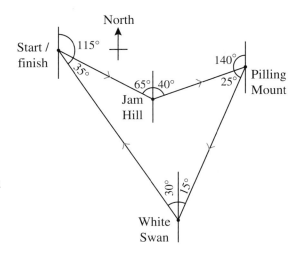

Note – the remaining Questions need to be *calculated*. Do not use a protractor.
Give your answers to a sensible degree of accuracy.

4 Hannah leaves Wes and walks 3 km due north then 7 km due east. If Wes now walks
directly to Hannah, on what bearing must he travel?

5 Kieran leaves Molly and jogs 5 km due south then 2 km due west. If Molly now runs
directly to Kieran, on what bearing must she run (**Be careful!**)?

6 A plane flies 50 miles on a bearing at 038°.

(a) How far North has the plane flown?

(b) How far East has the plane flown?

7 A ship sails 43 km on a bearing of 255°.

(a) How far South has the ship sailed?

(b) How far West has the ship sailed?

8 A submarine travels 40 miles South and 27 miles East. What is the bearing from its
original position to its new position?

9

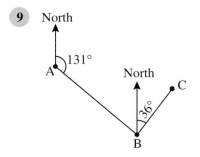

Barney walks 6 km from A to B on a bearing of
131° then 2 km from B to C on a bearing of 036°.

(a) How far East of A is C?

(b) How far South of A is C?

(c) Find the distance from A to C.

(d) Find the bearing of C from A.

10 Charlene walks 300 m from her house due south down Bedford Street then turns left
and walks 470 m along Harris Lane to Kevin's house. Calculate the bearing of
Charlene's house from Kevin's house.

11

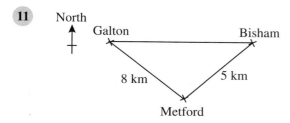

Bisham is due east of Galton.

Metford is on a bearing of 119°
from Galton and on a bearing of 222°
from Bisham.

How far is Bisham from Galton?

M | Angles of elevation and depression

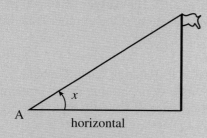

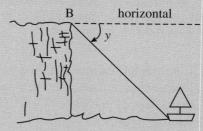

x is the *angle of elevation* of
the top of the flagpole from A
(the angle *above the horizontal*)

y is the *angle of depression* of
the boat from B
(the angle *below the horizontal*)

Harry sees a kite in the sky. The angle
of elevation of the kite from Harry is 21°.
The kite is 27 m above the ground.
How far must Harry walk so that he is
standing directly below the kite?

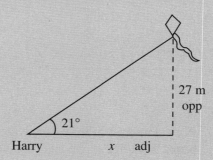

SOHCAHTOA

$$\text{Adj} = \frac{\text{Opp}}{\tan \theta}$$

$$x = \frac{27}{\tan 21°}$$

$$x = 70.3 \text{ (1 dec. place)}$$

so Harry must walk 70.3 m

In this exercise, give your answers to a sensible degree of accuracy.

1 Jody walks 300 m along horizontal ground from the foot of a transmitter. The angle of elevation from Jody to the top of the transmitter is 11°. How tall is the transmitter?

2 Arlene is standing 120 m from the wall of a church tower. The church tower is 21 m tall. What is the angle of elevation of the top of the church tower from Arlene?

3 Jarvis is standing on top of a building looking down on the street below. He can see his own car. The angle of depression of the car from Jarvis is 81°. His car is 6 m from the front of the building. How tall is the building?

4 A climber has climbed 62 m up the face of a vertical cliff. His partner stands 20 m from the foot of the cliff face. What is the angle of elevation of the climber from his partner?

5 Caroline has taken a ride in a balloon. The balloon is 130 m high when Caroline looks down and sees the ideal landing point. The angle of depression of the landing point from Caroline is 22°. What is the horizontal distance of the balloon to the landing point?

6

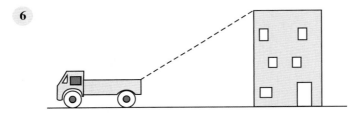

The back of a truck is 1.5 m tall. It is parked 17 m from the front of a building. Otto climbs onto the back of the truck and measures the angle of elevation of the top of the building as 58°. How tall is the building?

7 Rory stands 12 m from an advertising board. The angle of elevation of the top of the board is 32.7° and the angle of elevation of the bottom of the board is 10.9°. What is the vertical length of the advertising board?

8 A 29 m building is due east of Crimson. The angle of elevation of the top of the building from Crimson is 6.4°. A 16 m building is due west of Crimson with the angle of elevation of the top of this building from Crimson being 4.6°. How far apart are the two buildings?

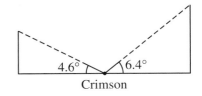

9 The angle of depression of a section of railway track down a mountain side is 7°. If the section drops a vertical height of 110 m from start to finish, how long is the section?

18B   **Algebra work**

1. Make x the subject of the formula $y = 6x - 17$

2. (a) Draw the graph of $y = 3x^2 - 5x$ for x-values from -3 to 3

     (b) Use your graph to solve $3x^2 - 5x = 0$

3. Factorise   (a) $4xy^2 - 12xy$ (b) $4x^2 - 1$ (c) $4x^2 - 4x - 3$

4. $3^x \times 3^y = 3^{13}$ and $3^x \div 3^y = 3^5$. Find the values of x and y.

5. r, l and w represent lengths. Which expressions below could represent areas?

$\pi l w$	$\pi(r + w)$	$5l^2 w$	$\dfrac{4lw^2}{\pi r}$	$8w^2$	$3\pi l w r$

6. Solve $5(1 - 2x) > 35$

7. Write down three inequalities which together describe the shaded region opposite.

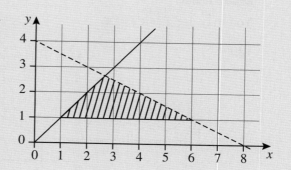

8. (a) Factorise $x^2 - 5x + 6$

     (b) Simplify $\dfrac{6}{x - 3} - \dfrac{2x}{x^2 - 5x + 6}$

9. Make y the subject of the formula $y - 3 = xy + p$

10.

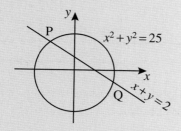

The line $x + y = 2$ meets the circle $x^2 + y^2 = 25$ at P and Q.

     (a) Show that the x co-ordinates at P and Q can be found from the equation $2x^2 - 4x - 21 = 0$.

     (b) Solve $2x^2 - 4x - 21 = 0$, giving your answer to 2 decimal places.

A point in 3-D space has co-ordinates (x, y, z) using 3 axes.

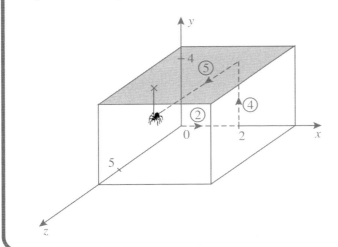

Start at the origin 0.
This has co-ordinates (0, 0, 0).
To get to the spider, move 2 units
parallel to the x-axis then 4 units
parallel to the y-axis then 5 units
parallel to the z-axis.
The spider is at (2, 4, 5).

M18.4

You may use a calculator.

1

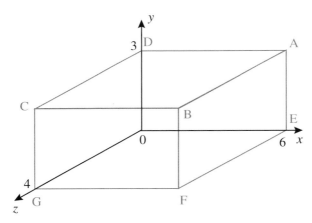

A has co-ordinates (6, 3, 0).
B has co-ordinates (6, 3, 4).
Write down the co-ordinates of
C, D, E, F and G.

2 (a) Write down the co-ordinates of
the vertices L, M, N, O, P, Q, R
and S.

(b) Write down the co-ordinates of
the midpoint of edge PL.

(c) Calculate the length of QS.

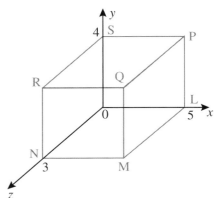

3

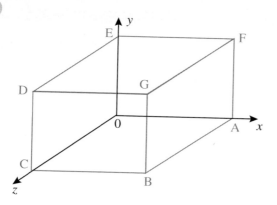

The co-ordinates of G are (6, 4, 10).

(a) Write down the co-ordinates of the vertices O, A, B, C, D, E and F.

(b) Calculate the length AG.

(c) Write down the co-ordinates of the midpoint of edge FG.

(d) Write down the co-ordinates of the midpoint of edge BC.

4

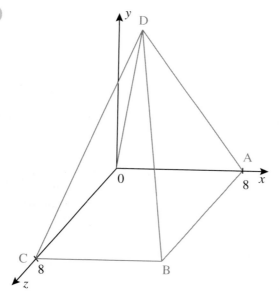

OABCD is a square-based pyramid. D is directly above the centre of the square base.

The pyramid has a height of 10 units.

Write down the co-ordinates of vertex D.

5 (a) Write down the co-ordinates of the vertices P, Q, R, S, T, U, V and W.

(b) Write down the co-ordinates of the midpoint of edge VR.

(c) Write down the co-ordinates of the midpoint of edge PS.

(d) Calculate the length PR.

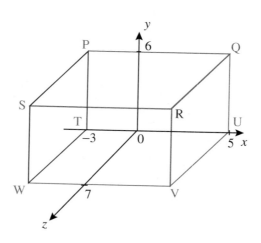

18C **Shape and space work**

1.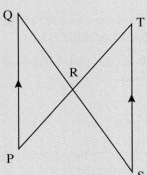

PQ = ST.

Prove that triangles PQR and RST are congruent.

2.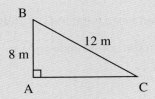

Work out the length of AC. Leave your answer in surd form.

3.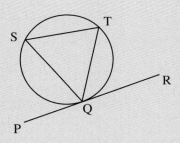

PR is a tangent to the circle. PQ̂S = 68° and ST = QT.

Work out RQ̂T, giving reasons for your answer.

4. (a) Describe *fully* the single transformation that maps A onto B.

(b) Copy the grid and shapes opposite.

Enlarge triangle B by a scale factor $-\dfrac{1}{2}$ about the point (1, 0). Label the image C.

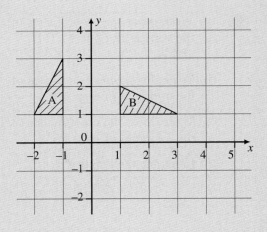

5. PQRSTUVW is a cuboid. Calculate PR̂T.

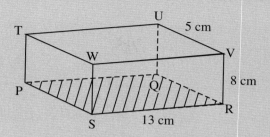

6.

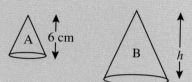

Two cones are similar.

The surface area of A = 18π cm².

The surface area of B = 288π cm².

Find h.

7. Denise is 4 km from home on a bearing of 063°. Simon is 7 km from home on a bearing of 158°. How far is Denise from Simon?

8.

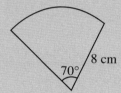

This is the sector of a circle of radius 8 cm.

Calculate the perimeter of the sector.

9.

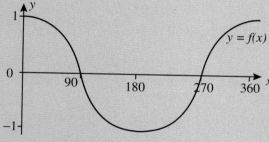

(a) Write down the actual equation of $f(x)$

(b) Sketch the curve for $y = f(x - 45)$

10.

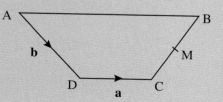

AB is twice the magnitude of DC.

AB is parallel to DC.

M is the midpoint of BC.

(a) Express $\overrightarrow{AB}$ in terms of a

(b) Express $\overrightarrow{AM}$ in terms of a and b

Key Facts

Use the *sine rule* to find angles and sides in triangles with **no right angle** (use basic trigonometry if the triangle contains a right angle).

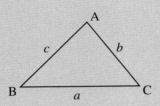

$$\frac{a}{\sin A} = \frac{b}{\sin B} = \frac{c}{\sin C}$$

Use this to find sides.

To find angles, it is easier to invert the formula and use

$$\frac{\sin A}{a} = \frac{\sin B}{b} = \frac{\sin C}{c}$$

(a)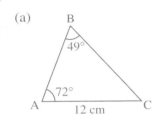

Find BC.

let BC = a (opposite $\hat{A}$)

and 12 = b (opposite $\hat{B}$)

$$\frac{a}{\sin A} = \frac{b}{\sin B}$$

$$\frac{BC}{\sin 72°} = \frac{12}{\sin 49°}$$

$$BC = \frac{12}{\sin 49°} \times \sin 72°$$

BC = 15.1 cm (3 sig. figs)

(b)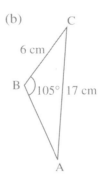

Find BÂC.

6 cm is opposite BÂC

17 cm is opposite 105°

$$\frac{\sin A}{a} = \frac{\sin B}{b}$$

$$\frac{\sin B\hat{A}C}{6} = \frac{\sin 105°}{17}$$

$$\sin B\hat{A}C = 6 \times \frac{\sin 105°}{17}$$

$$\sin B\hat{A}C = 0.341$$

$\boxed{\text{SHIFT/INV}}$ $\boxed{\sin}$

BÂC = 19.9° (1 dec. pl.)

Use a calculator and give all answers to 3 significant figures.

1 Find the value of each letter.

(a)

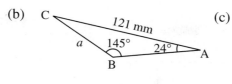

(b)

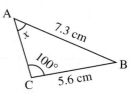

(c)

(d)

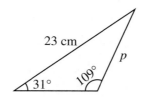

(e)

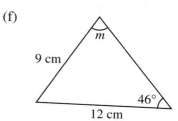

(f)

2 In triangle ABC, AC = 74 mm, BC = 83 mm and BÂC = 62°. Find AB̂C.

3 In triangle PQR, PQ = 7.1 cm, PR = 9.2 cm and PQ̂R = 93°. Find PR̂Q.

4 Find *x*, *y* and *z* in the following triangles:

(a)

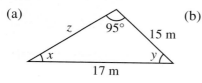

(b)

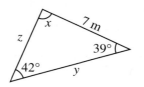

(c)

(d)

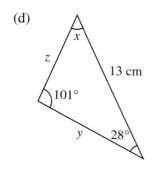

(e)

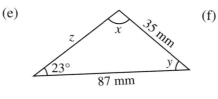

(f)

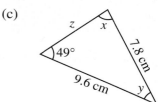

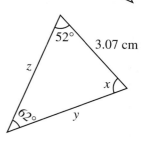

5 Hepford is due east of Sandhay. Alchurch is on a bearing of 128° from Sandhay and on a bearing of 207° from Hepford. If Hepford is 9 miles from Alchurch, how far is Hepford from Sandhay?

6

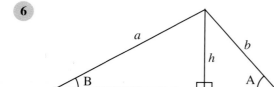

By finding *h* in two different ways, *prove* that

$$\frac{a}{\sin A} = \frac{b}{\sin B}$$

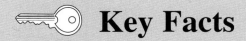

Key Facts

In triangles with **no right angle**, use the *cosine rule* to find an unknown side if the other two sides and the angle between them are known.

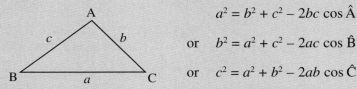

$$a^2 = b^2 + c^2 - 2bc \cos \hat{A}$$

or $$b^2 = a^2 + c^2 - 2ac \cos \hat{B}$$

or $$c^2 = a^2 + b^2 - 2ab \cos \hat{C}$$

If an angle needs to be found and all 3 sides are known, we rearrange the cosine rule and use one of the following:

$$\cos \hat{A} = \frac{b^2 + c^2 - a^2}{2bc} \quad \text{or} \quad \cos \hat{B} = \frac{a^2 + c^2 - b^2}{2ac} \quad \text{or} \quad \cos \hat{C} = \frac{a^2 + b^2 - c^2}{2ab}$$

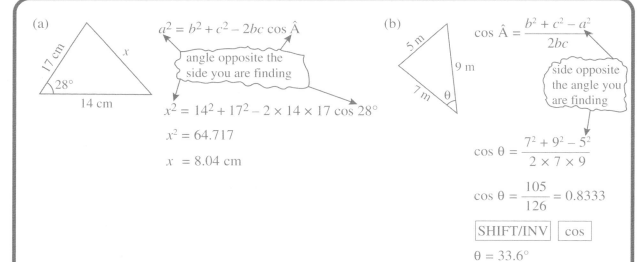

(a)

$$a^2 = b^2 + c^2 - 2bc \cos \hat{A}$$

angle opposite the side you are finding

$$x^2 = 14^2 + 17^2 - 2 \times 14 \times 17 \cos 28°$$

$$x^2 = 64.717$$

$$x = 8.04 \text{ cm}$$

(b)

$$\cos \hat{A} = \frac{b^2 + c^2 - a^2}{2bc}$$

side opposite the angle you are finding

$$\cos \theta = \frac{7^2 + 9^2 - 5^2}{2 \times 7 \times 9}$$

$$\cos \theta = \frac{105}{126} = 0.8333$$

SHIFT/INV cos

$$\theta = 33.6°$$

Note – if cos θ turns out to be negative, angle θ will be obtuse (your calculator will automatically give the correct obtuse angle)

Use a calculator and give all answers to 3 significant figures.

1 Find x in the following triangles:

(a)

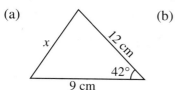

(b)

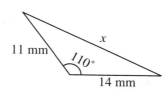

(c)

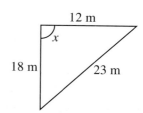

(d)

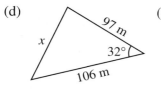

(e)

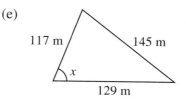

(f)

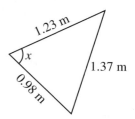

2 A man walks 300 m from a point P in a straight line and then turns through an angle θ and walks 120 m in a straight line. If he ends up 340 m from P then find θ.

3 A triangle ABC is such that AB = 3.8 cm, BC = 5.1 cm and the angle at B is 40°. Find the length of AC.

4 Jesse walks 5 km due north and then 4 km on a bearing of 120°.

(a) Draw a clear sketch of this journey, stating all known lengths and angles.

(b) How far is she from where she started?

5 A triangle XYZ is such that XY = 19 mm and YZ = 23 mm. If XZ = 35 mm, find the angle at Y.

6 A boat sails due south for 28 km then travels on a bearing of 127° for 15 km. How far is the boat from its starting position?

7 A car travels from its base on a bearing of 030° for 12 km. It then turns and drives a further 8 km on a bearing of 100° after which it breaks down.

(a) Draw a clear sketch of this journey, stating all known lengths and angles.

(b) A recovery vehicle leaves base to pick up the car. How far must it travel and on what bearing should it head?

8 A triangle ABC is such that BC is 3 cm longer than AB. The angle at B is 60° and AC = $\sqrt{37}$ cm. Suppose that the length of AB is x.

(a) Use the cosine rule to express AC^2 in terms of the other two sides.

(b) Hence show that $37 = x^2 + (x + 3)^2 - x(x + 3)$

(c) Rearrange this in the form $ax^2 + bx + c = 0$ and solve this to find x.

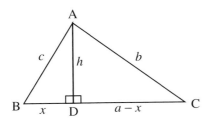

(a) Show that $x = c \cos \hat{B}$.

(b) Find h^2 in two different ways.

(c) Combine the two expressions for h^2 then substitute for x with $c \cos \hat{B}$.

(d) Rearrange to show that
$b^2 = a^2 + c^2 - 2ac \cos \hat{B}$

Using the sine and cosine rules

Two hikers walk 5 km on a bearing of 146° then 9 km on a bearing of 224°. On what bearing must they travel to return to their starting point and how much further must they walk?

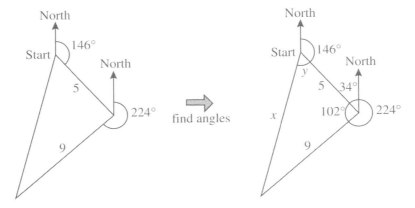

Find x and y.

Use the cosine rule first:

$x^2 = 5^2 + 9^2 - 2 \times 5 \times 9 \times \cos 102° = 124.71$

$x = 11.167 = 11.2$ km

Now use the sine rule:

$$\frac{\sin y}{9} = \frac{\sin 102°}{11.167} \quad \text{so} \quad \sin y = 9 \times \frac{\sin 102°}{11.167} = 0.7883$$

$$y = 52.0°$$

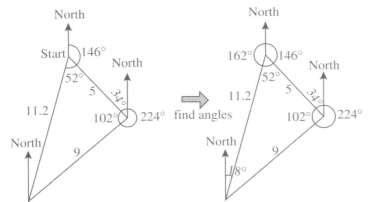

The hikers must travel on a bearing of 018° and must walk a further 11.2 km.

Use a calculator and give all answers to 3 significant figures when appropriate.

1 A plane travels 20 km on a bearing of 060°. It then travels 30 km on a bearing of 310°. Show that it is 29.8 km away from its starting point.

2 Carl runs 5 miles on a bearing of 205° and Avril, starting from the same place, jogs 3 miles on a bearing of 328°. How far apart are Carl and Avril now?

3 Find x, y and z in the following triangles:

(a)

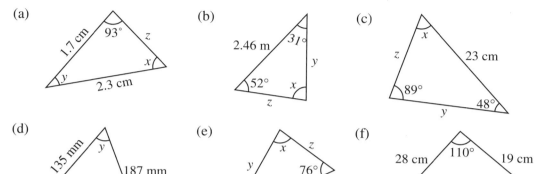

(b)

(c)

(d)

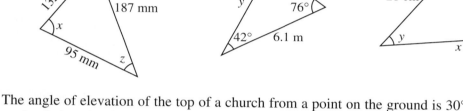

(e)

(f)

4 The angle of elevation of the top of a church from a point on the ground is 30°. The angle of elevation increases by 4° when measured from a second point, also on the ground but 22 m nearer the church than the first point.

(a) Find the distance from the top of the church to the second point.

(b) Find the height of the church (to the nearest m).

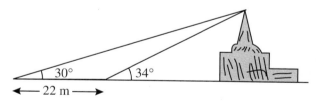

5 A yacht travels on a bearing of 241° for 14 km then on a bearing of 340° for 9 km. How far is the yacht from its starting point?

6 Two ships leave a port at noon. One travels at 12 km/h on a bearing of 040°, the other travels at 15 km/h on a bearing of 170°. How far away are they from each other at 2 p.m?

543

7

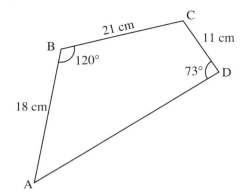

(a) Find the length of AC.

(b) Find the area of the triangle ABC (remember: area of a triangle ABC is $\frac{1}{2} ab \sin \hat{C}$)

(c) Find $C\hat{A}D$ and $A\hat{C}D$.

(d) Hence find the area of the quadrilateral ABCD.

8 A man runs 5 km on a bearing of 030°. He then runs 3 km on a bearing of 070°. He finally walks back to his starting point.

(a) How far is his total journey?

(b) What area has his journey enclosed?

9 A triangle ABC is such that AB is 2 cm longer than BC. The angle at B is 60° and the length of AC is $\sqrt{39}$.

(a) By letting BC = x cm, use the cosine rule to write down an equation involving x.

(b) Express this as a quadratic equation.

(c) Solve this to find x.

10

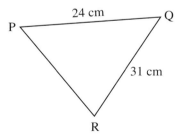

The area of this triangle is 254 cm². $P\hat{Q}R$ is acute.

Find the length of PR.

11 A car travels 15 km from A on a bearing of 100° to a point B. It then travels 12 km from B on a bearing of 175° to a point C. It then returns to A.

(a) Find the area enclosed by this journey.

(b) Find the time (to the nearest minute) it takes to travel from C to A if the car travels at 80 km/h.

544

18D **Data handling work**

1.

Time taken, t (mins)	Frequency
$0 < t \leqslant 5$	7
$5 < t \leqslant 10$	24
$10 < t \leqslant 20$	47
$20 < t \leqslant 30$	19
$30 < t \leqslant 50$	3

The table shows how long it takes 100 students to travel to college each morning.

Calculate an estimate of the mean time taken by these students (give your answer to the nearest whole number).

2. Sam has 3 red ties and 7 blue ties. He picks two ties at random.

   (a) Draw a tree diagram to show which ties he may have selected.

   (b) Work out the probability that Sam took two red ties.

   (c) Work out the probability that Sam took two ties of the same colour.

3. The following marks were obtained by 15 students in a science test:

   32   38   41   41   44   46   52   53   57   57   58   67   72   74   83

   (a) Write down the values of the lower quartile and the upper quartile.

   (b) Draw a box plot to illustrate this data.

4. (a) Explain what is meant by 'simple random sampling'.

   (b) Josh wishes to survey 60 people from a large firm about where they go for their holidays. The employees of the firm are classified by their salaries as shown in the table below.

Salary (£1000s)	4–10	11–15	16–25	26–40	41+
Number of people	120	154	132	96	38

   Josh wishes to take a stratified sample.

   Calculate how many people he should sample from each salary group.

5. A doctor asked her patients how many units of alcohol they drank each week. The data is shown in the unfinished histogram and table below.

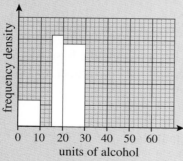

units of alcohol u	frequency
$0 \leqslant u < 10$	
$10 \leqslant u < 15$	16
$15 \leqslant u < 20$	21
$20 \leqslant u < 30$	
$30 \leqslant u < 60$	39

   (a) Use the information shown on the histogram to copy and complete the table.

   (b) Use the information shown in the table to copy and complete the histogram.

Lengths and angles often have to be found in three-dimensional situations. Triangles need to be identified then Pythagoras and trigonometry used.

Using Pythagoras

Find the length of QW.

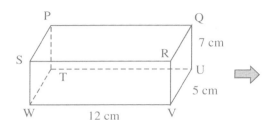 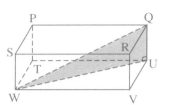

Use triangle QWU to find QW but we do not have enough information.

Use triangle UWV first:

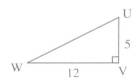

$UW^2 = 5^2 + 12^2$ (Pythagoras)

$UW^2 = 25 + 144$

$UW^2 = 169$

$UW = 13$ cm

Now use triangle QWU:

$QW^2 = 7^2 + 13^2$ (Pythagoras)

$QW^2 = 49 + 169$

$QW^2 = 218$

$QW = \sqrt{218} = 14.8$ cm (3 sig. figs)

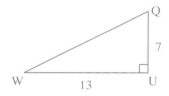

E18.4

Use a calculator and give all answers to 3 significant figures when appropriate.

1

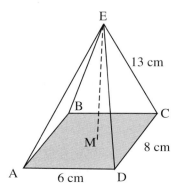

This pyramid has a rectangular base ABCD which is horizontal. EM is vertical. M is the midpoint of AC.

Find

(a) The length of AM.

(b) The height EM of the pyramid.

2

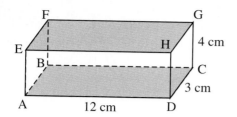

Find the following lengths:

(a) AC

(b) BE

(c) AH

(d) AG

3 A tin in the shape of a cuboid is 6 cm wide, 8 cm long and 5 cm tall.

(a) What is the length of a diagonal of the base of the tin?

(b) What is the longest thin pole that can be fitted in the tin (ignoring the thickness of the pole)?

4

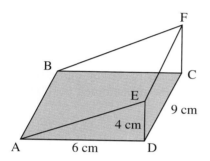

In this wedge, the rectangle DEFC is perpendicular to rectangle ABCD.

Find

(a) AC

(b) DF

(c) AF

5 Find the length of PV.

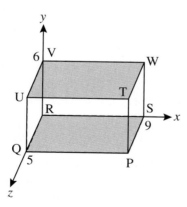

6 One plane is 7 km due south of an airport and another plane is 5 km due east of the same airport. If the difference in their heights is 500 m then find the distance between the two planes.

7 A cuboid has lengths in the ratio 3:4:12. If the distance from one corner of the box to the corner which is furthest away is 65 mm then find the dimensions of the box.

8 This pyramid has a rectangular base PQRS which is horizontal. MT is vertical. M is the midpoint of PR.

If MT = 18 cm, find:

(a) PM

(b) PT

(c) TN where N is the midpoint of SR.

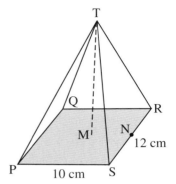

9 A cable is attached to the top of a vertical pole which is 120 m high. The other end of the cable is attached to a point on the ground which is 18 m to the north of the foot of the pole and 24 m to the east of the foot of the pole. Find the length of the cable.

10 An office block is 200 m further away from an underground station than a tall monument is from the same station. The office block is due east of the station and the monument is due north of the station. The distance between the top of the office block and the top of the monument is 600 m and the office block is 100 m taller than the monument.

(a) By letting x be the distance from the foot of the monument to the underground station, find an equation involving x.

(b) Solve this equation to find x.

E | **The angle between a line and a plane**

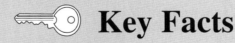

Key Facts

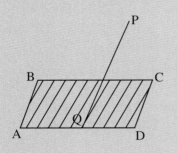

The angle between the line PQ and the flat surface (plane) ABCD is found by drawing any line from P perpendicular to the plane ABCD then forming the right-angled triangle as shown.

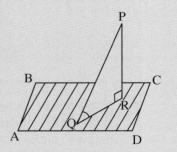

The angle between the line PQ and the plane ABCD is PQ̂R.

548

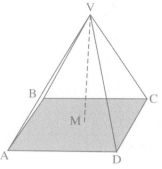

This pyramid has a horizontal square base ABCD. VM is vertical. M is the midpoint of AC.

AD = 120 cm and VM = 180 cm.

(a) Find DM.　　　　(b) Show that VD = $60\sqrt{11}$ cm.

(c) Calculate the angle between the line VD and the plane ABCD.

(d) Calculate AD̂V.

(a)

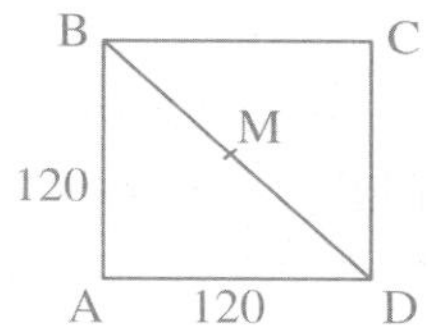

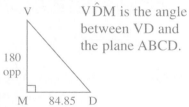

$BD^2 = 120^2 + 120^2$ (Pythagoras)

$BD^2 = 28800$

$BD = 169.7$

$DM = 169.7 \div 2$

$DM = 84.85$

$DM = 84.9$ cm (3 sig. figs)

(b)

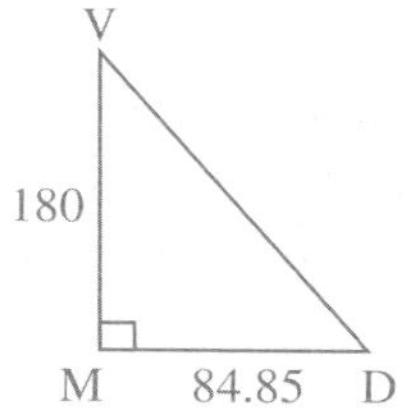

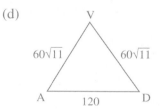

$VD^2 = VM^2 + MD^2$ (Pythagoras)

$VD^2 = 180^2 + 84.85^2$

⇩ using exact value from part (a) ⇩

$VD^2 = 32400 + 7200$

$VD^2 = 39600$

$VD^2 = 3600 \times 11$

$VD = 60\sqrt{11}$ cm.

(c)

VD̂M is the angle between VD and the plane ABCD.

SOHCAHTOA

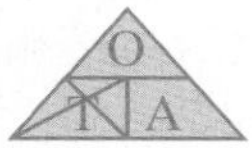

$\tan \theta = \dfrac{\text{Opp}}{\text{Adj}}$

$\tan V\hat{D}M = \dfrac{180}{84.85}$

$V\hat{D}M = 64.8°$ (3 sig. figs)

(d)

Cut the triangle in half and use basic trigonometry or use the cosine rule.

$\cos \hat{A} = \dfrac{b^2 + c^2 - a^2}{2bc}$

$\cos A\hat{D}V = \dfrac{120^2 + (60\sqrt{11})^2 - (60\sqrt{11})^2}{2 \times 120 \times 60\sqrt{11}}$

$\cos A\hat{D}V = 0.3015$

$A\hat{D}V = 72.5°$ (3 sig. figs)

Use a calculator and give all answers to 3 significant figures.

1

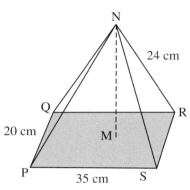

The pyramid has a horizontal rectangular base PQRS. NM is vertical. M is the midpoint of PR.

Find

(a) PM   (b) NM

(c) NP̂M   (d) PN̂S

(e) QN̂S

2

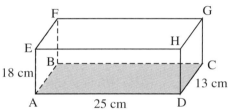

ABCDEFGH is a cuboid.

Find

(a) AC   (b) ED   (c) DG

(d) DF   (e) GÂC   (f) DÊC

(g) EB̂G

3 The pyramid has a horizontal square base ABCD. NM is vertical. M is the midpoint of AC and P is the midpoint of AD. DC = 20 cm and NM = 25 cm.

(a) Show that DM = $10\sqrt{2}$ cm.

(b) Calculate the angle between the line ND and the plane ABCD.

(c) Find ND.

(d) Find the angle between the line NP and the plane ABCD.

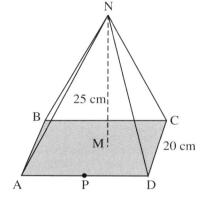

4

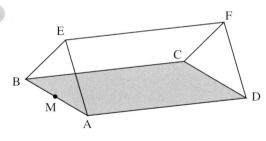

A tent has a horizontal base ABCD with AB = 1.4 m and AD = 2.3 m. EF is horizontal and EF = 1.7 m. The height of the tent is 1 m. The ends AEB and DFC make the same angle with the horizontal. The sides EBCF and AEFD make the same angle with the horizontal.

(a) Calculate the length of EM where M is the midpoint of AB.

(b) Show that the length of EA is 1.26 m.

(c) Show that EÂD is 76.2°.

(d) Calculate EÂB.

(e) Calculate the length of AX where X is the point on EA such that MX is perpendicular to EA.

5 A rectangular pencil case is made 5 cm wide, 11 cm long and 3 cm high.

(a) What is the longest distance between two corners of this box?

(b) A thin pencil of length 12 cm is jammed in the box (when closed) with one end in the bottom corner of the pencil case and the other end touching its roof. What angle does this pencil make with the floor of the pencil case?

6

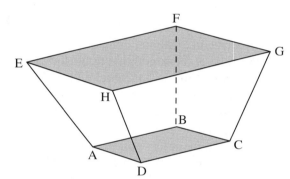

PQ̂R, PQ̂S and QR̂S are right angles.

QRS is horizontal and PQS is vertical.

Find

(a) PŜR

(b) the angle between the line PR and the plane QRS.

7 This diagram shows a gift box. ABCD and EFGH are horizontal squares of side lengths 12 cm and 20 cm respectively. The 4 slanting sides AE, BF, CG and DH are all 28 cm long and all make the same angle with the horizontal base.

(a) Calculate AÊH.

(b) If X is the point on the top of the box which is vertically above D then find HX.

(c) Hence find the vertical height of the gift box.

WATCH YOUR MONEY! – Old age pensions

Hopefully you will have a long and happy life. How will you pay for things when you get a lot older? What kind of life will you be able to have?

By 2050 there will be 14 million people over 65 in the UK.

If you do not save some money during your working years you will rely on the government for your money. How much might that be?

The state pension

The state pension at the time of writing is £3150 per annum for a single person. That is £60.58 each week. The government might give a person allowances to make sure the amount is at least £90 a week. How would you manage?

1 Billy receives £90 a week pension and allowances. He has no other savings. He owns his own house. He has to spend the following *each week*:

Food	£40
Electricity	£11
Gas	£7
Water rates	£7
Council tax	£16
Phone	£6

(a) How much money does Billy have left for each week?

(b) Billy needs to buy clothes, see friends and family. He wants to have the occasional drink and he would still like to run a car. He is 67 years old. What is your advice to Billy?

2 Caroline receives £90 a week pension and allowances. She has no other savings. She lives in a council bungalow and the rent is paid for her. Can you design a weekly budget for her, allowing for the fact that she has to pay for food, electricity, gas, water rates and the council tax. *Discuss your budget with your teacher.*

3 Mike started paying a *small amount* of money into a *personal pension* plan each month when he was 26 years old. He carried on paying a small amount each month throughout his working life. Mike is now 65 years old and has a pension of £14000 per annum. When he adds his state pension of £3150, he has £329.81 each week. *Compare* the life he could now lead compared to Billy in Question **1**.

4 Throughout your working life a small amount of money could be saved each month towards a pension.

(a) Write down (*or discuss with your teacher*) reasons for saving.

(b) Write down (*or discuss with your teacher*) reasons for *not* saving like this.

National Insurance payments

This is another tax that the government collects from each person's pay. This tax is used to pay for state pensions and the other state benefits like unemployment benefit. *Discuss with your teacher.*

Get wise!

State pensions are low. Pay a small amount of money into a pension pot throughout your life. A small amount each month does not have to greatly affect your life but will help you to have a better quality of life in old age.

1. Drawing and using plans and elevations

(a)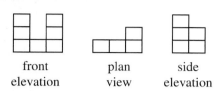

front elevation   plan view   side elevation

Draw this object on isometric paper.

(b)

Draw and label the plan and a side elevation for this solid (called a frustum)

(c)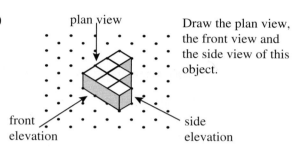

plan view

front elevation   side elevation

Draw the plan view, the front view and the side view of this object.

2. Measuring and calculating bearings

(a) Use a protractor to measure the bearing of:

  (i) Ambleford from Cayton

  (ii) Berwick from Cayton

  (iii) Berwick from Ambleford

  (iv) Cayton from Ambleford

(b) Pepton is 6 km due west of Cowley. North Sutton is 8 km due south of Cowley. Calculate the bearing of Pepton from North Sutton.

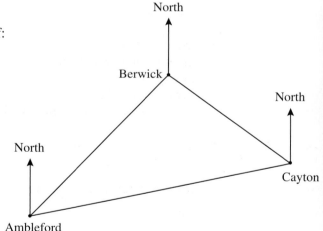

North

Berwick

North

North

Cayton

Ambleford

3. Using angles of elevation and depression

(a) Shane is looking at a bird sitting in a tree. The angle of elevation of the bird from Shane is 12° and Shane is standing 40 m from the tree. How high above the ground is the bird?

(b)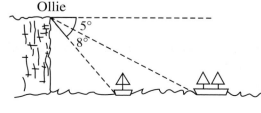

Ollie

5°
8°

From the top of a 73 m cliff, Ollie can see two boats due East of him. The angles of depression of the two boats are 5° and 13°. Find the distance between the two boats.

553

4. Using 3 co-ordinates for a point in 3-D space

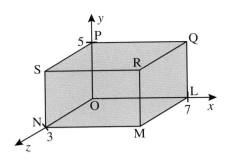

(a) Write down the co-ordinates of the vertices L, M, N, O, P, Q, R and S.

(b) Write down the co-ordinates of the midpoint of edge NS.

(c) Calculate the length of LN.

5. Using the sine and cosine rules

(a) Find x and y.

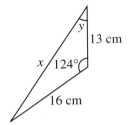

(b) Calculate the area of triangle PQR.

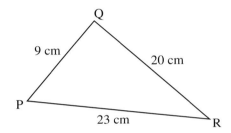

(c) High Cross is 45 km due south of Paulton. Tamwell is 41 km from Paulton on a bearing of 219°.

(i) How far is Tamwell from High Cross?

(ii) What is the bearing of Tamwell from High Cross?

6. Solving three-dimensional problems using trigonometry

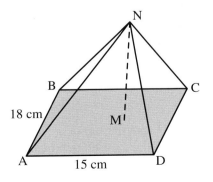

The pyramid has a horizontal rectangular base ABCD. NM is vertical. M is the midpoint of AC. NM = 12 cm.

Find

(a) AM

(b) AN

(c) the angle which ND makes with the plane ABCD.

(d) A long, thin metal box is 5 mm wide, 12 mm high and 84 mm long. What is the longest rod that can be fitted into this box?

Mixed examination questions

1 A car is 2.86 m long.
Two scale models are made of the car.
Model A is made to a scale of 1:30.
Model B is 38 mm long.

What is the difference between the length of model A and the length of model B? (OCR)

2 A lighthouse, L, is 3.2 km due West of a port, P.
A ship, S, is 1.9 km due North of the lighthouse, L.

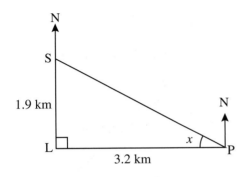

(a) Calculate the size of the angle marked x.
Give your answer correct to 3 significant figures.

(b) Find the bearing of the port, P, from the ship, S.
Give your answer correct to 3 significant figures.

(EDEXCEL)

3 Calculate the length of the longest thin straight rod that will fit inside this cuboid.

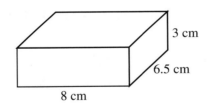

(OCR)

4

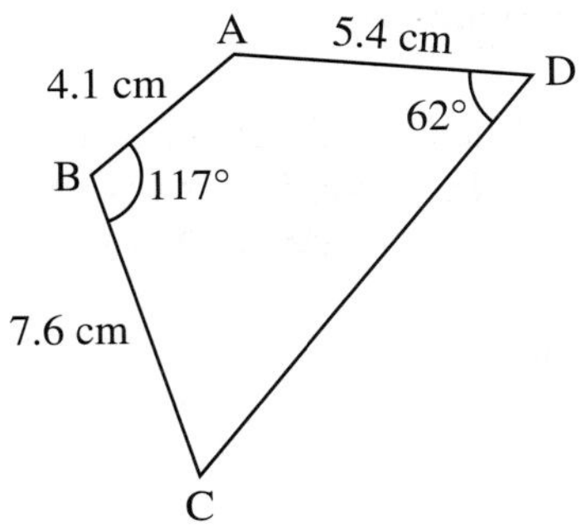

The diagram shows a quadrilateral *ABCD*.
AB = 4.1 cm.
BC = 7.6 cm.
AD = 5.4 cm.
Angle ABC = 117°.
Angle ADC = 62°.

(a) Calculate the length of AC.
Give your answer correct to 3 significant figures.

(b) Calculate the area of triangle ABC.
Give your answer correct to 3 significant figures.

(c) Calculate the area of the quadrilateral ABCD.
Give your answer correct to 3 significant figures. (EDEXCEL)

5

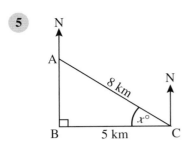

The diagram shows the positions of three telephone masts A, B and C.

Mast C is 5 kilometres due east of Mast B.
Mast A is due north of Mast B, and 8 kilometres from mast C.

(a) Calculate the distance of A from B.
   Give your answer in kilometres, correct to three significant figures.

(b) (i) Calculate the size of the angle marked $x°$.
        Give your angle correct to one decimal place.

    (ii) Calculate the bearing of A from C.
        Give your bearing correct to one decimal place.

    (iii) Calculate the bearing of C from A.
        Give your bearing correct to one decimal place.   (EDEXCEL)

6   Jenna is walking due north along a straight path, ABC.

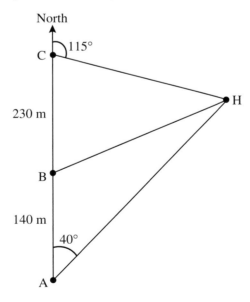

The distance from A to B is 140 m and the distance from B to C is 230 m.
There is a hut at H.
The bearing of H from A is 040° and the bearing of H from C is 115°.

How far is Jenna from the hut when she is at B?   (AQA)

7 ABCDEFGH is a cuboid with sides of 5 cm, 5 cm and 12 cm as shown.

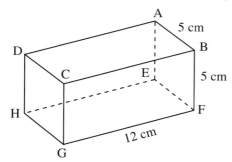

Calculate angle DFH.

(AQA)

8 Two ships, A and B, leave Dover Docks at the same time.
Ship A travels at 25 km/h on a bearing of 120°.
Ship B travels at 30 km/h on a bearing of 130°.
Calculate how far apart the two ships are after 1 hour.

(OCR)

9 ABCD is a quadrilateral with diagonal AC.

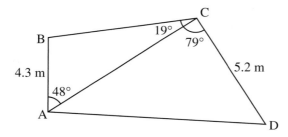

AB = 4.3 m and CD = 5.2 m.
Angle BAC = 48°, angle BCA = 19° and angle ACD = 79°.
Calculate the length of AD.

(OCR)

10 The diagram shows a glass paperweight in the form of a pyramid, having vertex A and a square base, BCDE. The edges AB, AC, AD and AE are each 58 mm long. The edges, BC, CD, DE and EB are each 52 mm long. The diagonals of BCDE intersect at F.

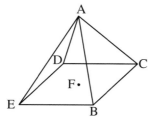

(a) Calculate

(i) The length of BF,

(ii) The angle between the edge AB and the base of the paperweight,

(iii) The height of the paperweight.

(b) X is the mid-point of BC. Calculate the angle between AX and the base of the pyramid.

(WJEC)

557

UNIT 1

Page 2   M1.1

1. (a) 31   (b) 61   (c) 81   (d) 33   (e) 12

(f) 121   (g) 35   (h) 36   (i) 169

2. (a) 3   (b) 1   (c) 5   (d) 9   (e) 2   (f) 7

3. (a) 1702   (b) 10332   (c) 18126   (d) 46   (e) 63   (f) 36

4. 74   **5.** 42   **6.** 4096

7. (a) 5.93   (b) 0.015   (c) 0.0027   (d) 0.01

(e) 1.2   (f) 15.287   (g) 0.126   (h) 150

(i) 0.9   (j) 21.4   (k) 0.95   (l) 6.2

(m) 0.0784   (n) 8.532   (o) 32.5   (p) 1.8096

8. £12.45   **9.** 16

10. (a) 10   (b) 27   (c) 34   (d) 49   (e) 40   (f) 13

(g) 4   (h) 2   (i) 8   (j) 1   (k) 33   (l) 25

Page 3   M1.2

1. (a) 35   (b) $\frac{1}{24}$ (c) $\frac{3}{14}$ (d) $\frac{3}{10}$ (e) $6\frac{3}{5}$ (f) $8\frac{1}{8}$

(g) $10\frac{2}{3}$ (h) 16   (i) $\frac{8}{9}$ (j) $\frac{18}{35}$ (k) $\frac{1}{16}$ (l) $1\frac{5}{6}$

(m) $\frac{3}{8}$ (n) $\frac{4}{5}$ (o) $1\frac{13}{21}$ (p) $1\frac{1}{28}$

2. 9   **3.** 8

4. (a) $\frac{29}{35}$ (b) $\frac{2}{9}$ (c) $\frac{17}{40}$ (d) $\frac{29}{60}$

(e) $\frac{29}{45}$ (f) $\frac{11}{12}$ (g) $\frac{1}{3}$ (h) $\frac{17}{56}$

5. (a) $4\frac{5}{12}$ (b) $1\frac{1}{8}$ (c) $\frac{7}{8}$ (d) $4\frac{17}{30}$

6. B by $1\frac{2}{5}$ m²   **7.** A → S, B → P, C → Q   **8.** $\frac{5}{12}$

9. $\frac{19}{40}$ **10.** $1\frac{1}{6}$ miles   **11.** $48\frac{1}{2}$

12. (a)

$\frac{1}{2}$	−	$\frac{1}{6}$	→	$\frac{1}{3}$
×		÷		
$\frac{1}{4}$	÷	$\frac{1}{5}$	→	$\frac{5}{4}$
↓		↓		
$\frac{1}{8}$	×	$\frac{5}{6}$	→	$\frac{5}{48}$

(b)

$\frac{2}{3}$	×	$\frac{1}{3}$	→	$\frac{2}{9}$
−		÷		
$\frac{1}{2}$	+	$\frac{3}{8}$	→	$\frac{7}{8}$
↓		↓		
$\frac{1}{6}$	+	$\frac{8}{9}$	→	$\frac{19}{18}$

13. (a) $\frac{1}{3}$ (b) $\frac{9}{32}$ (c) $\frac{19}{21}$ (d) $\frac{21}{40}$ (e) $6\frac{4}{5}$ (f) $\frac{319}{350}$

14. 8   **15.** $3\frac{5}{6}$ m²   **16.** $1\frac{83}{140}$ **17.** $\frac{1}{2}$ **18.** $\frac{1}{2}$

Page 5   Can you still? 1A

1. (a) 0.2   (b) 0.9   (c) 2.64   (d) 0.1   (e) 36.72   (f) 14.183

2. A, B, D

3. 1A 17.97, 3A 11, 6A 830, 8A 14.52, 9A 224, 11A 12, 12A 88, 13A 31.8, 14A 3.3, 1D 1.98, 2D 900, 4D 138.268, 5D 30.43, 9D 2.23, 7D 3.02, 10D 418, 12D 83

Page 6   M1.3

1. A → R, B → P, C → S, D → U, E → Q, F → T.

2. 45.2   **3.** (a) £143   (b) 185 km

4. (a) $\frac{26}{99}$ (b) $14\frac{2}{5}$ (c) $13\frac{3}{4}$ (d) $17\frac{16}{25}$

5. 1A 6.92, 3A 11.9, 5A 40.12, 7A 735, 9A 49, 10A 34.8, 11A 81, 12A 245, 1D 6.8, 2D 250.848, 3D 11.27, 4D 94.65, 6D 91.68, 8D 31.45, 10D 34

6. (a) 136.68   (b) 0.63   (c) 5.15   (d) 0.38   (e) 3.47   (f) 47.82

7.

+	$\frac{3}{8}$	$\frac{7}{20}$	$2\frac{1}{2}$	$1\frac{2}{3}$
$\frac{1}{4}$	$\frac{5}{8}$	$\frac{12}{20}$	$2\frac{3}{4}$	$1\frac{11}{12}$
$\frac{3}{5}$	$\frac{39}{40}$	$\frac{19}{20}$	$3\frac{1}{10}$	$2\frac{4}{15}$
$2\frac{1}{3}$	$2\frac{17}{24}$	$2\frac{41}{60}$	$4\frac{5}{6}$	4
$2\frac{3}{10}$	$2\frac{27}{40}$	$2\frac{13}{20}$	$4\frac{4}{5}$	$3\frac{29}{30}$

8. (a) 62.5   (b) 7.87   (c) 1.59   (d) 147   (e) 3.62   (f) 0.559

Page 8   Can you still? 1B

1. (a) −12   (b) −42   (c) −16   (d) −3   (e) 8   (f) −3

(g) 32   (h) 80   (i) 5   (j) 5   (k) 6   (l) −8

2. (a) −3   (b) −9   (c) −4   (d) −2   (e) −5

(f) −3   (g) 2   (h) −5   (i) −1

3. In order   (a) −2, −8, −7, 21   (b) 4, −5, −15, −7

4. (a) 30   (b) 84   (c) −40   (d) 2   (e) −10

(f) −3   (g) −9   (h) −22   (i) −45

5. (a) 1   (b) −10   (c) −12   (d) 20   (e) −2   (f) 5

6. (a) 64   (b) −0.0032   (c) 0.004   (d) −0.42   (e) 36   (f) −27

(g) −38   (h) −19   (i) −4   (j) 2   (k) 2   (l) −2

Page 9   M1.4

1. (a) $\frac{3}{5}$ (b) $\frac{2}{25}$ (c) $\frac{3}{4}$ (d) $\frac{43}{200}$

(e) $\frac{209}{250}$ (f) $\frac{517}{1000}$ (g) $\frac{291}{400}$ (h) $\frac{1}{16}$

2. $\frac{1}{8} = 0.125$, $\frac{3}{40} = 0.075$, $\frac{1}{25} = 0.04$, $\frac{7}{200} = 0.035$, $\frac{17}{50} = 0.34$,

$\frac{9}{16} = 0.5625$, $\frac{3}{32} = 0.09375$, $\frac{11}{64} = 0.171875$, $\frac{37}{500} = 0.074$

3. (a) $0.1\dot{8}$ (b) $0.\dot{5}$ (c) $0.\dot{6}$ (d) $0.6\dot{3}$

(e) $0.4\dot{6}$ (f) $0.\dot{4}$ (g) 0.16 (h) $0.58\dot{3}$

4. $0.\dot{5}7142\dot{8}$ **5.** $0.\dot{8}5714\dot{2}$, $0.\dot{8}4615\dot{3}$, $\frac{6}{7}$ is larger

Page 10   E1.1

1. (a) $10f = 7.\dot{7}$ $9f = 7$ $f = \frac{7}{9}$

(b) $100f = 31.\dot{3}\dot{1}$ $99f = 31$ $f = \frac{31}{99}$

2. (a) $\frac{8}{9}$ (b) $\frac{89}{99}$ (c) $\frac{17}{99}$ (d) $\frac{73}{99}$ (e) $\frac{17}{111}$ (f) $\frac{83}{333}$

(g) $\frac{91}{99}$ (h) $\frac{22}{37}$ (i) $\frac{1}{6}$ (j) $\frac{13}{30}$ (k) $\frac{161}{198}$ (l) $\frac{4304}{990} = 4\frac{172}{495}$

Page 12   E1.2

1. (a) $2\sqrt{3}$ (b) $2\sqrt{11}$ (c) $3\sqrt{5}$ (d) $5\sqrt{2}$ (e) $5\sqrt{3}$ (f) $2\sqrt{6}$
(g) $3\sqrt{7}$ (h) $10\sqrt{2}$ (i) $4\sqrt{10}$ (j) $5\sqrt{6}$ (k) $4\sqrt{3}$ (l) $3\sqrt{15}$
(m) $6\sqrt{5}$ (n) $36\sqrt{6}$ (o) $7\sqrt{5}$ (p) $7\sqrt{7}$

2. (a) $\sqrt{15}$ (b) $2\sqrt{7}$ (c) $\sqrt{55}$ (d) 3   (e) 6
(f) $2\sqrt{6}$ (g) $2\sqrt{15}$ (h) 6   (i) $4\sqrt{3}$

3. (a) $\sqrt{14}$ (b) $\sqrt{5}$ (c) $\sqrt{3}$ (d) $\sqrt{2}$ (e) $2\sqrt{2}$ (f) $\sqrt{2}$

4. (a), (c) and (f) are true

5. (a) $15\sqrt{10}$ (b) $6\sqrt{21}$ (c) 18   (d) $42\sqrt{3}$ (e) 50   (f) 45
(g) $63\sqrt{15}$ (h) $24\sqrt{6}$ (i) $2\sqrt{2}$ (j) $15\sqrt{21}$ (k) $54\sqrt{2}$ (l) $81\sqrt{3}$

6. $\sqrt{6} \times \sqrt{2}$, $\dfrac{2\sqrt{6}}{\sqrt{2}}$, $\sqrt{12}$, $5\sqrt{3} - 3\sqrt{3}$

7. (a) $2\sqrt{2}$ (b) $7\sqrt{3}$ (c) $3\sqrt{5}$ (d) $5\sqrt{3}$ (e) $3\sqrt{3}$
(f) $5\sqrt{3}$ (g) $8\sqrt{5}$ (h) $12\sqrt{2}$ (i) $13\sqrt{2}$ (j) $5\sqrt{15}$
(k) $4\sqrt{5}$ (l) $2(\sqrt{3} + \sqrt{5})$

Page 13   Can you still? 1C

1. 3600   **2.** 12000
3. (a) 5   (b) 100   (c) £3000   (d) 1   (e) 0.2 kg
(f) 2   (g) 100   (h) £2000   (i) 400

Page 15   E1.3

1. (a) $9 + 5\sqrt{3}$ (b) $3 + \sqrt{5}$ (c) $-8 + 2\sqrt{3} - 4\sqrt{5} + \sqrt{15}$
(d) $3 + \sqrt{6} + \sqrt{10} + \sqrt{15}$ (e) $-2 - \sqrt{6} + \sqrt{10} + \sqrt{15}$
(f) $\sqrt{6} + \sqrt{14} + \sqrt{15} + \sqrt{35}$

3. (a) $3 + 2\sqrt{2}$ (b) $8 + 2\sqrt{15}$ (c) $7 - 2\sqrt{10}$ (d) 1   (e) 4
(f) 1   (g) $10 - 2\sqrt{21}$ (h) 4   (i) $9 + 4\sqrt{5}$

4. (a) $\dfrac{\sqrt{5}}{5}$ (b) $\dfrac{\sqrt{3}}{3}$ (c) $\dfrac{\sqrt{7}}{7}$ (d) $3\sqrt{2}$ (e) $2\sqrt{5}$ (f) $3\sqrt{7}$
(g) $\dfrac{3\sqrt{5}}{2}$ (h) $\dfrac{3\sqrt{11}}{5}$ (i) $\dfrac{\sqrt{15}}{5}$ (j) $\dfrac{\sqrt{14}}{7}$ (k) $\dfrac{5\sqrt{21}}{7}$ (l) 2

5. (a) $\sqrt{2} + \sqrt{6}$ (b) $2\sqrt{5} - 5$ (c) $\sqrt{6} + \sqrt{15}$ (d) $6\sqrt{2} - 2\sqrt{6}$

6. (a) $\dfrac{(\sqrt{2} + \sqrt{6})}{2}$ (b) $\dfrac{(5\sqrt{5} - \sqrt{10})}{5}$ (c) $\dfrac{(\sqrt{6} + \sqrt{15})}{3}$ (d) $\dfrac{(2\sqrt{3} - \sqrt{2})}{2}$

7. (a) using difference of squares formula $(a + b)(a - b) = a^2 - b^2$,
multiply both numerator and denominator by $\sqrt{5} + 2$

$\rightarrow \dfrac{3}{(\sqrt{5} - 2)} \times \dfrac{(\sqrt{5} + 2)}{(\sqrt{5} + 2)} = 3\sqrt{5} + 6$

(b) $\dfrac{5}{(1 + \sqrt{2})} \times \dfrac{(1 - \sqrt{2})}{(1 - \sqrt{2})} = \dfrac{5 - 5\sqrt{2}}{-1} = -5 + 5\sqrt{2}$

Multiply numerator and denominator by $(a - \sqrt{b})$.

8. (a) 20   (b) 9   (c) 20   (d) 2   (e) 2
(f) 6   (g) $\sqrt{10} - \sqrt{5} + 3\sqrt{2} - 3$ (h) -2 (i) $3\sqrt{10} - 3\sqrt{15}$
(j) 2   (k) $11\sqrt{2} + 9\sqrt{3}$ (l) $38 + 17\sqrt{5}$

9. (a) $7 + 4\sqrt{3}$ (b) $\dfrac{3}{2}\sqrt{2} + \sqrt{6}$ (c) $\sqrt{35} + 3\sqrt{7} - 6 - 2\sqrt{2}$

10. (a) $\dfrac{\sqrt{5}}{2}$ cm³   (b) $3\sqrt{5}$ cm³

Page 18   WYM1

5. 300 minutes   **6.** £12   **7.** Tariff P   **8.** Tariff Q
9. (b) 200   (c) Tariff Z   (d) Tariff Y

Page 19   Test yourself on unit 1

1. (a) 196   (b) 3   (c) 15768   (d) 26   (e) 256
(f) 5   (g) A 0.03, B 1.651, C 6, D 0.019

2. (a) $\dfrac{29}{30}$ (b) 35   (c) $1\dfrac{17}{30}$ (d) $6\dfrac{3}{5}$ (e) $\dfrac{21}{32}$ (f) $\dfrac{73}{160}$

3. (a) 5.96   (b) 0.466   (c) 566000   (d) 5.37   (e) 0.0689   (f) 174

4. (a) $\dfrac{7}{20} = 0.35$, $\dfrac{4}{5} = 0.8$, $\dfrac{7}{8} = 0.875$, $\dfrac{17}{40} = 0.425$,

$\dfrac{57}{200} = 0.285$, $\dfrac{19}{25} = 0.76$ (b) $0.\dot{7}$ (c) $0.5\dot{3}$

5. (a) $\dfrac{23}{99}$ (b) $\dfrac{22}{45}$ (c) $\dfrac{719}{999}$

6. (a) iii, v, vi are true   (b) (i) $3\sqrt{3}$ (ii) $4\sqrt{5}$ (iii) $12\sqrt{10}$
(iv) 48   (v) $4\sqrt{2}$ (vi) $\sqrt{2}$

7. (a) $\sqrt{6} - \sqrt{10} + \sqrt{15} - 2$ (b) $\sqrt{5} + \sqrt{15} - 3\sqrt{3} - 3$
(c) -7 (d) $2\sqrt{5} - \sqrt{15}$ (e) $4 + 2\sqrt{3}$ (f) $54 - 14\sqrt{5}$
(g) $\dfrac{\sqrt{11}}{11}$ (h) $\dfrac{3\sqrt{2}}{2}$ (i) $\dfrac{\sqrt{35}}{7}$ (j) $\dfrac{(\sqrt{6} - 5\sqrt{2})}{2}$ (k) 8 cm

Page 21   Mixed examination questions

1. (a) $\dfrac{1}{6}$, $\dfrac{3}{8}$, $\dfrac{1}{2}$, $\dfrac{2}{3}$, $\dfrac{3}{4}$ (b) $\dfrac{3}{5}$, 65%, $\dfrac{2}{3}$, 0.72, $\dfrac{3}{4}$

2. 8   **3.** 1.84   **4.** 24 cm   **5.** (a) $\dfrac{1}{2}$, $\dfrac{4}{7}$, $\dfrac{3}{5}$ (b) $\dfrac{2}{7}$

6. (i) 69.3   (ii) 6.93   (iii) 0.0693

7. (a) $3\sqrt{2}$ (b) $7\sqrt{2}$ **8.** (a) 10   (b) 3   (c) 2

9. (a) 5   (b) 18   **10.** (a) $\dfrac{7}{9}$ (b) $\dfrac{43}{90}$ **11.** (a) 46   (b) $4\sqrt{6}$

UNIT 2

Page 24   M2.1

1.

60	38	3		63	90	38	11		66	15
Y	O	U		K	N	O	W		I	T

40	12	63	50	9		9	50	90	9	50
M	A	K	E	S		S	E	N	S	E

2. b   **3.** 67.5 g   **4.** A   **5.** £22880   **6.** £165,600
7. (a) £60   (b) £292.50   **8.** £7.72
9. (a) 1.25   (b) 1.175   (c) 0.94   (d) 0.965   (e) 0.37   (f) $1 + \dfrac{P}{100}$
10. (a) £292.80   (b) £60.48   (c) £19.68   (d) £9.53
11. 11270   **12.** £2883   **13.** £484.10   **14.** £945.14
15. £2276.85   **16.** (a) £2726   (b) £1989.98
17. (a) £323.13   (b) £274.66   **18.** (a) £646.25   (b) £529.93

Page 27   M2.2

1. 8%   **2.** 15%   **3.** $33\dfrac{1}{3}$%   **4.** 3%   **5.** 22.5%   **6.** 10.2%
7. Lager 125%, Crisps 140%, Bitter 117.4%, Nuts 177.8%
8. 20%   **9.** 3.6%   **10.** 73.3%   **11.** 44%   **12.** 20%

Page 28   Can you still? 2A

1. 16.937   **2.** 38.888   **3.** 0.048   **4.** 4.68   **5.** 0.9

6. 3.2   **7.** Yes   **8.** 0.181   **9.** 0.27   **10.** 1.3

Page 29   M2.3

1. £6615   **2.** (a) £10112.24   (b) £4764.06   (c) £2809   (d) £674.16

3. (a) £392   (b) £274.40   **4.** 7077888   **5.** 6912

6. (a) £53.05   (b) £54.64   (c) £77.90

7. (a) Geena   (b) £2.42   **8.** £4800   **9.** £1683.06

10. (a) 0.85   (b) £5129   **11.** £630, £694.58, £765.77, £977.34

12. 2670000, 2376300, 2114907, 1882267   **13.** £37178.76

14. 10 years   **15.** (a) 21600   (b) 23328   (c) 16.64%

Page 32   M2.4

1. £26000   **2.** 68 kg   **3.** 70   **4.** £2480   **5.** £60

6. £18   **7.** £34   **8.** (a) £27 (b) £48.50 (c) £9.30 (d) £110

9 £56.40   **10.** £624   **11.** £112   **12.** £1170   **13.** £27

14. Jane, divide 85.1 by 1.15   **15.** (a) 5600   (b) 5880

16. 86 p   **17.** £752   **18.** £1020   **19.** 120 mm × 160 mm

Page 33   Can you still? 2B

1. $\frac{3}{10}$ **2.** $\frac{6}{7}$ **3.** $\frac{3}{10}$ **4.** $2\frac{2}{5}$

5.

+	$\frac{1}{10}$	$\frac{1}{4}$	$\frac{2}{9}$
$\frac{2}{5}$	$\frac{1}{2}$	$\frac{13}{20}$	$\frac{28}{45}$
$\frac{3}{8}$	$\frac{19}{40}$	$\frac{5}{8}$	$\frac{43}{72}$
$\frac{1}{3}$	$\frac{13}{30}$	$\frac{7}{12}$	$\frac{5}{9}$

6. $\frac{14}{15}$ m   **7.** $8\frac{1}{3}$ m

Page 34   M2.5

1. 5:1   **2.** 3:2

3. (a) 6:7   (b) 8:5   (c) 8:3:5   (d) 10:1

(e) 1:40   (f) 1:30   (g) 3:12:2   (h) 3:100

4. £18.62   **5.** £82.20   **6.** Omar £120, Molly £40, Sachin £160

7. 16 blue, 40 yellow   **8.** $p = 108°$, $q = 36°$, $r = 72°$, $s = 144°$

9. 180 g Flour, 420 ml Milk, 3 eggs

10. 330 g butter, 360 g sugar, 3 spoons water, 6 eggs 300 g Flour,
3 spoons cocoa

11. (a) 18 (b) 20   **12.** 20   **13.** 94   **14.** £2500   **15.** $\frac{5y}{6}$

16. Dopey £120, Doc. £135, Happy £60, Bashful £45,
Grumpy £150, Sneezy £105, Sleepy £180, Total £795

Page 36   M2.6

1. (a) 16   (b) 243   (c) 32   (d) 125   (e) 72   (f) 100

2. (a) 3^6 (b) 2^8 (c) 8^3 (d) 6^2 (e) 9^6 (f) 4^{12}

3. (a) 5^6 (b) 7^5 (c) 6^7 (d) 9^3 (e) 5^3 (f) 4

(g) 5^6 (h) 7^8 (i) 1   (j) 5^{18} (k) 1   (l) 4^{10}

4. (a) 3^{11} (b) 2^{18} (c) 6^9 (d) 7^3 (e) 5^2

(f) 9^3 (g) 8^2 (h) 4^6 (i) 2^5

5. (a) 3^6 (b) 6^2 (c) 9^3 (d) 4^2 (e) 9

(f) 4^6 (g) 3^6 (h) 8^5 (i) 4^{12}

6. (a) a^7 (b) x^{11} (c) x^5 (d) n^6 (e) a^4 (f) x^9

(g) 1   (h) p^9 (i) m^6 (j) 1   (h) a^{13} (l) 1   **7.** B

8. (a) x^2 (b) a^4 (c) m (d) a^4 (e) n^2 (f) x^4 **9.** 3^8 cm^2

10. (a) 4   (b) 1   (c) 0   (d) 20   (e) 16

(f) 7   (g) 4   (h) 3   (i) 6

11. (a) $10a^7$ (b) $15a^8$ (c) $10p^5$ (d) $24a^6$ (e) $5a^9$ (f) $-18b^7$

12. (a) $3a^4$ (b) $5a^2$ (c) $4c^7$ (d) $4m^5$ (e) $8a^4$ (f) $7m^5$

13. $3x^5$ **14.** 1

15. (a) $9a^4$ (b) $8b^9$ (c) $125p^{12}$ (d) $49a^6$

16. (a) $x^6 + x^5$ (b) $n^9 - n^5$ (c) $x^9 + x^{12}$

Page 38   Can you still? 2C

1. $4\sqrt{3}$ **2.** $5\sqrt{3}$ **3.** $\sqrt{3}$ **4.** 20   **5.** 3   **6.** 2

7. $\sqrt{15} - \sqrt{5} + 2\sqrt{3} - 2$ **8.** $16 + 6\sqrt{7}$

9. (a) $\frac{\sqrt{5}}{5}$ (b) $2\sqrt{3}$ (c) $\frac{(2 + \sqrt{2})}{2}$

Page 39   E2.1

1. (a) $\frac{1}{36}$ (b) $\frac{1}{3}$ (c) $\frac{1}{216}$

2. (a) $\frac{1}{9}$ (b) $\frac{1}{1000}$ (c) $\frac{1}{2}$ (d) $\frac{1}{10}$ (e) $\frac{1}{64}$ (f) $\frac{1}{4}$

(g) $\frac{1}{27}$ (h) $\frac{1}{16}$ (i) $\frac{1}{49}$ (j) $\frac{1}{256}$ (k) $\frac{1}{20}$ (l) $\frac{1}{625}$

3. a and d **4.** (a) 5^{-3} (b) 6^{-4} (c) 3^{-7} (d) 9^{-5}

5. (a) 6^{-2} (b) 2^{-4} (c) 5^{-3} (d) 2^{-10}

6. (a) 3   (b) $2\frac{7}{9}$ (c) $\frac{9}{49}$

7. (a) 2   (b) $\frac{7}{2}$ (c) $\frac{9}{4}$ (d) 64   (e) $\frac{81}{4}$ (f) $\frac{10}{3}$

(g) 256   (h) $\frac{81}{25}$

8. a, d, f, h, i are true.

9. (a) x^2 (b) a^{-6} (c) x^{-8} (d) $9x^{-4}$ (e) $\frac{1}{2}b^8$ (f) $8a^{-15}$

10. (a) 8^{-1} (b) 8^1 (c) 8^0 (d) 8^2 (e) 8^{-2} (f) 8^{-3}

Page 41   E2.2

1. (a) 3   (b) 3   (c) $\frac{1}{6}$

2. (a) 2   (b) 2   (c) 5   (d) 2   (e) 3   (f) $\frac{1}{3}$

(g) $\frac{1}{2}$ (h) $\frac{1}{8}$ (i) $\frac{1}{13}$ (j) $\frac{1}{10}$ (k) $\frac{1}{3}$ (l) $\frac{1}{2}$

3. (a) $\frac{1}{2}$ (b) $-\frac{1}{3}$ (c) $-\frac{1}{2}$ (d) $\frac{1}{3}$

4. (a) 64^1 (b) $64^{\frac{1}{2}}$ (c) $64^{\frac{1}{3}}$ (d) $64^{\frac{1}{6}}$ (e) 64^0

(f) 64^{-1} (g) $64^{-\frac{1}{2}}$ (h) $64^{-\frac{1}{6}}$ (i) $64^{-\frac{1}{3}}$

5. (a) 3   (b) 4   (c) 9   (d) 10   (e) 2   (f) 11

(g) $\frac{1}{12}$ (h) $\frac{1}{7}$ (i) $\frac{1}{5}$ (j) $\frac{2}{3}$ (k) $\frac{1}{3}$ (l) $\frac{3}{4}$

(m) $\frac{4}{5}$ (n) $\frac{7}{6}$ (o) $\frac{6}{5}$ (p) $\frac{2}{5}$

6. (a) f^3 (b) r^2 (c) s^3 (d) q^{-5} (e) e^{-2}

(f) x^5 (g) $2x$ (h) $3y^2$ (i) $8z^6$ (j) $2w^5$

(k) $2q^2$ (l) $\frac{1}{2k^4}$ (m) $3a^2b$ (n) $4m^2n$ (o) $2hk^2$

Page 42   Can you still? 2D

1. $\frac{4}{9}$ **2.** $\frac{39}{99}$ **3.** $\frac{523}{990}$ **4.** $\frac{712}{999}$ **5.** $\frac{92}{990}$

Page 43   E2.3

1. (a) 16   (b) 32   (c) $\frac{1}{1000}$

2. (a) 125   (b) 4   (c) 27   (d) 8   (e) 10000   (f) $\frac{1}{32}$

(g) $\frac{1}{16}$ (h) $\frac{1}{25}$ (i) $\frac{1}{27}$ (j) $\frac{1}{16}$ (k) 343   (l) $\frac{1}{64}$

3. (a) 2   (b) $\frac{2}{3}$ (c) $-\frac{2}{3}$ **4.** (a) $\frac{16}{9}$ (b) $\frac{625}{16}$ (c) $\frac{729}{343}$

5. (a) $\frac{1000}{1331}$ (b) 8   (c) $\frac{64}{27}$ (d) $\frac{10000}{81}$

6. c, d, e are true

7. (a) $4p^6$ (b) $4a^2b^4$ (c) $\frac{1}{9j^{12}}$ (d) $\frac{f^{12}}{16}$ (e) $\frac{8a^3}{b^6}$ (f) $\frac{125b^{15}}{a^3}$

(g) $2z^{-5/2}$ (h) $r^{5/6}$ (i) $3x^{3/2}$

Page 45   E2.4

1. (a) −3   (b) 0   (c) 6   (d) 3   (e) −2

(f) −3   (g) −3   (h) −2   (i) −2

2. (a) $x = -5$ (b) $x = -6$

3. (a) $\frac{1}{5}$ (b) $\frac{1}{4}$ (c) $\frac{1}{3}$ (d) $\frac{1}{2}$ (e) $\frac{1}{2}$ (f) $\frac{1}{3}$

(g) $\frac{1}{5}$ (h) $\frac{1}{2}$ (i) −1   (j) $-\frac{1}{4}$ (k) $-\frac{1}{3}$ (l) $-\frac{1}{9}$

4. (a) $\frac{10}{3}$ (b) −1   (c) $-\frac{3}{2}$ (d) $\frac{11}{8}$ (e) 10   (f) $\frac{3}{2}$

5. (a) −5   (b) $-\frac{3}{2}$ (c) $-\frac{2}{3}$ (d) 1   (e) $\frac{3}{2}$ (f) $\frac{3}{2}$

6. (a) −2   (b) 3   (c) −3   (d) −2   (e) $-\frac{5}{2}$

(f) −10   (g) $-\frac{4}{3}$ (h) −2   (i) $-\frac{2}{3}$

Page 46   E2.5

1. (a) $\frac{1}{16}$ (b) 7   (c) $\frac{1}{9}$ (d) 125

(e) 5   (f) 1   (g) $\frac{7}{9}$ (h) $\frac{2}{5}$

2. (a) 2^{17} (b) 2^5 (c) $2^{1/2}$

3. (a) $8a^6$ (b) $25a^2b^4$ (c) $8a^2$ (d) $5ab^3$ (e) $32a^{15}$ (f) $81m^8n^{16}$

4. 10^6 **5.** $h = 3^{3/2}$

6. (a) $2a^8b^2$ (b) $12m^4n^4$ (c) $2a^3b^6$

7. (a) $\frac{5}{2}$ (b) $\frac{3}{2}$ (c) $-\frac{1}{3}$ (d) $\frac{1}{2}$ (e) 8   (f) 7

8. $£2^{13}$ **9.** $3m^{-1} = \frac{3}{m}$

10. (a) $\frac{5}{4}$ (b) 2   (c) $\frac{2}{25}$ (d) $\frac{3}{8}$

11. (a) $\frac{2}{3}$ (b) $\frac{125}{27}$ (c) $\frac{49}{9}$ (d) $\frac{9}{16}$

12. (a) 5   (b) 2

Page 48   WYM2

1. £684   **2.** £642   **3.** £1652   **4.** £834   **5.** £2810

6. £840   **7.** £5580   **8.** £2284   **9.** £2587   **10.** £6360

Page 49   Test yourself on unit 2

1. (a) £600   (b) £19474   (c) £8050000   (d) £369   (e) £1468.75

2. (a) 12%   (b) 15%   (c) 15%   (d) 7.87%

3. (a) £4494.40   (b) 1329   (c) 568.62

4. (a) £200   (b) £25800   (c) £11562.50   (d) £524

5. (a) Chloe 35, Lewis 10   (b) $x = 81°$, $y = 63°$, $z = 36°$

(c) £31.95   (d) 3:20   (e) 600 cm²

6. (a) 7^5 (b) 6^6 (c) 5^{16} (d) 3^3 (e) 8^7 (f) 6^2

(g) a^3 (h) n^2 (i) x^2 (j) $6n^6$ (k) $3a^2$ (l) $64a^6$

7. (a) $\frac{1}{36}$ (b) $\frac{1}{5}$ (c) $\frac{1}{8}$ (d) $\frac{25}{4}$ (e) $\frac{3}{7}$ (f) 16

(g) 0.09   (h) $\frac{27}{64}$ (i) a^{-5} (j) $\frac{1}{4a^2}$ (k) m^{-5}

8. (a) 8   (b) 5   (c) 25   (d) 4   (e) $\frac{10}{3}$ (f) $\frac{36}{25}$

(g) a^3 (h) $5m^2$ (i) $9a^6b^2$

9. (a) 4   (b) −5   (c) −2   (d) $\frac{1}{3}$ (e) $-\frac{1}{4}$ (f) 1

(g) $\frac{3}{4}$ (h) $-\frac{7}{2}$

Page 52   Mixed examination questions

1. £72340, £14468   **2.** Oleg's by £16.98   **3.** £40   **4.** 72.7%

5. (a) 150 g   (b) 100 g   **6.** (a) x^8 (b) y^4 (c) $4w^2$

7. (a) (i) a^3 (ii) p^4 (iii) $9n^6$ (b) (i) $6a^5b^3$ (ii) $\frac{1}{3a^2}$

8. (a) $\frac{9}{49}$ (b) 125 a^3b^{12} **9.** (i) f^5 (ii) k^6

10. (a) 12 a^5b^3 (b) $\frac{125p^9}{q^3}$ (c) $\frac{4t^3}{u}$ **11.** $\frac{2}{7}$ **12.** £76.50

13. £275   **14.** (a) (i) 15 (ii) 1   (b) −3

15. (a) $n = 7$ (b) $p = 0$ (c) $q = \frac{5}{2}$ **16.** (a) £5062.50 (b) 0.4096

UNIT 3

Page 55   M3.1

1. 50°   **2.** 61°   **3.** 30°   **4.** $d = 80°$, $e = 100°$

5. $f = 60°$, $g = 60°$ **6.** $h = 125°$ **7.** $i = 45°$ **8.** $j = 60°$

9. $k = 78°$ **10.** $l = 90°$ **11.** $m = 60°$ **12.** $n = 40°$

13. $p = 50°$ **14.** $q = 10°$ **15.** $r = 70°$ **16.** $s = 62°, t = 118°$

17. $u = 80°, v = 80°$ **18.** $w = 35°, x = 145°$ **19.** $y = 120°$

20. $z = 57°, a = 57°$ **21.** $b = 45°, c = 135°$

22. $d = 36°, 4d = 144°$ **23.** $e = 151°$ **24.** $f = 42°, g = 96°, h = 96°$

Page 57   M3.2

1. $a = 56°$ **2.** $b = 60°, c = 120°$ **3.** $d = 40°, e = 140°$

4. $f = 156°, g = 24°$ **5.** $h = 42°, i = 138°$

6. $j = 107°, k = 73°, l = 73°$ **7.** $m = 37°, n = 37°, p = 143°$

8. $q = 71°, r = 71°, s = 80°, t = 100°$

9. $u = 48°, v = 48°, w = 27°, x = 27°$

10. $y = 90°, z = 117°, a = 117°$ **11.** $b = 30°, c = 80°, d = 70°$

12. $e = 40°, f = 65°, g = 75°$ **13.** $h = 85°, i = 60°, j = 35°$

14. $k = 35°, l = 35°$ **15.** $m = 100°, n = 100°, p = 38°, q = 142°$

Page 58   Can you still? 3A

1. (a) 82.4 p   (b) 78 p   **2.** £97.50   **3.** £376   **4.** 5%

5. 25%   **6.** £14,403.90   **7.** (a) £1348.32   (b) £2149.02

8. 25%   **9.** £3200   **10.** £1270

Page 59   M3.3

1. Sum of angles = 1080°

2. (a) 1260°   (b) 900°   (c) 1440°   (d) 1800°

3. $x = 80°$ **4.** 110°   **5.** 85°   **6.** 80°   **7.** 79°   **8.** 62°

9. 146°   **10.** 144°   **11.** $h = 54°, 2h = 108°, 3h = 162°$

12. $i = 120°$ **13.** 3780°   **14.** 168°

Page 61   M3.4

1. a 108°, b 120°, c 144°

2. $a = 66°, b = 141°, c = 122°, d = 67°, e = 51°, f = 128°,$
$g = 113°, h = 122°, i = 85°, j = 92°, k = 88°$

3. (a) 30°   (b) 150°   **4.** (a) 40°   (b) 140°

5. (a) 24°   (b) 18°   (c) 6°   (d) 4°

6. (a) 156°   (b) 162°   (c) 174°   (d) 176°

7. 45   **8.** 18   **9.** 30   **10.** 172°   **11.** 15   **12.** 105°

13. $a = 18°, b = 81°, c = 18°, d = 162°$

14. 36   **15.** $x = 36°, y = 144°$

Page 63   Can you still? 3B

1. Pupils' drawings   **2.** Square   **3.** Square, rectangle

4. Square, Kite, rhombus   **5.** Kite, parallelogram, rhombus

6. Pupils' drawings   **7.** Kite

Page 64   M3.5

1. to **5.** proofs   **6.** $a = 42°, b$ 96°   **7.** $c = 110°, d = 70°, e = 55°$

8. $f = 72°, g = 108°$ **9.** $h = 40°$ **10.** $i = 28°, j = 76°, k = 28°$

11. $l = 108°$ **12.** $m = 83°$ **13.** $n = 150°, p = 30°$ **14.** $q = 30°$

Page 67   E3.1

1. a 90°, b 49°   **2.** c 22°   **3.** d 36°   **4.** e 48°   **5.** f 43°

6. g 48°   **7.** h 106°   **8.** i 134°   **9.** j 38°

10. k 27°, l 69°   **11.** m 52°, n 34°, p 65°   **12.** q 45°

13. r 124°, s 62°   **14.** t 117°   **15.** u 36°, v 54°   **16.** w 53°

17. (a) 42°   (b) 84°   (c) 48°   **18.** 77°

19. (a) 32°   (b) 58°   (c) 61°   (d) 29°

20. (a) 28°   (b) 28°   (c) 28°   (d) 152°

21. $a = 11°$ **22.** $b = 30°$ **23.** $c = 78°$

24. $d = 2°$ **25.** $e = 56°$ **26.** $f = 22°$

Page 70   E3.2

1. $a = 73°$ **2.** $b = 111°, c = 67°$ **3.** $d = 117°$

4. $e = 95°, f = 122°$ **5.** $g = 93°, h = 79°$ **6.** $i = 117°$

7. $j = 35°, k = 110°, l = 55°, m = 125°$

8. $n = 68°$ **9.** $p = 46°, q = 92°$ **10.** $r = 108°, s = 36°$

11. $t = 27°, u = 66°$ **12.** $v = 94°, w = 94°$

13. (a) 38°   (b) 72°   (c) 36°   **14.** (a) 68°   (b) 136°

15. a 36°   **16.** 34°   **17.** $c = 30°$ **18.** d 53°   **19.** e 23°   **20.** f 23°

Page 72   E3.3

1. $a = 20°$ **2.** $b = 72°$ $c = 36°$ **3.** $d = 40°$ **4.** $e = 130°, f = 65°$

5. $g = 140°$ **6.** $h = 52°$ **7.** $i = 150°, j = 75°$ **8.** $k = 126°, l = 54°$

9. (a) 42°   (b) 42°   (c) 96°   **10.** BÂC = 54°, CÂO = 26°

11. (a) 104°   (b) 52°   (c) 128°   (d) 26°   (e) 52°   (f) 26°

12. 15 cm   **13.** 11.3 cm   **14.** 60.9°   **15.** 40.4°   **16.** $a = 10°$

17. $b = 18°$ **18.** $c = 18°$ **19.** $d = 30°, e = 75°$

Page 74   Can you still? 3C

1. (b) and (f) are true   **2.** (a), (b) and (e)

3. (a) $\dfrac{1}{16}$ (b) $\dfrac{3}{2}$ (c) $\dfrac{9}{16}$ (d) $\dfrac{8}{125}$

4. (a) $\dfrac{7}{3}$ (b) -3 (c) $\dfrac{3}{5}$

5. (a) $64m^9$ (b) a^{-10} (c) $2m^2n^3$

Page 76   E3.4

1. $a = 38°$ **2.** $b = 72°$ **3.** $c = 25°, d = 94°$ **4.** $e = 38°, f = 76°$

5. $g = 62°, h = 124°, i = 28°$ **6.** $j = 47°, k = 73°, l = 60°$

7. $m = 86°, n = 86°$ **8.** $p = 49°, q = 49°, r = 49°$

9. $s = 82°, t = 16°, u = 16°$ **10.** $v = 48°, w = 42°, x = 48°$

11. $y = 50°$ **12.** $z = 56°$ **13.** (a) 67°   (b) 62°   (c) 51°

14. (a) 37°   (b) 128°   (c) 101°

15. (a) 63°   (b) 63°   (c) 75°   (d) 42°

16. (a) 56°   (b) 85°   (c) 39°

17. a 44°, b 44°, c 21°   **18.** d 44°, e 68°, f 46°

19. g 38°, h 52°, i 90°, j 36°

20. $k = 55°, l = 55°, m = 120°, n = 120°$ **21.** $p = 37°, q = 19°$

Page 78   E3.5

8. (a) $(90 - x)°$ (b) $x°$ (c) $y°$ (d) $(x + y)°$

Page 81   WYM3

1. 290 ε   **2.** 6944 Pesos   **3.** \$358.50   **4.** 10782 Rand   **5.** £165

6. £600   **7.** £68   **8.** 3105.36   **9.** £700   **10.** £1500

11. Japan   **12.** Australia   **13.** Shabina   **14.** £76.80   **15.** £38.80

Page 82   Test yourself on unit 3

1. (a) $a = b = 44°$ (b) $c = 57°$, $d = 66°$ (c) $e = 20°$

(d) $f = 104°$, $g = 52°$ (e) $h = 30°$ (f) $i = 128°$, $j = 134°$

2. (a) $a = 56°$, $b = 56°$, $c = 96°$, $d = 96°$

(b) $e = 65°$, $f = 65°$, $g = 51°$, $h = 64°$

(c) $i = 56°$, $j = 63°$, $k = 61°$

3. (a) $1080°$ (b) $135°$ (c) $72°$ (d) $24°$ (e) $81°$

4. (a) $a = 58°$, $b = 116°$ (b) $c = 66°$, $d = 33°$

(c) $e = 52°$, $f = 104°$ (d) $g = 16°$, $h = 137°$

(e) $i = 32°$ (f) $j = 98°$, $k = 49°$, $l = 29°$

Page 85   Mixed examination questions

1. $x = 50°$ $y = 110°$ **2.** $140°$ **3.** (a) $x = 85°$ (b) (i) $y = 74°$

4. 9   **5.** (a) (i) $90°$ (ii) $25°$ (b) $137°$

6. (a) $129°$ (b) $32°$ **7.** (a) (i) $50°$ (ii) $65°$ (iii) $25°$ (iv) $65°$ (v) $25°$

8. (a) $90°$ (b) $49°$ (c) $98°$ **9.** (a) (i) $112°$ (ii) $136°$ (c) $36°$

UNIT 4

Page 89   M4.1

1. 18   **2.** 35   **3.** 31   **4.** 9   **5.** 9   **6.** 0   **7.** 0

8. 73   **9.** 42   **10.** 24   **11.** 36   **12.** 8   **13.** 1   **14.** 292

15. 36   **16.** 12   **17.** −6   **18.** 36   **19.** 72   **20.** 80   **21.** 64

22. 36   **23.** 52   **24.** −14   **25.** 8   **26.** 48   **27.** −3   **28.** −2

29. 32   **30.** 56   **31.** 1   **32.** 10   **33.** 3   **34.** 107   **35.** −1

36. 63   **37.** 38   **38.** 216   **39.** 6   **40.** −28   **41.** −1   **42.** −2

43. 7   **44.** −140   **45.** 270

Page 90   M4.2

1. (a) 60   (b) 45   (c) 120   **2.** (a) 4   (b) 50

3. (a) 80   (b) 16   **4.** (a) 490   (b) 19.6   **5.** (a) 10   (b) 20

6. (a) 5   (b) 7   **7.** (a) 500   (b) 4000   **8.** (a) 72   (b) 528

9. (a) 11.9   (b) 17.7   **10.** (a) 4   (b) 5.20   **11.** (a) 6   (b) 73.0

12. (a) 1 ohms   (b) $\frac{12}{7}$ ohms (or 1.71)

Page 92   M4.3

1. (a) $8y$ (b) $48x$ (c) $8ab$ (d) $5c^2$ (e) $14a^2$ (f) $6x$

(g) $7n$ (h) $8p$ (i) $54c^2$ (j) $12abc$ (k) $-36y$ (l) $-20cd$

(m) $18cd$ (n) $-3y$ (o) $-7q$ (p) $35p^2$

2. T   **3.** F   **4.** T   **5.** F   **6.** F   **7.** T

8. T   **9.** F   **10.** F   **11.** $2a + 6$ **12.** $24x - 12$

13. $21x - 35$ **14.** $5a - 5b$ **15.** $21x + 7y$ **16.** $18x + 12$

17. $4p + 8q$ **18.** $36c + 72d$ **19.** $2x^2 + xy$ **20.** $ab + a^2$

21. $2c^2 + cd$ **22.** $a^2 - 7a$ **23.** $3a^2 - 4a$ **24.** $5xy + 10$

25. $4a^2 + 8ab$ **26.** $24ab - 48ac$ **27.** $-2x - 12$ **28.** $-3a + 6$

29. $-5c - 50$ **30.** $-12p + 20$ **31.** $-6c - 12$ **32.** $-ab - ac$

33. $-2p^2 - pq$ **34.** $-a^2 - ab$ **35.** $-2x^2 + xy$ **36.** $-m^2 + m$

37. $-2p - 5q$ **38.** $-24a + 12ab$ **39.** $a^3 - 2ab$ **40.** $4x^3 + x^2y$

41. $10b^3 + 15b^2$ **42.** $3p^2q + 6p^3$

Page 93   M4.4

1. $2x + 11$ **2.** $10x + 8$ **3.** $14x + 8$ **4.** $18x + 13$

5. $4a + 12$ **6.** $27y + 12$ **7.** $9a + 12$ **8.** $9x + 24$

9. $12x + 18$ **10.** $14a + 18$ **11.** $26x + 25$ **12.** $26d + 32$

13. $10a + 10$ **14.** $6x - 1$ **15.** $4x + 10$ **16.** $9a + 7$

17. 13   **18.** $10c + 22$ **19.** $4y - 13$ **20.** $5x + 17$

21. $14a - 5$ **22.** $3n + 21m$ **23.** $7a + 2b$ **24.** $8x + 22$

25. $13a^2 + 7a$ **26.** $9x^2 + 17x$ **27.** $3y^2$ **28.** $3a^2 + 4b^2 + 16ab$

29. $18m^2 + 5mp$ **30.** $9x^2 + 30xy$ **31.** $5a^2 + 22ab - 4bc$

32. $14x^2 + 12xy + 7xz + 6yz$

Page 93   Can you still? 4A

1. 225 g   **2.** $a = 75°$, $b = 90°$, $c = 15°$ **3.** 1:8:5

4. Yasmin £260, Janet £455, Wayne £390   **5.** (a) 6 cm   (b) 42 m

Page 95   M4.5

1. (a) $x^2 + 7x + 12$ (b) $a^2 - 2a - 15$ (c) $m^2 - 14 + 49$

2. $x^2 + 8x + 12$ **3.** $p^2 + 6p + 5$ **4.** $a^2 + 10a + 21$

5. $m^2 + 2m - 3$ **6.** $y^2 - 4y - 12$ **7.** $n^2 - 3n - 10$

8. $b^2 - 5b - 24$ **9.** $x^2 + 2x - 48$ **10.** $c^2 - 11c + 24$

11. $q^2 - 9q + 14$ **12.** $f^2 - 12f + 20$ **13.** $a^2 + 5a - 36$

14. $6x^2 + 11x + 4$ **15.** $5y^2 + 17y + 6$ **16.** $8p^2 + 32p + 14$

17. $15a^2 - 14a - 8$ **18.** $12f^2 + 16f - 3$ **19.** $36y^2 - 34y + 8$

20. $21x^2 - 22x - 8$ **21.** $21q^2 - 31q + 4$ **22.** $20b^2 - 27b + 9$

23. $8z^2 - 24z + 18$ **24.** $4x^2 + 19x - 63$ **25.** $30a^2 - a - 20$

26. $x^2 + 12x + 36$ **27.** $x^2 + 10x + 25$ **28.** $a^2 + 20a + 100$

29. $y^2 - 2y + 1$ **30.** $p^2 - 6p + 9$ **31.** $b^2 - 18b + 81$

32. $4a^2 - 4a + 1$ **33.** $25x^2 + 40x + 16$ **34.** $9y^2 - 30y + 25$

35. $2a^2 + 11a + 12$ **36.** $-10y^2 + 11y + 6$ **37.** $3x^2 - 2x - 8$

38. $6p^2 - 26p + 28$ **39.** $2x^2 + 2xy - 12y^2$ **40.** $6a^2 - 19ab + 15b^2$

41. $2x^2 + 8x + 10$ **42.** $12 - 12a$ **43.** $8 - 4y$

44. $3p^2 + 22p + 45$ **45.** $a^2 + 4a + 3$ **46.** $x^2 + 12x + 35$

47. $x^3 + 9x^2 + 26x + 24$ **48.** $x^3 + 8x^2 + 17x + 10$

Page 97   M4.6

1. $3(2a + 5)$ **2.** $7(n - 5)$ **3.** $8(6b - 5)$

4. $a(b - c)$ **5.** $x(x + 6)$ **6.** $3b(b - 4)$

7. $3x(y + 5z)$ **8.** $4x(3x - 2)$ **9.** $m(6m - 1)$

10. $a^2(a + 5b)$ **11.** $6(m + 7)$ **12.** $5(5a - 7)$

13. $4(6m - 5n)$ **14.** $4(4x - 1)$ **15.** $8(7a + 4b)$

16. $9(3p + 2)$ **17.** $5(2a + 3b + 5c)$ **18.** $4(7x - 9y + 4)$

19. $f(e + g)$ **20.** $x(x - 8)$ **21.** $a(a + 5)$

22. $2p(q + 2r)$ **23.** $4b(2a - 3c)$ **24.** $3y(2x - 3z)$

25. $5x(x - 3)$ **26.** $5s(t + 7)$ **27.** $8p(r - 5q)$

28. $2b(3a + 2)$ **29.** $a(3a + 8)$ **30.** $4x(3 - 4x)$

31. $3x(x + 7y)$ **32.** $a^2(b - c)$ **33.** $a(a + bc)$

34. $x(5x - 6y)$ **35.** $10p(2p - 3q)$ **36.** $4b(9ac - 4b)$

37. $7x(7x + 6y)$ **38.** $7a(9a - 5b)$ **39.** $3xy(3x + 2y)$

40. $5pq(2r + 3q)$ **41.** $8ab(2b + c)$ **42.** $5fg(5h - 4e)$

43. $2ab(4b - 3)$ **44.** $4x^2(3x + 2)$ **45.** $3p^2(2q + 5p)$

46. $6ab(3ab - 2c)$ **47.** $3ab(3c + 5a - 2b)$ **48.** $3xy(4xy - 3yz - 6xz)$

49. $7pq^2r(6p^2r + 4qr - 7p)$ **50.** $8a^2bc^2(4b^2c - 3abc + 5)$

Page 98   M4.7

1. $(x + 3)(x + 7)$ **2.** $(x - 3)(x - 4)$ **3.** $(x + 5)(x - 2)$

4. $(a + 5)(a + 6)$ **5.** $(y + 3)(y + 5)$ **6.** $(b + 2)(b + 10)$

7. $(p + 3)(p + 2)$ **8.** $(x + 2)(x + 2)$ **9.** $(f + 5)(f + 5)$

10. $(c + 4)((c + 1)$ **11.** $(y + 2)(y + 1)$ **12.** $(x + 5)(x + 7)$

13. $(m - 1)(m - 5)$ **14.** $(x - 2)(x - 15)$ **15.** $(n - 1)(n - 8)$

16. $(a - 4)(a - 4)$ **17.** $(q - 1)(q - 13)$ **18.** $(w + 8)(w - 3)$

19. $(x + 4)(x - 7)$ **20.** $(m + 5)(m - 7)$ **21.** $(y + 2)(y - 6)$

22. $(n + 7)(n - 2)$ **23.** $(p + 3)(p - 2)$ **24.** $(x + 4)(x - 5)$

25. $(y - 2)(y - 5)$ **26.** $(a + 8)(a - 5)$ **27.** $(q + 6)(q - 7)$

28. $(x + 6)(x - 4)$ **29.** $(n - 2)(n - 3)$ **30.** $(y + 6)(y - 10)$

31. $x + 8$ **32.** $a + 7$ **33.** $(x - 9)(x - 11)$

34. $(y - 5)(y - 5)$ **35.** $(m + 6)(m + 7)$ **36.** $(p - 2)(p - 12)$

37. $(n - 7)(n - 10)$ **38.** $(z + 2)(z - 20)$ **39.** $(h + 2)(h + 13)$

40. $(m + 10)(m - 13)$ **41.** $(q + 12)(q - 5)$

Page 99   Can you still? 4B

1. $4\sqrt{5}$ **2.** $5\sqrt{5}$ **3.** $\sqrt{5}$ **4.** 4 **5.** 7 **6.** $\sqrt{15}$

7. 3 **8.** $6\sqrt{15}$ **9.** $2\sqrt{3}$ **10.** $\sqrt{3} - 1$ **11.** 5

12. $15 + 5\sqrt{3} + 3\sqrt{2} + \sqrt{6}$ **13.** $\sqrt{21} - \sqrt{14}$ **14.** $14 - 6\sqrt{5}$

15. 2 cm² **16.** $\dfrac{\sqrt{2}}{2}$ **17.** $\dfrac{3\sqrt{5}}{5}$ **18.** $\dfrac{4\sqrt{3}}{9}$ **19.** $\dfrac{(\sqrt{2} - \sqrt{10})}{2}$

Page 100   E4.1

1. $(a + 2)(a - 2)$ **2.** $(2x + y)(2x - y)$ **3.** $(3p + 2q)(3p - 2q)$

4. $(m + n)(m - n)$ **5.** $(p + q)(p - q)$ **6.** $(a + 2)(a - 2)$

7. $(n + 7)(n - 7)$ **8.** $(n + 7)(n - 7)$ **9.** $(x + 2)(x - 2)$

10. $(y + 9)(y - 9)$ **11.** $(m + 1)(m - 1)$ **12.** $(8 + a)(8 - a)$

13. $(10 + y)(10 - y)$ **14.** $(x + \frac{1}{4})(x - \frac{1}{4})$ **15.** $(2b + c)(2b - c)$

16. $(p + 4q)(p - 4q)$ **17.** $(5m + 2)(5m - 2)$ **18.** $(3x + 1)(3x - 1)$

19. $(6y + 5)(6y - 5)$ **20.** $(9b + 2c)(9b - 2c)$ **21.** $(7a + 4b)(7a - 4b)$

22. $(10x + 7y)(10x - 7y)$ **23.** $(5m + \frac{n}{2})(5m - \frac{n}{2})$

24. 12000 **25.** 1600000 **26.** 380

27. $a(4 + a)(4 - a)$ **28.** $3(n + 5)(n - 2)$ **29.** $4(p + 1)(p - 1)$

30. $m(m + 5)(m - 5)$ **31.** $6(p + 2)(p - 2)$ **32.** $n(n + 1)(n - 1)$

33. $5(s + 1)(s + 1)$ **34.** $3(t + 1)(t + 2)$ **35.** $3(3 + 2x)(3 - 2x)$

36. $10(y + 2)(y - 4)$ **37.** $2(x + 7)(x - 4)$ **38.** $7(a - 6)(a - 1)$

Page 101   E4.2

1. $b(a + c) - d(a + c) = (a + c)(b - d)$

2. $z(x + y) - y(x + y) = (x + y)(z - y)$ **3.** $(f + g)(e + h)$

4. $(m + n)(q - p)$ **5.** $(a - d)(b + c)$ **6.** $(m + y)(n + x)$

7. $(a - b)(d - c)$ **8.** $(q - s)(r - p)$ **9.** $(e - g)(h + f)$

10. $(a + 2)(c - 3)$ **11.** $(3 - d)(1 - e)$ **12.** $(2a + b)(3c + 2d)$

13. $(3z + 2x)(4y - 3w)$ **14.** $(4m - 5n)(2p - 3q)$

Page 102   E4.3

1. $(3x + 2)(x + 3)$ **2.** $(5q + 2)(q - 2)$ **3.** $(2x + 3)(x + 2)$

4. $(3x + 2)(x + 4)$ **5.** $(3a + 4)(2a + 1)$ **6.** $(2y + 9)(2y + 1)$

7. $(4z + 1)(z + 3)$ **8.** $(3q - 4)(2q - 1)$ **9.** $(4p - 9)(p - 1)$

10. $(8h - 3)(h + 1)$ **11.** $(5t - 1)(2t + 3)$ **12.** $(4r + 1)(3r - 4)$

13. $(5e + 7)(5e - 7)$ **14.** $(4s + 5)(4s - 5)$ **15.** $(3x - 2)(x - 4)$

16. $(2a + 7)(a - 3)$ **17.** $(4p + 1)(p - 4)$ **18.** $(3u - 4)(5u + 1)$

19. $(3x + 2)(2x + 5)$ **20.** $(2b + 1)(2b + 5)$ **21.** $(2p + 1)(2p + 9)$

22. $(8w + 5)(w - 3)$ **23.** $(14x + 3)(3x - 1)$

Page 103   Can you still? 4C

1. $a = 27°$, $b = 27°$ **2.** $c = 74°$ **3.** $d = 115°$

4. $e = 40°$, $f = 105°$ **5.** $g = 65°$ **6.** $h = 72°$

7. $i = 108°$ **8.** $j = 45°$ **9.** $k = 113°$

Page 104   E4.4

1. $x = -5$ or -4 **2.** $m = 6$ or -1 **3.** $r = 0$ or 6 **4.** -3 or -4

5. -3 or -2 **6.** -4 **7.** -6 or -3 **8.** 2 or 4

9. 3 or 7 **10.** 6 or 4 **11.** 5 or 2 **12.** 3 or -2

13. 10 or -2 **14.** 5 or -3 **15.** 3 or -10 **16.** 5 or -4

17. 1 or -9 **18.** 3 or 8 **19.** 8 or -7 **20.** 0 or -2

21. 0 or 3 **22.** 2 or -10 **23.** -1 **24.** 0 or -1

25. 1 or 2 **26.** 5 or 6 **27.** 1 or -7 **28.** $\dfrac{5}{2}$ or -2

29. 0 or 2 **30.** -3 or -12 **31.** 6 or -2 **32.** 5 or -1

33. 7 or -2 **34.** $\dfrac{1}{7}$ or $-\dfrac{3}{4}$ **35.** $\dfrac{4}{3}$ or $-\dfrac{1}{2}$ **36.** -4 or $-\dfrac{1}{3}$

37. $\dfrac{5}{3}$ or $\dfrac{1}{2}$ **38.** 3 or $-\dfrac{1}{2}$ **39.** $\dfrac{2}{3}$ or $-\dfrac{5}{2}$ **40.** $-\dfrac{1}{4}$ or $-\dfrac{4}{5}$

41. $\dfrac{7}{2}$ or $-\dfrac{3}{2}$ **42.** $\dfrac{2}{9}$ or -1 **43.** 6 or -6 **44.** $+\dfrac{1}{3}$ or $-\dfrac{1}{3}$

45. $\dfrac{4}{5}$ or $-\dfrac{4}{5}$ **46.** $\dfrac{4}{3}$ or $\dfrac{5}{3}$ **47.** $\dfrac{2}{7}$ or $-\dfrac{2}{7}$ **48.** $\dfrac{5}{2}$ or $-\dfrac{1}{2}$

49. $\dfrac{1}{2}$ or $\dfrac{9}{2}$ **50.** $\dfrac{3}{2}$ or $-\dfrac{1}{2}$ **51.** 0 or $\dfrac{4}{5}$ **52.** $\dfrac{2}{3}$ or $-\dfrac{2}{3}$

53. -2 or $-\dfrac{3}{8}$ **54.** 0 or 2 **55.** -1 or $-\dfrac{1}{6}$ **56.** -3 or $-\dfrac{1}{2}$

Page 106   Can you still? 4D

1. 82°   **2.** 73°   **3.** 79°   **4.** 64°   **5.** 59°   **6.** 98°

7. 71°   **8.** I$\hat{F}$H = 70°, F$\hat{G}$H = 127°   **9.** A$\hat{O}$C = 126°, A$\hat{B}$C = 54°

Page 107   E4.5

1. (a) $x + 4$ (b) $\frac{1}{2}x(x + 4) = 30 \Rightarrow x^2 + 4x - 60 = 0$ (c) $x = 6$

2. (a) $x + 5$ (b) $x(x + 5)$ (c) $x^2 + 5x - 36 = 0$ (d) $x = 4$

3. (a) $x^2 - 1 = 3x + 9$ (c) $x = 5$

4. (a) $x + 5$ (b) $\frac{x}{2}(x + 5) = 5$ (c) $x = 8$

5. (a) $x + 7$ (b) $x^2 + (x + 7)^2 = 13^2$ (c) $x = 5$

6. (a) $x^2 + 8x - 33 = 0$ (b) $x = 3$

7. (a) $(2x + 4)$ by $(2x + 8)$ (b) $(2x + 4)(2x + 8) - 32$ (c) $x = 2$

8. (a) $x(2x + 3) = 44$ (b) $x = 4$

9. (a) $x(x - 1) = 10(x - 3)$ (b) $x = 5$ or 6

10. (a) $(12 - 2x)$ by $(8 - 2x)$ (b) $4x^2 - 40x + 96$

    (c) $4x^2 - 40x + 64 = 0$ (e) $x = 2$ $(x \neq 8)$

11. (a) $14 - w$ (b) $w(14 - w) = 40$ (c) $w = 4$ $(w \neq 10)$

12. (a) $n + 2$ (b) $n^2 + (n + 2)^2 = 244$ (d) $n = 10$ **13.** 5 and 6

14. (a) 210   (b) $n^2 + n - 110 = 0$ (c) $n = 10$ **15.** $x = 11$

Page 110   WYM4

1. (a) £963.50   (b) £528.75   (c) £740.25

2. 'Electrics'   **3.** £213.85   **4.** £3231.25

5. Total £92, V.A.T. £16.10. Total bill £108.10   **6.** No

7. Yes   **8.** Total Bill £502.90   **9.** £370   **10.** £11400

Page 111   Test yourself on unit 4

1. (a) 14   (b) 13   (c) 12   (d) 4   (e) 60

    (f) 63   (g) 67   (h) 3.5   (i) 11

2. (a) $5x + 15$ (b) $6a - 12$ (c) $y^2 - 5y$ (d) $8b^2 + 4b$

    (e) $8a + 21$ (f) $5x + 27$ (g) $2y - 13$ (h) $2p^2 + 14p$

3. (a) $x^2 + 10x + 21$ (b) $y^2 - 4y - 12$ (c) $a^2 - 8a + 15$

    (d) $p^2 - 4p + 4$ (e) $15b^2 - b - 6$ (f) $9x^2 + 12x + 4$

4. (a) $5(x + 3)$ (b) $c(d - e)$ (c) $7(5p - 3)$ (d) $x(x - 4y)$

    (e) $2q(3p - 5r)$ (f) $5a(a + 6b)$ (g) $4yz(2y + 5)$ (h) $6ab(3b - 2a)$

5. (a) $(x + 2)(x + 1)$ (b) $(m - 6)(m - 1)$ (c) $(b + 3)(b - 2)$

    (d) $(u + 4)(u - 2)$ (e) $(h + 13)(h + 2)$ (f) $(y - 16)(y + 3)$

6. (a) $(y + z)(y - z)$ (b) $(m + 4)(m - 4)$ (c) $(3x + 5)(3x - 5)$

    (d) $(6n + 7p)(6n - 7p)$ (e) $(10 + 9a)(10 - 9a)$ (f) $x(x + 6)(x - 6)$

7. (a) $(k + l)(m + n)$ (b) $(q - y)(x - p)$ (c) $(4 + 3b)(2a - 1)$

8. (a) $(3x - 2)(x - 2)$ (b) $(2y - 5)(2y + 1)$

    (c) $(n - 2)(4n - 3)$ (d) $(3p + 1)(2p - 5)$

9. (a) $x = -7$ or -2 (b) $n = 3$ or 2 (c) $y = 12$ or -2

    (d) $m = 0$ or 8 (e) $a = \frac{1}{2}$ or $-\frac{3}{2}$ (f) $p = -\frac{3}{5}$ or $\frac{2}{3}$

10. (a) (i) $x + 3$ (ii) $x(x + 3) = 40 \rightarrow x^2 + 3x - 40 = 0$

    (iii) $x = 5$ (iv) 5 cm

    (b) (i) $x^2 + (x + 17)^2 = (x + 18)^2$ (ii) $x = 7$ (iii) 7, 24, 25

    (c) (i) $x(x + 3) = 6x$ (ii) $x = 0$ or 3 (iii) $x = 3$

Page 113   Mixed examination questions

1. (a) $8a^2 + 12a$ (b) $6x^2 - x - 2$ (c) $6x^2 + xy - 2y^2$

2. (a) $x^2y - x^2$ (b) $6n + 11$

3. $2x^2 + 8xy - 5y^2$ **4.** (i) $5(2x + 1)$ (ii) $x(x + 7)$

5. $2a(3a + 5b)$ **6.** (a) $3x^2 + y^2$ (b) $(a + b)(a - b)$

7. (i) $(x - 4)(x - 2)$ (ii) $x = 4$ or 2 **9.** $x = -2$ or -6

10. (a) $3(d + 2e)$ (b) $4x(x + 2y)$ (c) $(x - 6)(x - 5)$ (d) $(5x + 1)(5x - 1$

11. (a) $10x + 3$ (b) $6x^2 + 5xy - 4y^2$

12. (a) $2x^2 - x - 21$ (b) (i) $(x + 5)(x - 1)$ (ii) $x = 1$ or -5

13. $(3a + 2b)(2a + b)$ **14.** (b) (i) $x = \frac{3}{2}\left(\text{or} - \frac{13}{3}\right)$ (ii) 8 cm

15. $x = -2$ or $-\frac{1}{2}$

16. (i) $3x^2 + 14x - 5$ (ii) $x^4 + y^2 + 2x^2y$ (iii) $4xy$

17. (i) $p^3r^3(r + p^2)$ (ii) $(5p + 2q)(5p - 2q)$

UNIT 5

Page 117   M5.1

1. (a) 1, 2, 4, 7, 14, 28   (b) 1, 2, 5, 10, 25, 50

    (c) 1, 2, 3, 4, 6, 8, 12, 16, 24, 48

2. No   **3.** 21, 28   **4.** 77

5. (a) 12, 24, 36, 48, 60   (b) 15, 30, 45, 60, 75   (c) 60

6. (a) 60   (b) 70   (c) 60

7. (a) 1, 2, 4, 8, 16, 32   (b) 1, 2, 4, 5, 8, 10, 20, 40   (c) 8

8. (a) 16   (b) 12   (c) 5   **9.** No   **10.** 15, 30

Page 118   M5.2

1. (a) 20   (b) 30   (c) 45   (d) 42   (e) 165   (f) 100

2. (a) $2 \times 2 \times 2 \times 3 \times 3$ (b) $2 \times 2 \times 3 \times 7$

3. (a) 2×3^2 (b) $2^2 \times 7$ (c) 2×11 (d) 2^5 (e) 3^4

    (f) $2^5 \times 3$ (g) $2^3 \times 5^2$ (h) $2^3 \times 3 \times 5$ (i) $2^2 \times 7^2$ (j) $5 \times 7 \times 11$

    (k) $2^2 \times 3 \times 5 \times 7$ (l)$2^3 \times 7^2$ **4.** see above   **5.** 7

6. (a) 25   (b) $2 \times 3 \times 5^2 \times 11 \times 13$ (21450)

7. (a) 4   (b) 20   (c) 28

8. (a) $2^5 \times 7$ (224)   (b) $2^5 \times 3 \times 5$ (480)   (c) $2^3 \times 3 \times 5^2 \times 7$ (4200

9. (a) 75   (b) $3^3 \times 5^3$ (3375)

10. (a) $2^2 \times 7$ (28)   (b) $2^4 \times 3 \times 7 \times 11$ (3696)

11. (a) $315 = 3^2 \times 5 \times 7$, $525 = 3 \times 5^2 \times 7$ (b) $3^2 \times 5^2 \times 7$ (1575) (c)

12. (a) H.C.F = 10, L.C.M = $2 \times 3 \times 5^2 \times 7 \times 11$ (11550)

    (b) 115500   (c) same answer

Page 120 Can you still? 5A

1. 36 cm **2.** $\frac{17}{25}$ m^2 **3.** $\frac{1}{6}$ **4.** $\frac{11}{24}$ m **5.** 76

6. A $\frac{17}{24}$, B $\frac{3}{4}$, C $\frac{1}{16}$, D $\frac{2}{3}$ **7.** £7.20

Page 121 M5.3

1. (a) 10^5 (b) 8.2×10^4 (c) 6.4×10^3 (d) 8×10^{-2} (e) 6.7×10^{-5}

(f) 5.2×10^{-2} (g) 4×10^{-1} (h) 4.2×10^4 (i) 8.2×10^{-4}

2. (a) 6×10^4 (b) 9×10^2 (c) 5.8×10^3 (d) 6.9×10^5

(e) 8.5×10^2 (f) 7.4×10^7 (g) 4.7×10^4 (h) 4×10^6

(i) 8×10^{-4} (j) 3×10^{-3} (k) 7×10^{-8} (l) 9.5×10^{-1}

(m) 2×10^{-1} (n) 6.1×10^{-3} (o) 6.2×10^{-5} (p) 7.2×10^7

(q) 4.2×10^4 (r) 6.25×10^{-2} (s) 8.12×10^{-1} (t) 2.13×10^8

3. 1.5×10^5 **4.** 5×10^8 **5.** 4.126×10^6 **6.** 7×10^{-6}

7. 8×10^{-1} **8.** 1.7×10^{-24} **9.** 3.5×10^6

10. (a) 500 (b) 6800 (c) 810000 (d) 0.07

(e) 0.00098 (f) 61200 (g) 0.0037 (h) 0.0841

(i) 2500000 (j) 0.46 (k) 0.000172 (l) 536000

11. b, c, d, f

12. (a) 2×10^{-2} (b) 6×10^{-4} (c) 2.09×10^2 (d) 3.16×10^4

(e) 5.8×10^6 (f) 3.168×10^2 (g) 3.271×10 (h) 6.5×10^{-3}

(i) 3×10^9 (j) 7.3×10^{-2} (k) 5×10^{-3} (l) 5.9×10^5

Page 123 M5.4

1. (a) 3.6×10^6 (b) 2.1×10^{10} (c) 4.7×10^{-3} (d) 3.8×10^6

(e) 8×10^{11} (f) 7.1×10^{-7} (g) 5.86×10^{12} (h) 4.13×10^{-7}

2. (a) 8×10^8 (b) 9×10^{12} (c) 6×10^{12}

(d) 7.5×10^{15} (e) 1.6×10^9 (f) 1.2×10^{14}

(g) 7.5×10^5 (h) 3.6×10^9 (i) 1.5×10^{11}

3. (a) 4×10^8 (b) 3×10^{13} (c) 3×10^{13}

(d) 1.5×10^{13} (e) 2.7×10^{25} (f) 2×10^{-10}

(g) 1.5×10^{18} (h) 5×10^{17} (i) 3×10^{11}

4. 1.45×10^7 **5.** 1.08×10^{-16} **6.** 20 hours

7. 9.2×10^{10} m^2 **8.** 1.8×10^{23} **9.** 7.3×10^9

10. (a) 4.3×10^7 (b) 8.3×10^{-8}

11. (a) 3.6×10^4 (b) 8.5×10^9 (c) 5.91×10^{12}

(d) 4.6×10^3 (e) 1.4×10^5 (f) 3.29×10^3

(g) 3.2×10^{-7} (h) 5.9×10^{-12} (i) 5.83×10^{-5}

12. (a) 4.26×10^9 (b) 3.14×10^9 (c) 1.222×10^{10}

13. 4.2×10^{-6} m **14.** 4.41×10^{-14}

15. (a) 7.69×10^9 km (b) 5.21×10^9 km

Page 125 M5.5

1. (a) 1.5×10^8 (b) 4.14×10^{20} (c) 2.88×10^{-17} (d) 2.88×10^{-30}

(e) 2.4×10^{40} (f) 1.2×10^{22} (g) 3×10^{11} (h) 3.09×10^{-10}

(i) 4.82×10^{19} **2.** 40 **3.** 6.94×10^{-15} m^2

4. (a) 2.56×10^{53} (b) 1.97×10^{-14} (c) 5.04×10^{39} (d) 3.89×10^{-28}

5. 4.55×10^{-15} **6.** 9.5×10^{12} km

7. (a) 2.42×10^{18} (b) 5.04×10^{34} (c) 4.15×10^{29}

(d) 2.80×10^{57} (e) 2.57×10^{22} (f) 1.01×10^{-40}

8. (a) 2×10^{-5} seconds (c) 18 secs

9. (a) (i) 1.6×10^5 (ii) 1.34×10^5

Page 128 M5.6

1. (a) 13.5 cm (b) 14.5 cm **2.** (a) 41.5 m (b) 42.5 m

3. (a) 21.45 mm (b) 21.55 mm **4.** (a) 3.55 kg (b) 3.65 kg

5. (a) 78.5 – 79.5 (b) 32.25 – 32.35 (c) 9.05 – 9.15

(d) 15.65 – 15.75 (e) 6.315 – 6.325 (f) 8.165 – 8.175

6. 10.25 g **7.** £24711500 **8.** 525 m **9.** 10.115 s

10. (b) $92.55 \le l < 92.65$ (c) $16.15 \le d < 16.25$

(d) $1150 \le c < 1250$ (e) $3.855 \le h < 3.865$

11. 1.3, 1.5 litres **12.** 2175 m, 2225 m

Page 129 Can you still? 5B

1. 20% **2.** £3.36 **3.** £6932.50 **4.** 25% **5.** £90

6. 15% **7.** £20 million **8.** 162 **9.** 12% **10.** £912.93

Page 130 E5.1

1. (a) $156.25 \le l < 156.35$ (b) $71.75 \le w < 71.85$

(c) lower 11210.94 m^2, higher 11233.75 m^2

2. 32.55 cm **3.** 320.625 cm^3

4. (a) 11.8 (b) 26.0775 (c) 0.401 (d) 21.3 (e) 4.9

5. (a) $6945 \le A < 6955$ (b) $94.5 \le l < 95.5$ (c) $72.72 \le w < 73.60$

6. $490 \le S < 508$ **7.** (a) 35.75 m$^2 \le Ar < 48.75$ m^2

(b) 7.07 m$^2 \le Ac < 19.6$ m^2 (c) 16.1 m$^2 \le Ag < 41.7$ m^2

8. (a) 4.16 (b) 3.90 **9.** 9.6 m/s $\le Sp < 9.8$ m/s

10. (a) 2.85 ohms (b) 2.89 ohms

Page 132 Can you still? 5C

1. (a) 5^4 (b) 3^8 (c) 5^7 (d) 1

2. (a) $\frac{1}{2}$ (b) $\frac{1}{27}$ (c) 5 (d) $\frac{1}{9}$

3. (a) $12xy^2$ (b) $\frac{3m}{2n}$ (c) $27a^6$ (d) $6n^2$

4. (a) 4 (b) 9 (c) $\frac{5}{3}$ (d) $\frac{4}{9}$

5. (a) -3 (b) $-\frac{1}{4}$ (c) $\frac{10}{3}$ (d) 3

Page 134 E5.2

1. (a)

5	13	15	23
10	26	30	26

(b)

8	14	18	20
12	21	27	30

(c)

8	10	24	38
20	25	60	95

2. (a) A = 3P (b) 72 (c) 24

3. (a) $v \propto t$ (b) $v = kt$ (c) 21 m/s (d) 14 seconds

4. (a) C = kT (b) £56.25 (c) 0.8 cm

5. (a) S = 3.5t (b) 56 (c) 8

6. (a) $h = 4.2T$ (b) 147   (c) 50

7. (a) $u = 2t$ (b) 14   (c) 2.5

Page 135   E5.3

1. (a) (i) $s = \dfrac{v^2}{5}$ (ii) $s = \dfrac{45^2}{5} = 405$ m

2.

2	4	5	8
8	32	50	128

3.

2	3	6	8
40	135	1080	2560

4. (a) $m = kl^3$ (b) $k = 2$ (c) 1024 kg   (d) 5 cm

5. (a) $E = ke^2$ (b) $k = 6$ (c) 54 joules   (d) 8 cm

6. (a) $T = 0.8\sqrt{l}$ (b) 3.2 secs   (c) 49 cm

7. (a) $y = 6x^{\frac{1}{3}}$ (b)

8	64	216	1000
12	24	36	60

8. 43.2 amps.   **9.** (a) $H = 5r^{\frac{1}{3}}$ (b) 50   (c) 64

10. (a) $y \propto x^3$ (b) $y = 3x^3$ (c) 11

Page 137   Can you still? 5D

1. $2x(x + 2)$ **2.** $(x + 3)(x - 7)$ **3.** $(x + 5)(x - 5)$

4. $(x + 3)(x + 2)$ **5.** $(x - 9)(x + 2)$ **6.** $x(x - 6)$

7. $(x + 6)(x - 3)$ **8.** $(x + 9)(x - 9)$ **9.** $(x - 5)(x - 2)$

10. $2x(4x + 3)$ **11.** $(x - 4)(x + 3)$ **12.** $(x + 1)(x - 1)$

13. $(m - n)(p + q)$ **14.** $(2x - 1)(5x + 2)$ **15.** $x(x + 2)(x - 2)$

16. $(c - d)(a - b)$ **17.** $(y + z)(x - y)$ **18.** $(3x + 5)(x + 3)$

19. $(4x - 3)(3x + 2)$ **20.** $x(x + 6)(x - 6)$ **21.** $(2x + 7)(2x - 7)$

22. $x(x + 1)(x + 1)$ **23.** $2(4x + 1)(4x - 1)$ **24.** $5(3x - 1)(3x - 1)$

Page 138   E5.4

1. (a) $F = \dfrac{120,000}{r}$ (b) 500   (c) 120

2. (a) $Y = \dfrac{48}{x^2}$ (b) 12   (c) $\dfrac{1}{2}$

3. (a) $V = \dfrac{800}{P}$ (b) $4m^3$ (c) 50 N/m²

4. (a) $F = \dfrac{108}{d^2}$ (b) 108 N   (c) 2 cm

5. (a) $Q = \dfrac{36}{\sqrt{t}}$ (b) 9   (c) 4

6. (a) $P = \dfrac{1000}{r^3}$ (b) $P = 1$ (c) 2

7. (a) $\dfrac{1}{2}$ (b) $\dfrac{1}{4}$

8. (a) $l = \dfrac{300}{\sqrt[3]{V}}$ (b) 30 cm   (c) 15625 cm³

9.

2	3	6	10
225	100	25	9

10. 8   **11.** $y = \dfrac{200}{x^2}$

Page 141   WYM5

1. £40.19   **2.** £47.25   **3.** £116.52

4. (a) $17 - 26 - 19$ (b) 32718425   (c) www.sb.co.uk

(d) 419327   (e) the amount figures and words do not agree

5. £35.14

Page 142   Test yourself on unit 5

1. (a) 51, 68, 85   (b) 1, 3, 5, 9, 15, 45

(c) $2 \times 3 \times 5^2$ (d) $x = 3, y = 2, z = 13$

(e) $3 \times 5 \times 7 : 2 \times 3 \times 5 \times 11$, H.C.F. 15, L.C.M $2 \times 3 \times 5 \times 7 \times 11$ (2310)

2. (a) 2.73×10^5 (b) 3.8×10^2 (c) 5.2×10^4 (d) 8×10^{-1}

(e) 1.8×10^{-3} (f) 9×10^6 (g) 7.126×10^2 (h) 8.7×10^{-6}

(i) 720   (j) 0.0521   (k) 0.00059   (l) 6140000

3. (a) 3×10^{12} (b) 1.5×10^{14} (c) 3×10^{11} (d) 6×10^{11}

(e) 5.3×10^7 (f) 6.3×10^{-6}

4. (a) 3×10^{11} (b) 6.08×10^{25} (c) 2.07×10^9 (d) 1.78×10^{16}

5. (a) 57.5 kg $\le m < 58.5$ kg   (b) 3.65 m $\le w < 3.75$ m

(c) $72.55 \le h < 72.65$ cm   (d) $8.115\,l \le c < 8.125\,l$

(e) 7.75 km $\le d < 7.85$ km

6. (a) 1.8   (b) 8.5   (c) 30   (d) 1.49 m

7. (a)

5	8	11	13
25	40	55	65

(b) (i) $S = 3t^2$ (ii) 147 (iii) 1

(c) 1296 joules

8. (a) (i) $m = \dfrac{240}{N}$ (ii) 16   (iii) 10

(b) (i) $R = \dfrac{20.25}{d^2}$ (ii) 0.25 ohms   (iii) 5 mm

Page 144   Mixed examination questions

1. (a) $2^3 \times 3$ (b) 120

2. (a) (i) 50100   (ii) 9×10^{-4} (b) 2.4×10^9

3. 2.3×10^7 **4.** 2.4×10^5 **5.** $c = 4, d = 23$

6. $S = \dfrac{8000}{f^2}$ (b) 500

7. (a) 79.5 cm   (b) 40.5 cm   (c) 3260.25 cm²

8. (a) $P = 20r^2$ (b) £3.20

9. (a) (i) 3×10^7 (ii) 0.00002   (b) 6×10^2

10. 750   **11.** No   **12.** (a) $2^2 \times 3^3$ (b) 12

13. (a) $w = 3\sqrt{P}$ (b) 15   (c) 49

14. (a) 175.4 mm²   (b) $26.8 \le AC < 27.0$ (c) 37.4°

15. (a) 160   (b) $3\frac{1}{3}$ **16.** (a) 42.5 cm   (b) 31

17. (a) $y = \dfrac{80}{x^2}$ (b) 3.2

UNIT 6

Page 148   M6.1

1. $\dfrac{4}{5}$ **2.** 56   **3.** -4 **4.** 10   **5.** -5 **6.** -6 **7.** -7

8. 4   **9.** $-4\frac{1}{2}$ **10.** $\dfrac{3}{4}$ **11.** -15 **12.** -5 **13.** -20 **14.** 4

15. -3 **16.** $-\dfrac{1}{2}$ **17.** $-\dfrac{3}{4}$ **18.** 9   **19.** -6 **20.** 4   **21.** 10

22. 11   **23.** –1   **24.** $-\frac{5}{6}$ **25.** –4   **26.** –5   **27.** –5   **28.** 4

29. 4   **30.** 5   **31.** 5   **32.** $\frac{1}{7}$ **33.** 4   **34.** $-\frac{5}{6}$ **35.** –5

36. 2   **37.** 20   **38.** 21   **39.** 25   **40.** –30   **41.** 8   **42.** 10

43. –12   **44.** 15   **45.** $\frac{8}{3}$ **46.** $\frac{21}{5}$ **47.** –7

Page 149   M6.2

1. 3   **2.** 1   **3.** 5   **4.** 5   **5.** –1   **6.** $-\frac{1}{4}$

7. –2   **8.** –3   **9.** $-\frac{3}{10}$ **10.** $-\frac{7}{20}$ **11.** $\frac{5}{6}$ **12.** $-\frac{7}{40}$

13. –20   **14.** 3   **15.** 5   **16.** 3   **17.** $-\frac{2}{7}$ **18.** $2\frac{1}{2}$

19. $\frac{2}{9}$ **20.** 4   **21.** 13   **22.** $\frac{7}{10}$ **23.** –18   **24.** 3

25. –4   **26.** 7   **27.** 10   **28.** 5   **29.** 4

Page 151   M6.3

1. 15   **2.** 12   **3.** 15   **4.** 18   **5.** 54   **6.** 16   **7.** 12

8. 7   **9.** 9   **10.** $5\frac{1}{3}$ **11.** 5   **12.** –9   **13.** 5   **14.** 3

15. 11   **16.** 14   **17.** $\frac{5}{4}$ **18.** $\frac{13}{6}$ **19.** $-\frac{9}{5}$ **20.** 3   **21.** 6

22. 5   **23.** 7   **24.** 10   **25.** 9   **26.** 8   **27.** $\frac{5}{8}$ **28.** $\frac{3}{2}$

29. –4   **30.** 27   **31.** $\frac{1}{2}$ **32.** $\frac{7}{3}$ **33.** $-\frac{19}{5}$

Page 152   M6.4

1. (a) $10x = 180°$ (b) $x = 18°$ (c) $36°, 54°, 90°$

2. (a) $5x + 80 = 180°$ (b) $x = 20°$ (c) $40°, 70°, 70°$

3. (a) $4x + 6 = 78 \rightarrow 18, 19, 20, 21$

4. (a) $8x + 10 = 58$ (b) $x = 6$ (c) l 20 cm, w 9 cm   **5.** 7 cm

6. 5 cm   **7.** (a) $12x + 120 = 360$ (b) $x = 20°$ (c) $80°, 110°, 110°, 60°$

8. l 12, w 4   **9.** 4 yrs, 7 yrs, 10 yrs   **10.** $20°, 80°, 80°$

11. (a) $x + 2, x + 4, x + 6$ (b) 51, 53, 55, 57   **12.** 50 cm

13. £59, £131   **14.** 10, 12, 14   **15.** 4   **16.** 34

Page 154   Can you still? 6A

1. $12a - 8$ **2.** $5x^2 + 3x$ **3.** $2p^2 - 6pq$

4. $17b + 23$ **5.** $8y + 7$ **6.** $3a - 2b + 2ab$

7. $7m - 13m^2$ **8.** $x^2 + 7x + 12$ **9.** $n^2 - 3n - 4$

10. $w^2 - 7w + 10$ **11.** $z^2 - 2z - 24$ **12.** $6a^2 + 23a + 20$

13. $15m^2 + 22m - 5$ **15.** $x^2 + 6x + 9$ **16.** $x^2 - 10x + 25$

Page 155   M6.5

1. 13.7   **2.** 6.1   **3.** 18.3   **4.** (a) 4.4   (b) 4.5   (c) 5.4

5. 8.66   **6.** 8.61   **7.** (a) 4.41   (b) 5.07   (c) 7.04

8. (a) $7x^2 = 300$ (b) 6.55   **9.** 6.11   **10.** (a) 2.6   (b) 2.5

11. $3.3 \times 3.3 \times 8.3$ cm   **12.** (a) 7.2 or 2.8 cm

Page 157   M6.6

1. $\frac{a}{6} = b$ **2.** $8a = b$ **3.** $n = mp$

4. (a) $y + 9$ (b) $12y$ (c) $y - 20$ (d) $\frac{y}{8}$

(e) $3y$ (f) $y - b$ (g) $\frac{y}{m}$ (h) $y + w$

5. (a) $\frac{(x-2)}{3} = y$ (b) $\frac{(x+9)}{4} = y$ **6.** (a) $\frac{(y-8)}{2}$ (b) $\frac{(y+5)}{6}$

(c) $\frac{(y+10)}{8}$ (d) $3(y-2)$ (e) $5(y+6)$ (f) $2(y+4)$

7. (a) $\frac{(y-q)}{p}$ (b) $\frac{(y+h)}{c}$ (c) $\frac{(y+2p)}{r}$

(d) $\frac{(q-3s)}{c}$ (e) $\frac{(2f-5c)}{b}$ (f) $\frac{(y-b+c)}{a}$

8. (a) $\frac{(y-cd)}{c}$ (b) $\frac{(q+mn)}{m}$ (c) $\frac{(y-5r)}{r}$

(d) $\frac{(3b-7a)}{a}$ (e) $\frac{(y+fg)}{f}$ (f) $\frac{(4b+st)}{s}$

9. (a) $\frac{(yh+g)}{f} = x$ (b) $\frac{(yc-2h)}{p}$

10. (a) $\frac{(4e-d)}{a}$ (b) $\frac{(py-3c)}{b}$ (c) $\frac{(5q+r)}{a}$

(d) $\frac{(7y+2d)}{c}$ (e) $\frac{(yb+3c)}{a}$ (f) $\frac{(8y+qr)}{p}$

11. $\frac{(h-m)}{3}$ **12.** $\frac{(v-u)}{f}$ **13.** $\frac{(ya+3)}{c}$ **14.** $\frac{(ym-3c)}{3}$

Page 160   M6.7

1. (a) $x = \sqrt{(z+w)}$ (b) $m = \sqrt[3]{(p-3c)}$ (c) $y = \left(\frac{4n}{m}\right)^2$

2. (a) $\sqrt{(b-7)}$ (b) $\sqrt{(z+t)}$ (c) $\sqrt{(4p-q)}$ (d) $\sqrt[3]{(c+a)}$

(e) $\sqrt[3]{\left(\frac{r}{q}\right)}$ (f) $\sqrt{\left(\frac{n}{b}\right)}$ (g) $\sqrt{(cb)}$ (h) $(m-n)^2$

(i) $(p+2q)^3$ (j) $(yw)^3$ (k) $\left(\frac{a}{b}\right)^2$ (l) $(n-2m)^2$

3. (a) $(p+r)^2 - q = x$ (b) $(3B(N+M))^2 = A$

4. (a) $p^2 + r$ (b) $9q^2 - 2r$ (c) $b^3 - 5c$

(d) $\sqrt{w} - t$ (e) $q + \sqrt{(2p-y)}$ (f) $(8h-m)^2 + g$

(g) $y - w^2$ (h) $(3m + 4k)^2 + h$ (i) $(5(d-c))^2$

(j) $(z(y+2w))^2$ (k) $\sqrt{(e(b-3c))}$ (l) $w + \sqrt[3]{xyz}$

5. (a) $\frac{m}{(3R-Q)} = N$ (b) $\frac{(v+yw)}{y} = x$

6. (a) $\frac{m}{q}$ (b) $\frac{n}{c}$ (c) $\frac{2m}{3a}$ (d) $\frac{x}{(m+z)}$

(e) $\frac{2a}{(b^2-3c)}$ (f) $\frac{r}{(q-5n)}$ (g) $\frac{3d}{(5a^2-4c)}$ (h) $\frac{t}{(q-3r)}$

(i) $\frac{a}{b^3} - c$ (j) $\frac{c^2}{f} - 3a$ (k) $\frac{k}{5m} + 4n$ (l) $\frac{m}{6p^2} - n$

7. $\frac{ym}{f} + h$ **8.** $\frac{x}{w^3}$ **9.** $\sqrt{(m^2 - n)}$ **10.** $\sqrt{(w^2 - n^3)}$

Page 161   Can you still? 6B

1. $\frac{78}{99}$ **2.** $\frac{4}{90}$ **3.** $\frac{86}{99}$ **4.** $\frac{364}{999}$ **5.** $\frac{261}{990}$

Page 162   E6.1

1. (a) $b = \dfrac{h^2 + c}{a^2 - f}$ (b) $x = \dfrac{pr + k}{m + rq}$ **2.** $\dfrac{pn}{n - p}$ **3.** $\dfrac{yb}{3b + y}$

4. (a) $\dfrac{e - g}{f - d}$ (b) $\dfrac{y + wz}{y - w}$ (c) $\dfrac{3c + b}{a + b}$ (d) $\dfrac{nz + my}{m - n}$

(e) $\dfrac{cd - b}{f + c}$ (f) $\dfrac{3z}{y^2 + w}$ (g) $\dfrac{pr + t}{p - s}$ (h) $\dfrac{a(c + 1)}{cd - b}$

(i) $\dfrac{f - mg}{mk + 1}$ (j) $\dfrac{4}{y - z}$ (k) $\dfrac{c - nd}{nk - m}$ (l) $\dfrac{s - fd}{5f + r}$

5. $\dfrac{rq - qx + q}{p + q + r}$ **6.** (a) $n = \dfrac{m(2p^2 - 1)}{1 + p^2}$ (b) $f = \dfrac{g(k - 6)}{3 + k}$

7. (a) $\dfrac{y(2z^3 - 1)}{1 - z^3}$ (b) $\dfrac{ax - cq^2}{bq^2 + 1}$ (c) $\dfrac{9y^2z}{9y^2 - 1}$ (d) $\dfrac{a - c\sqrt{b}}{\sqrt{b} + 1}$

(e) $\dfrac{b(\sqrt{z} - 1)}{c + \sqrt{z}}$ (f) $\dfrac{2n}{5m + 2p}$ (g) $\dfrac{bm + an}{a - bd}$ (h) $\dfrac{4p^2b}{4p^2 - aq^2}$

(i) $\dfrac{1 + 8n^3}{8pn^3 - m}$ **8.** $\dfrac{c - 12p}{3zp + t}$ **9.** $\dfrac{r^2 - mp}{w - mpq - n}$

Page 164   E6.2

1. (a) 11   (b) 39   (c) −9   (d) −1

2. (a) 33   (b) −9   (c) −30   (d) $8\dfrac{1}{2}$

3. (a) 49   (b) 0   (c) $\dfrac{1}{16}$ (d) 16

4. (a) 0   (b) 3   (c) 8   (d) 35

5. (a) 0   (b) 9   (c) 49   (d) $(w - 4)^2$

6. (a) 10   (b) −2   (c) 130   (d) $y^3 + y$

7. (a) 3   (b) −1   (c) $\dfrac{3}{z} + 2$ (d) ∞

8. (a) $-\dfrac{2}{3}$ (b) −7   (c) $\dfrac{p^2 - 7}{3p + 1}$

9. 7   **10.** −2   **11.** ± 5   **12.** $q = 0$ or 3

13. $a = -6$ or 3   **14.** 2 or −4   **15.** 4 or −3   **16.** 0 or −8

17. −5   **18.** −8   **19.** $20x + 11$

20. (a) $2x + 6$ (b) $6x - 3$ (c) $10x - 8$ (d) $1 - 2x$

21. (a) $18x + 8$ (b) $18x + 1$ (c) $-9x - 4$ (d) $-36x - 16$

22. (a) $4x^2 - 8x + 5$ (b) $3x^2 - 6x - 3$ (c) $-2x^2 + 4x - 2$ (d) $-x^2 + 2x + 3$

23. (a) $2x - 2x^3$ (b) $x^3 - x - 9$ (c) $4 + 3x - 3x^3$ (d) $-3 + 5x - 5x^3$

24. $f(x) = 5x + 3$

Page 166   Can you still? 6C

1. 53°   **2.** 109°   **3.** 49°   **4.** 15°   **5.** 128°

6. 95°   **7.** 22°   **8.** 26°   **9.** 160°

Page 167   M6.8

1. $y = 2, 4, 6, 8$ **2.** $y = 1, 4, 7, 10$ **3.** $y = 3, 5, 7, 9$

4. $y = 6, 5, 4, 3, 2, 1$ **5.** $y = 0, 2, 4, 6, 8$

6. $y = -15, -11, -7, -3, 1, 5, 9$

Page 169   M6.9

1. (a) 16   (b) −12   (c) 18   (d) 10   (e) 12

2. (a) −2   (b) 1   (c) 4   (d) 2   (e) −1

3. $y = 9, 4, 1, 0, 1, 4, 9$

4. (a) $y = 10\ 5\ 2\ 1\ 2\ 5\ 10$ (b) $y = 7, 2, -1, -2, -1, 2, 7$

(c) $y = 18\ 8\ 2\ 0\ 2\ 8\ 18$ (d) $y = 27, 12, 3, 0, 3, 12, 27$

(e) $y = 19\ 9\ 3\ 1\ 3\ 9\ 19$ (f) $y = 20, 5, -4, -7, -4, 5, 20$

5. (a) y values 14, 8, 4, 2, 2, 4, 8

6. $y = 6, 2, 0, 0, 2, 6, 12$

7. (a) $y = 14, 8, 4, 2, 2, 4, 8$ (b) 1.75

8. (a) $y = 2, -2, -4, -4, -2, 2, 8$ (b) −4.25

9. (a) $(-2, -7)$ (b) $\left(\dfrac{3}{2}, \dfrac{3}{4}\right)$ (c) $\left(-\dfrac{1}{4}, -6\dfrac{1}{8}\right)$

(d) $\left(-\dfrac{3}{2}, 6\dfrac{1}{4}\right)$ (e) $\left(\dfrac{5}{6}, \dfrac{47}{12}\right)$ (f) $\left(\dfrac{3}{2}, \dfrac{9}{4}\right)$

Page 171   E6.3

1. $y = (-27), -8, -1, 1, 8, 27$

2. (a) $y = -29, -9, -1, 1, 3, 11, 31$ (b) $5\dfrac{7}{8}$

3. (a) $y = -26, -8, -2, -2, -2, 4, 22$ (b) $-1\dfrac{5}{8}$

4. (a) $y = -41, -9, 5, 9, 3, -1, 1, 15, 47$ (b) $-\dfrac{1}{8}$

9. (a) $y = -0.2, -0.25, -0.\dot{3}, -0.5, -1, \infty, 1, 0.5, 0.\dot{3}, 0.25, 0.2$

(b) 0.4   **10.** (b) 1.25

13. (e), (j) linear; (a), (c), (f), (l) quadratic; (b), (d), (g) cubic; (h), (i), (k) reciprocal

14. (a) → 2   (b) no match   (c) → 4   (d) → 3   (e) → 1

Page 174   E6.4

1. (a) → 2   (b) → 3   (c) → 1   **2.** £28

3. (a) → 5   (b) → 1   (c) → 6   (d) → 3   (e) → 2   (f) → 4

4. A → 3, B → 1, C → 2

5. (b) 3.8 secs   (c) 148 m   **6.** (b) 8 ohms   (c) 2.7 amps

7. (a) $10 - 2x$ (d) 74 cm³   (e) 1.7

8. (c) 2.6   (d) 17.2 cm³

Page 177   M6.10

1. A 4, B $\dfrac{3}{2}$, C $\dfrac{1}{4}$ **2.** P −2, Q −5, R $-\dfrac{1}{3}$, S $\dfrac{3}{2}$, T $\dfrac{5}{2}$

3. (a) 2   (b) 3   (c) −2   (d) $\dfrac{3}{2}$ (e) −1   (f) $-\dfrac{1}{2}$

(g) $\dfrac{1}{2}$ (h) $\dfrac{5}{3}$ (i) 0   (j) $-\dfrac{2}{3}$ (k) $-\dfrac{1}{6}$ (l) ∞

4. (a) $-\dfrac{2}{3}$ (b) −3   (c) −1   **5.** 23   **6.** 6

Page 180   M6.12

1. 3, 4   **2.** 2, −5   **3.** 8, −1   **4.** 1, 6   **5.** −4, −2

6. −4, 3   **7.** −1, −2   **8.** −5, 2   **9.** −1, 3   **10.** −2, 4

11. $\dfrac{1}{3}$, −7   **12.** 5, 1   **13.** −4, 5   **14.** 6, −3   **15.** $-\dfrac{2}{5}, \dfrac{3}{5}$

16. $\dfrac{3}{4}$, −6   **17.** $\dfrac{5}{3}$, −1   **18.** $\dfrac{5}{4}, \dfrac{1}{2}$ **19.** −4, 6   **20.** $\dfrac{5}{7}, -\dfrac{2}{7}$

25. A, $y = 3x - 1$; B, $y = \frac{1}{2}x + 1$; C, $y = -x - 2$

26. (a), (d) and (e) **27.** $y = 5x + 4$ **28.** $y = -4x + 2$

29. $y = 3x - 4$ **30.** $y = x - 6$ **31.** $y = 3x - 7$

32. $y = 4x - 23$ **33.** $y = 3x + 13$ **34.** $y = -2x + 7$

35. $y = 2x - 1$ **36.** $y = -\frac{1}{5}x + 1\frac{1}{5}$

Page 182   E6.5

1. (a) -3 (b) $\frac{1}{3}$ (c) -1 **2.** $-\frac{1}{2}$ (b) 2 (c) -1

4. $-\frac{1}{4}$ **5.** $-\frac{1}{4}$

Page 184   E6.6

1. (a) $-\frac{1}{7}$ (b) -1 (c) $\frac{1}{4}$ (d) $\frac{1}{8}$ (e) -3 (f) $-\frac{5}{2}$

(g) 6 (h) $\frac{4}{3}$ (i) $\frac{2}{9}$ (j) 2 (k) -5 (l) ∞

2. (a) $-\frac{1}{3}$ (b) $\frac{3}{2}$ (c) $\frac{8}{5}$

3. (a) $y = -3x + 3$ (b) $y = 5x - 2$ (c) $y = 4x - 3$ (d) $y = -\frac{1}{2}x + 6$

(e) $y = -2x + 6$ (f) $y = 3x + 20$ (g) $y = \frac{1}{3}x - 2$ (h) $y = -\frac{1}{2}x + 1$

(i) $y = x + 7$ (j) $y = \frac{1}{2}x - 1$

4. $y = 5x - 15$ **5.** $y = -\frac{1}{2}x + 6$

6. (a) and (e), (c) and (f), (g) and (j), (i) and (d), (b) and (h)

Page 186   WYM6

1. £353.15 **2.** £1044.98 **3.** £1016.34 **4.** £125.60 **5.** £785.29

6. £65 **7.** £807.03 **8.** £785.08 **9.** £785.08

10. money taken to pay bills

11. money taken from a cash machine

12. Amount overdrawn (owed to bank)

Page 186   Test yourself on unit 6

1. (a) 8 (b) 3 (c) $5\frac{1}{3}$ (d) 3 (e) $\frac{1}{6}$

(f) -2 (g) -1 (h) 44 (i) $2\frac{1}{2}$

2. (a) $30°, 70°, 80°$ (b) $8x + 2 = 42, 98\ cm^2$ (c) $33, 35, 37$

3. (a) 6.4 (b) 7.17

4. (a) $\frac{y - c}{m}$ (b) $\frac{q}{c} + p$ (c) $a(m - k)$ (d) $\frac{ny - z}{w}$

(e) $\frac{a}{m + p}$ (f) $\frac{c}{3z + 4y}$ (g) $\sqrt[3]{(w - z)}$ (h) $9b^2 - n$

5. (a) y values $-11, -9, -7, -5, -3, -1, 1$

(c) y values $13, 8, 5, 4, 5, 8, 13$

(d) y values $-3, -6, -7, -6, -3, 2, 9, 18$

6. (a) 2 (b) $\frac{3}{2}$ (c) $-\frac{1}{3}$ (d) AB, 4; BC, -4; AC, -2

7. (a) $2, -6$ (b) $-1, -8$ (c) $-\frac{3}{5}, \frac{8}{5}$ (d) $y = -2x + 1$ (e) $y = 5x - 6$

8. (a) $\frac{m - p}{1 + x}$ (b) $\frac{d + ab}{c - a}$ (c) $\frac{d}{f - k^2}$ (d) $\frac{c^3 - a}{k - m}$

9. (a) -25 (b) 12 (c) 8 (d) 6 (e) 0 or 7

10. (a) y values $-8, 6, 8, 4, 0, 2, 16$

(b) y values $-8, -10, -13.3, -20, -40, \infty, 40, 20, 13.3, 10, 8$

(c) (iv) $15.5\ m, 4.5\ m$ (v) $100\ m^2$ (vi) $10\ m \times 10\ m$

11. (a) 4 (b) $\frac{1}{5}$ (c) $x + 4y = 1$ and $y = 4x - 3$ (d) $y = -\frac{1}{3}x + 2$

Page 190   Mixed examination questions

1. (a) $p = 9$ (b) $q = 8\frac{1}{2}$ (c) $r = -7$

2. 4.8 **3.** 3.3 **4.** $x = \frac{1}{2}$ **5.** (c) (i) 0.4 (ii) 1.2

6. (a) y : $6, 1, -2, -3, -2, 1, 6$ (c) 2.73 or 0.73

7. $q = \frac{8p}{tp - 8}$ **8.** $x = \pm\sqrt{5y + 4}$

9. (a) -2 (b) $y = -2x + 3$ (c) $y = \frac{1}{2}x + 3$

10. (i) c (ii) d **11.** (a) $y = 3x - 7$ (b) $\frac{1}{-3}$

12. (a) y: $3, 0, -2, -3, -3, -2, 0, 3$ (c) 1.85 or -1.35

13. $r = \pm\sqrt{\left(\frac{2p + 12}{3}\right)}$ **14.** $r = st^2$ **15.** (a) $y = -2x + 4$ (b) $\frac{1}{2}$

UNIT 8

Page 202   M8.1

1. (a) 50 (b) 0.18

2. (a) $0.24, 0.38, 0.45, 0.44, 0.45, 0.42, 0.48, 0.43, 0.42, 0.44, 0.43,$
$0.44, 0.43, 0.43$ (c) 0.43

3. (a) Maria (b)

Total	0	1	2	3
770	188	267	126	189

biased (c) 0.25

Page 203   Can you still? 8A

1. $\frac{5}{12}$ **2.** $\frac{1}{3}$ **3.** $\frac{3}{4}$ **4.** $\frac{73}{90}$ **5.** $\frac{79}{150}$ **6.** $\frac{7}{24}$

7. 0.48 **8.** 0.021 **9.** 0.82

10.

0.39	–	0.21	→	0.18
+		÷		
0.1	×	0.7	→	0.07
↓		↓		
0.49	×	0.3	→	0.147

11. $\frac{19}{22}$ **12.** $7\frac{3}{4}$

Page 204   M8.2

1. (a) $\frac{4}{13}$ (b) $\frac{7}{13}$ (c) 0 (d) $\frac{2}{13}$

2. (a) $\frac{1}{9}$ (b) $\frac{2}{9}$ (c) $\frac{1}{3}$

3. (a) $\frac{4}{11}$ (b) $\frac{5}{11}$ (c) $\frac{6}{11}$ **4.** (a) $\frac{1}{5}$ (b) $\frac{2}{5}$ (c) $\frac{3}{5}$

5. (a) $\frac{1}{2}$ (b) $\frac{3}{10}$ (c) $\frac{1}{2}$

6. (a) $\frac{1}{3}$ (b) $\frac{1}{5}$ (c) $\frac{2}{3}$ (d) 0

7. (a) $\frac{1}{10}$ (b) $\frac{2}{5}$ (c) $\frac{1}{2}$

8. (a) $\frac{1}{52}$ (b) $\frac{1}{2}$ (c) $\frac{1}{4}$ (d) $\frac{3}{13}$

9. (a) $\frac{5}{12}$ (b) $\frac{7}{12}$ **10.** (a) $\frac{1}{12}$ (b) $\frac{1}{2}$ (c) $\frac{5}{12}$

11. (a) $\frac{1}{2}$ (b) $\frac{1}{3}$ (c) $\frac{1}{2}$

12. (a) $\frac{4}{11}$ (b) $\frac{1}{4}$ **13.** (a) $13 - x$ (b) $\frac{x}{13}$ (c) $\frac{(13-x)}{13}$

14. $\frac{m}{(m+n)}$ **15.** (a) $10 + y$ (b) $10 - x$ (c) $\frac{(10-x)}{(10+y)}$

Page 206 M8.3

1. 60 **2.** (a) 30 (b) 30 (c) 90 (d) 60 **3.** 24

4. 4 **5.** (a) 28 (b) 20 (c) 32 **6.** 48 **7.** 180

8. 12 **9.** 25 **10.** (a) 0.3 (b) 1500

Page 208 M8.4

1. Cereal juice , Cereal tea, toast juice, toast tea

2. TS, TB, TR, SB, SR, BR

3. H1, H2, H3, H4, H5, H6, T1, T2, T3, T4, T5, T6

4. (a) HHH, HHT, HTH, HTT, THH, THT, TTH, TTT (b) $\frac{1}{8}$

5. (b) $\frac{3}{9}$

6. (a) BBBB, BBBG, BBGB, BGBB, GBBB, BBGG, BGBG, GBGB, GGBB, GBBG, BGGB, GGGB, GGBG, GBGG, BGGG, GGGG.

(b) $\frac{1}{16}$

7. (2, 1) (2, 4) (2, 9) (2, 16) (3, 1) (3, 4) (3, 9) (3, 16) (5, 1) (5, 4) (5, 9) (5, 16) (7, 1) (7, 4) (7, 9) (7, 16), 16 outcomes

8. (b) $\frac{5}{36}$ (c) $\frac{1}{2}$ (d) $\frac{1}{6}$ (e) $\frac{7}{36}$ (f) $\frac{1}{4}$

9. (a) HHHH, HHHT, HHTH, HTHH, THHH HHTT, HTHT, HTTH, TTHH, THHT, THTH, TTTH, TTHT, THTT, HTTT, TTTT.

(b) (i) $\frac{1}{16}$ (ii) $\frac{6}{16}$ (iii) $\frac{4}{16}$ (iv) $\frac{15}{16}$

10. Game is fair. p(win) = $\frac{1}{6}$ for both.

Page 209 Can you still? 8B

1. 5.14×10^3 **2.** 8×10^{-2} **3.** 7.2×10^{-1} **4.** 8.3×10^5

5. 5.6×10^2, 560; 6.5×10^{-3}, 0.0065; 6.5×10^3, 6500; 5.6×10^{-2}, 0.056.

6. 7.5×10^{12} **7.** 1.8×10^{17} **8.** 4×10^{-5} **9.** 4×10^{18}

10. 4.8×10^3 **11.** 8.7×10^{19} **12.** 2.32×10^9

13. 3.37×10^{-35} **14.** 9.3775×10^{-13} **15.** 8.7256×10^8

Page 210 M8.5

1. (b) and (e) **2.** (a) 0.8 (b) 0.2 **3.** (a) 0.9 (b) 0.1 **4.** 0.2

5. (a) 0.4 (b) 0.2 (c) 12 **6.** (a) 0.2 (b) 0.2 (c) 15

7. $\frac{12}{13}$ **8.** (a) 0.6 (b) 0.15 (c) 15

9. (a) $\frac{3}{8}$ (b) $\frac{15}{16}$ (c) $\frac{9}{16}$ (d) 2 **10.** (a) and (c) are true

Page 212 Can you still? 8C

1. 74° **2.** 53° **3.** 72° **4.** 30°

5. 60° **6.** 66° **7.** 113° **8.** 67.5°

Page 213 M8.6

1. $\frac{1}{12}$ **2.** $\frac{1}{4}$ **3.** (a) $\frac{1}{16}$ (b) $\frac{1}{4}$ **4.** (a) $\frac{1}{104}$ (b) $\frac{3}{26}$

5. (a) $\frac{9}{64}$ (b) $\frac{25}{64}$ **6.** $\frac{1}{216}$ **7.** (a) $\frac{1}{169}$ (b) $\frac{1}{4}$

8. (a) $\frac{1}{196}$ (b) $\frac{9}{196}$ (c) $\frac{9}{49}$ **9.** (a) 0.24 (b) 0.06 (c) 0.14

10. $\frac{1}{64}$ **11.** $\frac{1}{243}$ **12.** (a) $\frac{16}{121}$ (b) $\frac{56}{121}$

Page 216 M8.7

1. (b) $\frac{64}{121}$ (c) $\frac{24}{121}$ **2.** (b) $\frac{49}{144}$ (c) $\frac{25}{144}$ (d) $\frac{35}{72}$

3. (b) $\frac{49}{225}$ (c) $\frac{112}{225}$ **4.** (b) 0.16 (c) 0.48 **5.** (b) $\frac{9}{100}$ (c) $\frac{42}{100}$

6. (b) $\frac{1}{169}$ (c) $\frac{24}{169}$ **7.** (b) $\frac{1}{8}$ (b) $\frac{7}{8}$ (c) $\frac{3}{8}$

8. (b) $\frac{27}{512}$ (c) $\frac{135}{512}$ (d) $\frac{387}{512}$ **9.** (b) 0.343 (c) 0.973 (d) 0.441

10. (b) 9% (c) 41% (d) 86% **11.** (b) $\frac{2}{9}$ (c) $\frac{2}{27}$ (d) $\frac{26}{27}$

12. (a) $\frac{91}{216}$ (b) $\frac{15}{216}$

Page 220 E8.1

1. (b) $\frac{1}{13}$ (c) $\frac{6}{13}$ **2.** (b) $\frac{3}{11}$ (c) $\frac{6}{11}$ **3.** (b) $\frac{2}{21}$ (c) $\frac{10}{21}$

4. (a) $\frac{3}{8}$ (b) $\frac{1}{2}$ (c) $\frac{1}{2}$ **5.** (b) $\frac{1}{30}$ (c) $\frac{29}{30}$ (d) $\frac{1}{2}$

6. (b) $\frac{91}{460}$ (c) $\frac{27}{92}$ (d) $\frac{369}{460}$ **7.** (b) $\frac{21}{55}$ (c) $\frac{27}{55}$ (d) $\frac{219}{220}$

8. (a) $\frac{11}{850}$ (b) $\frac{997}{1700}$ (c) $\frac{117}{850}$ **9.** (b) $\frac{4}{7}$ (c) $\frac{74}{105}$

10. $\frac{1}{5}$ **11.** (a) $\frac{n}{20} \times \frac{(n-1)}{19}$ (b) $1 - \frac{n(n-1)}{380}$

12. (a) $\frac{x}{(x+y)} \times \frac{(x-1)}{(x+y-1)}$ (b) $\frac{2xy}{(x+y)(x+y-1)}$

Page 222 E8.2

1. (b) 15% (c) 37.5% **2.** (b) 0.675 **3.** (b) 35.5% **4.** (b) 46%

5. 2.4% **6.** 0.645 **7.** (b) $\frac{11}{45}$ **8.** $\frac{23}{40}$ **9.** $\frac{19}{20}$

10. $\frac{34}{63}$ **11.** (b) 0.24 (c) 0.12 **12.** 10 **13.** 4 **14.** 5

Page 226 WYM8

1. $53164 - 51083 = 2081$

$2081 \times 9.3 = 19353.3$ p = £193.53

5% of £193.53 = £9.68

Total bill £203.21

2. £119.13   **3.** £131.91   **4.** £61.37   **5.** £109.16
6. £94.54   **7.** £110.72   **8.** £159.51   **9.** 48

Page 226   Test yourself on unit 8

1. (a) (i) 5 (ii) 25 (iii) 25   (b) (i) 45 (ii) 135 (iii) 90

2. (a) 0.46, 0.58, 0.62, 0.68, 0.68, 0.62, 0.6, 0.63, 0.64, 0.62, 0.64,
0.63, 0.64, 0.64   (c) 0.64   (d) 1280

3. (a) (i) $\frac{1}{8}$ (ii) $\frac{3}{8}$ (iii) $\frac{1}{4}$ (iv) $\frac{3}{8}$ (b) (i) $\frac{1}{3}$ (ii) $\frac{1}{6}$ (iii) $\frac{7}{12}$

4. (a) (i) F.H.A, F.H.Dt., F.G.A, F.G.Dt., L.H.A, L.H.Dt., L.G.A,
L.G.Dt., S.H.A, S,H,Dt, S.G.A., S.G.Dt.   (ii) 12

(b) (ii) $\frac{1}{8}$ (iii) $\frac{11}{24}$

5. (a) (i) $\frac{5}{6}$ (ii) $\frac{1}{6}$ (b) (i) 0.2 (ii) 0.3 (iii) 25

6. (a) (i) $\frac{1}{12}$ (ii) $\frac{1}{26}$ (b) $\frac{1}{32}$

7. (a) (ii) $\frac{9}{121}$ (iii) $\frac{48}{121}$ (b) (ii) 0.216 (iii) 0.784 (iv) 0.432

8. (a) (ii) $\frac{3}{28}$ (iii) $\frac{13}{28}$ (iv) $\frac{9}{14}$ (b) (ii) 0.435

Page 230   Mixed examination questions

1. (b) (i) 0.42 (ii) 0.54   (c) 116   **2.** (a) 0.54 (b) 0.17

3. (b) $\frac{44}{132}\left(=\frac{1}{3}\right)$ **4.** (i) $\frac{1}{6}$ (ii) $\frac{1}{4}$

5. (a) Diamond 0.15   (b) 0.75   **6.** (a) $\frac{3}{10}$ (b) 200   **7.** $\frac{14}{45}$

8. (a) (i) $\frac{1}{5}$ (ii) $\frac{3}{10}$ (iii) 0   (b) (i) $\frac{14}{30}$ (ii) $\frac{8}{15}$

(c) (i) $\frac{x}{5+x} \times \frac{x-1}{4+x} = \frac{1}{6}$ → $x^2 - 3x - 4 = 0$ (ii) 9

9. (a) (i) $(2x-7)(x-14)$ (ii) $x = 14$ or $3\frac{1}{2}$ (b) (i) $\frac{7}{n+7}$ (ii) $n > 0$

(c) $2\left[\frac{n}{n+7} \times \frac{7}{n+7}\right] = \frac{4}{9}$ → $2n^2 - 35n + 98 = 0$ (d) $\frac{1}{9}$

UNIT 9

Page 234   M9.1

3. (a) 3   (b) 1   (c) 2   (d) 1   (e) 4
(f) 2   (g) 4   (h) 2   (i) 5   (j) 8
(k) 5   (l) 1   (m) 6   (n) 6   (o) 4   (p) 4

Page 235   M9.2

2. (a) 3   (b) 2   (c) 2   **3.** cube

Page 236   Can you still? 9A

1. $2 \times 3 \times 3 \times 3$ **2.** $2 \times 2 \times 5 \times 11$ **3.** $p = 3, q = 2, r = 7$
4. $2 \times 3 \times 5 \times 7$ **5.** $2^4 \times 3 \times 7$ **6.** $2 \times 3 \times 7$ (42)
7. $2^4 \times 3 \times 5 \times 7$ (1680) **8.** HCF = 15, LCM = $3 \times 5 \times 11 \times 23$ (3795)
9. HCF = 36, LCM = $2^2 \times 3^2 \times 7 \times 13$ (3276)

Page 237   M9.3

1. (a) $\begin{pmatrix} -3 \\ -1 \end{pmatrix}$ (b) $\begin{pmatrix} 1 \\ -4 \end{pmatrix}$ (c) $\begin{pmatrix} -2 \\ -2 \end{pmatrix}$ (d) $\begin{pmatrix} 3 \\ -2 \end{pmatrix}$

(e) $\begin{pmatrix} -3 \\ 2 \end{pmatrix}$ (f) $\begin{pmatrix} 1 \\ 2 \end{pmatrix}$ (g) $\begin{pmatrix} -4 \\ 0 \end{pmatrix}$ (h) $\begin{pmatrix} 4 \\ -3 \end{pmatrix}$

2. (a) $\begin{pmatrix} 1 \\ -3 \end{pmatrix}$ (b) $\begin{pmatrix} 3 \\ -7 \end{pmatrix}$ (c) $\begin{pmatrix} -4 \\ -9 \end{pmatrix}$ (d) $\begin{pmatrix} 1 \\ -10 \end{pmatrix}$ (e) $\begin{pmatrix} 0 \\ -6 \end{pmatrix}$ (f) $\begin{pmatrix} 2 \\ -8 \end{pmatrix}$

(g) $\begin{pmatrix} 5 \\ 0 \end{pmatrix}$ (h) $\begin{pmatrix} 4 \\ 3 \end{pmatrix}$ (i) $\begin{pmatrix} -2 \\ -4 \end{pmatrix}$ (j) $\begin{pmatrix} -7 \\ 2 \end{pmatrix}$ (k) $\begin{pmatrix} -5 \\ -6 \end{pmatrix}$ (l) $\begin{pmatrix} 9 \\ 0 \end{pmatrix}$

(m) $\begin{pmatrix} 7 \\ 4 \end{pmatrix}$ (n) $\begin{pmatrix} -3 \\ 4 \end{pmatrix}$ (o) $\begin{pmatrix} -2 \\ -3 \end{pmatrix}$ (p) $\begin{pmatrix} -9 \\ 6 \end{pmatrix}$ (q) $\begin{pmatrix} 5 \\ 6 \end{pmatrix}$ (r) $\begin{pmatrix} -5 \\ 7 \end{pmatrix}$

3. (f) $\begin{pmatrix} 4 \\ 4 \end{pmatrix}$ (g) $\begin{pmatrix} -2 \\ -8 \end{pmatrix}$ (h) $\begin{pmatrix} 0 \\ 8 \end{pmatrix}$

Page 239   M9.4

7. (d) Reflection x axis
8. (a) $x = 3$ (b) y axis   (c) $y = -1$ (d) x axis
9. (e) (−3, 6) (−3, 4) (−2, 4)   **10.** (e) $x = 1$
11. (f) Reflection in y axis

Page 241   Can you still? 9B

1. 9   **2.** 21   **3.** 2   **4.** 4   **5.** $\frac{5}{7}$ **6.** 42
7. 32   **8.** 6   **9.** 10   **10.** −4   **11.** −5   **12.** −10
13. $3(3x - 1) = 24, x = 3$ **14.** 38, 40, 42, 44
15. (a) $5x + 250 = 360$ (b) $x = 22$ (c) 12°, 94°, 143°, 111°
16. Rose £190, Imran £265, Megan £305

Page 243   M9.5

3. (a) (7, 5) (b) (5, $4\frac{1}{2}$)   (c) (5, 4)   (d) (2, 8)
4. (f) Rotation 90° clockwise centre (−3, 5)
7. (a) Reflection in $y = x + 1$
(b) Rotation 180° centre (0, 2)
(c) Rotation 90° Anti-clockwise centre (−1, 1)
8. (g) Rotation 90° clockwise centre (−2, −2)

Page 247   M9.6

1. Scale factor 2, centre (1, 0)
2. S.F. 3, centre (2, 4)
3. S.F. 4, centre (−6, 5)
4. S.F. 2, centre (4, 3)
5. S.F. 2, centre (−5, 5)

Page 250   E9.1

2. (d) $\begin{pmatrix} 6 \\ -3 \end{pmatrix}$ **3.** (e) $\begin{pmatrix} -3 \\ 0 \end{pmatrix}$ **4.** S.F. −3 centre (2, 1)
5. S.F. $1\frac{1}{2}$, centre (2, −1)   **6.** (f) Back to A   **7.** (f) $\begin{pmatrix} 6 \\ 0 \end{pmatrix}$

Page 252   E9.2

1. (a) Rotation 180°, centre (3, 4)
(b) Rotation 90° clockwise, centre (3, 1)
(c) Translation $\begin{pmatrix} 3 \\ 2 \end{pmatrix}$

2. (c) Translation $\begin{pmatrix} -5 \\ 3 \end{pmatrix}$

3. (a) Reflection in x axis   (b) Translation $\begin{pmatrix} -4 \\ 1 \end{pmatrix}$

    (c) Rotation 180°, centre (–1, 0)   (d) Translation $\begin{pmatrix} 2 \\ 1 \end{pmatrix}$

4. (g) Translation $\begin{pmatrix} 6 \\ 0 \end{pmatrix}$

6. (a) Translation $\begin{pmatrix} 9 \\ -5 \end{pmatrix}$ (b) Enlargement S.F. $\frac{1}{2}$, centre (0, 0)

    (c) Reflection in $y = 1$ (d) Rotation 180° centre (4, 3)

    (e) Rotation 180° centre (0, 0)

7. (d) Rotation 90° clockwise, centre (1, –1)

    (g) Enlargement S.F. –2, centre (4, 0)

    (i) Reflection in $y = 5$

8. (e) Enlargement S.F. 2 centre (1, 0)

    (h) Rotation 90° clockwise, centre (–3, 2)

    (i) Translation $\begin{pmatrix} 7 \\ 3 \end{pmatrix}$

Page 254   Can you still? 9C

1. (a) 31   (b) –23   **2.** (a) 60 (b) 0   **3.** (a) 121 (b) 0

4. (a) $\frac{2}{3}$ (b) $-\frac{1}{6}$ **5.** 6   **6.** $x = 2$ or 3   **7.** $z = 0$ or 10

8. $w = 1$ **9.** $4x^2$ **10.** $5x - 11$

Page 256   E9.3

1. SSS   **2.** SAS   **3.** No   **4.** ASA

Page 260   WYM9

1. (a) £42   (b) £504   (c) £546   (d) £126

2. (a) £84   (b) £558   (c) £642   (d) £82

3. (a) Total credit price £820, Extra cost £85   (b) £440, £50

    (c) £13752, £1352   (d) £250, £20   (e) £594.64, £129.64

4. £988   **5.** £980

Page 261   Test yourself on unit 9

1. (a) (i) 2   (ii) 2   (b) (i) 6   (ii) 6   (c) (i) 1   (ii) 1   (d) ∞

2. (a) 3   **3.** (c) Translation $\begin{pmatrix} -5 \\ 1 \end{pmatrix}$ **4.** 1 unit

5. (b) (i) Rotation 90° anticlockwise, centre (1, –1)

    (ii) Rotation 90° clockwise, centre (0, 0)

6. (a) S.F. 2, Centre (3, 9)

7. (b) Enlargement S.F. $-\frac{1}{2}$ Centre (–3, 1)

Page 265   Mixed examination questions

1. (a) Rotation 90° clockwise centre (0, 0)   (b) Reflection in $y = x$

3. (a) (ii) $y = x + 1$ (b) Rotation 90° Anti-clockwise, centre (–1, 0)

5. (a) Reflection in $x = 2$ (b) Translation $\begin{pmatrix} -6 \\ -5 \end{pmatrix}$

UNIT 10

Page 268   M10.1

1. (a) 4 kg   (b) 0.7 l   (c) 2 m   (d) 330 ml

2. (a) 0.8 cm   (b) 0.35 km   (c) 9500 g   (d) 375 g

    (e) 0.575 kg   (f) 6200 kg   (g) 1.832 l   (h) 4500 ml

    (i) 2.48 m   (j) 5830 litres   (k) 7300 cm^3 (l) 0.872 m^3

3. 2.43 kg   **4.** 220   **5.** 12

6. (a) 2 pounds   (b) 2 pints   (c) 7 pounds   (d) 22 yards

7. (a) 64   (b) 6720   (c) 34   (d) 58   (e) 3520   (f) 76

    (g) 5   (h) 4   (i) 54   (j) 5600   (k) $8\frac{1}{2}$ (l) 54

8. 13 Stone 8 pounds   **9.** $6\frac{3}{4}$ **10.** GALLON

Page 270   M10.2

1. (a) 10   (b) 90   (c) 450   (d) 225   (e) 45

2. (a) 6.6   (b) 11   (c) 7.7   (d) 18.7   (e) 13.64

3. (a) 9   (b) 40.5   (c) 90   (d) 24.75   (e) 20.7

4. Tom's   **5.** Ed.

6. (a) 300   (b) 9   (c) 8   (d) 20   (e) 15

    (f) 8.8   (g) 30   (h) 7   (i) 12   (j) 630

    (k) 132   (l) 5   (m) 180   (n) 22.4   (o) 16

7. B   **8.** D   **9.** £32.40   **10.** 38.4

11. No   **12.** a metre   **13.** Yes   **14.** 3

Page 271   Can you still? 10A

1. 4   **2.** (a) 3, 7   (b) –2, 3   (c) $-\frac{2}{5}, \frac{1}{5}$ (d) $\frac{7}{3}$, 2

3. (a) $y = 2x - 1$ (b) $y = -\frac{1}{2} x + 3$, $x + 2y = 6$

4. $y = 4x + 3$ **5.** $y = 2x + 7$

Page 273   M10.3

1. $1\frac{1}{2}$ hrs.   **2.** 140 km/h   **3.** 20 miles   **4.** $9\frac{1}{2}$ hrs.

5. (a) 60 M.P.H.   (b) 36 M.P.H.   (c) 45 M.P.H.

    (d) 72 M.P.H.   (e) 40 M.P.H.

6. 11 miles   **7.** 18 km   **8.** 11.35   **9.** 20 secs

10. (a) 10.8   (b) 72   (c) 2.808   (d) 0.108

11. (a) 5   (b) 32   (c) 17   (d) 6.8

12. Nerys   **13.** 60 km/h   **14.** 970 km/h   **15.** 3 m 20 secs.

16. (a) (i) 20 km/h (ii) 5.56 m/s   (b) 20 km/h, 5.56 m/s

17. (a) 99 km   (b) 09.45   (c) 08.45   (d) 20 km/h   (e) 13.8̇   (f) 10 m/s

Page 276   M10.4

1. 4 g/cm^3, 16 g/cm^3, 104 g, 864 g, 15 cm^3, 30 g, 4 g/cm^3, 20 cm^3,

    190 cm^3, 4.2 g/cm^3, 16 g

2. 164 g   **3.** 19.3 g/cm^3 **4.** 1.54 g/cm^3 **5.** 200 cm^3

6. B by 0.5 g **7.** 263 cm³ **8.** 415 g **9.** 70 cm³

10. 333 cm³ **11.** £6000 **12.** £171 **13.** £21.95 **14.** 218.75

Page 277 Can you still? 10B

1. 7.4 cm **2.** 6.8 **3.** (a) 13.2 (b) 4.76

Page 278 M10.5

1. (a) 7.81 (b) 4.47 (c) 5 (d) 10.72

2. (a) 24 (b) 12.21 (c) 10.80 (d) 11.11

(e) 15.01 (f) 40.95 (g) 8.41 (h) 16.19

3. 12.50 **4.** 14.56 **5.** 37.64 **6.** 7.32

Page 280 M10.6

1. 5.50 m **2.** B by 0.57 **3.** 4.90 m **4.** 10.39 m

5. 14.42 km **6.** 11.40 km **7.** 23.71 inches **8.** 79.65 km

9. 2.58 km **10.** 5.02 m **11.** 721 **12.** 10

13. 8.49 **14.** (b) (8, 1) (c) $\left(5, -\frac{1}{2}\right)$ (d) 6.71

15. (b) (−1, −2) (c) (0, 0) (d) 8.94 **16.** 9.17 cm

17. (a) 6.32 (b) 10.91 (c) 12.69

18. 31.75 cm² **19.** 110.85 cm²

20. (a) 17 cm (b) 11.18 cm (c) 7.21 cm

Page 283 Can you still? 10C

1. $\frac{y}{a}$ **2.** $\frac{y-c}{a}$ **3.** $\frac{y}{c} + q$ **4.** $ct - r$ **5.** $\frac{zy-c}{m}$

6. $p(m+b)$ **7.** $\frac{5z-n}{b}$ **8.** $\frac{p-q-r}{c}$ **9.** $\sqrt{(p-m)}$ **10.** $(v^2 - q)^2$

11. $\sqrt[3]{\left(\frac{y-w}{p}\right)}$ **12.** $\frac{w^2+b}{a}$ **13.** $\frac{qr+p}{n-m}$ **14.** $\frac{b+z}{a+m}$ **15.** $\frac{4h-3qx}{q-k}$

16. $\frac{bx}{c-a}$ **17.** $\frac{k+mn}{m-n}$ **18.** $\frac{zx}{m^3-p}$ **19.** $\frac{9am^2}{bc^2-9a^2}$

Page 284 M10.7

1. A. **2.** H. **3.** A. **4.** H. **5.** O. **6.** O

7. H **8.** A

Page 286 M10.8

1. 5.00 cm **2.** 21.1 cm **3.** 11.4 cm **4.** 11.2 cm **5.** 4.53 cm

6. 17.9 cm **7.** 6.38 cm **8.** 30.8 cm **9.** 67.9 cm **10.** 30.1 cm

11. 32.6 cm **12.** 8.46 cm **13.** 15.0 cm **14.** 17.9 cm **15.** 9.16 cm

16. 49.9 cm **17.** 6.25 cm **18.** 4.23 cm **19.** $r = 11.1$ cm, $s = 21.5$ cm

20. $t = 15.0$ cm, $u = 7.95$ cm **21.** $v = 22.5$ cm **22.** $w = 9.01$ cm

Page 289 M10.9

1. 28.6° **2.** 47.3° **3.** 77.9° **4.** 38.0° **5.** 46.1° **6.** 66.8°

7. 55.3° **8.** 37.8° **9.** 61.7° **10.** 61.9° **11.** 63.7° **12.** 82.8°

13. (i) 13.4 cm (ii) 44.8° **14.** (i) 3.82 cm (ii) 18.2° **15.** 29.8°

Page 290 M10.10

1. 14.3 cm **2.** 54.3° **3.** 73.7° **4.** 10.0 cm **5.** 9.02 cm

6. 18.7° **7.** 3.00 m **8.** 20.2° **9.** (a) 11.3 m (b) 13.8 m

10. 17.7° **11.** 47.2° **12.** (a) 11.5° (b) 33.9° (c) 67.6°

13. 10.3 cm **14.** 19.1 cm **15.** 6.6 cm **16.** (a) 45° (b) 3.83 cm

17. 4.08 m **18.** 5.49 cm **19.** 29.9 cm **20.** 13.4 cm

21. 9.92 cm **22.** 6.45 cm, 16.8 cm **23.** (a) 9 cm (b) 13.5 cm

24. 26 cm **25.** $x = 28.6$ m, $h = 34.1$ m

Page 294 Can you still? 10D

1. (a) $-\frac{1}{2}$ (b) 4 (c) $-\frac{3}{4}$ (d) $\frac{5}{7}$ (e) $\frac{5}{3}$ **2.** $-\frac{1}{5}$

3. 3 **4.** $y = 3x - 2$ **5.** $y = 2x - 1$ **6.** $y = 2x + 7$

Page 296 E10.1

1. $a = \begin{pmatrix} 1 \\ 3 \end{pmatrix}$, $b = \begin{pmatrix} -3 \\ -2 \end{pmatrix}$, $c = \begin{pmatrix} -2 \\ 2 \end{pmatrix}$, $d = \begin{pmatrix} -2 \\ 4 \end{pmatrix}$, $e = \begin{pmatrix} 4 \\ -1 \end{pmatrix}$, $f = \begin{pmatrix} -2 \\ -3 \end{pmatrix}$, $g = \begin{pmatrix} -3 \\ 1 \end{pmatrix}$,

$h = \begin{pmatrix} -3 \\ -3 \end{pmatrix}$, $\overrightarrow{AB} = \begin{pmatrix} -1 \\ 2 \end{pmatrix}$, $\overrightarrow{CD} = \begin{pmatrix} 4 \\ 2 \end{pmatrix}$, $\overrightarrow{EF} = \begin{pmatrix} 0 \\ 2 \end{pmatrix}$, $\overrightarrow{GH} = \begin{pmatrix} 1 \\ -1 \end{pmatrix}$, $\overrightarrow{MN} = \begin{pmatrix} 4 \\ 4 \end{pmatrix}$

$\overrightarrow{PQ} = \begin{pmatrix} -4 \\ 0 \end{pmatrix}$, $\overrightarrow{RS} = \begin{pmatrix} -1 \\ -2 \end{pmatrix}$, $\overrightarrow{XY} = \begin{pmatrix} 5 \\ -3 \end{pmatrix}$

3. $a \sqrt{5}$, $b \sqrt{10}$, $c \sqrt{29}$, $d \sqrt{3}$, $e \sqrt{2}$, $|\overrightarrow{AB}| \sqrt{20}$, $|\overrightarrow{CD}| \sqrt{37}$, $|\overrightarrow{EF}|$ 5,
$|\overrightarrow{GH}|$ 2, $|\overrightarrow{MN}| \sqrt{41}$

4. (a) 3

Page 299 E10.2

1. (a) $\begin{pmatrix} 6 \\ 10 \end{pmatrix}$ (b) $\begin{pmatrix} 6 \\ -3 \end{pmatrix}$ (c) $\begin{pmatrix} 1 \\ 6 \end{pmatrix}$ (d) $\begin{pmatrix} 2 \\ 12 \end{pmatrix}$ (e) $\begin{pmatrix} 0 \\ 0 \end{pmatrix}$ (f) $\begin{pmatrix} -2 \\ 1 \end{pmatrix}$

(g) $\begin{pmatrix} 13 \\ 13 \end{pmatrix}$ (h) $\begin{pmatrix} 9 \\ 2 \end{pmatrix}$ (i) $\begin{pmatrix} -11 \\ 12 \end{pmatrix}$ (j) $\begin{pmatrix} -10 \\ -8 \end{pmatrix}$

2. (a) $\begin{pmatrix} 2 \\ -7 \end{pmatrix}$ (b) $\begin{pmatrix} -5 \\ 3 \end{pmatrix}$ (c) $\begin{pmatrix} -2 \\ 7 \end{pmatrix}$ (d) $\begin{pmatrix} -3 \\ -4 \end{pmatrix}$

(e) $\overrightarrow{AB} + \overrightarrow{BC} = \overrightarrow{AC}$ (f) (8, 10) (g) (10, 3)

3. (a) w (b) c (c) z (d) m (e) s (f) n

(g) q (h) q (i) k (j) w (k) m

4. (a) b (b) −2a (c) 3a (d) a + b (e) 2a + 2b

(f) 2a + b (g) a + 2b (h) −2a − b (i) 3a + 2b

(j) −a − 3b (k) −4a − b (l) a + 4b

5. (a) $\overrightarrow{LW}$ (b) $\overrightarrow{LP}$ (c) $\overrightarrow{LD}$ (d) $\overrightarrow{LT}$

(e) $\overrightarrow{LU}$ (f) $\overrightarrow{LH}$ (g) $\overrightarrow{LA}$ (h) $\overrightarrow{LE}$

6. (a) $\begin{pmatrix} 5 \\ -1 \end{pmatrix}$ (b) $\begin{pmatrix} -3 \\ -3 \end{pmatrix}$ (c) $\begin{pmatrix} 8 \\ 2 \end{pmatrix}$ (d) $\begin{pmatrix} -5 \\ 1 \end{pmatrix}$ (e) $\begin{pmatrix} 3 \\ 3 \end{pmatrix}$ (f) $\begin{pmatrix} -2 \\ -2 \end{pmatrix}$

7. (a) b (b) −a (c) a − b (d) a + b

8. (a) −3p (b) p + q (c) 2p − q (d) q − 3p

9. (a) −2m (b) m + 2n (c) −m − n (d) 2n − 2m (e) m − n

10. (a) b + c (b) −a − b (c) a + b − c (d) −a − b − c (e) b + c − a

11. Yes, $\overrightarrow{CD} = 2\overrightarrow{AB}$ **12.** Yes, $\overrightarrow{WZ} = 3\overrightarrow{PQ}$ **13.** B, C and E

Page 304 E10.3

1. (a) a + b (b) $\frac{1}{2}(a + b)$ (c) $\frac{1}{2}b - \frac{1}{2}a$

2. 2b (b) 3a + 2b (c) 2b (d) 2b − 3a (e) −3a

3. (a) b (b) 2b (c) b − a (d) 2b − 2a

(e) 2b − a (f) b − 2a

4. (a) (i) $\frac{1}{2}\mathbf{q}$ (ii) $\frac{1}{2}\mathbf{p}$ (iii) $\mathbf{p}+\mathbf{q}$ (iv) $\frac{1}{4}(\mathbf{p}+\mathbf{q})$

(v) $\frac{1}{4}\mathbf{p}-\frac{1}{4}\mathbf{q}$ (vi) $\frac{1}{4}\mathbf{p}-\frac{1}{4}\mathbf{q}$

(b) MR is parallel to RN $\therefore$ M, R and N are co-linear (c) 1:1

5. (a) (i) $\mathbf{s}-\mathbf{r}$ (ii) $\mathbf{r}+\mathbf{s}$ (iii) $\frac{2}{3}(\mathbf{s}-\mathbf{r})$

(iv) $\frac{2}{3}\mathbf{s}+\frac{1}{3}\mathbf{r}$ (v) $\frac{1}{3}\mathbf{s}$ (vi) $\frac{1}{3}(\mathbf{s}+\mathbf{r})$

(b) from (ii) and (vi) $\overrightarrow{YX}=\frac{1}{3}\overrightarrow{AC}$ $\therefore$ YX is parallel to AC

(c) 1:3

6. (a) (i) $\mathbf{q}-\mathbf{p}$ (ii) $\frac{1}{2}(\mathbf{q}-\mathbf{p})$ (iii) $\frac{1}{2}(\mathbf{p}+\mathbf{q})$ (iv) $\frac{1}{3}(\mathbf{p}+\mathbf{q})$

(c) from b $\overrightarrow{BF}=\frac{3}{2}\overrightarrow{BG}$ $\therefore$ parallel. B, F and G are co-linear

(d) $\overrightarrow{CG}=\frac{1}{3}\mathbf{p}-\frac{2}{3}\mathbf{q}$, $\overrightarrow{CD}=\frac{1}{2}\mathbf{p}-\mathbf{q}$ $\therefore$ $\overrightarrow{CD}=\frac{3}{2}\overrightarrow{CG}$

(e) BF, CD and AE

7. (a) $\frac{3}{2}\mathbf{p}$ (b) $\mathbf{p}+\frac{1}{4}\mathbf{q}$ (c) $\mathbf{p}+\mathbf{q}$ (d) $\frac{1}{2}(\mathbf{p}+\mathbf{q})$

(e) $\overrightarrow{XY}=\frac{1}{4}\mathbf{q}-\frac{1}{2}\mathbf{p}$, $\overrightarrow{YZ}=\frac{1}{4}\mathbf{q}-\frac{1}{2}\mathbf{p}$

(f) XY parallel to YZ so X, Y and Z co-linear

8. (a) (3, 6)   (b) (4, 0)   (c) 4.2

9. (a) $2\mathbf{q}-2\mathbf{p}$ (b) $\mathbf{q}-\mathbf{p}$ (c) RQ = 2NL, RQ parallel to NL

(d) $\overrightarrow{PL}=\mathbf{q}$, $\overrightarrow{LM}=\mathbf{p}$, $\overrightarrow{NM}=\mathbf{q}$, $\overrightarrow{PN}=\mathbf{p}$

10. (a) (i) $\mathbf{b}-\mathbf{a}$ (ii) $\mathbf{c}-\mathbf{a}$ (iii) $\mathbf{c}-\mathbf{b}$

(iv) $\frac{1}{2}\mathbf{a}-\mathbf{b}+\frac{\mathbf{c}}{2}$ (v) $\frac{1}{2}\mathbf{a}+\frac{1}{2}\mathbf{b}-\mathbf{c}$ (vi) $\frac{1}{2}\mathbf{b}+\frac{1}{2}\mathbf{c}-\mathbf{a}$

(b) $\frac{1}{3}(\mathbf{a}+\mathbf{b}+\mathbf{c})$ (c) $\frac{1}{3}(\mathbf{a}+\mathbf{b}+\mathbf{c})$ (d) $\frac{1}{3}(\mathbf{a}+\mathbf{b}+\mathbf{c})$

(e) they meet at a point   (f) (5, 4)

11. (a) (i) $\frac{3}{4}\mathbf{p}$ (ii) $\frac{3}{8}\mathbf{q}$ (iii) $\frac{1}{4}(\mathbf{p}+\mathbf{q})$

(iv) $\frac{1}{4}\mathbf{q}-\frac{1}{2}\mathbf{p}$ (v) $\frac{1}{8}\mathbf{q}-\frac{1}{4}\mathbf{p}$

(b) $\overrightarrow{MX}=2\overrightarrow{XN}$ so MX is parallel to XN. M, X and N are co-linear Ratio 2:1

Page 308   WYM10

1. £149.90   **2.** £3037.57   **3.** £3057.57

4. £1942.43   **5.** £4936.57   **6.** £246.83

7. £46.83   **8.** £5001.73   **9.** £5021.73

Page 309   Test yourself on unit 10

1. (a) 762 g   (b) 12 st, 3 pounds (c) 25 cm   (d) 11

(e) 40   (f) 10 km   (g) 54

2. (a) $4\frac{1}{2}$ hrs.   (b) $1\frac{1}{2}$ mins   (c) 4980 g   (d) 19.3 g/cm³

3. (a) 7 cm   (b) 12.7 cm   (c) 9.8 cm

(d) 6.4   (e) 26.5 m   (f) 116.1 cm²

4. (a) 55.4°   (b) 8.7 cm   (c) 35.8 cm   (d) 7.7 cm

5. (a)

(b) (i) $\begin{pmatrix}6\\4\end{pmatrix}$ (ii) $\begin{pmatrix}2\\-11\end{pmatrix}$ (iii) $\begin{pmatrix}6\\-33\end{pmatrix}$ (iv) $\begin{pmatrix}-1\\26\end{pmatrix}$ (v) 10   (vi) (7, 5)

6. (a) (i) $3\mathbf{a}-\mathbf{b}$ (ii) $\frac{1}{4}(3\mathbf{a}-\mathbf{b})$ (iii) $\frac{1}{4}(7\mathbf{a}+3\mathbf{b})$ (iv) $\mathbf{b}-\frac{7}{2}\mathbf{a}$

(b) (i) $\mathbf{u}+\mathbf{v}$ (ii) $\mathbf{u}+\frac{1}{2}\mathbf{v}$ (iii) $\mathbf{v}+\frac{1}{2}\mathbf{u}$ (iv) $\frac{1}{2}(\mathbf{u}+\mathbf{v})$

(v) $\mathbf{u}$ (vi) $\mathbf{v}-\mathbf{u}$ (vii) $\frac{1}{3}(2\mathbf{u}+\mathbf{v})$ (ix) 1:2

Page 311   Mixed examination questions

1. (a) 22   (b) 5 litres   **2.** 50 kg   **3.** (a) 5.29 cm

(b) 41.4°   (c) 12.4 cm   **4.** (a) 13.6 cm   (b) 14.5 cm

(c) 69.8°   **5.** (a) $\mathbf{a}$ (b) $\mathbf{a}+\mathbf{b}$ (c) $-\mathbf{b}$

(d) $\frac{3}{2}\mathbf{b}$ (e) $\mathbf{a}-\frac{1}{2}\mathbf{b}$ **6.** 150 km/h

7. (a) $3\mathbf{a}-\mathbf{b}$ (b) $-\frac{1}{4}\mathbf{a}+\frac{3}{4}\mathbf{b}$ **8.** 250 cm²   **9.** 8.79 m

10. (a) (i) $2\mathbf{x}+\mathbf{y}$ (ii) $\frac{3}{2}\mathbf{x}+\frac{3}{4}\mathbf{y}$ (iii) $\frac{3}{2}\mathbf{x}-\frac{3}{4}\mathbf{y}$

(b) (i) $2\mathbf{x}-\mathbf{y}$ (ii) co-linear

UNIT 11

Page 315   M11.1

1. (a)

	P.Choc	M.Choc	W.Choc	Total
F.	19	19	5	43
M.	21	27	9	57
Total	40	46	14	100

(b) 40

2. (a)

	Cinema	Swim	Cycle	Total
B.	18	17	12	47
G.	15	10	8	33
Total	33	27	20	80

(b) 27

3. (a)

	Art.	P.E.	Maths	Science	Total
B.	20	53	28	18	119
G.	31	28	8	14	81
Total	51	81	36	32	200

(b) $\frac{36}{200}$

4. (a)

	Smoke	Drink Alcohol	Neither	Smoke and Drink	Total
Y.10	21	40	88	24	173
Y.11	23	56	110	38	227
Total	44	96	198	62	400

(b) $\frac{198}{400}$

(c) 24.7%

5. (a)

	Car Accident	No Car Accident	Total
17 – 25	123	481	604
26 – 60	65	637	702
Over 60	98	396	494
Total	286	1514	1800

(b) 15.9%

(c) 17–25,   20.4%
    26–60,   9.2%
    60+,   19.8%

Page 316   Can you still? 11A

1. $\frac{7}{17}$ **2.** (a) $\frac{1}{13}$ (b) $\frac{1}{4}$

3. (a) 0.15   (b) 0.45   (c) 16

4. $\frac{1}{6}$ **5.** $\frac{1}{8}$ **6.** (a) $\frac{1}{8}$ (b) $\frac{1}{4}$

Page 317   M11.2

1. Arsenal 60°, Liverpool 60°, Chelsea 80°, Man U. 100°, Everton 24°, A. Villa 36°.

2. Shakespeare 90°, Churchill 108°, Newton 42°, Elizabeth I 72°, Brunel 48°.

3. Crisps 120°, Fruit 70°, Nuts 20°, Biscuits 36°, Chocolate 68°, Other 46°.

4. Simpsons 50, 150°; Bugs Bunny 8, 24°; Jungle Book 20, 60°; Tom and Jerry 30, 90°; Scooby Doo 12, 36°

(a) 20   (b) 40   (c) 8   (d) 12

5. (a) £225   (b) £150   (c) £525

6. (a) 50   (b) 30   (c) 18   (d) 90   (e) 40   (f) 12

7. Homer 70, 140°; Bart 40, 80°; Mr Burns 32, 64°; Marge 22, 44°; Lisa 16, 32°

8. (a) Carl wrong (240:250)   (b) Jasmin wrong (160:150)

9. B   **10.** C

Page 320   Can you still? 11B

1. $\frac{11}{20}$, $\frac{112}{200}$, 0.563, 58.2%, 0.595, $\frac{3}{5}$

2. 53   **3.** £1237.35   **4.** 0.00283   **5.** 2.1×10^{15} **6.** £18400

7. a = 3, b = 2, c = 13   **8.** $2\sqrt{3}$ **9.** 1   **10.** 0.96

11. $\frac{38}{99}$ **12.** $\frac{4\sqrt{5}}{5}$ **13** (a) 18   (b) 8

14. (a) $P = \frac{12}{\sqrt{Q}}$ (b) 3   (c) 2.25

Page 321   M11.3

1. (a) none   (b) negative   (c) none   (d) positive

2. (c) about 66   **3.** (c) about 14

4. (a) weak positive   (b) weak positive   (c) positive   (d) none

5. (b) negative   (d) about 58

Page 324   Can you still? 11C

1. (a) $\frac{1}{10}$ (b) $\frac{21}{40}$ **2.** (a) $\frac{4}{15}$ (b) $\frac{8}{15}$

3. (a) $\frac{1}{27}$ (b) $\frac{1}{9}$ (c) $\frac{19}{27}$

4. $\frac{55}{323}$ (b) $\frac{268}{323}$ (c) $\frac{440}{969}$

Page 326   M11.4

1. (b) 11, 11, 16, 21, 23, 24, 24, 24, 24

(c) Sales increase steadily and then stay constant

2. (b) 30   (c) 31   (d) 32, 33, 27, 23, 23, 27, 27, 26, 31, 30, 29, 29

(e) sales go down in the summer and then recover

3. (b) 47, 43, 45, 47, 56, 55, 53, 52, 52

(d) there is a gradual increase and then a slow decrease. Lower wages – team demoted?

4. (b) 3.9, 3.9, 3.8, 3.7, 3.6, 3.2, 2.6, 2.1, 2.2, 2, 2.4, 3

(c) profits fell steadily and then increased from 2004

5. (b) 920, 1060, 1080, 1080, 1100, 1140, 1190, 1170, 1270, 1270

(d) attendance went up steadily

Page 329   Can you still? 11D

1. 7   **2.** 4   **3.** 56   **4.** –2 or –4   **5.** 4 or 5

6. 6   **7.** 0 or 6   **8.** 8 or –2   **9.** –9   **10.** 0 or 1

11. $-\frac{1}{5}$ or $\frac{3}{2}$ **12.** $\frac{2}{3}$ or $\frac{5}{4}$

13. (a) $(x + 6)^2 = (x + 4)^2 + (x + 2)^2$ (b) x = 4, 6 cm, 8 cm, 10 cm

14. (a) $(n + 5)(n + 3) – 15$ (b) $n^2 + 8n – 65 = 0$ (c) n = 5

Page 330   E11.1

1. For discussion, d and e are ok

2. (a) no, whole day not covered   (b) yes   (c) no, biased sample

(d) the telephone directory will not have people without landlines

(e) no, bias   (f) yes   (g) yes   (h) no, age bias

Page 332   E11.2

1. 24   **2.** (vertically) 12, 11,11, 8, 8

3. (a) systematic

(b) the sample is biased because only customers are asked

5. 36, 15, 11, 5, 17, 7, 7

6. (a) 14   (b) There are more females than males, choose 11 females and 9 males   (c) 5

7. (a) mean = 66.3   (b) mean = 65.6

(c) method in part (a) is more reliable because it has more values

(d) random sampling

8. 33 dogs, 34 cats, 22 rabbits, 19 hamsters

Page 335   WYM11

1. £160.01   **2.** £139.65   **3.** £303.86   **4.** £879.83

5. £2.71   **6.** £3.91   **7.** £6165, £1165

8. £16939.08, £1939.08   **9.** £1119.12, £119.12   **10.** £157.20

Page 336   Test yourself on unit 11

1. (a)

	AUST.	INDIA	USA	TOTAL
FEMALE	23	32	16	71
MALE	24	8	17	49
TOTAL	47	40	33	120

(b) $\frac{1}{3}$

2. (a) Inherited 69°, Business 114°, Music 84°, Sport 57° Other 36°

(b) (i) 18   (ii) 36   (iii) 12   (iv) 42

3. (b) Strong negative   (d) about 42   (c) 2.2 → 2.3

4. (b) 4-point averages : 410, 355, 335, 260, 195, 220, 235, 325, 415

(d) decrease in summer – better weather

5. (b) (ii) $\frac{80}{374} = 0.214$ →   Spain 13, Greece 10, U.S.A. 18 Australia 8, Thailand 6, France 17, India 4, China 4

Page 338   Mixed examination questions

1. (a) $\frac{4}{5}$ (b) $\frac{6}{125}$ **2.** (b) 6 days   (d) 24 g

3. (a) (i) None (ii) length of hair   (b) (i) positive   (ii) waist measurement

4. 182, 178, 180, 184   **5.** 24

6. (a) He should have sampled more boys than girls   (b) 15   **7.** 112

8. 0–16, 19; 17–29, 12; 30–44, 9; 45–59, 8; 60 + 2; Total 50

UNIT 12

Page 342   M12.1

1. (b) $y = 2$ (c) $x = 4$ **2.** (b) $y = 3$, $x = 1$

Page 343   M12.2

1. (a) $x = 3$, $y = 2$ (b) $x = 0$, $y = 5$ (c) $x = 1$, $y = 6$

2. (d) $x = 4$, $y = 3$ **3.** $x = 1\frac{1}{2}$, $y = 4\frac{1}{2}$

4. $x = 1\frac{1}{2}$, $y = 3\frac{1}{2}$ **5.** $x = 5$, $y = 3$

6. (a) $x = 10$, $y = 1$ (b) $x = 3$, $y = 8$ (c) $x = 1$, $y = 4$

Page 344   M12.3

1. $x = 3$, $y = 1$ **2.** $x = 2$, $y = 4$ **3.** $x = -1$, $y = 5$

4. $x = 4$, $y = 3$ **5.** $x = 2$, $y = 1$ **6.** $x = 2$, $y = -2$

7. $x = 6$, $y = 3$ **8.** $x = 1$, $y = 2$ **9.** $x = 5$, $y = 2$

10. $x = -3$, $y = 1$ **11.** $x = 4$, $y = -2$ **12.** $x = -3$, $y = -3$

Page 346   M12.4

1. $a = 2$, $b = 1$ **2.** $c = 3$, $d = 1$ **3.** $x = 3$, $y = 2$

4. $p = 5$, $q = 4$ **5.** $u = 4$, $v = -1$ **6.** $p = 7$, $q = -2$

7. $a = 5$, $b = -2$ **8.** $m = 3$, $n = 4$ **9.** $p = 5$, $q = -1$

10. $g = 3$, $h = 4$ **11.** $m = 4$, $n = 1$ **12.** $b = 5$, $c = 2$

13. $x = 3$, $y = -1$ **14.** $r = 7$, $s = -3$ **15.** $p = 3$, $q = 2$

16. $b = 2$, $c = -3$ **17.** $x = -2$, $y = 4$ **18.** $m = -3$, $n = -2$

19. $x = 1$, $y = 5$ **20.** $x = -2$, $y = 5$ **21.** $a = -1$, $b = -1$

22. $x = 0.25$, $y = -0.5$ **23.** $a = 0.5$, $b = 3$ **24.** $r = 0.4$, $s = -0.75$

Page 347   M12.5

1. Shirt £42, Tie £16   **2.** 5 gellos, 12 inkos

3. Adult £5.50, Child £3.50   **4.** 25   **5.** 13, 6

6. 1st £205.50, 2nd £129.50   **7.** A £13.50, B £18.   **8.** $m = 3$ $c = -1$

9. (a) $m = 6d$ (b) $m + 2$ (c) $d + 2$

(d) $m + 2 = 5$ $(d + 2)$ (e) daughter 8, mother 48

10. $a = 3$, $b = 5$, $c = 2$ **11.** 74 standard, 37 luxury.

Page 348   Can you still? 12A

1. (a) Translation $\binom{-5}{-4}$ (b) Reflection in $y = x + 1$

(c) reflection in y axis   (d) Rotation 90° Clockwise, Centre (3, –2)

(e) Enlargement s.f. $\frac{1}{2}$, Centre (0, 0)

(f) Enlargement s.f. 2, Centre (1, –4)

2. (h) (1, 1), (1, –5), (–2, –5)

Page 349   M12.6

1. 162, 486, × 3 each time   **2.** $2\frac{1}{2}$, 3, add $\frac{1}{2}$ each time

3. 50, 0, take 10, then take 10 more each time

4. 2.9, 3.3, add 0.4 each time

5. 0.03, 0.003 divide by 10 each time

6. $\frac{1}{1250}$, $\frac{1}{6250}$, increase the divisor by 5 times each time

7. (a) 48   (b) 96   **8.** 31, 42   **9.** 63, 90   **10.** 46, 64

11. 37, 53   **12.** 121, 169   **13.** 50, 70   **14.** 79, 109   **15.** 32, 43

16. 21, 34, add the previous 2 numbers   **17.** 24, 44

18. (a) 1, 7, 21, 35, 35, 21, 7, 1   (b) 1, 2, 4, 8, 16 ..., doubles each time

19. 6, 9, 14, 21, 30, 41

20. (a) 1, 5, 9, 13   (b) 0, 3, 8, 15   (c) 9, 12, 17, 24

(d) 2, 4, 8, 16   (e) $\frac{1}{3}$, $\frac{3}{5}$, $\frac{5}{7}$, $\frac{7}{9}$ (f) 0, 1, 3, 6

Page 351   M12.7

1. (a) $2n + 6$ (b) $4n - 1$ (c) $4n + 1$ (d) $3n - 1$

2. (a) $6n - 3$ (b) $7n - 3$ (c) $10n + 3$ (d) $5n + 3$ (e) $8n - 7$

(f) $9n - 2$ (g) $14 - 2n$ (h) $21 - 4n$ (i) $\frac{1}{2}n + 2$ (j) $49 - 9n$

3. (a) $6n - 1$ (b) 239   (c) 80th

4. (a) $7n - 4$ (b) 493   (c) 102nd

5. (a) $11n - 3$ (b) 129   (c) 23rd

6. (b) $s = 4n + 1$ (c) 201

7. (b) $s = 2n + 1$ (c) 101

8. (b) $4n + 1$ (c) 201   **9.** (b) $s = 9n + 1$ (c) 451

10. (a) $5n + 20$ (b) 65   (c) 14th

11. (b) 8, 10, 12   (c) $w = 2n + 6$ (d) 86

12. (a) $250n + 34750$ (b) 24   **13.** (a) $3n + 1$ (b) 334

14. (a) $46 - 8n$ (b) $104 - 11n$ (c) 20

Page 355   E12.1

1. $n^2 + 2$ **2.** $n^2 - 1$ **3.** $n^2 - 4$ **4.** $n^2 + 10$ **5.** $n^2 + n$

6. $n^2 - 2n$ **7.** (a) $n^2 + 3n$ (b) 460

8. (a) $d = n^2 + 2n$ (b) 960

9. (a) $n^2 + n + 3$ (b) $n^2 + 3n - 2$ (e) $2n^2 + n$ (d) $3n^2 + 4n + 1$

10. (a) $2n^2 - 2n + 1$ (b) 761   **11.** $\frac{1}{2}(n^2 + n)$

12. (a) 2^{2n} (b) $2^n - 1$ (c) $n^3 - 1$ (d) 3^{n-1}

Page 356   Can you still? 12B

1. $a = 23°$ **2.** $b = 39°$ **3.** $c = 38°$ **4.** $d = 43°$

5. $f = 64°$ **6.** $g = 120°$ **7.** $h = 35°$ **8.** $i = 78°$

Page 358   E12.2

1. $(x + 4)^2 - 9$ **2.** $(x - 6)^2 - 11$ **3.** $(x + 9)^2 - 6$

4. $(x - 3)^2 - 4$ **5.** $(x - 5)^2 - 42$ **6.** $(x + 6)^2 - 33$

7. $\left(x + \frac{3}{2}\right)^2 - \frac{5}{4}$ **8.** $\left(x + \frac{7}{2}\right)^2 - \frac{37}{4}$ **9.** $\left(x + \frac{1}{2}\right)^2 + \frac{3}{4}$

10. $x = 1$ or -9 **11.** $x = 1 \pm \sqrt{8}$ **12.** $-2 \pm \sqrt{3}$

13. $3 \pm \sqrt{2}$ **14.** $5 \pm \sqrt{5}$ **15.** $-4 \pm \sqrt{5}$

16. $-1 \pm \sqrt{8}$ **17.** $-6 \pm \sqrt{11}$ **18.** $-\frac{11}{2} \pm \frac{3}{2}\sqrt{13}$

19. $\frac{-7}{2} \pm \frac{\sqrt{61}}{2}$ **20.** $-\frac{1}{2} \pm \frac{\sqrt{13}}{2}$ **21.** $a = 2, b = 3, c = 5$

22. $p = 3, q = 2, r = -7$ **23.** $a = 5, b = 1, c = -8$ **24.** $-1 \pm \sqrt{5}$

25. $-\frac{5}{2} \pm \frac{\sqrt{23}}{2}$ **26.** $\frac{3}{14} \pm \frac{\sqrt{37}}{14}$ **27.** $(5, -22)$

28. $(2, -3)$ **29.** (a) 1   (b) None

Page 360   E12.3

1. -6.19 or -0.807 **2.** -2.41 or 0.414 **3.** 4.54 or -1.54

4. 0.540 or -0.740 **5.** 2.08 or -1.33 **6.** -0.232 or -1.43

7. 0.0938 or -1.52 **8.** 1 or -0.6 **9.** 1.19 or -1.69

10. -0.407 or -1.84 **11.** -0.314 or -1.22 **12.** 0.631 or -1.41

13. 1.64 or -4.04 **14.** 1.32 or -0.687 **15.** 0.777 or -0.920

16. 0.828 or -4.83 **17.** 0.608 or -4.11 **18.** 5.37 or -0.372

19. $\frac{-5 \pm \sqrt{21}}{2}$ **20.** $\frac{-3 \pm \sqrt{17}}{2}$ **21.** $\frac{3 \pm \sqrt{229}}{10}$

22. $\frac{-1 \pm \sqrt{13}}{6}$ **23.** $\frac{-5 \pm \sqrt{221}}{14}$ **24.** $\frac{-8 \pm \sqrt{108}}{2}$ or $-4 \pm \sqrt{27}$

Page 361   E12.4

1. (a) $(2x + 3)^2 = x^2 + 4^2$ (c) $x = 0.517$ **2.** 4.87 **3.** 46.3 m

4. (a) $2x + 1$ (b) $(2x + 1)^2 = x^2 + 49$ (c) 3.39

5. 4.24 **6.** (a) $x + 23$ (c) $x = 33$

7. (a) $(x + 17)^2 + x^2 = 305^2$ (b) 207 mm   **8.** 4.96×11.96

9. (a) $d(d + 4) - \frac{\pi d^2}{4} - 4\pi = 50$ (b) 10.1 cm   **10.** 2.32 m

Page 364   E12.5

1. $x = 3, y = 8$ **2.** $a = 7, b = 2$ **3.** $p = 1, q = 1$ **4.** $a = 48, b = 9$

5. $c = 12, d = 2$ **6.** $x = 3, w = 10$ **7.** $x = 1, y = 2$ or $x = -2, y = -1$

8. $x = 1, y = 5$ or $x = -\frac{7}{2}, y = -4$

9. $x = -1, y = -2$ or $x = -\frac{2}{3}, y = -1$

10. $x = 4, y = 3$ **11.** $x = 2, y = 12$ or $x = -1, y = 3$

12. $x = 5, y = 12$ or $x = -12, y = -5$

13. $x = 2, y = 8$ or $x = -\frac{7}{2}, y = -\frac{17}{2}$

14. $x = 4, y = 5$ or $x = 5, y = 4$ **15.** $(6, 8)$ and $(-8, -6)$

16. $(3, 4)$ and $(5, 0)$

Page 365   Can you still? 12C

1. 17.2 cm   **2.** 4.8 cm   **3.** 10.8 cm   **4.** 7.8 cm   **5.** 15.2 cm

6. 44.4°   **7.** 20.4°   **8.** 7.8 cm   **9.** 5.4   **10.** 6.1 cm

Page 366   E12.6

1. (a)

t	0	1	2	3	4	5
N	1	2	4	8	16	32

(c) 4.64

2. (a)

x	-3	-2	-1	0	1	2	3
y	$\frac{1}{64}$	$\frac{1}{16}$	$\frac{1}{4}$	1	4	16	64

(b) 2.45   (c) 8

3. (a)

t	0	1	2	3	4	5
y	10	5	2.5	1.25	0.625	0.3125

(c) 1.32   (d) No

4. (a) £119.10   (b) £126.25   (c) £179.08   (e) 5.8 yrs

5. (a) 8653   (b) 11842   (c) 17529   (e) 10.3 yrs

6. (a)

x	-2	-1	0	1	2	3
y	9	3	1	$\frac{1}{3}$	$\frac{1}{9}$	$\frac{1}{27}$

(b) -1.46

7. 3.21 yrs   **8.** $a = 3$ $b = 5$

Page 369   E12.7

1. (a)

x	-3	-2	-1	0	1	2	3	4	5
y	11	4	-1	-4	-5	-4	-1	4	11

(c) 3.2 or -1.2 (d) 4.2 or -2.2

2.

x	-6	-5	-4	-3	-2	-1	0	1	2
y	15	8	3	0	-1	0	3	8	15

(c) -1 or -3 (d) 0.45 or -4.45 (e) 1.3 or -5.3

3. (a) 0.6 or 3.4   (b) 4.45 or -0.45 (c) 3.7 or 0.3

4. (a) $y = x$ (b) $y = x + 4$ (c) $y = 3x - 4$ (d) $y = 3 - 2x$

5. (a) 1.6 or -2.6 (b) 2.2 or -3.2 (c) ± 2.45 (d) 0.6 or -1.6

6. (a) 2.3 or -1.3 (b) ± 2.65 (c) 0 or 1

(d) 3.8 or -0.8 (e) 2.3 or -1.3

7. (a) 2.4 or -0.4 (b) ± 2.65 **8.** (a) 3.2 or -1.2 (b) 2.3 or -1.3

9. (a) 2.4 or -0.4 (b) 1 or 4   **10.** (a) -0.17 or -5.8 (b) 0.3 or -3.3

Page 372   WYM12

1. A   **2.** B   **3.** B   **4.** B   **5.** A

6. Plates: 1 of 50 + 1 of 20, cups: 2 of 30 + 1 of 12   **7.** A   **8.** B

Page 373   Test yourself on unit 12

1. (a) (ii) (0, 2), (6, 0)

2. (a) $x = 2$, $y = 3$ (b) $x = 1$, $y = 3$ (c) $x = 3$, $y = 2$

3. (a) $x = 4$, $y = 2$ (b) $a = -3$, $b = 7$ (c) $m = 5$, $n = \frac{1}{2}$

(d) 13 rows of 18 seats, 17 rows of 25 seats

4. (a) $3n + 2$ (b) 223   (c) (i) $3n + 47$ metres (ii) 12th

5. (a) $n^2 - 4n$ (b) 2596   (c) $t = 2n^2 - 1$

6. (a) $-3 \pm \sqrt{10}$ (b) $4 \pm \sqrt{7}$ (c) $p = 2$, $q = 5$, $r = 3$

7. (a) 0.72 or -1.17 (b) 0.77 or -0.43

(c) (i) $x + 3$ (ii) $x^2 + (x + 3)^2 = 11^2$ (iii) 6.13 (or -9.13)

8. (a) $x = 2$, $y = 4$ or $x = -8$, $y = -26$ (b) (3, 0) and (0, -3)

9. (a) £12960   (b) £9450   (c) £5580   (e) 4.5 yrs.

10. (a) 2.3 or -1.3 (b) 2.6 or -1.6 (c) ± 1.7 (d) 2.6 or 0.4

Page 376   Mixed examination questions

1. $x = 4\frac{1}{2}$, $y = -3$ **2.** $x = 4$, $y = \frac{1}{2}$ **3.** (i) $x + 3$ (ii) $3n - 1$

4. (a) G(0, 5) H(10, 0)   (b) (ii) $x = 2$, $y = 4$ **5.** $x = 2\frac{1}{2}$, $y = -2$

6. $a = 5$, $b = -7$ **7.** $x = -6.19$ or -0.81

8. (a) $a = 11$, $b = 5$ (b) $x = 8.32$ or 1.68   **9.** $n^2 - 1$

10. (b) (i) -4.25 (ii) $x = 2.6$, -1.6 **11.** (b) $x = 2.6$

12. $n = £2$, $s = £11.50$ **13.** $k = 10$, $n = \frac{1}{3}$ **14.** $n^2 - n$

15. (-3, 5), (-5, 3)   **16.** (b) $x = 2.4$ or -1.9 (c) $y = 2\frac{1}{2}$

17. $p = 8$, $q = \frac{9}{4}$, $k = 27$ **18.** (a) $x^2 + 8x + 16$ (c) 1.74 or -5.74

UNIT 13

Page 379   M13.1

1. 62 cm^2 **2.** 50 cm^2 **3.** 3.03 cm^2 **4.** 754.8 cm^2

5. 307.9 cm^2 **6.** 319.9 cm^2 **7.** 126.6 cm^2 **8.** B

9. 6.51 cm^2 **10.** 35.3 cm^2 **11.** 69 cm^2 **12.** 33.5 cm^2

13. 11.6 cm^2 **14.** 12 cm   **15.** 10 cm, 20 cm

16. 48 cm^2 **17.** 60 cm^2 **18.** 36.5 cm^2 **19.** 173.8 cm^2

Page 382   E13.1

1. 84.9 cm^2 **2.** 124.7 cm^2 **3.** 16.3 cm^2 **4.** 60.4 cm^2 **5.** 22.0 cm^2

6. 142.9 cm^2 **7.** (a) 27.6°   (b) 22.3°   (c) 87.9°   **8.** 20.2 cm

Page 383   Can you still? 13A

1. 13.46 litres   **2.** 9 inches   **3.** 0.5 kg   **4.** Less   **5.** 5 gallons

6. (a) 120 cm   (b) 32 km   (c) 15 kg

(d) 22.5 cm   (e) 54 litres   (f) 14.4 pints

7. Beth by $\frac{2}{5}$ km.   **8.** 4.6 pints

Page 384   E13.2

1. 7.0 cm   **2.** 6.1 cm   **3.** 14.2 cm   **4.** 7.5 cm

5. 20.5 cm   **6.** 86.0 cm   **7.** 28.3 cm   **8.** 157.6°

9. 22.0 cm   **12.** $9.\dot{7}\pi + 32$ cm   **13.** $2.1\pi + 18$

14. 17.5 cm   **15.** 20 cm

Page 387   E13.3

1. 7.9 cm^2 **2.** 104.6 cm^2 **3.** 942.9 cm^2

4. 7.7 cm^2 **7.** $(3.5\pi + 66)$ cm^2 **9.** 25°

10. 7.95 cm   **11.** (a) 18.4 cm^2 (b) 69.2 cm^2

12. (a) 4.85 cm^2 (b) 5.89 cm^2 (c) 1.54 cm^2

13. (a) 19.1 cm^2 (b) 19.5 cm^2 (c) 85.6 cm^2

14. (a) OX = 6.4 cm, AX = 7.7 cm   (b) 24.6 cm^2

(c) 43.6 cm^2 (d) 19.0 cm^2

15. (a) 9.5 cm   (b) 17.4 cm^2 **16.** 15.3 cm^2

17. (a) 36.9°   (b) 24 cm^2 (c) 32.2 cm^2 **19.** 135.3 cm^2

Page 390   Can you still? 13B

1. (a) $x(x + 5)$ (b) $(2x + 1)(2x - 1)$ (c) $(x - 2)(x - 5)$

(d) $(a - x)(a + y)$ (e) $(3x - 2)(2x + 5)$

2. (a) x^3 (b) $x^{-11/3}$ (c) $4x^5y^2$ **3.** (a) -3 (b) $\frac{1}{6}$ (c) $\frac{1}{2}$

4. (a) 7   (b) 12   (c) 8 or -3 **5.** 45   **6.** 10 or 0

7. (a) $x - 35$ (b) $x^2 + y^2 + 2xy$ (c) $x^2 - 2x + 1$

8. (a) $p(2r + q)$ (b) $(z - 3)^2 - 3y$ (c) $\frac{3h - g}{f - 2}$

9. (a) $(x + 7)$ m   (b) $(x + 7)^2 + x^2 = 97^2$ (c) 65 m

Page 392   M13.2

1. (a) 160 m^3 (b) 160,000,000 cm^3 **2.** 2 m

3. (a) 1,000,000 (b) 2,000,000 (c) 4,700,000 (d) 10,000 (e) 30,000

(f) 8   (g) 3.5   (h) 92,500   (i) 1000

(j) 7000   (k) 5.6   (l) 3,900,000.

4. (a) 216 cm^3 (b) 816 m^3 (c) 3950 cm^3

5. (a) 132 cm^2 (b) 1324 cm^2 **6.** 2 m

7. (a) 339.3 cm^3 (b) 1400 cm^3 (c) 1963.5 cm^3 (d) 175.9 cm^3

8. 1910 litres   **9.** A   **10.** 23.3 cm^3 **11.** 10   **12.** 4.0

13. 12.8 cm   **14.** 1.2 m   **15.** (a) 16.2 m^2 (b) 4854.4 m^3

16. 12.7 cm   **17.** 9168.4 g   **18.** 81π

19. (a) yes (b) 1770.8 cm^3 **20.** 824668 cm^3 **21.** 3526.5 cm^3

22. (b) 71.4 cm^3 (c) 14277.9 cm^3

Page 396   E13.4

1. (a) 3050 cm^3 (b) 1010 cm^3 (c) 1130 mm^3

(d) 133 cm^3 (e) 189 cm^3 (f) 56.5 m^3

2. 1530 cm^3 **3.** 1770 g   **4.** 233 g   **5.** 18.0 cm

6. (a) 100π cm^3 (b) $\frac{16\pi}{3}$ cm^3 (c) 504π cm^3 **7.** 17500 mm^3

8. (a) 69π cm³   (b) 1269π cm³   (c) 378 cm³   **9.** 15 cm

10. 16.1 mm   **11.** 7.98 cm   **12.** 855 cm³   **13.** 3.6 mm

14. (a) $\frac{50\pi}{3}$ cm³   (b) $\frac{4\pi}{3}$ (c) 1.6 mm

15. (a) 269 cm³   (b) 80.8 litres

16. (b) 7 cm   (c) (i) 14π cm   (ii) 101° (3 s.f.)

17. (a) 8π cm   (b) 4 cm   (c) 3cm   **18.** 2722.7 cm³

Page 400   E13.5

1. (a) 1130 cm²   (b) 81.7 cm²   (c) 154 cm²

2. (a) 108π cm²   (b) 70π cm²   (c) (72π + 112) cm²

3. B by 209 cm²   **4.** 314 cm²   **5.** 1.91 cm   **6.** 109 cm²

7. 2.96 cm   **8.** 151 cm²

9. (a) 174 cm²   (b) 704 cm²   (c) 1850 cm²

10. 3.24 cm   **11.** 8 cm

12. (a) 75.4 cm²   (b) 12.6 cm   (c) r = 2 cm   (e) 11.8 cm

13. £223   **14.** 192 cm²

Page 402   M13.3

1. (a) 9 cm   (b) 3 cm   (c) 4 cm   (d) $7\frac{1}{2}$ cm

2. 40.5 cm   **3.** All sides increased in same ratio (× 1.5)

4. (b) 5 cm   (c) 4.5 cm   **5.** (b) 12.5 cm   (c) 12 cm

6. (a) 9 m   (b) 13.5 cm   (c) 21 m

Page 404   M13.4

1. 6 cm   **2.** 6 cm   **3.** 5 cm   **4.** 8 cm   **5.** 7.5 cm   **6.** 7 cm

7. 6 cm   **8.** 88.125 m   **9.** PQ = 6 cm, PT = 4 cm   **10.** 9.375 m

11. x = 7 cm, y = 4 cm   **12.** 12 cm   **13.** x = 3.6 cm, y = 6 cm

14. 1 cm   **15.** 20 cm

Page 406   Can you still?   13C

1. (a) $\begin{pmatrix} -6 \\ -18 \end{pmatrix}$ (b) $\begin{pmatrix} -5 \\ 3 \end{pmatrix}$ (c) $\sqrt{34}$ **2.** (a) **m**   (b) **w**   (c) **f**

3. (a) $\frac{1}{2}$**a**   (b) **b** − **a**   (c) **b** − $\frac{1}{2}$**a**   **4.** Parallel

5. (a) $-\frac{1}{2}$**b**   (b) 2**a**   (c) 2**a** − $\frac{1}{2}$**b**   (d) −**a** + $\frac{1}{4}$**b**   (e) $\frac{5}{4}$**b**

Page 408   E13.6

1. (a) 1 : 125   (b) 8 : 729   **2.** (a) 1 : 7   (b) 5 : 12   (c) 1 : 3   (d) 5 : 29

3. 378 m²   **4.** 16 cm³   **5.** 8.1 m²   **6.** 560 cm³   **7.** 28 cm

8. 0.65 m   **9.** 90 cm   **10.** 9 cm   **11.** 11.0 cm   **12.** 633 cm³

13. 74.52 cm²   **14.** 66.1 mm   **15.** 152 cm   **16.** 1.664 l   **17.** £19.60

18. 8.44 l   **19.** 25.4 cm   **20.** (b) $\frac{h}{h+8} = \sqrt[3]{\frac{216}{1728}}$ (c) h = 8

Page 411   E13.7

1. (a) 1 : 16   (b) 1 : 4   (c) 1 : 64   (d) 2304 cm³

2. (a) 1 : 343   (b) 1 : 7   (c) 1 : 49   (d) 29 cm²

3. 33.0 cm²   **4.** 5.87 litres   **5.** (a) 16.6 kg   (b) 2560 cm²

6. 594 cm³   **7.** (a) £2.22   (b) £28.20   **8.** 1 litre

9. 1.39 m²   **10.** 17.4 cm   **11.** 413 cm²   **12.** 25.8 cm

Page 413   WYM13

1. £20.67   **2.** £57.70   **3.** £31.67

4. £504, £42   **5.** £1071, £89.25 **6.** £562.50, £46.88

7. £748, £62.33   **8.** £348, £29   **9.** £848, £70.67

10. (a) £42.67   (b) £64   (c) £21.33   **11.** £34.25

Page 414   Test yourself on unit 13

1. (a) 166.8 cm²   (b) 240 cm²   (c) 108.8 cm²   (d) 27.5 cm²

2. (a) 385 m³   (b) (i) 5,000,000   (ii) 72000 cm²   (iii) 0.26 m²

　　 (c) 37,699   (d) 5 m

3. (a) 28 cm   (b) 4 cm   (c) AB = 6.6 cm, DE = 6 cm

4. (a) 6.6 cm   (b) π + 18 cm   (c) 23.9 cm

5. (a) 114.6 cm²   (b) 2.5π   (c) 4.3 cm²   (d) 14.5 cm²

6. (a) 339.3 cm³   (b) 486π   (c) 1045.3 cm³   (d) 11.3 cm

7. (a) 1608.5 cm²   (b) 368π   (c) 562.2 cm²   (d) 2 cm

8. (a) 4.05 litres   (b) 9.0 cm   (c) 10.5 cm²

Page 418   Mixed examination questions

1. 147.5 cm²   **2.** 38.6 cm   **4.** (a) 703.7 cm²   (b) 2.0 m

5. 20 cm   **6.** (i) 10 cm (ii) 4.8 cm   **7.** 170 g

8. 6 million   **9.** (a) (i) 57.7 cm³ (ii) 92.3 cm²   (b) 12.7 cm³

10. 57.2 cm³   **11.** (a) 24 cm   (b) 40.5 cm

12. (a) 113 cm³   (b) 3 cm   (c) 2.25   **13.** 428 cm³

UNIT 14

Page 423   M14.1

1. (a) Mean 7, Median 8, Mode 8, Range 5

　　 (b) Mean 15, Median 15.5, Mode 16, Range 5

　　 (c) Mean 6, Median 6, Mode 5 and 9, Range 7

　　 (d) Mean 5.9, Median 5.5, Mode 4, Range 5

2. (a) 13   (b) 14   (c) 13.4

3. (a) 7   (b) 7.35   (c) mode is the most common shoe size

4. (a) 11   (b) 1   (c) Median, The 70 distorts the mean

7. 6, 12   **8.** (a) Median   (b) £7050   **9.** 420 kg

10. (a) 32 m   (b) 159 cm   **11.** 312   **12.** (a) 224 (b) 220 (c) 37

13. 62.24%   **14.** 31   **15.** The mean

Page 425   M14.2

1. (a) 9   (b) 8   **2.** B   **3.** (a) 0–2   (b) 0–2

4. (a) 1   (b) 1   **5.** (a) 40–49   (b) 40–49

6. (a) Easitech 11–15, compfix 7–10   (b) Easitech, higher median

Page 427   M14.3

1. (a) 164   (b) 1.64   **2.** (a) 225   (b) 2.25   **3.** (a) 202   (b) 1.01

4. (a) Paradise 16.53, De-Vere 16.46, Tropic 16.36   (b) Tropic

Page 429   M14.4

1. (a)

No. of trips Abroad	Frequency	Mid Value
0–2	6	1
3–5	8	4
6–10	5	8
11–15	1	13

(b) 91   (c) 4.55

2. (a) 3258   (b) 3.26   **3.** (a) 2900   (b) 14.5

4. 38.9 lengths   **5.** Kabinseal, about £14500   **6.** 27 hrs

Page 431   M14.5

1. (a)

Stem	Leaf
14	666788999
15	1233355578
16	122234

(b) 18

2. (a)

Stem	Leaf
2	4568
3	022266788
4	022238
5	11
6	355589
7	00014
8	2

(b) 33   (c) £42   (d) £58

3. (a) 88   (b) 23   **4.** (a) 1.75 litres   (b) 1.4 litres

5. (a) Median 47, Range 39 yrs   (b) Median 36, Range 38 yrs

(c) ages at Grindley HS are lower and a little less spread out

Page 433   M14.6

1. (a) 7   (b) 3   (c) 10   (d) 3

2. (a) 11   (b) 8   (c) 16   (d) 8

3. (a) 8   (b) 4   (c) 10   (d) 6

4. (a) 6   (b) 2   (c) 8   (d) 6

5. (a) 18   (b) 16   (c) 21   (d) 5

6. (a) Chelsea 5 yrs, Man. U. 4 yrs   (b) medians: Chelsea 24 yrs
Man. U. 29 yrs

Page 436   M14.7

1. (a) 34 hrs.   (b) 23 hrs.   (c) 48 hrs   (d) 25 hrs

2. (b) (i) 28   (ii) 15 or 16

3. (a) 100, 225, 400, 625, 775, 900, 975, 1000

(c) (i) 154 cm   (ii) 25 cm   (d) 68%

4. (a) 16, 28, 39, 46, 52, 57, 59, 60

(c) (i) 11 mm   (ii) 15 mm   (d) 27.5%

5. (b) (i) £220 000 (ii) £62000   (c) 30

6. (b) (i) D + C Median 11, Grand parents median 14

(ii) D + C I.Q.R $14\frac{1}{2}$, Grand parents I.Q.R 19

Page 438   Can you still? 14A

1. $x = 5$, $y = -2$ **2.** $x = 7$, $y = -1$ **3.** $x = 2$, $y = 7$ **4.** $x = 4$, $y = 1$

5. (a) $7x + 3y = 220$, $4x + 5y = 175$ (b) $x = 25$, $y = 15$

Page 439   M14.8

1. (a) 9 years   (b) 16   (c) 5   (d) 11   (e) 6

4. Salaries higher at Naylor's and with a greater range

5. (b) over 65s watched more and there was a higher number around the median

6. (b) girls' marks were more spread out and slightly lower

Page 441   Can you still? 14B

2. yr. 10 – Boys 14, girls 12; year 11 – Boys 11, girls 13

3. Audi 11, Peugeot 16, Vauxhall 25, Mitsubishi 8

Page 442   E14.1

1. (a) $0–5 \rightarrow 4$; $5–10 \rightarrow 5$; $10–12.5 \rightarrow 8$; $12.5–15 \rightarrow 6$; $15–17.5 \rightarrow 4$; $17.5–20 \rightarrow 2$

2.

21	32	37	29	18
4.2	6.4	7.5	2.9	0.9

3.

Class width	Frequency density
5	1.2
5	1.8
5	2.2
10	0.5
10	0.4
20	0.1

4.

Frequency	Frequency density
20	1
37	3.7
62	6.2
51	5.1
30	1.5
8	0.2

Page 445   E14.2

1. (a) frequencies: 25, 30, 32, 24   (b) 111   **2.** 830   **3.** 78

4. frequencies: 160, 160, 240, 430, 570

5. (a) 18, 13, 8, 15, 3,   (b) 57   (c) 31.58%

6. (a) frequencies: 4, 5, 4, 6, 9   (b) 28   (c) 68%

7. (a) frequencies: 56, 64, 48, 56, 48

Page 447   Can you still? 14C

1. $a = 6$, $b = -28$ **2.** $p = -2$, $q = 3$

3. (a) $2 \pm \sqrt{7}$ (b) $-10 \pm \sqrt{95}$ **4.** $p = 4$, $q = 3$, $r = 2$

5. (a) 1.27 or −6.27   (b) 0.41 or −2.41

Page 448   E14.3

1. (a) 10A median 69, range 45: 10B median 65, range 51

2. (a) Ash Lane mean 1.75 range 4   (b) Tibbs Drive mean 2.1, range

3. (a) Science Median 61, I.Q.R 18: Maths Median 60, I.Q.R 26

(c) Marks more spread out for maths test. Median about the same for both subjects.

4. Both the average age and range of ages is lower for the men.

5. People in area A lived longer

Page 451   WYM14

1. £15000 − £4745 = £10255, 10% of £1960 = £196,

     22% of £8295 = £1824.90

     Total Income Tax = £196 + £1824.90 = £2020.90

2. £13400 − £4745 = £8655, 10% of £1960 = £196,

     22% of £6695 = £1472.90

     Total tax = 196 + 1472.90 = £1668.90

3. (a) £23755 (b) £4990.90   **4.** (a) £17400 (b) £3592.80 (c) £299.40

5. £125.50   **6.** (a) £16640   (b) £11895 (c) £2381.70 (d) £45.80

7. None   **8.** £27.49

Page 452   Test yourself on unit 14

1. (a) (i) 7 (ii) 6 (iii) 5 (iv) 8   (b) 69.7 kg   **2.** (a) 2   (b) 2

3. (a) (i) 204 (ii) 2.72   (b) 13.5

4. (a)

1	99
2	0136778
3	12567
4	23678
5	01338
6	2

   (b) 36   (c) 43 yrs

5. (b) 37 yrs   (c) 15 yrs   **6.** (a) 10   (b) 8   (c) 14   (d) 6

7. (b) lower median and range for Ellis Gate. Ellis Gate might be a junior school and Avalon Meadow a senior school.

8. (a) missing frequencies 285 and 510

9. The median height of the boys is about 5.5 cm greater and the spread is similar for both.

Page 455   Mixed examination questions

1. (a) 56   (b) 53   (c) 25   **2.** 79.3   **3.** £1060

4. The spread of the times was similar but the median was lower for spelling names forwards.

5. (a) 60–70   (b) 60.75 hrs   (c) 0, 4, 22, 90, 169, 200   (e) 13.5

6. (a) 65   (b) 48   (c) 42   **7.** (a) 10–25, 60; 25–30, 40

9. (a) (i) 152 (ii) 177

10. 150–160, 35; 165–170, 18; 170–180, 22; 190–210, 12

UNIT 16

Page 465   M16.1

1. (a) $x \le -2$ (b) $-5 \le x < 1$ (c) $-6 < x < -1$

2. (a) $x \le 6$ (b) $x > -3$ (c) $x \ge 4$

     6   −3   4

(d) $x \ge 2$ (e) $3 < x \le 8$ (f) $0 < x < 4$

     2   3   8   0   4

3. (a) $a > 5$ (b) $x < -45$ (c) $b < 3$ (d) $y \le 5$

   (e) $n > 3$ (f) $c \le 4$ (g) $x \ge -5$ (h) $a < 7$

   (i) $n \ge 36$ (j) $x \ge 6$ (k) $n > 7$ (e) $x < 3$

4. (a) 1, 2, 3 (b) 1, 2, 3, 4, 5, 6 (c) −2, −1, 0, 1, 2 (d) −3, −2, −1, 0

5. (a) 3   (b) 7   (c) 2   (d) 41   (e) 1   (f) 6

6. (a) $5 \le x < 7$ (b) $12 \le x \le 28$ (c) $-12 < x < -9$

   (d) $10 \le x < 15$ (e) $4 \le x < 7$ (f) $-2 < x \le 2$

   (g) $-\frac{1}{2} < x < 4$ (h) $-1 \le x \le 2$ (i) $3 < x \le 4$

Page 467   M16.2

1. $-5 < x < 5$ **2.** $-9 \le m \le 9$ **3.** $y < -2$ or $y > 2$

4. $-20 \le z \le 20$ **5.** $b \le -12$ or $b \ge 12$ **6.** $-2.5 < n < 2.5$

7. $m \le -4$ or $m \ge 4$ **8.** $x < -1$ or $x > 1$ **9.** $-3 < n < 3$

10. $a \le -5$ or $a \ge 5$ **11.** $x < -1$ or $x > 1$ **12.** $-7 < x < 7$

13. (a) $-11 < y < 11$ (b) $m \le -2$ or $m \ge 2$ (c) $n < -6$ or $n > 6$

    −11   11   −2   2   −6   6

   (d) $-3.5 < p < 3.5$ (e) $-14 \le x \le 14$ (f) $m \le -2$ or $m \ge 2$

    −3.5   3.5   −14   14   −2   2

Page 468   M16.3

1. (a) $x < 1$ (b) $2 < y \le 4$ (c) $x + y \le 5$ (d) $y < 2x + 3$

3. (a) $y \ge 2 - x$ (b) $y < 2x - 1$ (c) $y > \frac{1}{2}x + 1$

4. $y \ge \frac{1}{2}x$ **5.** $y \ge 4, y < 3x + 4, y \le 9 - 2x$

7. $y < x + 6, y \ge x^2$

Page 470   Can you still?   16A

1. (a) 73.5 cm²   (b) 38 cm²   **2.** (a) 96π (b) 576π

3. 245 cm²   **4.** 0.42 cm   **5.** 13.1 cm

Page 472   M16.4

1. Area   **2.** Volume   **3.** $2abc$

4. (a) A   (b) L   (c) A   (d) A   (e) L   (f) V   (g) A

   (h) V   (i) A   (j) V   (k) V   (l) A   (m) L   (n) L

   (o) V   (p) A   (q) A   (r) V   (s) L   (t) A

5. $\pi r^2 \to A, 4r^2l^2 \to$ none, $\pi rl \to A, 2\pi r \to L, \pi r^2 l \to V$

Page 473   M16.5

[L = Length, A = Area, V = Volume, N.M. = No Meaning]

1. N.M.   **2.** L   **3.** b, e, f, k, r, t all meaningless

4. $5a^2b \to V, 3(2a + b^2) \to$ N.M., $\frac{\pi a^3}{4b} \to A, 6ab(3a - 4) \to$ N.M.

   $4\pi(3a + 2b) \to L, \frac{5(\pi a^2 + 3ab)}{\pi a} \to L$

5. (a) A   (b) A   (c) N.M.   (d) L   (e) A   (f) V

   (g) L   (h) A   (i) N.M.   (j) N.M   (k) A   (l) L

   (m) A   (n) N.M.   (o) V   (p) A

6. 2   **7.** yes.   **8.** 3

Page 475   Can you still? 16B

1. (a) 5.54 or −0.54   (b) 1 or $-\dfrac{7}{5}$ (c) 4.23 or −9.23

2. (a) $\dfrac{-5 \pm \sqrt{17}}{2}$ (b) $\dfrac{-7 \pm \sqrt{73}}{6}$ **3.** 8.3 cm

Page 476   E16.1

1. $\dfrac{a}{c}$ **2.** $\dfrac{m}{n}$ **3.** $\dfrac{2a}{5b}$ **4.** $\dfrac{a}{4b}$ **5.** $\dfrac{m-n}{mn}$ **6.** $\dfrac{m-n}{2mn}$

7. 3   **8.** $p + 2q$ **9.** $b + c$ **10.** $\dfrac{n-p}{p}$ **11.** 2   **12.** $\dfrac{5x}{y+z}$

13. (a) F   (b) T   (c) F   (d) T   (e) T   (f) F

14. $\dfrac{1}{x-3}$ **15.** $\dfrac{6n}{5m}$ **16.** $\dfrac{2}{3}$ **17.** $\dfrac{a-2b}{a+2b}$ **18.** 4   **19.** $\dfrac{x-3}{2}$

20. $\dfrac{x+2}{x}$ **21.** $\dfrac{x-1}{x+2}$ **22.** $x + 1$ **23.** $m + 2$ **24.** $a + 1$ **25.** $b - 5$

26. $\dfrac{n+2}{n+4}$ **27.** $2y + 1$ **28.** $5x - 1$ **29.** $2m - 1$

Page 477   E16.2

1. $\dfrac{5}{3n}$ **2.** xy **3.** $6m$ **4.** $\dfrac{2x-3}{2}$ **5.** $\dfrac{a}{4(a-b)}$ **6.** $5m - 10$

7. $\dfrac{3ab}{4}$ **8.** $\dfrac{y}{6}$ **9.** $\dfrac{4}{5}$ **10.** 6   **11.** $\dfrac{9}{5}$ **12.** $\dfrac{c}{2}$

15. (a) $\dfrac{2}{5}$ (b) $\dfrac{m+7}{6}$ (c) $\dfrac{x+1}{x-2}$ (d) $\dfrac{b+2}{b+1}$

(e) $\dfrac{xy}{(x-2)^2}$ (f) $\dfrac{3}{m+9}$ (g) $\dfrac{(c-6)(c+1)}{2(c-1)}$ (h) $\dfrac{2}{n-5}$

(i) $b - 2$ (j) $\dfrac{a(a+1)}{a+2}$ (k) $\dfrac{x+7}{2x+5}$ (l) $\dfrac{n-2}{n+3}$

Page 478   Can you still? 16C

1. $5n - 3$ **2.** $6n - 2$ **3.** 777   **4.** B   **5.** $n^2 + n$

6. (b) $P = 4n + 2$ **7.** 4415   **8.** $2^n - 1$

Page 479   E16.3

1. $\dfrac{5x}{6}$ **2.** $\dfrac{8x+15y}{20}$ **3.** $\dfrac{a^2+b^2}{ab}$ **4.** $\dfrac{3b-10a}{2ab}$ **5.** $\dfrac{5m+6n^2}{15n}$

6. $\dfrac{x^2-4y^2}{2xy}$ **7.** $\dfrac{20y-6x}{12xy}$ **8.** $\dfrac{3n^2+2m}{2mn}$ **9.** $\dfrac{8x+10}{15}$

10. $\dfrac{13x+25}{42}$ **11.** $\dfrac{-2m-8}{12}$ **12.** $\dfrac{33-3n}{40}$ **13.** B and D

14. (a) $\dfrac{7x+10}{(x+1)(x+2)}$ (b) $\dfrac{9m+39}{(m+3)(m+5)}$ (c) $\dfrac{3n+17}{(n-1)(n+3)}$

(d) $\dfrac{2y-32}{(y+5)(y-2)}$ (e) $\dfrac{13x+45}{(2x+1)(x+6)}$ (f) $\dfrac{18m+34}{(m-3)(3m+2)}$

(g) $\dfrac{-30a-5}{(a+6)(1-4a)}$ (h) $\dfrac{1}{x-2}$ (i) $\dfrac{9}{m-n}$

15. (a) $\dfrac{5x+19}{x^2-9}$ (b) $\dfrac{2x+9}{x^2+4x+3}$ (c) $\dfrac{7-2x}{x^2-1}$ (d) $\dfrac{2-2x}{x^2-x-6}$

(e) $\dfrac{11m-3}{m(m^2-1)}$ (f) $\dfrac{5y+11}{(y-4)(y+1)(y+2)}$ (g) $\dfrac{5}{m^2-mn}$

(h) $\dfrac{7a+11}{a(a-3)(a-2)(a+5)}$ (i) $\dfrac{3x-41}{(x+5)(x+2)(x-2)}$

Page 481   E16.4

2. 7   **3.** $\dfrac{13}{7}$(1.86)   **4.** 3.73 or 0.268   **5.** 4.24 or −0.236   **6.** ±1.58

7. 1.45 or −3.45   **8.** −0.551 or −5.45   **9.** 1.63 or −0.0510

10. 0.285 or −1.10   **11.** 2.27 or 1.07   **12.** −0.209 or −4.79

13. 0.789, 0.211   **14.** $\dfrac{20}{x+1} + \dfrac{3}{x} = 10$, $x = \dfrac{3}{2}$ $\left(\text{or} -\dfrac{1}{5}\right)$

15. (a) $\dfrac{60}{n} - \dfrac{60}{n+1} = 3$ (b) $n = 4$

16. (a) $\dfrac{100}{V} + \dfrac{200}{V-1} = 36$ (b) 9.03 m/s (or 0.3 m/s but V−1 > 0)

17. A = (1, 3), B = $\left(-\dfrac{3}{2}, -2\right)$ **18.** (b) V = 60 km/h.

Page 482   Can you still? 16D

1. $x = 3$, $y = 11$ or $x = -1$, $y = 3$

2. $x = 1$, $y = 2$ or $x = -\dfrac{3}{2}$, $y = 4\dfrac{1}{2}$

3. $x = 2$, $y = 3$ **4.** $x = 3$, $y = 4$ or $x = -4$, $y = -3$

5. $x = 10$, $y = 2$ or $x = -2$, $y = -10$

Page 483   E16.5

8. (a) $n(n + 2)$ **11.** (a) $n(n + 1)^2$

12. (a) $12n^2 + 24n + 12$ (b) $12n^2 + 24n + 12 = 12(n + 1)^2$

Page 485   WYM16

1. (a) £122,500   (b) £17,500   (c) £20,900

2. (a) £120,000   (b) yes   (c) £650

3. (a) £167,500   (b) £1675

4. (a) £91,000   (b) £66,500   (c) £153,770   **5.** £1540

Page 486   Test yourself on unit 16

1. (a) $x \leq 3$ (b) $x < -2$ (c) $-1 < x \leq 11$

(d) $x > -9$ (e) $x < -3$, $x > 3$

2. (a) $x + 2y \leq 4$, $y \geq -1$, $y < 2x$

3. (a) Area   (b) Length   (c) Volume   (d) Volume

(e) Area   (f) Meaningless   (g) Meaningless   (h) Volume

(i) Length   (j) Volume   (k) Meaningless   (l) Area

4. (a) $\dfrac{x-1}{x+3}$ (b) $\dfrac{4}{x-2}$ (c) $\dfrac{2y}{x+3}$

5. (a) $\dfrac{x^2-y^2}{xy}$ (b) $\dfrac{x+4}{6}$ (c) $\dfrac{9x+7}{(x+3)(x-2)}$ (d) $\dfrac{32-7x}{(x-4)(x+3)}$

6. (a) $x = 4.1$ (b) $x = 3$ or −1   (c) P = 0.0466 or −1.43   (d) (ii) $x = 2$

Page 488   Mixed examination questions

1. (a) −1, 0, 1, 2, 3   (b) $x \geq 5$ **2.** 1, 2, 3, 4   **3.** $2\pi b^2$, πab, $2(a^2 + b)$

4. −2, −1, 0, 1   **5.** (a) −1, 0, 1   **6.** πpq, $\dfrac{qr}{2}$, $r(p+q)$

7. $\dfrac{x}{x+2}$ **8.** $\dfrac{-x}{x+6}$ **9.** $\dfrac{x}{x+7}$ **10.** $\dfrac{x^2+1}{x^2-1}$

1. (i) $3ab$, $2a^2 + bc$ (ii) $2a^2c$, $ab(b + 2c)$ **14.** $x = \dfrac{4}{5}$

5. (a) $(2x + 1)(x + 3)$ (b) $\dfrac{3x + 1}{(2x + 1)(x + 3)}$ **16.** (a) 73×67

7. (a) $\dfrac{15}{x} + \dfrac{11}{x - 2}$ (b) $\dfrac{15}{x} + \dfrac{11}{x - 2} = 4$ (c) (ii) $x = 7\frac{1}{2}$

8. (a) $5n$ **19.** (b) 1.56 or −2.56

UNIT 17

Page 492   M17.1

1. 4 m   **2.** 1.3 km   **3.** 150 km   **4.** 9 cm
5. (a) 54 km   (b) 78 km   (c) 48
6. 5.5 cm   **7.** 12 cm²   **8.** 90°   **9.** 0.96 km²

Page 493   Can you still? 17A

1. 25.5 cm   **2.** 8π **3.** 36 cm   **4.** 21.4 cm²
5. (a) 7.4 cm²   (b) 2.9 cm²   **6.** 37100 cm³

Page 496   M17.3

1. (a) 3.5 cm   (b) 10 cm   **8.** 7 cm
9. (a) 3.7 cm   (b) 4.4 cm   **13.** (b) square-based pyramid

Page 503   Can you still? 17B

1. 14 cm   **2.** 50 cm²   **3.** 21 cm
4. 10 cm   **5.** 209 cm³   **6.** 500 mm³

Page 505   E17.1

θ	0	30	60	90	120	150	180	210	240	270	300	330	360
cos θ	1	0.87	0.5	0	−0.5	−0.87	−1	−0.87	−0.5	0	0.5	0.87	1

2. (a), (d), (e)   **3.** (b), (c), (d)
4. (a)

θ	0	20	40	60	80	100	120	140	160	180
tan θ	0	0.4	0.8	1.7	5.7	−5.7	−1.7	−0.8	−0.4	0

θ	200	220	240	260	280	300	320	340	360
tan θ	0.4	0.8	1.7	5.7	−5.7	−1.7	−0.8	−0.4	0

(b) error, i.e. no possible value.

5. $y = \cos x$ **6.** $y = \sin x$, $y = \tan x$,   **7.** No
9. A(0, 1), B(180, −1), C(270, 0)   **10.** (b) yes

Page 507   E17.2

1. 328°   **2.** 292°   **3.** 162°   **4.** 310°
5. (a) 105°   (b) 47°   (c) 22°   (d) 220°
6. 60°, 300°   **7.** 55.1°, 124.9°   **8.** 109.9°, 250.1°   **9.** 143.1°, 216.9°
10. (a) −sin 85°   (b) cos 70°   (c) −cos 65°   (d) sin 10°   (e) −sin 25°
(f) −cos 55°   (g) cos 25°   (h) −sin 65°   (i) −cos 68°
11. (a) tan 40°   (b) tan 74°   (c) −tan 75°   (d) −tan 60°
12. 63.4°, 243.4°   **13.** 30°, 210°

Page 509   Can you still? 17C

1. (b) 1.2 litres   (c) 0.9 litres   (d) 19%
2. (a) $15 \le d < 18$ is 3, $18 \le d < 20$ is 3   (c) 4

14. (a) 45°, 135°   (b) 60°, 240°   (c) 60°, 120°   (d) 135°, 225°
(e) 45°, 225°   (f) 150°, 210°   **15.** eg. 60°, 300°, 420°, 660°
16. (a) eg. 45.2°, 134.8°, 405.2°, 494.8°   (b) eg. 80°, 260°, 440°, 620°
(c) eg. 126.9°, 233.1°, 486.9°, 593.1°
17. 19.5°, 160.5°   **18.** 3 hours, 9 hours
19. 60°, 120°, 240°, 300°   **20.** 15°, 75°, 195°, 255°

Page 511   E17.3

1. (b) (0, 1)   (c) (0, 3)   (d) (−1, −3)
6. (c) $y = \sin x$ **7.** $g(x) = f(x) - 2$
8. (a) (2, 1)   (b) (−2, 1)   (c) (1, 1)

Page 514   E17.4

2. (b) stretch scale factor 4 parallel to y-axis
(c) stretch scale factor $\dfrac{1}{3}$ parallel to y-axis
4. (a) A(−2, 0), B(−1, −8), C(2, 12), D(4, 0)
(b) A(−6, 0), B(−3, −2), C(6, 3), D(12, 0)
(c) A(−1, 0), B$\left(-\dfrac{1}{2}, -2\right)$, C(1, 3), D(2, 0)
10. $g(x) = 3f(x)$
11. (a) stretch scale factor $\dfrac{1}{4}$ parallel to x-axis
(b) stretch scale factor 10 parallel to y-axis
12. (a) $y = 27x^3 + 9x$ (b) $y = \cos 6x$ (c) $y = \dfrac{8}{x}$

Page 516   E17.5

2. (c) (3, −6)   **3.** (b) (−3, 0), (0, 9)
5. (a) (−6, 3)   (b) (−2, −3)   (c) (−2, 15)
(d) (−1, 3)   (e) (−2, 6)   (f) (2, 6)
7. (a) stretch scale factor $\dfrac{1}{3}$ parallel to x-axis
(b) translation through $\begin{pmatrix} 2 \\ 0 \end{pmatrix}$
(c) reflection in the x-axis or in the y-axis
8. (a) $y = x^2 - 3x + 4$ (b) $y = \sin(-x)$ (c) $y = -x^3 - 3$

Page 518   WYM17

1. £1420   **2.** (a) £1675   (b) £167.50   **3.** £598.50
4. £191   **5.** none   **6.** £355   **7.** £106.50

Page 519   Test yourself on unit 17

1. (a) (i) 13.8 km   (ii) 10.8 km   (b) 1.5 cm
2. (a) 6 cm   (b) 3.5 cm
4. (b) 0°, 180°, 360°   (c) max at 1, min at −1
5. (a) A   (b) C   (c) 32.9°, 327.1°   (d) 210°, 330°
6. (a) translation through $\begin{pmatrix} 4 \\ 0 \end{pmatrix}$

Page 521   Mixed examination questions

3. (b) −336°, −204°, 156°   **4.** −80.8°, 99.2°

6. (a) (2, 18)   (b) (−1, 12)   (c) (−2, 12)   (d) $\left(\frac{1}{2}, 12\right)$

7. (c) (−2b, 0)   (d) (0, a + c)   **8.** (b) 105°, 165°, 285°, 345°

9. (a) g(x) = f(x + 2)   (b) h(x) = 2f(x + 4)

11. (a) (ii) 120°   (b) 225°

12. (a) (i) (5, −4)   (ii) (2, −9)   (iii) (2, 4)

(iv) (1, −4)   (b) f(x) = x² − 4x

UNIT 18

Page 527   M18.1

1. (a)   (b)   (c)

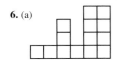

2. (a)   (b)   (c)

3. (a)   (b)   (c)

4. (a)   (b)   (c)

5. (a)   (b)   (c)

6. (a)   (b)   (c)

7. (a)   (b)   (c)

plan   side   plan   side   plan   side

Page 528   Can you still? 18A

1. 0.034   **2.** m = 3, n = 2,   **3.** £2800   **4.** £41.50

5. 3.264 × 10⁻²⁵   **6.** $\frac{17}{90}$

7. (a) $\frac{1}{8}$ (b) 1   (c) 3   (d) $\frac{16}{9}$

8. n = 2   **9.** 4   **10.** 2   **11.** £444.16   **12.** 22

Page 529   M18.2

1. A − 031°, B − 338°, C − 279°, D − 056°, E − 073°, F − 311°

2. (a) 225°   (b) 083°   (c) 315°   (d) 264°

3. (a) 115°   (b) 040°   (c) 195°   (d) 330°

4. 066.8°   **5.** 201.8°   **6.** (a) 39.4 miles   (b) 30.8 miles

7. (a) 11.1 km   (b) 41.5 km   **8.** 146°

9. (a) 5.7 km   (b) 2.32 km   (c) 6.15 km   (d) 112°

10. 302.6°   **11.** 10.3 km

Page 532   M18.3

1. 58.3 m   **2.** 9.9°   **3.** 37.9 m   **4.** 72.1°   **5.** 322 m

6. 28.7 m   **7.** 5.39 m   **8.** 457 m   **9.** 903 m

Page 533   Can you still? 18B

1. $x = \frac{y + 17}{6}$ **2.** (b) 0, 1.7

3. (a) 4xy(y − 3)   (b) (2x + 1)(2x − 1)   (c) (2x − 3)(2x + 1)

4. x = 9, y = 4   **5.** $\pi lw, \frac{4lw^2}{\pi r}, 8w^2$ **6.** x < −3

7. y ≥ 1, y ≤ x, x + 2y < 8   **8.** (a) (x − 2) (x − 3)   (b) $\frac{4}{x − 2}$

9. $y = \frac{p + 3}{1 − x}$ **10.** (b) −2.39, 4.39

Page 534   M18.4

1. C(0, 3, 4), D(0, 3, 0), E(6, 0, 0), F(6, 0, 4), G(0, 0, 4)

2. (a) L(5, 0, 0), M(5, 0, 3), N(0, 0, 3), O(0, 0, 0), P(5, 4, 0),
Q(5, 4, 3), R(0, 4, 3), S(0, 4, 0)

(b) (5, 2, 0) (c) 5.83

3. (a) O(0, 0, 0), A(6, 0, 0), B(6, 0, 10), C(0, 0, 10), D(0, 4, 10),
E(0, 4, 0), F(6, 4, 0)

(b) 10.8   (c) (6, 4, 5)   (d) (3, 0, 10)   **4.** (4, 10, 4)

5. (a) P(−3, 6, 0), Q(5, 6, 0), R(5, 6, 7), S(−3, 6, 7), T(−3, 0, 0),
U(5, 0, 0), V(5, 0, 7), W(−3, 0, 7)

(b) (5, 3, 7) (c) $\left(−3, 6, 3\frac{1}{2}\right)$ (d) 10.6

Page 536   Can you still? 18C

2. $\sqrt{80} = 4\sqrt{5}$ **3.** 56°   **4.** (a) rotation 90° clockwise about (0, 0

5. 29.9°   **6.** 24 cm   **7.** 8.4 km   **8.** 25.8 cm

9. (a) f(x) = cos x   **10.** (a) 2a   (b) $\frac{3}{2}$a + $\frac{1}{2}$b

Page 539   E18.1

1. (a) 23.5 cm   (b) 85.8 mm   (c) 49.1°   (d) 31.5 m

(e) 12.5 cm   (f) 73.6°   **2.** 51.9°   **3.** 50.4°

4. (a) x = 61.5°, y = 23.5°, z = 6.80 m

(b) x = 99°, y = 10.3 m, z = 6.58 m

(c) x = 68.3°, y = 62.7°, z = 9.18 cm

(d) x = 51°, y = 10.3 cm, z = 6.22 cm

(e) x = 76.2°, y = 80.8°, z = 88.4 mm

(f) x = 66°, y = 2.74 cm, z = 3.18 cm

5. 14.3 miles

Page 541   E18.2

1. (a) 8.03 cm   (b) 20.6 mm   (c) 98.1°

(d) 56.6 m   (e) 72.0°   (f) 75.7°

2. 81.1°   **3.** 3.28 cm   **4.** (b) 4.58 km

5. 113°   **6.** 38.9 km   **7.** 16.5 km on 057.1°

8. (a) $37 = x^2 + (x + 3)^2 - 2x(x + 3)\cos 60°$

(c) $x^2 + 3x - 28 = 0$, $x = 4$

Page 543   E18.3

2. 7.10 miles

3. (a) $x = 47.6°$, $y = 39.4°$, $z = 1.46$ cm

(b) $x = 97°$, $y = 1.95$ m, $z = 1.28$ m

(c) $x = 43°$, $y = 15.7$ cm, $z = 17.1$ cm

(d) $x = 108°$, $y = 29.0°$, $z = 43.5°$

(e) $x = 62°$, $y = 6.70$ m, $z = 4.62$ m

(f) $x = 38.8$ cm, $y = 27.4°$, $z = 42.6°$

4. (a) 158 m   (b) 88.2 m   **5.** 15.4 km   **6.** 49.0 km

7. (a) 33.8 cm   (b) 164 cm²   (c) $C\hat{A}D = 18.1°$, $A\hat{C}D = 88.9°$

(d) 350 cm²   **8.** (a) 15.5 km   (b) 4.82 km²

9. (a) $39 = x^2 + (x + 2)^2 - 2x(x + 2)\cos 60°$ (b) $x^2 + 2x - 35 = 0$

(c) $x = 5$ **10.** 21.2 cm   **11.** (a) 86.9 km²   (b) 16 mins

Page 545   Can you still? 18D

1. 15 mins   **2.** (b) $\frac{1}{15}$ (c) $\frac{8}{15}$ **3.** (a) 41, 67

4.

Salary	4–10	11–15	16–25	26–40	41+
People in sample	13	17	15	11	4

5. 0–10 range is 12, 20–30 range is 38

Page 546   E18.4

1. (a) 5 cm   (b) 12 cm

2. (a) 12.4 cm   (b) 5 cm   (c) 12.6 cm   (d) 13 cm

3. (a) 10 cm   (b) 11.2 cm

4. (a) 10.8 cm   (b) 9.85 cm   (c) 11.5 cm

5. 11.9   **6.** 8.62 km   **7.** 15 mm, 20 mm, 60 mm

8. (a) 7.81 cm   (b) 19.6 cm   (c) 18.7 cm

9. 123.7 m   **10.** (a) $x^2 + (x + 200)^2 = 350000$ (b) 306 m

Page 550   E18.5

1. (a) 20.2 cm   (b) 13.0 cm   (c) 32.8°   (d) 93.6°   (e) 114.2°

2. (a) 28.2 cm   (b) 30.8 cm   (c) 22.2 cm   (d) 33.4 cm

(e) 32.6°   (f) 22.9°   (g) 61.8°

3. (b) 60.5°   (c) 28.7 cm   (d) 68.2°

4. (a) 1.04 m   (d) 56.2°   (e) 0.389 m

5. (a) 12.4 cm   (b) 14.0°   **6.** (a) 64.3°   (b) 36.9°

7. (a) 81.8°   (b) 5.66 cm   (c) 27.4 cm

Page 552   WYM18

1. (a) £3

Page 553   Test yourself on unit 18

2. (a) (i) 259°   (ii) 307°   (iii) 044°   (iv) 079°   (b) 323°

3. (a) 8.5 m   (b) 518 m

4. (a) L(7, 0, 0), M(7, 0, 3), N(0, 0, 3), O(0, 0, 0), P(0, 5, 0),
Q(7, 5, 0), R(7, 5, 3), S(0, 5, 3)

(b) $\left(0, 2\frac{1}{2}, 3\right)$ (c) 7.62

5. (a) $x = 25.6$ cm, $y = 31.1°$ (b) 89.2 cm²

(c) (i) 29.0 km   (ii) 297°

6. (a) 11.7 cm   (b) 16.8 cm   (c) 45.7°   (d) 85 mm

Page 555   Mixed examination questions

1. 57.3 mm   **2.** (a) 30.7°   (b) 120.7°   **3.** 10.7 cm

4. (a) 10.1 cm   (b) 13.9 cm²   (c) 41.2 cm²

5. (a) 6.24 km   (b) (i) 51.3°   (ii) 321.3°   (iii) 141.3°

6. 256.2 m   **7.** 21°   **8.** 6.91 km   **9.** 12.3 m

10. (a) (i) 36.8 mm   (ii) 50.7°   (iii) 44.9 mm   (b) 59.9°

Index